MACMILLAN/McGRAW-HILL

Math

Assessment Guide

Grade 5

- Inventory and Final Test
- Chapter Tests
- Unit Tests
- Portfolio and Performance Assessment

- Self-Assessment
- Teacher Interviews
- Journal Writing
- Scoring Rubrics and Prescription Tables
- Teacher Forms

Macmillan
McGraw-Hill

GRADE 5
CONTENTS

How to Use the Assessment Guide

Macmillan/McGraw-Hill Math includes opportunities to assess students' knowledge on both a formal and an informal basis. This Assessment Guide is intended to assist you in developing, organizing, and managing multiple assessment strategies.

It is the philosophy of this series that the primary purpose of assessment is to improve students' learning, not just to grade their work. Assessment should provide an occasion for students to learn and to evaluate their own work. It should be an integral part of instruction, not simply an end point. Therefore, strategies for monitoring progress as well as summative measures, such as chapter tests, are all included in this guide.

The following is a brief description of the seven assessment strategies provided in this program.

Teacher Interview

The Teacher Interview is an informal assessment strategy designed to help you measure your students' understanding of math concepts. This guide includes a **Teacher Interview Questionnaire** (see page 15) that you can use to document your interviews with students. It also provides information on questioning strategies and help with interviewing techniques.

Journal Writing

Journal Writing is another informal assessment strategy. Here students are given the opportunity to write down how they think about math concepts in their journals. The program provides numerous opportunities for journal writing.

Journal Writing: Problem Solving

The problem-solving section of journal writing contains specifically designed problems based on the material covered in each chapter. These problems give students the opportunity to express their math thinking and problem-solving skills in a written setting. You may use these questions as either a formal or informal assessment tool.

How to Use the Assessment Guide *(continued)*

Paper-and-Pencil Tests

Inventory, chapter, unit, and final tests in this Assessment Guide provide a snapshot of the content that the student has mastered. These tests are available in multiple-choice and free-response formats. They are easy to grade, and they measure student understanding, skill level, and problem-solving ability.

Performance Assessment

Each unit test contains a Performance Assessment. Here, students are asked to perform math procedures and make problem-solving decisions that require an understanding of math concepts. The emphasis is on problems set in realistic situations outside of school.

Portfolio Assessment

Portfolios give you a means of evaluating students' understanding of concepts and abilities to reason and communicate mathematically. Blackline Masters are provided for both student and teacher to help with selecting and documenting student portfolios.

Self-Assessment

Self-assessment gives students the opportunity to look at their work and assess how well they are doing. This guide provides a checklist for students to use as they review their work.

Teacher Interview

The **Teacher Interview** is an informal technique designed to be part of the process of monitoring student progress. Interviews can help you assess your students' knowledge of math concepts. The purpose of the interview is to try to discern a student's thinking well enough to determine what to do next. By using questioning strategies, you can learn how each of your students is understanding the concepts you are teaching.

Where to Begin

A generic **Teacher Interview Questionnaire** (see page 15) is included in this Assessment Guide. You may customize this questionnaire to suit your needs. In addition, later in this guide you will find a Teacher Interview section for each chapter. These interview questions focus on the major ideas of each chapter. Another possibility is the **Write About It!** question in each Pupil Edition lesson as a starting point for the interview.

Classroom Management

Select a time when groups of students are engaged in different activities. As students work, you can either interview small groups or individuals at your desk, or move around the room to talk to students. Conduct the interviews in whatever manner best suits your own teaching style. Target a few students each day. Over the course of two weeks, you should be able to interview all the students in your class.

Recordkeeping. One of the most important things to remember is to date the notes you take. In this way a student's progress can be monitored. If you are using the **Teacher Interview Questionnaire** (see page 15), you can write student responses on this form. Another technique would be to keep a class roster with enough space under each student's name for you to take notes about the student's answers to questions.

Teacher Interview *(continued)*

Some Hints for Questioning Strategies

• Try to ask open-ended questions.

• The question could be a follow-up to work the student has done or to a response the student has made.

• Clarifying Questions: "What do you mean by…?" or "How did you do that?"

• Probing Questions: "Do you think that will always be the case?" or "How can you prove that your answer is right?"

• Challenging Questions: "What if the problem was changed in the following way?"

• Try not to pose questions that lead the students to the correct answer.

Interviewing Techniques

• Try to keep a relaxed atmosphere. Get students off to a positive start with a question you are sure that they can handle.

• Tell the students what you are doing. Explain that you are questioning them so that you can learn how they think when they solve math questions. Emphasize the thinking process as opposed to getting a correct answer.

• Rephrase your question if the student doesn't understand it.

• The interview session is not a time for you to teach or correct a student's errors. Concentrate on learning more about the student's thought processes. You may want to take notes on problems you need to help the student with at another time.

• Observe your student's behavior during the interview. You can often gain insight into a student's thinking through his or her actions.

• After you've asked a question, give the student some time to answer. Your focus should be on observing. Allowing the students to do most of the talking will supply you with a wealth of information on the way they think about math.

*See page 15 in this Assessment Guide for the **Teacher Interview Questionnaire.***

Journal Writing

Journal Writing is the second component of monitoring student progress. Journals provide an opportunity for students to use writing and drawing to show their understanding of math concepts. Math journals can provide you with valuable information about how and what your students are thinking about math.

The Value of Journal Writing

Writing helps students develop thinking skills. Expressing understanding of a concept in writing is also a means of discovering that understanding. Journal writing gives the student the opportunity to clarify, reflect on, and summarize math lessons. Students can pose a question, explore a train of thought, support an argument, or come to a conclusion. Writing can itself be a form of problem solving.

Journal Writing can:

• Help students become comfortable with reflecting on their own learning

• Promote self-assessment of the student's math thinking

• Give students the opportunity to restate information they just learned

• Provide you with information on how a student is thinking about concepts taught

Where to Begin

Macmillan/McGraw-Hill Math provides several opportunities for students to write in their journals. You will find a feature on journal writing for each chapter of this guide. In addition, journal prompts can be found in the **Writing for Math** and **Performance Assessment** sections of the Pupil Edition. All prompts are specific to the material covered in the unit.

Journal Writing *(continued)*

Talking to Your Students About Journal Writing

Emphasize clarity and focus, rather than fluency, in math journals. Tell your students that the idea is to explain a math idea, using illustrations when appropriate, in a way that is to the point.

Discuss the prompts and notify the students if any of their journal entries will be seen by their peers.

Classroom Management

Students can use folders, spiral notebooks, or sections of binders in which to keep their journals. Just be sure that they keep their writing together so that you can easily keep up a dialog with the student.

Assessment and Feedback

It would be best to read and respond to the journals at least once each unit. You may want to write directly in the journal. Encourage students to respond to your entries. Try to provide constructive feedback that will help students further their understanding of a particular topic.

Journal Writing: Problem Solving

Problem Solving questions are word problems specifically designed to assess the material covered in each chapter. See the specific chapter sections in this *Assessment Guide* for the **Problem Solving** question for each chapter.

The Intent of Problem Solving Questions

These word problems give students the opportunity to express their math thinking and problem solving skills in a written setting. You may use these questions as either a formal or informal assessment tool.

Scoring Problem Solving Questions

If you would like to have a numerical score for the **Problem Solving** questions, you may want to use the following 4-point holistic scoring rubric.

Scoring Rubric

Category 4
- Shows a full understanding of the problem
- Uses a systematic and effective math strategy
- Develops a solution that is accurate and complete
- Explains math reasoning in a clear and logical way

Category 3
- Shows an understanding of the problem
- Uses a workable strategy
- Forms a solution that is mostly accurate and complete
- Describes reasoning in a way that makes sense

Category 2
- Shows a partial understanding of the problem
- Uses an appropriate strategy
- Forms a solution that is mostly inaccurate and/or incomplete
- Displays little reasoning

Category 1
- Shows little or no understanding of the problem
- Uses an inappropriate strategy or no strategy
- Forms an inaccurate solution or no solution
- Displays no reasoning

Paper-and-Pencil Tests

Macmillan/McGraw-Hill Math includes four levels of paper-and-pencil tests. The **inventory test** is given at the beginning of the school year. **Chapter tests** and **unit tests** are available to measure student progress throughout the school year. The **final test** is designed to assess student understanding of the content of the entire year. *All* tests provide a multiple-choice format (Form A) and a free-response format (Form B) that contain different item content. Both forms test the same objectives and have the same number of items.

By using both the multiple-choice and the free-response formats, you may help ensure that students get practice taking standardized tests and also have an opportunity to demonstrate higher level thinking skills.

Inventory Test

The inventory test is given at the beginning of the school year. Its intent is to provide a measure of individual and class level of performance at the beginning of the program, establishing a baseline. The inventory test for each grade is the equivalent of the final test of the grade previous to it. There are 40 questions in each form. The inventory test is designed to be scored by the previous grade's objectives and by total test.

Chapter Tests

The chapter tests in this Assessment Guide are aligned with the 28 chapters in the **Macmillan/McGraw-Hill Math** Pupil Edition. The chapter tests measure progress on individual chapter objectives as the students progress through the program. There are about 20 questions in each form of every chapter test. Each test is designed to be scored by objective and by total test.

Unit Tests

The unit tests in this Assessment Guide are aligned with the 14 units in the **Macmillan/McGraw-Hill Math** Pupil Edition, occurring after every 2 chapters. The unit tests measure progress on individual chapter objectives within that particular unit. There are about 40 questions in each form of every unit test. Each test is designed to be scored by objective and by total test.

Final Test

The final test is given at the end of the school year and measures student progress on skills covered throughout the school year. There are 40 questions in each form. The final test is designed to be scored by the year's objectives and by total test.

Paper-and-Pencil Tests *(continued)*

Administering the Tests

The tests are not timed. In most cases they may be administered in one sitting. For the multiple-choice tests, students may mark their answers on the generic **Student Answer Sheet** (see page 16) or on the test page. Responses to the free-response Form B tests should be marked directly on the test.

It is very important that your students understand exactly what they are supposed to do. Review the directions and the test items before giving the test. During the test, monitor the students to make sure that they are following directions, working on the appropriate task, and indicating their responses correctly.

Try to make the environment as comfortable as possible. Make an effort to minimize distracting noises or activities that might draw the students' attention away from the test.

Evaluating Test Scores

Each test provides an indication of each student's general math achievement at different periods. Achievement on all tests is reported by objective AND by total test. Scores on these tests may indicate if a student has mastered one or more of the math areas tested. The test scores, therefore, can be used to plan further activities, either for reteaching or enrichment.

*See page 16 in this Assessment Guide for the **Student Answer Sheet.***

*See pages 17–18 in this Assessment Guide for the **Monitoring Student Progress** form.*

*See page 19 in this Assessment Guide for the **Monitoring Class Progress** form.*

Performance Assessment

In math, performance assessment emphasizes what the student *does* and *thinks* with problems that involve realistic situations outside of school. Students are asked to perform math procedures and make problem-solving decisions that require an understanding of math concepts.

The Goals of Performance Assessment

The **Performance Assessment** tasks at the end of each unit:

- Assess the "big ideas" in the unit
- Balance concept and process, knowing and doing
- Elicit reasoning
- Provide opportunities for varied learning styles and intelligences
- Set a "real-world" context as often as possible
- May involve teamwork

Where to Begin

At the end of each unit of the Pupil Edition, there is a Performance Assessment task. This task is designed to allow students to apply their knowledge of the unit in a practical situation. The problem-solving, activity-based assignments in each unit also offer important assessment opportunities with more extended time frames and greater potential for students to explore math in engaging situations.

Evaluating Student Performance

Responses in this type of assessment are not simply right or wrong, but rather show a continuum of the degree of understanding. To evaluate students in a fair and consistent way, **Macmillan/McGraw-Hill Math** provides you with scoring rubrics. At the end of each unit in the Teacher Edition you will find a scoring rubric specifically designed for that unit's **Performance Assessment** task. These rubrics are 3-point scales that provide you with specific criteria on which to evaluate students' work. You might want to distribute these rubrics to your students so that they understand how they will be assessed. Students should receive feedback about their performance with respect to the criteria. In this way, assessment will serve to improve student performance, not just monitor it.

Portfolio Assessment

A portfolio is a collection of students' work that can be used as an important assessment tool. Portfolio assessment:

- Focuses attention on performance criteria
- Documents the improvement of students' work over time
- Fosters students' self-assessment and reflection
- Develops students' ownership in learning
- Communicates with students, parents, and other teachers
- Evaluates the instructional program

What Goes in a Portfolio?

The portfolio is a place for student work that highlights their understanding of concepts, problem solving, reasoning, communication, and connection making. Any task that provides evidence of these abilities is a candidate for inclusion in the portfolio. In particular, **Macmillan/McGraw-Hill Math** provides the following features for use in the portfolio:

- Performance Assessment
- Journal Writing
- Write About It!
- Reading Math and Science
- Applying Math and Science
- Decision Making
- Unit Enrichment

One important goal of the portfolio is to foster student ownership of his or her work. Therefore, material to go in the portfolio should always be selected with the student. You may prefer to keep a "working" portfolio where all student work is held. Then every three or four weeks, you and the student can determine which pieces will go in the "showcase" portfolio, which is shared with external audiences, such as parents and next year's teacher.

Selecting the Showcase Portfolio

Selecting the showcase portfolio is very important. It is a significant part of a student's self-assessment. Have your students use **My Portfolio** (see page 20) to write about the selections they've made. In addition, each piece may be annotated by the student or teacher indicating where it demonstrates specific portfolio criteria, such as using appropriate problem-solving criteria. Since portfolios collect student work over time, be sure to include work that shows improvement. Remember to write the date on all work.

You may also want to consider a multimedia portfolio. Here students who are not strong in writing can demonstrate their math proficiency through photographs, audio or video tapes, and computer software.

Classroom Management

Working portfolios need to be used in ongoing instruction and therefore must be accessible to students. Cardboard boxes or milk crates can be used to house working portfolios. As students complete performance tasks and other appropriate exercises, they will need to store drafts of their work. When students revise their work they will need access to their portfolios again. If possible, allow students to move about the room to access their portfolio material. Learning to take responsibility for one's own work can be a fruitful by-product of using a portfolio.

As selections are made for the showcase portfolio, those materials not selected can be sent home to parents or discarded. Showcase portfolios need not be accessible on a daily basis and may be stored in a file cabinet or closet.

Small-Group Strategies

Teachers who use portfolios often find that by using flexible grouping strategies they are able to work intensively with small groups of students on particular topics while other students work independently. Since students generally finish performance-oriented tasks at different rates, this approach works well with portfolio work. It can also free you up to confer with individuals or groups concerning portfolio work.

Reviewing Portfolios

A good strategy for reviewing portfolios is to look at just a few each day. Even if each portfolio is reviewed every two weeks, this schedule can provide you with enough information to meet with students to discuss their portfolios.

*See page 20 in this Assessment Guide for the student's **My Portfolio** form.*
*See page 21 in this Assessment Guide for the teacher's **Portfolio Assessment Form.***

Self-Assessment

Self-assessment empowers the students and gives them the sense that they are in control of an important aspect of their school work. Students should be able to look at their work and assess how well they are doing. Self-assessment is an important aspect of the process of selecting a showcase portfolio as well.

Checklist

Macmillan/McGraw-Hill Math provides a checklist for students to use in the self-assessment process. The **Self-Assessment Checklist** (see page 22) uses simplified language to provide students with a means of comparing their work against established criteria. This list correlates to the teacher's blackline master **Portfolio Assessment Form** (see page 21). It is particularly suitable for extended tasks, such as performance assessment tasks. To promote and guide student self-assessment, you might want to attach checklists to the work in the student's portfolio. Then use this information in conferences to improve your student's understanding of classroom standards.

*See page 22 in this Assessment Guide for the student's **Self-Assessment Checklist.***

Teacher Interview Questionnaire

Student Name _____ Date _____

Chapter _____ Lesson _____

For Individual Students

Tell how you got your result.

_____

_____

What were some of the things you were thinking when you solved the problem?

_____

_____

Show how to prove that your answer is right.

_____

_____

What would happen if (you changed)…

_____

_____

What have you learned in class that might have helped you solve this problem?

_____

_____

For Students in a Group

How would you solve this problem differently than the other students in your group suggested?

_____

_____

Tell me more about how you would solve this problem.

_____

_____

Student Answer Sheet

Student Name _____ Date _____

Macmillan/McGraw-Hill Math
GRADE 5

☐ Inventory ☐ Chapter _____ ☐ Unit _____ ☐ Final

Choose One

1. (A) (B) (C) (D)   21. (A) (B) (C) (D)
2. (F) (G) (H) (J)   22. (F) (G) (H) (J)
3. (A) (B) (C) (D)   23. (A) (B) (C) (D)
4. (F) (G) (H) (J)   24. (F) (G) (H) (J)
5. (A) (B) (C) (D)   25. (A) (B) (C) (D)
6. (F) (G) (H) (J)   26. (F) (G) (H) (J)
7. (A) (B) (C) (D)   27. (A) (B) (C) (D)
8. (F) (G) (H) (J)   28. (F) (G) (H) (J)
9. (A) (B) (C) (D)   29. (A) (B) (C) (D)
10. (F) (G) (H) (J)   30. (F) (G) (H) (J)
11. (A) (B) (C) (D)   31. (A) (B) (C) (D)
12. (F) (G) (H) (J)   32. (F) (G) (H) (J)
13. (A) (B) (C) (D)   33. (A) (B) (C) (D)
14. (F) (G) (H) (J)   34. (F) (G) (H) (J)
15. (A) (B) (C) (D)   35. (A) (B) (C) (D)
16. (F) (G) (H) (J)   36. (F) (G) (H) (J)
17. (A) (B) (C) (D)   37. (A) (B) (C) (D)
18. (F) (G) (H) (J)   38. (F) (G) (H) (J)
19. (A) (B) (C) (D)   39. (A) (B) (C) (D)
20. (F) (G) (H) (J)   40. (F) (G) (H) (J)

Monitoring Student Progress

Student Name _____

Inventory Test	Form A		Form B		Comments
	Score	%	Score	%	
	/40		/40		

Chapter	Form A		Form B		Comments
	Score	%	Score	%	
1	/20		/20		
2	/20		/20		
3	/20		/20		
4	/20		/20		
5	/20		/20		
6	/20		/20		
7	/20		/20		
8	/20		/20		
9	/20		/20		
10	/20		/20		
11	/20		/20		
12	/20		/20		
13	/20		/20		
14	/20		/20		
15	/20		/20		
16	/20		/20		
17	/20		/20		
18	/20		/20		
19	/20		/20		
20	/20		/20		
21	/20		/20		
22	/20		/20		
23	/20		/20		
24	/20		/20		
25	/20		/20		
26	/20		/20		
27	/20		/20		
28	/20		/20		

Student Name _____

Unit	Form A		Form B		Performance Assessment	Comments
	Score	%	Score	%		
1	/40		/40			
2	/40		/40			
3	/40		/40			
4	/40		/40			
5	/40		/40			
6	/40		/40			
7	/40		/40			
8	/40		/40			
9	/40		/40			
10	/40		/40			
11	/40		/40			
12	/40		/40			
13	/40		/40			
14	/40		/40			

Final Test	Form A		Form B		Comments
	Score	%	Score	%	
	/40		/40		

Monitoring Class Progress

GRADE 5

This chart is to be used in monitoring your class progress unit by unit. Please photocopy this page and use one page for every unit in the **Macmillan/McGraw-Hill Math** program. Fill in the correct chapter and unit numbers in the chart as you complete the columns.

UNIT _____ PA = Performance Assessment

Student	Chapter _____		Chapter _____		Unit _____		
	Form A	Form B	Form A	Form B	Form A	Form B	PA

My Portfolio

Student Name _____

Date	Type of Work	Title	I'm including this because...

Portfolio Assessment Form

Student Name _____ Grade _____

Teacher _____ Date _____

This portfolio shows evidence that the student:	Little Evidence	Partial Evidence	Adequate Evidence	Substantial Evidence
Understands concepts				
Selects appropriate strategies to solve problems				
Provides quality explanations				
Expresses concepts, ideas, and thinking in an organized and clear way				
Uses math representations (models, graphs, charts, pictures, diagrams, numerals, symbols, math vocabulary) appropriately and accurately				
Makes connections to real-world situations, other math ideas, or other subject areas				

I would characterize the quality of the work in this portfolio as —

_____

_____

This student shows growth in —

_____

_____

This student would benefit from instruction in —

_____

_____

Self-Assessment Checklist

Student Name _____ Date _____

Now you have a chance to look at your work and review it.
Check what you did.

Understanding

☐ My work shows that I understand the big math "idea."

Problem Solving

☐ I answered the whole question.

☐ I showed how I got my answer.

Reasoning

☐ I explained why I did my work the way I did.

☐ I explained why my solution is reasonable.

Communicating

☐ My writing was organized and clear.

☐ I used models, pictures, or charts to organize my work.

Now complete these sentences.

The math strategy I used to solve this problem was —

_____

_____

From this problem I learned —

_____

_____

Inventory Test – Monitoring Student Progress

☐ Form A   ☐ Form B

Name _____ Date _____

Directions: This test targets selected objectives. For each item that is answered incorrectly, cross out the item number. Then record the number of correct responses for each strand in the column labeled **Number of Correct Responses.** Add to find the **Total Number of Correct Responses** and record the total. Use this total to determine the **Total Test Score** and the **Total Percent Correct.**

Strand • Objective(s)	Item Numbers	Number of Correct Responses	
Number Sense • Read and write whole numbers in millions. Compare, order, and round whole numbers and money. • Add whole numbers and money. • Subtract whole numbers and money. • Multiply facts through 12. • Estimate products, including money. • Divide by 2-digit numbers. • Multiply by multiples of 10, 100, and 1,000. • Multiply multi-digit numbers. • Multiply by 2-digit numbers. • Estimate products. • Divide multi-digit numbers by 1-digit numbers. • Estimate quotients. • Find the better buy. • Divide multiples of 10 and multi-digit numbers by 2-digit numbers. • Identify, read, and write fractions and mixed numbers. • Add fractions with like and unlike denominators.• Round decimals. • Subtract fractions with like and unlike denominators. • Identify fraction and decimal equivalents. • Read and write decimals to tenths, hundredths, and thousandths. • Add decimals to thousandths. • Subtract decimals to thousandths.	1, 2, 3, 6, 7, 8, 9, 10, 12, 13, 14, 15, 17, 18, 21, 23, 24, 25, 27, 29, 31, 32, 33, 37	/24	/24
Algebra & Functions • Use properties of multiplication. • Convert customary units. • Evaluate expressions. • Estimate and determine perimeter, circumference, area, and volume.	5, 16, 20, 26, 30	/5	/5
Measurement and Geometry • Identify, describe, and classify 3-dimensional figures. • Tell time and find elapsed time. • Identify and describe circles. • Identify translations, reflections, and rotations.	22, 34, 38, 39	/4	/4
Statistics, Data, and Probability • Read and interpret data. • Find range, median, and mode. • Find and explore probability.	4, 11, 35	/3	/3
Mathematical Reasoning • Use skills and strategies to solve problems.	19, 28, 36, 40	/4	/4
Total Number of Correct Responses			
Total Test Score		/40	/40
Total Percent Correct		%	%

Name_____

Read each question carefully. Darken the circle on your answer sheet for the correct answer.

1. What is the standard form of three million, twenty-one thousand, ninety?

A. 3,210,900   **C.** 3,021,900

B. 3,210,090   **D.** 3,021,090

2.
$$53,432 - 25,674$$

F. 79,106   **H.** 32,242

G. 38,868   **J.** 27,758

3. Jan's lunch bill is $5.74. She pays with a $10 bill. How much change does she receive?

A. $5.74   **C.** $4.74

B. $5.26   **D.** $4.26

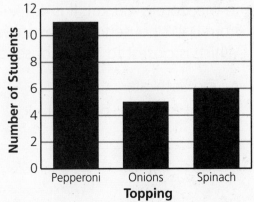

Favorite Pizza Topping

4. How many more students liked pepperoni than spinach?

F. 5 students   **H.** 3 students

G. 4 students   **J.** 2 students

5. $6 \times 0 = $ ☐

A. 6   **C.** $\frac{1}{6}$

B. 1   **D.** 0

6. Which is the best estimate?

208×76

F. 30,000   **H.** 16,000

G. 28,000   **J.** 10,000

7. $96 \div 8 = $ ☐

A. 9   **C.** 11

B. 10   **D.** 12

8. $54,218 + 2,896 = $ ☐

F 83,178   **H.** 56,004

G. 57,114   **J.** 51,322

9. ☐ $\times 8 = 56$

A. 9   **C.** 7

B. 8   **D.** 6

10. $4\overline{)\$170.24}$

F. $42.56   **H.** $42.06

G. $42.51   **J.** $42.01

GO ON ➤

11. Jenna had the following mini-golf scores: 65, 75, 63, and 66.

What was the median?

A. 68   **C.** 65

B. 66   **D.** 65.5

---

12. $48\overline{)1{,}490}$

F. 31 R2   **H.** 30 R5

G. 31   **J.** 30

---

13. $60 \times 4{,}000 =$ ▢

A. 240,000   **C.** 2,400

B. 24,000   **D.** 240

---

14. $34 \times 2{,}803 =$ ▢

F. 95,392   **H.** 90,000

G. 95,302   **J.** 19,702

---

15. Which is the best estimate?

$7{,}839 \div 91$

A. 900   **C.** 90

B. 700   **D.** 70

---

16. 20 qt = ▢ pt

F. 40   **H.** 5

G. 10   **J.** 2

---

17. Write a fraction for the shaded part.

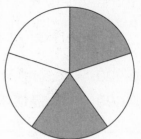

A. $\frac{4}{5}$ **C.** $\frac{2}{5}$

B. $\frac{3}{5}$ **D.** $\frac{1}{5}$

---

18. $\frac{3}{4} - \frac{2}{3} =$ ▢

F. $1\frac{5}{12}$ **H.** $\frac{5}{12}$

G. $\frac{7}{12}$ **J.** $\frac{1}{12}$

---

19. From Dan's house to the movie theater is 4.6 km. From his house to the bank is 5.1 km. From his house to the store is 4.3 km. It is 4.4 km from Dan's house to the gas station. Which is closest to Dan's house?

A. movie theater   **C.** store

B. bank   **D.** gas station

---

20. $s = 2t + 5$

$t = 3$

$s =$ ▢

F. 16   **H.** 8

G. 11   **J.** 6

GO ON

21. Which is the best estimate?

512×86

A. 50,000   **C.** 36,000

B. 45,000   **D.** 32,000

---

22. Identify the figure.

F. cone   **H.** sphere

G. cylinder   **J.** cube

---

23. $\frac{1}{4} + \frac{7}{8} =$ ▨

A. $1\frac{1}{4}$ **C.** 1

B. $1\frac{1}{8}$ **D.** $\frac{2}{3}$

---

24. Round 6.239 to the nearest tenth.

F. 6.3   **H.** 6.23

G. 6.24   **J.** 6.2

---

25. $31.90
       $\times \qquad 7$

A. $223.30   **C.** $133.30

B. $217.30   **D.** $22.33

---

26. Heather has a rectangular rug in her room that measures 5 feet by 8 feet. What is the area of the rug?

F. 40 ft^2 **H.** 20 ft^2

G. 26 ft^2 **J.** 13 ft^2

---

27. $5.498 + 0.03 =$ ▨

A. 5.798   **C.** 5.501

B. 5.528   **D.** 5.428

---

28. How many possible combinations of a soup and a sandwich are there when there is a choice of 3 sandwiches and 3 soups?

F. 12 combinations

G. 9 combinations

H. 6 combinations

J. 3 combinations

---

29. Write $\frac{13}{1,000}$ as a decimal.

A. 1.3   **C.** 0.013

B. 0.13   **D.** 0.0013

---

30. $(8 \times 4) \times 5 =$ ▨

F. 320   **H.** 32

G. 160   **J.** 17

GO ON ▶

31. $1.385 - 0.667 =$ ▢

    A. 2.052   **C.** 0.718

    B. 1.722   **D.** 0.628

32. Write $5\frac{9}{1,000}$ as a decimal.

    F. 5.9   **H.** 0.59

    G. 5.009   **J.** 0.45

33. Round $149.49 to the nearest dollar.

    A. $198   **C.** $149

    B. $150   **D.** $100

34. If a test starts at 11:45 A.M. and ends at 1:55 P.M., how long do you have to do the test?

    F. 9 hours, 50 minutes

    G. 2 hours, 10 minutes

    H. 1 hour, 50 minutes

    J. 40 minutes

35. If your bag of marbles has 5 cats-eyes and 7 aggies, what is the chance of pulling out an aggie on your first try?

    A. $\frac{7}{5}$ **C.** $\frac{7}{12}$

    B. $\frac{5}{7}$ **D.** $\frac{1}{12}$

36. Noam is 12 pounds heavier than Said. Ron is 4 pounds lighter than Alroy. Alroy is 5 pounds heavier than Said. Who is the heaviest?

    F. Ron   **H.** Said

    G. Alroy   **J.** Noam

37. $7 \times \$28.92 =$ ▢

    A. $196.00   **C.** $198.00

    B. $196.44   **D.** $202.44

38. A triangle with three sides of different lengths is always ▢ .

    F. equilateral   **H.** scalene

    G. obtuse   **J.** acute

39. A regular pentagon has exactly how many lines of symmetry?

    A. 0 line of symmetry

    B. 1 line of symmetry

    C. 3 lines of symmetry

    D. 5 lines of symmetry

40. Melba is offered 9 pencils for $2.52, or 5 pencils for $1.60. How much less would she pay for each pencil if she buys 9 instead of 5?

    F. $1.00   **H.** 4¢

    G. 25¢   **J.** 3¢

STOP

Name_____

Read each question carefully. Fill in the correct answer in the space provided.

1. What is the standard form of four million, one hundred five thousand, seventeen?

_____

_____

2.   41,731
    − 25,899
      ‾‾‾‾‾‾‾

_____

3. Rocco's lunch bill is $14.49. He pays with a $20 bill. How much change does he receive?

_____

Favorite Ice Cream

4. How many more students liked vanilla than rocky road?

_____

5. $11 \times 1 =$ _____

_____

6. Estimate.

    304×47

_____

_____

7. $84 \div 7 =$ _____

_____

8. $64{,}928 + 7{,}185 =$ _____

_____

9. _____ $\times 9 = 63$

_____

10. $6\overline{)\$270.24}$

_____

11. Gini had the following bowling scores: 71, 85, 63, and 73.

What is the median?

_____

12. 57)2,630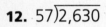

_____

13. 50 × 7,500 = _____

14. 41 × 1,981 = _____

15. Estimate.

8,109 ÷ 91

_____

16. 12 yd = _____ in.

_____

17. Write a fraction for the shaded part.

_____

_____

18. $\dfrac{7}{8} - \dfrac{1}{3} =$ _____

_____

19. From Chang-shah's house to the mall is 2.4 mi. From his house to the supermarket is 3.1 mi. From his house to the zoo is 4.3 mi. It is 2.7 mi from Chang-shah's house to the cinema. Which is closest to his house?

_____

20. $m = 3v - 4$

$v = 3$

$m =$ _____

GO ON

21. Estimate.

694 × 72

_____

_____

22. Identify the figure.

_____

_____

23. $\frac{3}{4} + \frac{3}{8} =$ _____

_____

24. Round 8.448 to the nearest tenth.

_____

25. $52.89
      ×   6

26. Martin has a soccer poster on his wall that measures 2 meters by 1.5 meters. What is the area of the poster?

_____

_____

27. 7.788 + 0.02 = _____

_____

28. If a menu offers a choice of 4 desserts and 3 hot drinks, how many possible combinations of a hot drink and a dessert are possible?

_____

_____

29. Write $\frac{33}{1,000}$ as a decimal.

_____

_____

30. (3 × 9) × 3 = _____

GO ON

31. $6.095 - 0.487 =$ _____

32. Write $7\frac{87}{1000}$ as a decimal.

_____

33. Round $199.45 to the nearest dollar.

_____

34. If you start a trip at 10:20 A.M. and get there at 1:40 P.M., how long did the trip take?

_____

35. What is the probability of getting an even number when tossing a number cube numbered from 1 to 6?

_____

36. Amy is 4 inches taller than Penny. Aleysha is 3 inches taller than Jane. Jane is 5 inches taller than Amy. Who is the tallest?

_____ _____

37. $8 \times \$16.89 =$ _____

38. A chord that passes through the center of a circle is the

_____

39. Two capital letters, when you rotate them, become other capital letters. Name them.

_____

40. Jerrod can buy 4 apples for $1.99, or 7 apples for $3.29. Which is the better buy?

_____

STOP

Chapter 1 – Teacher Interview

Core Concept: *Place Value and Number Sense*

Student Activity: Students demonstrate an understanding of place value and are able to compare and order whole numbers and decimals. Ask students to order them from least to greatest.

Teacher Question 1:

- List the following numbers in order from least to greatest.

  4.09, 4.109, 4.080

Understanding Student Response	Practice and Improvement
Students who say 4.09 is greatest.	Review lesson 3 to reinforce an understanding of place value with decimals.
Students who say 4.080 is greater than 4.09.	Review lesson 4 to help students recognize that 4.09 and 4.090 are equivalent decimals.

Teacher Question 2:

- Which symbol makes the sentence true?

  12.035 ◯ 12.08

Understanding Student Response	Practice and Improvement
Students who say the answer is >.	Review lesson 5 to help students learn to line up the decimal points of numbers.
Students who say the answer is =.	Review lesson 5 to help students learn the 3 steps for comparing decimals.

Teacher Question 3:

- How can you prove your answer is right?

Understanding Student Response	Practice and Improvement
Students who say 35 is greater than 8.	Review lesson 3 to reinforce an understanding of place value with decimals.
Students who say 12.035 is greater than 12.08.	Review lesson 5 to help students learn to line up the decimal points of numbers.

Chapter 1 – Journal Writing

Encourage students to generate their own journal entries related to math ideas in general or to concepts in this chapter. Present the following journal prompt and have students share their drawing/writing with a partner:

- When you are comparing numbers, why is it important to line up the decimal points of the numbers?

    (Responses should indicate that a number with fewer digits, such as 12.2 can be greater than a number with more digits, such as 11.087.)

JOURNAL WRITING/PROBLEM SOLVING

Jan's best times in the 200-meter dash were 24.45 seconds, 24.39 seconds, and 23.96 seconds. Write these times in order from fastest to slowest.

Read

Have students find the answer to the problem. Then ask them to write a few sentences telling—

- which information they used to find the answer

- what they did with the information

Have students make up another problem with different information for which they could have followed the same procedure. Then have students solve the problem and supply the correct response.

Plan

Students must correctly follow the steps for comparing decimals. Students must also recognize that the fastest time is the least of the three numbers and that the slowest time is the greatest number.

Solve

The correct response to the assigned problem is 23.96, 24.39, 24.45.

Look Back

A correct response demonstrates the ability to compare and order decimals. (See scoring rubric on page 7.)

Chapter 1 – Monitoring Student Progress

☐ **Form A**   ☐ **Form B**

Name _____ Date _____

Directions: For each item that is answered incorrectly, cross out the item number. Then record the number of correct responses in the appropriate Student Score column. If the student has not met the Criterion Score for an objective, circle the student's score. Recommended assignments are listed in the Prescription Table on the next page.

Objective	Item Numbers	Criterion Score	Student Score
A. Estimate quantities using benchmarks.	1, 2, 10	2/3	/3
B. Use place value to read and write whole numbers and decimals.	3, 4, 5, 7, 12, 15, 16	6/7	/7
C. Compare and order whole numbers and decimals.	6, 8, 9, 11, 13, 14	5/6	/6
D. Use skills and strategies to solve problems.	17, 18, 19, 20	3/4	/4
Total Test Score		16/20	/20
Total Percent Correct			%

Chapter 1 – Prescription Table

The following chart correlates the tested objectives for this chapter to supplementary materials that meet the individual needs of the students. The Reteach and Practice pages are designed for students who need further instruction in the math concepts taught in this chapter. The Enrich pages are designed for students who need advanced challenges.

Objective	Reteach	Practice	Enrich
A. Estimate quantities using benchmarks.	1	2	3
B. Use place value to read and write whole numbers and decimals.	4, 7, 10	5, 8, 11	6, 9, 12
C. Compare and order whole numbers and decimals.	13	14	15
D. Use skills and strategies to solve problems.	16	17	18

Read each question carefully. Darken the circle on your answer sheet for the correct answer.

1. Which is the most likely amount of juice in the full glass?

   A. 5 ounces   **C.** 10 ounces

   B. 6 ounces   **D.** 15 ounces

2. Which is most likely the number of marbles in the full jar?

   F. 60 marbles   **H.** 150 marbles

   G. 90 marbles   **J.** 300 marbles

3. Name the underlined place value.

321,654

   A. ones   **C.** hundreds

   B. tens   **D.** thousands

4. Write fifteen million, three hundred twenty-four thousand, fifty-seven in standard form.

   F. 1,532,457   **H.** 7,542,351

   G. 5,732,415   **J.** 15,324,057

5. $30,000,000 + 20,000 + 3,000 + 500 + 10 + 7 =$

   A. 323,517   **C.** 30,023,517

   B. 3,023,517   **D.** 32,003,517

6. Order from least to greatest.

0.235, 1.05, 0.073, 1.10

   F. 0.073, 0.235, 1.05, 1.10

   G. 1.10, 1.05, 0.235, 0.073

   H. 0.073, 0.235, 1.10, 1.05

   J. 1.05, 1.10, 0.235, 0.073

7. Name the underlined place value.

3,113.205

   A. thousands

   B. thousandths

   C. hundreds

   D. hundredths

8. Which number is greater than 86,507.508?

   F. 86,505.329   **H.** 86,507.041

   G. 86,507.093   **J.** 86,507.724

9. Which digit makes the sentence true?

$1{,}238 > 1{,}2\ \boxed{}\ 8$

   A. 2   **C.** 4

   B. 3   **D.** 5

10. Which is the most likely price for the second bunch of bananas?

$2.07

   F. $6   **H.** $12

   G. $8   **J.** $20   **GO ON**

11. Order from greatest to least.

1.092, 1.102, 0.805, 0.812

A. 1.092, 1.102, 0.812, 0.805

B. 1.092, 1.102, 0.805, 0.812

C. 1.102, 1.092, 0.812, 0.805

D. 1.102, 1.092, 0.805, 0.812

---

12. Which number has 7 in the tenths place?

F. 23.07   **H.** 17.34

G. 72.12   **J.** 56.75

---

13. Which number is less than 124.0234?

A. 125.0022   **C.** 124.0321

B. 124.0222   **D.** 124.1203

---

14. Which digit makes the sentence true?

0.0285 < 0.02 5

F. 6   **G.** 7   **H.** 8   **J.** 9

---

15. 40,000,000 + 700,000 + 60,000 + 200 + 90 + 1 = ▉

A. 40, 076,291   **C.** 47,600,291

B. 40,760,291   **D.** 47,629,100

---

16. Write the expanded form.

62,058.7

F. 60,000 + 2,000 + 50 + 8 + 0.7

G. 60,000 + 2,000 + 500 + 8 + 0.7

H. 600,000 + 20,000 + 500 + 80 + 7

J. 600,000 + 20,000 + 5,000 +80 + 7

---

17. In the solar system, four planets have a diameter larger than Earth's—Uranus (51,200 km), Saturn (120,540 km), Jupiter (142,980 km), and Neptune (49,500 km). List them from largest to smallest.

A. Jupiter, Saturn, Uranus, Neptune

B. Saturn, Jupiter, Uranus, Neptune

C. Jupiter, Saturn, Neptune, Uranus

D. Saturn, Jupiter, Neptune, Uranus

---

18. The populations of four cities are: Baltimore (651,154), Memphis (650,100), Milwaukee (596,974), Boston (589,141). Which two cities have about the same population?

F. Milwaukee and Boston

G. Baltimore and Memphis

H. Memphis and Milwaukee

J. Boston and Baltimore

---

19. Minneapolis has a population of 382,618. Miami has a population of 362,470. Which place value determines which number is greater?

A. millions

B. hundred thousands

C. ten thousands

D. thousands

---

20. In a 100-meter race, Erin had a time of 13.3 seconds, Dave's time was 14.1 seconds, Sara's was 13.9 seconds and Matias's was 14.2 seconds. List them in order from fastest to slowest.

F. Erin, Sara, Dave, Matias

G. Dave, Matias, Sara, Erin

H. Sara, Erin, Matias, Dave

J. Matias, Dave, Sara, Erin

STOP

Name _____

Read each question carefully. Fill in the correct answer in the space provided.

1. Which is the more likely number of pennies in the full jar, 300 or 600?

200 pennies

_____

2. Which is the more reasonable amount of juice in the full glass, 6 ounces or 12 ounces?

3 ounces

_____

3. Name the underlined place value.

892,917

_____

4. Write twenty-seven million, three hundred eight thousand, one hundred seven in standard form.

_____

5. $80,000,000 + 9,000,000 + 50,000 + 6,000 + 100 + 20 + 3 =$

_____

6. Order from least to greatest.

12.086, 12.105, 12.720, 12.009

_____

_____

7. Name the underlined place value.

847.253

_____

_____

8. Compare. Write >, <, or =.

156,842,370 ◯ 156,842,048

_____

9. Write a digit that makes the sentence true.

1.0786 < 1.0▢86

_____

10. Which is the more likely number of pages in the larger book? 150 or 500?

50 pages

_____

11. Order from greatest to least.

17.628, 17.268, 17.609, 17.097

_____

_____

12. Name the place of the 6 in the number 12.654.

_____

_____

13. Compare. Write >, <, or =.

13.2 ▨ 13.20

_____

_____

14. Write a digit that makes the sentence true.

180.065 > 1___5.324

_____

15. 70,000,000 + 4,000,000 + 3,000 + 900 + 8 =

_____

_____

16. Write the expanded form.

48,562.3

_____

_____

17. In the solar system, there are four large planets with a diameter smaller than Earth's—Mars (6,794 km), Venus (12,104 km), Pluto (2,200 km), and Mercury (4,878 km). List these planets from largest to smallest.

_____

_____

18. The populations of four cities are listed below.

Lexington   260,512
Newark   273,546
Anchorage   260,283
Louisville   256,231

Which two cities have about the same population?

_____

_____

19. Dallas has a population of 1,188,580. San Antonio has a population of 1,144,646. Which place determines which number is greater?

_____

_____

20. At a track meet, Miguel's longest jump was 11.3 meters, Paul's was 12.4 meters, Lina's was 11.2 meters, and Kylie's was 11.9 meters. List the jumpers in order from shortest to longest jump.

_____

_____

STOP

Chapter 2 – Teacher Interview

Core Concept: *Adding and Subtracting Whole Numbers and Decimals*

Student Activity: Students demonstrate an understanding of how to calculate and estimate sums and differences of whole numbers and decimals. Assign addition and subtraction problems such as 426.33 + 358.9 = ___ or 629.34 – 517.653 = ___.

Teacher Question 1:

• Can you tell me how you added 426.33 + 358.9 (and subtracted 629.34 – 517.653)?

Understanding Student Response	Practice and Improvement
Students who lined up the numbers on the left.	Review lesson 1 to reinforce an understanding of place value with decimals.
Students who lined up the numbers on the right.	Review lesson 1 to recall the steps for adding and subtracting numbers with decimals.

Teacher Question 2:

• How can you estimate to check whether your answer is reasonable?

Understanding Student Response	Practice and Improvement
Students who would estimate by adding 500 + 400.	Review lesson 2 to review how to raise or lower a decimal factor in estimating.
Students who would estimate by subtracting 600 – 600.	Review lesson 2 to review how to raise or lower a decimal factor in estimating.

Teacher Question 3:

• Suppose you changed the first problem to 426.33 + 358.9 + 175.2. How could you use the associative property to help you do the problem mentally?

Understanding Student Response	Practice and Improvement
Students who say 350 + 200 = 550	Review lesson 4 to review the addition properties.
Students who say 426.33 + 358.9 + 175.2 = 175.2 + 358.9 + 426.33	Review lesson 4 to help the student understand how the associative property can help with grouping and adding mentally (426.33 + 175.2) + 358.9 = 601.52 + 358.9 = 960.42

Chapter 2 – Journal Writing

Encourage students to generate their own journal entries related to math ideas in general or to concepts in this chapter. For students requiring guidance, present the following journal prompt:

- When you are problem solving, why is it important to categorize the information? What are some tools you can use to categorize the information in a word problem?

  (Responses should include references to necessary vs. unnecessary information. Some ways to organize information are to use a table or chart, or a graphic organizer.)

JOURNAL WRITING/PROBLEM SOLVING

Last year, Banner Sneaker Company had sales of $5,842,699.11. This year their sales were $6,785,443.51. About Sneakers had sales of $4,225,832.77 last year. Their sales were $3,844,922.66 this year. What was Banner's two-year total?

Read

Have students find the answer to the problem. Then ask them to write a few sentences telling—

- which information they used to find the answer

- what they did with that information

Have students make up another problem with different information for which they would have to follow the same procedure. Then have students solve the problem and supply the correct response.

Plan

Students must recognize that the appropriate operation is adding, lining up decimals in both numbers, and following through by computing correctly.

Solve

The correct response to the assigned problem is $12,628,142.62. Students had to know Banner's sales for last year ($5,842,699.11) and for this year ($6,785,443.51). Then they had to add these two numbers, lining the decimals up correctly and computing correctly.

Look Back

A correct response demonstrates the ability to discriminate between necessary vs. unnecessary information and apply the appropriate operation to solve the problem. (See scoring rubric on page 7.)

Chapter 2 – Monitoring Student Progress

☐ Form A   ☐ Form B

Name _____ Date _____

Directions: For each item that is answered incorrectly, cross out the item number. Then record the number of correct responses in the appropriate Student Score column. If the student has not met the Criterion Score for an objective, circle the student's score. Recommended assignments are listed in the Prescription Table on the next page.

Objective	Item Numbers	Criterion Score	Student Score
A. Add whole numbers and decimals.	1, 3, 7, 8, 13, 16	5/6	/6
B. Subtract whole numbers and decimals.	6, 11, 14	2/3	/3
C. Estimate sums and differences of whole numbers and decimals.	2, 5, 10, 15	3/4	/4
D. Identify and use the properties of addition.	4, 9, 12	2/3	/3
E. Use skills and strategies to solve problems.	17, 18, 19, 20	3/4	/4
Total Test Score		15/20	/20
Total Percent Correct			%

Chapter 2 – Prescription Table

The following chart correlates the tested objectives for this chapter to supplementary materials that meet the individual needs of the students. The Reteach and Practice pages are designed for students who need further instruction in the math concepts taught in this chapter. The Enrich pages are designed for students who need advanced challenges.

Objective	Reteach	Practice	Enrich
A. Add whole numbers and decimals.	19, 28, 29	20	21, 30
B. Subtract whole numbers and decimals.	31	32	33
C. Estimate sums and differences of whole numbers and decimals.	22	23	24
D. Use strategies to solve problems.	25, 26, 34	27, 35	36

Name _____

Read each question carefully. Darken the circle on your answer sheet for the correct answer.

1. $32.4 + 45.17 + 13.068 =$

   A. 17.909

   B. 62.09

   C. 90.638

   D. 91.25

2. Which is the best estimate?

   $456.102 + 129.96$

   F. 500   **H.** 700

   G. 600   **J.** 800

3.   124,089.019
  + 13,098.637

   A. 137,177.646

   B. 137,177.656

   C. 137,187.646

   D. 137,187.656

4. Identify the addition property used to rewrite the problem.

   $16 + 29 + 4 = 16 + 4 + 29$

   F. associative   **H.** identity

   G. commutative   **J.** distributive

5. Which is the best estimate?

   $31.682 - 15.123$

   A. 10   **C.** 20

   B. 15   **D.** 25

6. $6,307.89 - 379.2 =$

   F. 2,515.89   **H.** 6,038.69

   G. 5,928.69   **J.** 6,269.97

7. $18.0189 + 0.176 =$

   A. 18.0365   **C.** 18.1949

   B. 18.156   **D.** 18.365

8. $234.8 + 1.65 =$

   F. 69.8

   G. 218.3

   H. 236.45

   J. 233.25

9. Identify the addition property used to rewrite the problem.

   $(12 + 16) + 34 = 12 + (16 + 34)$

   A. associative   **C.** identity

   B. commutative   **D.** distributive

10. Which is the best estimate?

   $32.17 + 1.089 + 59.81$

   F. 80   **H.** 100

   G. 90   **J.** 110

GO ON

11. 3,124.5 − 897.08 = ☐

A. 2227.42   **C.** 3337.42
B. 2272.52   **D.** 3337.52

12. Identify the addition property used to write the problem.

864.17 + 0 = 864.17

F. associative   **H.** identity
G. commutative   **J.** distributive

13. 123 + 358 = ☐

A. 471   **C.** 481
B. 475   **D.** 485

14. 6,351 − 764 = ☐

F. 5,587   **H.** 6,587
G. 5,617   **J.** 6,617

15. Which is the best estimate?

3,729 − 2,156

A. 1,000   **C.** 2,000
B. 1,500   **D.** 2,500

16. 0.3875 + 0.127 = ☐

F. 0.3992   **H.** 0.4045
G. 0.4002   **J.** 0.5145

17. In 2000, the population of Chicago was 2,896,016. In 1990, the population of Chicago was 2,783,726. How many more people lived in Chicago in 2000?

A. 112,290 people
B. 112,710 people
C. 113,390 people
D. 113,710 people

18. Monday's baseball game was attended by 12,324 people. On Thursday, 9,827 people attended the baseball game. What was the total attendance at these two games?

F. 21,141 people
G. 21,151 people
H. 22,141 people
J. 22,151 people

19. The snow in Gina's yard is 4.25 inches deep. If the depth of the snow increases by 1.25 inches every hour, how deep will the snow be after 3 hours?

A. 5.5 inches   **C.** 8 inches
B. 7 inches   **D.** 8.5 inches

20. Mila's record in the long jump was 10.3 feet in March, 11.4 feet in April, and 12.5 feet in May. If this pattern continues, what will Mila's record be in July?

F. 12.5 feet   **H.** 14.7 feet
G. 13.6 feet   **J.** 15.8 feet

STOP

Read each question carefully. Fill in the correct answer in the space provided.

1. 13.7 + 36.23 + 8.059 = _____

_____

2. Estimate.

377.408 + 128.67

_____

3.   206,514.608
      + 32,706.521

_____

4. Identify the addition property used to write the problem.

164.589 + 0 = 164.589

_____

5. Estimate.

83.609 − 22.473

_____

6. 8,135.77 − 268.4 = _____

_____

7. 12.5086 + 0.535 = _____

_____

8. 606.2 − 8.44 = _____

_____

9. Identify the addition property used to rewrite the problem.

(23 + 18) + 42 = 23 + (18 + 42)

_____

10. Estimate.

64.25 + 5.067 + 37.19

_____

GO ON

Name _____

11.   5,910.8
       − 745.26

_____

12. Identify the addition property used to
rewrite the problem.

14 + 9 + 36 = 14 + 36 + 9

_____

13. 627 + 293 = _____

_____

14. 4,712 − 819 = _____

_____

15. Estimate.

6,213 − 3,867

_____

16. 0.6391 + 0.751 = _____

_____

17. In 2000, the population of Alabama
was 4,447,100. In 1990, the
population of Alabama was
4,040,587. How many more people
lived in Alabama in 2000?

_____

18. In June, the aquarium sold 18,694
tickets. In July, the aquarium sold
19,827 tickets. All together, how many
tickets were sold in June and July?

_____

19. Keisha's plant is 42.5 inches tall. If the
plant grows 2.5 inches every week,
how tall will the plant be in 4 weeks?

_____

20. Jessie jogged 2.2 miles each week in
June, 2.5 miles each week in July, and
2.8 miles each week in August. If this
pattern continues, how many miles will
Jessie jog each week in October?

_____

STOP

Unit 1 Performance Assessment

Balancing a Budget

- *Target Skill:* Add and subtract whole numbers and decimals.

- *Additional Skills:* Compare and order whole numbers and decimals; estimate sums and differences of whole numbers and decimals.

Task Description: This task requires students to find the total cost of a number of food items for a picnic, to compare the total cost to the amount budgeted for these items, and to suggest a way to reduce the total cost to the amount budgeted.

Preparing: You may wish to ask students to list the types of food they would like to eat at a picnic. You may ask students to research food prices, or assign prices to the foods they choose. Make sure students understand that the total cost of the food they buy must not exceed the budgeted amount.

Materials	Group Size	Time on Task
Calculator (optional) Work chart	3 to 4 students	1 to 2 days

Guiding: Tell students that the price of the items should include the dollar and cents amounts (such as $0.89; $1.49; etc.)

Remind students to align decimals when adding or subtracting.

Observing/ Monitoring: As you move among the students, post the following questions:

Why is it important to align numbers when adding or subtracting?

Are there other ways you might organize your information?

What are some ways you could check the accuracy of your results?

Unit 1 Performance Assessment Scoring Rubric

Balancing a Budget

Score	Explanation
3	Students demonstrate an efficient strategy and a thorough approach that enables them to solve the problem completely. A satisfactory answer: • shows a clearly completed chart; • shows steps used to calculate the difference between the total cost of the original food items and the amount budgeted; • shows the item or items that can be removed from the list to reduce the total cost of the items to the amount that has been budgeted. Students are able to complete the problem quickly and have all of the correct solutions.
2	Students demonstrate a strategy that enables them to solve most of the problem correctly. The strategy is somewhat disorganized, making it less efficient. A solution is found, but errors are contained. Students may: • make an error in calculating the total cost of the items, or the difference between the total cost and the amount budgeted. • make an error in choosing an item or items to be removed from the list. Students have some difficulty determining all solutions correctly but demonstrate an understanding of general concepts.
1	Students demonstrate a confused strategy, which leads to difficulty solving the problem. Most answers are incorrect, but students do demonstrate knowledge of at least one concept being assessed, such as calculating the total cost of the original items

Unit 1 Performance Assessment
Student Activity

Balancing a Budget

You will need
- a pencil
- a calculator (optional)

1. You are planning a picnic with some friends.
   You have a limited budget to spend on food and drinks.

Food Item	Cost
Exact Total Cost	

Amount budgeted to spend on food _____

Item that can be removed from the list to reduce the total cost to below the amount budgeted _____

Combination of items that can be removed from the list to reduce the total cost to below the amount budgeted _____

1. List the items in the chart. Include the price of each item.
   (Make sure prices include some decimals.)

2. Calculate the total cost of the items.

3. Calculate the difference between the total cost of the items and the amount budgeted.

4. Choose an item that can be removed from the list so that the total cost is less than the amount budgeted.

5. Choose a combination of items that can be removed from the list so that the total cost is less than the amount budgeted.

Unit I – Monitoring Student Progress

☐ Form A   ☐ Form B

Name _____ Date _____

Directions: This test targets selected objectives. For each item that is answered incorrectly, cross out the item number. Then record the number of correct responses in the column labeled **Number of Correct Responses.** Add to find the **Total Number of Correct Responses** and record the total. Use this total to determine the **Total Test Score** and the **Total Percent Correct.**

Strand • Objective(s)	Item Numbers	Number of Correct Responses
Number Sense, Concepts, and Operations • Use place value to read and write whole numbers and decimals. • Compare and order whole numbers and decimals. • Add whole numbers and decimals. • Subtract whole numbers and decimals. • Estimate sums and differences of whole numbers and decimals. • Identify and use the properties of addition. • Use skills and strategies to solve problems.	1, 2, 3, 4, 6, 7, 8, 9, 10, 11, 12, 13, 14, 15, 16, 17, 18, 19, 21, 22, 23, 24, 25, 26, 27, 28, 29, 30, 31, 32, 33, 34, 35, 36, 37, 38, 39	/37
Measurement • Estimate quantities using benchmarks.	5	/1
Algebraic Thinking • Use skills and strategies to solve problems.	20, 40	/2
Total Number of Correct Responses		
Total Test Score		/40
Total Percent Correct		%

Read each question carefully. Darken the circle on your answer sheet for the correct answer.

1. Name the place of the underlined digit.

9,7<u>6</u>5,281

  A. thousands
  B. ten thousands
  C. hundred thousands
  D. millions

2. $48.2 + 27.015 + 6.9583 =$

  F. 82.2333
  G. 82.1733
  H. 81.11733
  J. Not Here

3. Which number has the digit 9 in the hundredths place?

  A. 475.391
  B. 628.953
  C. 821.059
  D. 930.164

4. Which is the best estimate?

131.1007 + 520.79

  F. 500   **G.** 600   **H.** 800   **J.** 1,000

5. Which is the most likely amount of marbles in the full jar?

  A. 20 marbles
  B. 50 marbles
  C. 100 marbles
  D. 200 marbles

6. Which is the best estimate?

44.793 − 12.517

  F. 20   **H.** 40
  G. 30   **J.** 50

7. What is the value of 2 in 82,435,691?

  A. 200 thousand   **C.** 20 million
  B. 2 million   **D.** 2 billion

8.   71,842.956
       + 4,326.49

  F. 76,170.005   **H.** 72,274.605
  G. 76,169.446   **J.** 72,268.1546

9. $8,723.24 - 857.88 =$

  A. 7,865.36   **C.** 7,866.46
  B. 7,865.46   **D.** 7,866.76

10. In 1990, New York's population was 17,990,778. Illinois's was 11,430,602. To determine which state had more people, you need to compare digits in which place?

  F. ten millions
  G. millions
  H. hundred thousands
  J. ten thousands

GO ON

11. Which is the best estimate?

88,208 − 9,196

A. 60,000   **C.** 80,000

B. 70,000   **D.** 90,000

---

12. Which number is greater than 84,762.688?

F. 84,760.955   **H.** 84,762.599

G. 84,762.098   **J.** 84,762.777

---

13. Which is the best estimate?

453 + 384 + 117

A. 800   **C.** 1,100

B. 1,000   **D.** 1,200

---

14.   3,179,280.04
−   438,577.85

F. 2,741,713.29   **H.** 2,740,702.19

G. 2,740,702.29   **J.** 873,500.54

---

15. Which is the best estimate?

568.31 + 324.58

A. 800   **C.** 1,000

B. 900   **D.** 1,100

---

16.   762.9
+ 486.3

F. 1,248.102   **H.** 1,249.2

G. 1,248.12   **J.** 12,481.2

---

17. Last year, Tarmac Jean Company's sales were $20,219,753. This year's sales were $18,662,913. What is the best estimate of Tarmac's total sales for the two years?

A. $20,000,000   **C.** $40,000,000

B. $30,000,000   **D.** $50,000,000

---

18. In June, attendance at the baseball stadium was 10,808 people. In July, attendance was 12,794. In August, it was 14,825. What was the total attendance for the summer?

F. 37,317 people   **H.** 38,427 people

G. 38,417 people   **J.** 38,527 people

---

19. In 1962, Wilt Chamberlain averaged 50.4 points per game. In 1987, Michael Jordan averaged 37.1 points. What was the difference in their averages?

A. 12.3 points   **C.** 13.3 points

B. 12.7 points   **D.** 17.3 points

---

20. Brenda practices the high jump. She starts the bar at 2 feet 3 inches and raises it 1.5 inches after each successful jump. How high will the bar be during the 3rd successful jump?

F. 2 feet 4.5 inches

G. 2 feet 6 inches

H. 2 feet 7.5 inches

J. 2 feet 8 inches

GO ON

21. Name the value of the underlined digit.

5,<u>3</u>87,429

A. 3,000,000   **C.** 3,000

B. 300,000   **D.** 300

22. 54.1 + 17.0023 + 3.0150 = ▢

F. 20.0714   **H.** 101.25

G. 74.1173   **J.** 205,583

23. Which number has the digit 7 in the hundredths place?

A. 629.765   **C.** 603.587

B. 629.575   **D.** 603.567

24. Which is the best estimate?

4.9781 + 13.026

F. 14   **H.** 19

G. 18   **J.** 20

25. What is the standard form of seventeen billion, six hundred forty million, two hundred ten?

A. 17,640,210

B. 17,000,640,210

C. 17,640,000,210

D. 17,640,210,000

26. Which is the best estimate?

30.51704 − 6.889

F. 10   **H.** 30

G. 23   **J.** 38

27. What is the value of 5 in 751,280,811?

A. 50 billion   **C.** 5 million

B. 50 million   **D.** 500 thousand

28.   16,232.417
    + 8,400.36

F. 24,632.777   **H.** 17,072.453

G. 24,632.7   **J.** 17,077

29. 4,318.11 − 284.328 = ▢

A. 4,033.782   **C.** 1,477.782

B. 4,033.683   **D.** 1,474.83

30. California has an area of 158,706 square miles. Montana has an area of 147,046 square miles. To determine which state is larger, you need to compare the digits in which place?

F. hundred thousands

G. ten thousands

H. thousands

J. hundreds

GO ON

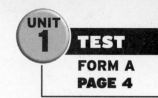
31. Which is the best estimate?

12,640 − 5,821

A. 8,000   **C.** 6,000

B. 7,000   **D.** 5,000

---

32. Identify the addition property shown.

7 + 38 + 13 = 7 + 13 + 38

A. Associative

B. Commutative

C. Identity

D. Distributive

---

33. Which is the best estimate?

395 + 211 + 324

A. 600   **C.** 900

B. 700   **D.** 1,200

---

34.   12,000,456
      − 8,987,689

F. 3,012,767   **H.** 4,123,767

G. 3,012,877   **J.** 4,123,877

---

35. Which is the best estimate?

287.35 + 417.6

A. 500   **C.** 900

B. 700   **D.** 1,000

---

36. 817 + 397 = ▨

F. 1,214   **H.** 1,114

G. 1,204   **J.** 1,104

---

37. Last year, the Clearwater CD Company had sales of $11,587,982. This year, the company had sales of $6,997,005. What is the best estimate of the company's total sales over two years?

A. $17,000,000   **C.** $20,000,000

B. $19,000,000   **D.** $21,000,000

---

38. During the first week of April, there were 383 visitors to the museum. During the second week, there were 142 visitors. There were 654 visitors during the third week. What is the best estimate of the total number of visitors to the museum for those three weeks?

F. 1,000 visitors   **H.** 1,300 visitors

G. 1,200 visitors   **J.** 1,400 visitors

---

39. The coach timed how fast his runners ran 1 mile. Eric ran a mile in 8.84 minutes, Kay ran a mile in 8.79 minutes, and Rosie ran a mile in 9.58 minutes. How much faster did Eric run than Rosie?

A. 0.69 minute   **C.** 0.79 minute

B. 0.74 minute   **D.** 0.76 minute

---

40. Kay's coach put her on a 4-week training program. She must increase the distance she runs each week by 0.5 miles. If she runs 1.5 miles the first week, how far will she run the last week?

F. 2 miles   **H.** 3 miles

G. 2.5 miles   **J.** 3.5 miles

STOP

Name _____

Read each question carefully. Fill in the correct answer in the space provided.

1. Name the place of the underlined digit.

18,076,352

_____

_____

2. 3.0378 + 23.9 + 54.816 =

_____

_____

3. Which number has the digit 3 in the thousandths place?

3,102.04   4.036   12.093

_____

_____

4. Estimate.

82.0637 + 294.51

_____

_____

5. Estimate the amount of juice in the full cup.

_____

6. Estimate.

28.726 − 11.418

_____

_____

7. What is the value of 6 in 612,038,541?

_____

_____

8.   36,142.833
       +   5,667.09

_____

9. 8,156.71 − 623.55 = _____

_____

10. In the 100-meter dash, Erik's time is 11.27 seconds. Darnel's time is 11.24 seconds. To determine the winner of the race, you need to compare digits to which place?

_____

11. Estimate.

57,816 − 8,149

_____

_____

12. Complete. Write <, > , or =

12.090 ⬤ 12.09

_____

_____

13. Estimate.

273 + 521 + 681

_____

_____

14.   8,459,126.38
      − 231,667.09

_____

15. Estimate.

655.13 + 249.78

_____

_____

16.   893.6
        + 358.7

17. A theme park's ticket sales were $15,789,021. Sales of food and drinks at the park were $9,328,602. Estimate the total sales at the park.

_____

_____

18. Kareem Abdul-Jabar scored 38,387 points during his career. Karl Malone scored 35,464 points. Wilt Chamberlain scored 31,419 points. How many points did they score altogether?

_____

_____

19. Carl is 1.37 meters tall. Shelly is 1.64 meters tall. What is the difference in their heights?

_____

_____

20. Georgia's best swimming time is 1 minute 56.7 seconds. Her time decreased by 1.3 seconds each week. What is Georgia's best swimming time after 2 weeks?

_____

21. Name the value of the underlined digit.

342,5̲92.093

_____

_____

22. 68.7 + 189.230 + 1.55 = _____

_____

23. Which number has the digit 3 in the tenths place?

31.065　　　19.372　　　24.035

_____

_____

24. 56.854 + 7.0396 = _____

_____

25. What is the standard form of forty-five billion, eight hundred thirty million, three thousand twenty-two?

_____

26. Estimate.

43.872 − 9.65

_____

_____

27. What is the value of 9 in 13,290,075?

_____

28.　　　56,142.783
　　　+　6,002.47
　　　‾‾‾‾‾‾‾‾‾‾

_____

29. 1,892.34 − 435.761 = _____

_____

30. Japan has an area of 234,800 square miles. Sweden has an area of 279,600 square miles. To determine which country is larger, you need to compare the digits in which place?

_____

GO ON

31. Estimate.

17,862 − 5,349

_____

_____

32. Identify the addition property shown.

234.85 + 0 = 234.85

_____

_____

33. Estimate.

514 + 398 + 832

_____

_____

34. 19,658,173
− 3,519,277

_____

35. Estimate.

514.99 + 176.34

_____

36. 341 + 568 = _____

37. Last week, 19,087,663 people bought tickets to see a new movie. This week, 6,813,420 people bought tickets. Estimate the number of people who bought tickets during these two weeks.

_____

_____

38. During November, 742 skiers bought season passes. During December 878 skiers bought season passes. During January, 566 skiers bought season passes. Estimate the number of season passes sold during those three months.

_____

_____

39. Ken earns $6.89 per hour. Larry earns $6.78 per hour. Tanya earns $7.23 per hour. How much more per hour does Tanya earn than Ken?

_____

40. Each week Karen increases the length of her bike ride by 0.6 miles. If Karen's bike ride is 2.1 miles during the first week, how long will her ride be during the fourth week?

_____

STOP

Chapter 3 – Teacher Interview

Core Concept: *Estimate products of whole numbers.*

Student Activity: Students demonstrate an understanding of rounding and multiplication of whole numbers. Ask students to estimate the product of two numbers such as 4.3 and 13.8.

Teacher Question 1:

- How will you round 4.3?

Understanding Student Response	Practice and Improvement
Students who say they will round to 5.	Review lessons 5 to allow students to practice rounding factors.
Student who say they will round to 43.	Review Chapter 1, lesson 2 to reinforce the concept of place value.

Teacher Question 2:

- How will you round 13.8?

Understanding Student Response	Practice and Improvement
Students who say they will round to 13.	Review lesson 5 to allow students to practice rounding factors
Students who say they will round to 10.	Review lesson 5 to allow students to practice rounding factors. Suggest that rounding to 14 will lead to a more accurate estimate.

Teacher Question 3:

- Estimate the product of 13.8 and 4.3.

Understanding Student Response	Practice and Improvement
Students who round correctly but do not give 56 as an answer.	Review lesson 3 to allow students to practice multiplying whole numbers.
Students who round correctly and say the answer is 416.	Review lesson 2 to reinforce the concept of regrouping.

Chapter 3 – Journal Writing

Encourage students to generate their own journal entries related to math ideas in general or to concepts in this chapter. Present the following journal prompt and have students share their drawing/writing with a partner:

- How can you use the distributive property to find the product of 3 and 17?

  (Responses should indicate that the students add the product of 3 and 10 to the product of 3 and 7.)

JOURNAL WRITING/PROBLEM SOLVING

Use the distributive property to find the product of 4 and 219.

Read

Have students find the answer to the problem. Then ask them to write a few sentences telling—

- which information they used to find the answer

- what they did with the information

Have students make up another problem with different information for which they could have followed the same procedure. Then have students solve the problem and supply the correct response.

Plan

Students must correctly write 219 as 2 hundreds, 1 ten and 9 ones. The student must then find the sum of $(4 \times 200) + (4 \times 10) + (4 \times 9)$.

Solve

The correct response to the assigned problem is 876.

Look Back

A correct response demonstrates the ability to compare and order decimals. (See scoring rubric on page 7.)

Chapter 3 – Monitoring Student Progress

☐ Form A ☐ Form B

Name _____ Date _____

Directions: For each item that is answered incorrectly, cross out the item number. Then record the number of correct responses in the appropriate Student Score column. If the student has not met the Criterion Score for an objective, circle the student's score. Recommended assignments are listed in the Prescription Table on the next page.

Objective	Item Numbers	Criterion Score	Student Score
A. Multiply whole numbers.	1, 2, 3, 4, 5	4/5	/5
B. Identify and use the properties of multiplication.	6, 7, 8, 9, 10	4/5	/5
C. Estimate products of whole numbers.	11, 12, 13, 14, 15	4/5	/5
D. Use skills and strategies to solve problems.	16, 17, 18, 19, 20	4/5	/5
Total Test Score		16/20	/20
Total Percent Correct			%

Chapter 3 – Prescription Table

The following chart correlates the tested objectives for this chapter to supplementary materials that meet the individual needs of the students. The Reteach and Practice pages are designed for students who need further instruction in the math concepts taught in this chapter. The Enrich pages are designed for students who need advanced challenges.

Objective	Reteach	Practice	Enrich
A. Multiply whole numbers.	38, 44	39, 45	40, 46
B. Identify and use the properties of multiplication.	41, 47	42, 48	43, 49
C. Estimate products of whole numbers.	50	51	52
D. Use skills and strategies to solve problems.	53	54	55

Read each question carefully. Darken the circle on your answer sheet for the correct answer.

1. $45 \times 21 =$ ▢

   A. 4,521   **C.** 945

   B. 946   **D.** 845

2. $50 \times 10 =$ ▢

   F. 600   **H.** 60

   G. 500   **J.** 50

3. $5 \times 4 =$ ▢

   A. 5   **C.** 15

   B. 10   **D.** 20

4. $2 \times 14 =$ ▢

   F. 14   **H.** 24

   G. 20   **J.** 28

5. $9 \times 39 =$ ▢

   A. 390   **C.** 271

   B. 351   **D.** 251

6. Identify the property shown.

   $65 \times 0 = 0$

   F. Identity property

   G. Associative property

   H. Commutative property

   J. Zero property

7. Which of the following is an example of the identity property?

   A. $9 \times 9 = 81$

   B. $3 \times 9 = 9 \times 3$

   C. $1 \times 8 = 8$

   D. $5 \times 0 = 0$

8. $3 \times 49 =$ ▢

   F. $(3 \times 50) + (3 \times 1)$

   G. $(3 \times 40) + (3 \times 9)$

   H. $(30 \times 4) + (30 \times 9)$

   J. 127

9. $12 \times (5 \times 7) =$ ▢

   A. $(12 \times 5) \times 7$

   B. $1 \times 2 \times 5 \times 7$

   C. $(12 \times 5) + (12 \times 7)$

   D. $(7 \times 5) \times 21$

10. $40 \times 1 \times 0 =$ ▢

   F. 0

   G. 40

   H. 41

   J. 400

GO ON

11. Estimate the sum of 287 + 322 + 301 by clustering.

 A. 700   **C.** 900

 B. 800   **D.** 1,000

12. Estimate the product of 12 × 76 by rounding.

 F. 1,200   **H.** 840

 G. 960   **J.** 800

13. Estimate the sum of 694 + 478 + 901 by clustering.

 A. 2,000   **C.** 2,200

 B. 2,100   **D.** 2,300

14. Estimate the product of 49 × 61 by rounding.

 F. 2,500   **H.** 3,000

 G. 2,940   **J.** 3,500

15. Estimate the product of 109 × 129 by rounding.

 A. 14,300   **C.** 20,000

 B. 15,000   **D.** 25,000

16. About 50,000 people showed up for a football game. If the stadium seats 60,000 people, how many empty seats were there?

 F. 10,000   **H.** 50,000

 G. 15,000   **J.** 60,000

17. A track meet has 19 events. Each event awards 3 medals. How many medals are required for the track meet?

 A. 50   **C.** 60

 B. 57   **D.** 67

18. John is mailing 31 Christmas cards. If each card costs 34 cents to mail, how much will it cost John to mail the cards?

 F. $10.64   **H.** $10.20

 G. $10.54   **J.** $9.30

19. Savannah has a population of 482,618. Richmond has a population of 362,470. By about how much is Savannah's population greater than Richmond's?

 A. 200,000 people

 B. 120,000 people

 C. 110,000 people

 D. 100,000 people

20. A group goes rafting on the Colorado River. Each raft carries 12 people. If there are 9 rafts, how many people went rafting?

 F. 96   **H.** 108

 G. 100   **J.** 120

STOP

Read each question carefully. Fill in the correct answer in the space provided.

1. 23 × 47 = _____

_____

2. 3 × 4 = _____

_____

3. 8 × 15 = _____

_____

4. 24 × 8 × 5 = _____

_____

5. 11 × 12 × 13 = _____

_____

6. Rewrite 4 × 115 using the Distributive Property.

_____

7. Identify the property shown.

12 × 21 = 21 × 12

_____

_____

8. According to the Identity Property, what does the product of any factor and 1 equal?

_____

_____

9. According to the Associative Property, what does 10 × (4 × 5) equal?

_____

_____

10. 42 × 0 = _____

GO ON

11. Estimate by clustering.

679 + 372 + 919

_____

_____

12. Estimate by rounding.

11 × 77

_____

_____

13. Estimate by clustering.

567 + 909 + 121 + 702

_____

_____

14. Estimate by rounding.

19 × 62

_____

_____

15. Estimate by rounding.

24 × 26

_____

16. James leaves about 9 coins in each pair of jeans he has. If he has 8 pairs of jeans, about how many coins does he have?

_____

_____

17. A pack of videotapes has 9 videotapes. How many videotapes are there in 6 packs?

_____

_____

18. Mary can drive about 500 miles a day. If Miami and San Francisco are about 3000 miles apart, how long will it take Mary to drive from Miami to San Francisco?

_____

_____

19. A bus can carry 100 passengers. If there are 12 empty seats, how many passengers are on the bus?

_____

_____

20. Each pound of bananas has 7 bananas. How many bananas are in 5 pounds of bananas?

_____

STOP

Chapter 4 – Teacher Interview

Core Concept: *Multiply Whole Numbers and Decimals*

Student Activity: Students demonstrate an understanding of how to multiply whole numbers and decimals. Assign multiplication problems, such as 2.7 × 400 or 3.2 × 0.6.

Teacher Question 1:

- Can you tell me how you multiplied 2.7 × 400?

Understanding Student Response	Practice and Improvement
Students who found the product and then moved the decimal point two places to the left.	Review Chapter 1, lesson 3 to reinforce an understanding of place value with decimals.
Students who multiplied 20 times 400 and 7 times 400.	Review Chapter 3, lesson 2 to help the student apply the Distributive Property correctly.

Teacher Question 2:

- How can you estimate to prove your answer is reasonable?

Understanding Student Response	Practice and Improvement
Students who would estimate by multiplying 2 times 400.	Review Chapter 3, lesson 5 to review how to raise or lower a decimal factor in estimating.
Students who multiply 4 by 2.7 and move the decimal point two places to the right.	Review Chapter 3, lesson 5 to review the concept of estimating.

Chapter 4 – Journal Writing

Encourage students to generate their own journal entries related to math ideas in general or to concepts in this chapter. For students requiring guidance, present the following journal prompt:

- When you are problem solving, why is it important to categorize the information? What are some tools you can use to categorize the information in a word problem?

  (Responses should include references to necessary vs. unnecessary information. Some ways to organize information are to use a table, chart, or graphic organizer.)

JOURNAL WRITING/PROBLEM SOLVING

Ms. Kiler bought 32 tickets to the science museum, 32 bus passes, 32 juice boxes and 32 bags of popcorn. The museum tickets cost $2.45, bus passes $0.40 each, juice boxes $0.75 each, and popcorn $1.25 per bag. How much did the museum tickets cost?

Read

Have students find the answer to the problem. Then ask them to write a few sentences telling—

- which information they used to find the answer

- what they did with the information

Have students make up another problem with different information for which they would have to follow the same procedure. Then have students solve the problem and supply the correct response.

Plan

Students must recognize that the operation is multiplication, know how to determine placement of a decimal point, and follow through by computing correctly.

Solve

The correct response to the assigned problem is $78.40. Student had to know how many tickets she bought (32) and how much each ticket cost ($2.45). Then they had to multiply those two numbers, computing correctly and inserting the decimal point correctly.

Look Back

A correct response demonstrates the ability to discriminate between necessary vs. unnecessary information and apply the appropriate operation to solve the problem. (See scoring rubric on page 7.)

Chapter 4 – Monitoring Student Progress

☐ Form A   ☐ Form B

Name _____ Date _____

Directions: For each item that is answered incorrectly, cross out the item number. Then record the number of correct responses in the appropriate Student Score column. If the student has not met the Criterion Score for an objective, circle the student's score. Recommended assignments are listed in the Prescription Table on the next page.

Objective	Item Numbers	Criterion Score	Student Score
A. Multiply whole numbers and decimals.	1, 2, 3, 4, 5	4/5	/5
B. Multiply decimals by decimals.	6, 7, 8, 9	3/4	/4
C. Express products as powers and evaluate exponential expressions.	10, 11, 12, 13, 14, 15	5/6	/6
D. Use skills and strategies to solve problems.	16, 17, 18, 19, 20	4/5	/5
Total Test Score		16/20	/20
Total Percent Correct			%

Chapter 4 – Prescription Table

The following chart correlates the tested objectives for this chapter to supplementary materials that meet the individual needs of the students. The Reteach and Practice pages are designed for students who need further instruction in the math concepts taught in this chapter. The Enrich pages are designed for students who need advanced challenges.

Objective	Reteach	Practice	Enrich
A. Multiply whole numbers and decimals.	56, 62	57, 63	58, 64
B. Multiply decimals by decimals.	59, 62	60, 63	61, 64
C. Express products as powers and evaluate exponential expressions.	71	72	73
D. Use skills and strategies to solve problems.	65, 68, 69	66, 70	67

Read each question carefully. Darken the circle on your answer sheet for the correct answer.

1. $7.56 \times 8 =$ ⬜

   A. 56.48   **C.** 60.48

   B. 60.08   **D.** 64.08

2. $6 \times \$5.95 =$ ⬜

   F. \$36   **H.** \$35.70

   G. \$35.95   **J.** \$35.30

3.   5.4
      $\times$ 4

   A. 20.8   **C.** 22

   B. 21.6   **D.** 28

4. $6.5 \times 1,000 =$ ⬜

   F. 65   **H.** 6,500

   G. 50   **J.** 65,000

5. $7 \times 4.5 =$ ⬜

   A. 28.5   **C.** 33.5

   B. 31.5   **D.** 35

6. 5.9×6.4

   F. 3.776   **H.** 377.6

   G. 37.76   **J.** 3776

7. 8.5×3.2

   A. 24   **C.** 25.5

   B. 24.5   **D.** 27.2

8. 4.7×2.2

   F. 11   **H.** 10.3

   G. 10.34   **J.** 103.4

9. 9.8×11.3

   A. 110.74   **C.** 117.6

   B. 115.64   **D.** 128.36

10. Write in exponential form.

   10,000

   F. 0^4 **H.** 10^4

   G. 1^4 **J.** 10^5

GO ON ➡

11. Write in standard form.

2^7

  A. 256   **C.** 64

  B. 128   **D.** 14

12. Write in exponential form.

10

  F. 1^1 **H.** 1^0

  G. 10^1 **J.** 11^0

13. Rewrite using a base and an exponent.

$3 \times 3 \times 3 \times 3 \times 3 \times 3$

  A. 3^3 **C.** 6^3

  B. 3^6 **D.** 6^6

14. Write in standard form.

$(0.9)^3$

  F. 0.729   **H.** 0.6561

  G. 0.81   **J.** 0.93

15. Write in exponential form.

121

  A. 1^{21}

  B. 12^1

  C. 121^0

  D. 11^2

16. A fence that surrounds a rectangular yard is 20 meters. If one side of the fence is 2 meters longer than the other, what are the lengths of the two sides?

  F. 4 meters, 6 meters

  G. 5 meters, 7 meters

  H. 6 meters, 8 meters

  J. 9 meters, 11 meters

17. Tom orders five bowls of chili. Each bowl costs $2.50. If he pays with a $20 bill, how much change does he receive?

  A. $7.50   **C.** $2.50

  B. $5   **D.** $0

18. In Mr. Trent's class of 18 students, there are twice as many females as males in the room. How many male students are there?

  F. 5   **H.** 7

  G. 6   **J.** 8

19. A cut-glass vase costs $3.50. How much do 8 vases cost?

  A. $24   **C.** $32

  B. $28   **D.** $40

20. Jane has 3 nickels. If she has 4 times as many pennies as she has nickels, how many coins does she have?

  F. 18   **H.** 12

  G. 15   **J.** 6

STOP

Read each question carefully. Fill in the correct answer in the space provided.

1. $35 \times 6.8 =$ _____

_____

2. $4 \times \$29.97 =$ _____

_____

3. $8 \times \$17.25 =$ _____

_____

4. $17.6 \times 25 =$ _____

_____

5. $\$4.32 \times 1,000 =$ _____

_____

6. 9.9×12.1

_____

7. 0.9×9.2

_____

_____

8. 5.9×5.9

_____

_____

9. 12.3×0.6

_____

_____

10. Write in exponential form.

256

_____

11. Write in standard form.

7^3

_____

_____

12. Rewrite using a base and an exponent.

$17 \times 17 \times 17$

_____

_____

13. Write in exponential form.

0.04

_____

_____

14. Write in standard form.

$(0.81)^2$

_____

_____

15. Rewrite using a base and an exponent.

$10 \times 10 \times 10 \times 10 \times 10 \times 10 \times 10$

_____

16. A mechanical pencil costs 50 cents and a pen costs 25 cents. If Will spends five dollars on 17 pens and pencils, how many of each does he buy?

_____

_____

17. Each pen in a box is either red, blue, or black. If there are 7 pens of each color in the box, how many pens are there in the box?

_____

_____

18. A group of 9 friends spent $12 each on dinner without tax. If the tax is $6, how much did the entire dinner cost?

_____

_____

19. Sarah has 4 quarters. If she has twice as many dimes as quarters, how many coins does she have?

_____

_____

20. The distance around a rectangular park is 400 meters. One side of the park is 50 meters longer than the other side. How long are the sides of the park?

_____

STOP

Unit 2 Performance Assessment

Building a Geodesic Dome

- *Target Skill:* Multiply whole numbers and decimals.
- *Additional Skills:* Estimate products of whole numbers and decimals.

**Task
Description:** This task requires students to calculate the total amount of metal pipe needed to build a geodesic dome.

Preparing: You may wish to show students pictures of geodesic domes. Point out that the domes are made of struts that connect to form a pattern of triangles. Explain that the struts must be cut to precise lengths in order to fit together. The figures given in this activity are correct for a geodesic dome with a frequency of 3 and a radius of 10 feet.

Materials	Group Size	Time on Task
Calculator (optional) Work chart	3 to 4 students	1 to 2 days

Guiding: Tell students that the lengths provided for each type of strut are given in feet. The decimal number represents a part of 1 foot, rather than a number of inches.

**Observing/
Monitoring:** As you move among the students, pose the following questions:

How could you use mental math to make these calculations easier?

Suppose you were building your own dome. How could you estimate these products to ensure that you bought enough material?

What are some ways you could check the accuracy of your results?

Unit 2 Performance Assessment Scoring Rubric

Building a Geodesic Dome

Score	Explanation
3	Students demonstrate an efficient strategy and a thorough approach that enables them to solve the problem completely. A satisfactory answer: • shows a clearly completed chart; • shows steps used to calculate the total length of metal pipe needed; • evaluates the estimate shown; • correctly calculates the cost of the pipe. Students are able to complete the problem quickly and have all of the correct solutions.
2	Students demonstrate a strategy that enables them to solve most of the problem correctly. The strategy is somewhat disorganized, making it less efficient. A solution is found, but errors are contained. Students may: • make an error in calculating the total length of metal pipe; • incorrectly evaluate the estimation; • make an error in calculating the cost of the pipe. Students have some difficulty determining all solutions correctly but demonstrate an understanding of general concepts.
1	Students demonstrate a confused strategy which leads to difficulty solving the problem. Most answers are incorrect, but students do demonstrate knowledge of at least one concept being assessed, such as multiplying whole numbers and decimals or estimating products of whole numbers and decimals.

Unit 2 Performance Assessment Student Activity

Building a Geodesic Dome

You will need
- a pencil
- a calculator (optional)

You are planning to build a geodesic dome made of metal pipe. The table below lists the number of three different lengths of pipe you will need.

Complete the table to find the total length of pipe you will need to buy.

Type	Length (in feet)	Number of Pipes	Total Length (in feet)
A	3.486	30	
B	4.035	40	
C	4.124	50	
		Total	

1. In your total, what is represented by the numbers to the right of the decimal point?

_____

2. A friend recommends that you find the total by estimating:

$(3.5 \times 30) + (4 \times 40) + (4 \times 50) =$ Total length needed

Do you think the estimate above is enough to build the dome? Explain.

_____

_____

_____

3. Suppose the cost of metal pipe is $0.55 per foot. How much will it cost to buy the pipe for your dome?

Unit 2 – Monitoring Student Progress

☐ **Form A**   ☐ **Form B**

Name _____ Date _____

Directions: This test targets selected objectives. For each item that is answered incorrectly, cross out the item number. Then record the number of correct responses in the column labeled **Number of Correct Responses.** Add to find the **Total Number of Correct Responses** and record the total. Use this total to determine the **Total Test Score** and the **Total Percent Correct.**

Strand • Objective(s)	Item Numbers	Number of Correct Responses
Number Sense, Concepts, and Operations • Multiply whole numbers and decimals. • Identify and use the properties of multiplication. • Estimate products of whole numbers and decimals. • Express products as powers and evaluate exponential expressions. • Use skills and strategies to solve problems.	1, 2, 3, 4, 5, 6, 7, 8, 9, 10, 11, 12, 13, 14, 15, 16, 17, 18, 19, 20, 21, 22, 23, 24, 25, 26, 27, 28, 29, 30, 31, 32, 33, 34, 35, 36, 37, 38, 39, 40	/40
Total Number of Correct Responses		
Total Test Score		/40
Total Percent Correct		%

Read each question carefully. Darken the circle on your answer sheet for the correct answer.

1. $7 \times 70 = \boxed{}$

   A. 490   **B.** 700   **C.** 770   **D.** 4,900

2. Which is the best estimate?

   $16 \times 4,125$

   F. 6,000   **H.** 80,000

   G. 8,000   **J.** 160,000

3. Rewrite using a base and an exponent.

   $7 \times 7 \times 7 \times 7 \times 7 \times 7$

   A. 6^7 **B.** 7^6 **C.** 7^7 **D.** 70^3

4. Which is the best estimate?

   $48 \times \$3.85$

   F. \$120 **G.** \$150 **H.** \$160 **J.** \$200

5. $1.9 \times 300 = \boxed{}$

   A. 5.70   **B.** 57.0   **C.** 570   **D.** 5,700

6. Identify the property shown.

   $3 \times 6 = 6 \times 3$

   F. Associative   **H.** Identity

   G. Commutative   **J.** Distributive

7. Which is the best estimate?

   5.12×8.2

   A. 4.5   **B.** 40   **C.** 400   **D.** 450

8. $\begin{array}{r} 7.003 \\ \times \quad 9 \\ \hline \end{array}$

   F. 6.327   **H.** 63.027

   G. 63.0027   **J.** 630.027

9. Which is the best estimate?

   23.6×127

   A. 200   **C.** 2,000

   B. 250   **D.** 4,000

10. Write in standard form.

   8^3

   F. 24   **G.** 64   **H.** 240   **J.** 512

11. $\begin{array}{r} 2.4 \\ \times \ 0.8 \\ \hline \end{array}$

   A. 1.092   **C.** 10.92

   B. 1.92   **D.** 19.2

GO ON

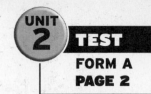
12. Which is the best estimate?

9.6×62.183

F. 54   **G.** 600   **H.** 5,400   **J.** 6,200

13. Identify the property shown.

$6 \times (3 + 4) = 6 \times 3 + 6 \times 4$

A. Associative   **C.** Identity

B. Commutative   **D.** Distributive

14. $0.6 \times 835 = \boxed{}$

F. 50.01   **G.** 50.1   **H.** 500.01   **J.** 501

15. Write in standard form.

10^4

A. 400   **C.** 10,000

B. 4,000   **D.** 100,000

16. Judi hiked through the Appalachian Mountains over summer vacation. Each day she hiked 12.35 miles. How far did she hike in 22 days?

F. 270.6 mi

G. 271.7 mi

H. 494 mi

J. 2,760 mi

17. A train trip cost $315.15 per person. How much did Fred's father pay for 5 tickets?

A. $15.55   **C.** $15,555.00

B. $1,575.75   **D.** $15,757.50

18. Mr. Hand takes 20 students to the science museum. Each student ticket costs $5.25. How much do the student tickets cost all together?

F. $10.50   **H.** $105.00

G. $52.50   **J.** $1,050.00

19. Kurt bought a CD and a book. The total cost of the CD and the book was $25 without tax. The CD cost $4 more than the book. How much did the book cost?

A. $8.00   **C.** $10.50

B. $9.50   **D.** $11.00

20. Earl bikes 19.78 miles in one day. Estimate how far he can bike in 2 weeks at that rate.

F. 40 mi   **H.** 148 mi

G. 140 mi   **J.** 280 mi

GO ON

21. $9 \times 8,000 =$ ▢

   A. 70,200   **C.** 702,000

   B. 72,000   **D.** 720,000

---

22. Which is the best estimate?

   $28 \times 11,151$

   F. 20,000   **H.** 100,000

   G. 30,000   **J.** 300,000

---

23. Rewrite using a base and an exponent.

   $6 \times 6 \times 6 \times 6 \times 6 \times 6 \times 6 \times 6 \times 6$

   A. 6^6 **C.** 9^6

   B. 6^9 **D.** 60

---

24. Which is the best estimate?

   $68 \times \$12.33$

   F. \$50   **H.** \$840

   G. \$60   **J.** \$1,200

---

25. $3.7 \times 60 =$ ▢

   A. 18.42   **C.** 184.2

   B. 22.20   **D.** 222

---

26. Rewrite using a base and an exponent.

   $11 \times 11 \times 11 \times 11 \times 11 \times 11$

   F. 6^1 **H.** 11^6

   G. 6^{11} **J.** 1,103

---

27. Which is the best estimate?

   8.77×41.2

   A. 20   **C.** 360

   B. 30   **D.** 3,600

---

28.   24.5
   $\times\ 12$

   F. 28.86   **H.** 288.6

   G. 29.4   **J.** 294

---

29. Which is the best estimate?

   75.8×391

   A. 240   **C.** 3,000

   B. 2,400   **D.** 32,000

---

30. Write in standard form.

   12^0

   F. 0   **H.** 12

   G. 1   **J.** 144

---

31.   6.6
   $\times\ 3.6$

   A. 5.94   **C.** 59.4

   B. 23.76   **D.** 237.6

GO ON

32. Which is the best estimate?

7.8×95.493

F. 78   **H.** 1,000

G. 780   **J.** 7,000

---

33. Write in standard form.

0^5

A. 0.25   **C.** 2.5

B. 1.0   **D.** 0

---

34. $0.7 \times 91.8 =$ ▨

F. 63.756   **H.** 637.56

G. 64.26   **J.** 642.6

---

35. Identify the property shown.

$10 \times 1 = 5 \times 2$

A. Associative   **C.** Identity

B. Commutative   **D.** Distributive

Solve.

36. Bev's family took a road trip to Alaska. They averaged 274.9 miles per day. How far did they drive in 9 days?

F. 1,836 mi

G. 2,474.1 mi

H. 24,668.1 mi

J. 24,741 mi

---

37. The French Club bought discount tickets to France for $328.19 per person. How much would 100 tickets cost?

A. $3,281.90

B. $32,819

C. $328,190

D. $3,281,900

---

38. Videos are on sale at Nelson's Video for $11.75 each. How much will 4 videos cost?

F. $15.75   **H.** $44.75

G. $44.00   **J.** $47.00

---

39. Kyle bought a T-shirt and a hat. The total cost of the T-shirt and the hat was $29.50 without tax. The T-shirt cost $13.50 more than the hat. How much did the hat cost?

A. $8.00   **C.** $13.50

B. $9.50   **D.** Not Here

---

40. Roman sells 39 tickets for the school play. Each ticket costs $3.75. Estimate how much money he should be paid.

F. $90   **H.** $1,200

G. $160   **J.** $1,600

STOP

Read each question carefully. Fill in the correct answer in the space provided.

1. $5 \times 80 =$ _____

_____

2. Estimate.

$19 \times 3,076$

_____

3. Rewrite using a base and an exponent.

$0 \times 0 \times 0 \times 0 \times 0 \times 0 \times 0$

_____

4. Estimate.

$62 \times \$53.05$

_____

5. $3.1 \times 400 =$ _____

6. Identify the property shown.

$7 \times 4 = 4 \times 7$

_____

_____

7. Estimate.

6.4×3.2

_____

_____

8. $3.526 \times 8 =$ _____

_____

9. Estimate.

13.5×450

_____

_____

10. Write in standard form.

13^0

_____

GO ON

11. $3.5 \times 0.7 =$ _____

_____

12. Estimate.

45.6×26.4

_____

13. Identify the property shown.

$5 \times (4 + 9) = (4 + 9) \times 5$

_____

14. $15.4 \times 0.8 =$ _____

_____

15. Write in standard form.

10^2

_____

16. Marcus went cross-country skiing over winter break. Every day he skied for 17.25 miles. How far did he ski in 8 days?

_____

17. Concert tickets cost $47 per person. How much did it cost for 16 people to attend the concert?

_____

18. A new backpack cost $29.96. If 19 students bought new backpacks, how much did they spend?

_____

19. Jeanine bought a book and a DVD. The total cost of the book and DVD was $37 without tax. The book cost $3 less than the DVD. How much did the DVD cost?

_____

20. Claire jogs 3.21 miles in one day. Estimate how far she can jog in a month at that rate.

_____

GO ON

21. $5 \times 3,000 =$ _____

_____

22. What is the best estimate?

$62 \times 23,094$

_____

23. Rewrite using a base and an exponent.

$3 \times 3 \times 3 \times 3 \times 3$

_____

24. What is the best estimate?

$45 \times \$82.97$

_____

25. $7.1 \times 70 =$ _____

26. Rewrite using a base and an exponent.

$15 \times 15 \times 15 \times 15$

_____

_____

27. What is the best estimate?

2.14×77.8

_____

28. $45.6 \times 15 =$ _____

_____

29. What is the best estimate?

19.3×857

_____

30. Write in standard form.

22^2

_____

GO ON

31. $6.3 \times 2.1 =$ _____

_____

32. What is the best estimate?

39.4×59.87

_____

33. Write in standard form.

0^2

_____

34. $0.7 \times 47.2 =$ _____

_____

35. Identify the property shown.

$6 \times 1 = 2 \times 3$

_____

36. Audrey's family took a road trip around Europe. They averaged 389.4 kilometers per day. How far did they drive in 17 days?

_____

37. Tickets for the student play cost $5.25. How much would 1,000 tickets cost?

_____

38. Laptops are on sale for $1,095 each. How much would 8 laptops cost?

_____

39. James bought a CD and a poster. The total cost of the CD and poster was $22 without tax. The poster cost $6 less than the CD. How much did the CD cost?

_____

40. Suzanne sold 73 raffle tickets for the school fund-raiser. Each ticket costs $2.25. Estimate how much money she should be paid.

_____

STOP

Chapter 5 – Teacher Interview

Core Concept: *Interpreting the Remainder*

Student Activity: Students solve real-world problems by dividing and demonstrating an understanding of what is represented by the remainder. Assign problems such as: 3 friends decide to share 14 balloons. How many balloons does each friend receive?

Teacher Question 1:

- What operation can you use to solve this problem?

Understanding Student Response	Practice and Improvement
Students who say multiplication.	Review lesson 1 to remind students of the relationship between multiplication and division.
Students who say subtraction.	Review lesson 1 to show students that division can be used to solve this type of problem in a single step, whereas subtraction would have to be repeated.

Teacher Question 2:

- What is 14 divided by 3?

Understanding Student Response	Practice and Improvement
Students who say 11.	Review lesson 3 so students can practice dividing with 1-digit divisors.
Students who say 4.	Review lesson 3 to reinforce the idea that the remainder must be a part of their answer.

Teacher Question 3:

- What does the remainder of 2 represent?

Understanding Student Response	Practice and Improvement
Students who cannot explain what the remainder represents.	Review lesson 5 so students can see that the remainder of a real-world problem represents a number of objects.
Students who say the remainder represents 2 of the friends.	Review lesson 5 to reinforce the idea that the remainder is a leftover part of the dividend.

Chapter 5 – Journal Writing

Encourage students to generate their own journal entries related to math ideas in general or to concepts in this chapter. Present the following journal prompt and have students share their drawing/writing with a partner:

• How do fact families show the relationship between multiplication and division?

(Responses should indicate that certain multiplication and division facts can be grouped together in fact families.)

JOURNAL WRITING/PROBLEM SOLVING

What multiplication and division facts belong in a fact family with $3 \times 4 = 12$?

Read
Have students find the answer to the problem. Then ask them to write a few sentences telling—

• which information they used to find the answer

• what they did with the information

Have students make up another problem with different information for which they would have to follow the same procedure. Then have students solve the problem and supply the correct response.

Plan
Students must correctly list other facts from this fact family.

Solve
Correct responses to the assigned problem are $4 \times 3 = 12$, $12 \div 3 = 4$, and $12 \div 4 = 3$.

Look Back
A correct response demonstrates the ability to relate multiplication and division facts. (See scoring rubric on page 7.)

Chapter 5 – Monitoring Student Progress

☐ **Form A**   ☐ **Form B**

Name _____ Date _____

Directions: For each item that is answered incorrectly, cross out the item number. Then record the number of correct responses in the appropriate Student Score column. If the student has not met the Criterion Score for an objective, circle the student's score. Recommended assignments are listed in the Prescription Table on the next page.

Objective	Item Numbers	Criterion Score	Student Score
A. Divide whole numbers by 1-digit numbers.	2, 5, 8, 11, 15	4/5	/5
B. Divide by 10, 100, and 1,000.	1, 4, 7, 10, 13	4/5	/5
C. Estimate quotients of whole numbers.	3, 6, 9, 12, 14	4/5	/5
D. Use skills and strategies to solve problems.	16, 17, 18, 19, 20	4/5	/5
Total Test Score		16/20	/20
Total Percent Correct			%

Chapter 5 – Prescription Table

The following chart correlates the tested objectives for this chapter to supplementary materials that meet the individual needs of the students. The Reteach and Practice pages are designed for students who need further instruction in the math concepts taught in this chapter. The Enrich pages are designed for students who need advanced challenges.

Objective	Reteach	Practice	Enrich
A. Divide whole numbers by 1-digit numbers. 76	76, 82, 85	77, 83, 86	78, 84, 87
B. Divide by 10, 100, and 1,000.	79	80	81
C. Estimate quotients of whole numbers.	79	80	81
D. Use skills and strategies to solve problems.	88	89	90

Read each question carefully. Darken the circle on your answer sheet for the correct answer.

1. 300 ÷ 50 = ☐

    A. 150   **C.** 15

    B. 60   **D.** 6

2. 4)$\overline{267}$

    F. 60 R1   **H.** 66 R1

    G. 60 R3   **J.** 66 R3

3. Which is the best estimate?

    615 ÷ 6

    A. 60   **C.** 100

    B. 90   **D.** 120

4. 36,000 ÷ 9 = ☐

    F. 4,000   **H.** 40

    G. 400   **J.** 4

5. 3)$\overline{589}$

    A. 150   **C.** 196 R1

    B. 193 R1   **D.** 200

6. Which is the best estimate?

    2,568 ÷ 8

    F. 240   **H.** 320

    G. 300   **J.** 400

7. 540,000 ÷ 900 = ☐

    A. 6   **C.** 60

    B. 600   **D.** 6,000

8. 2)$\overline{8,469}$

    F. 4,144 R1   **H.** 4,250 R1

    G. 4,234 R1   **J.** 4,414 R1

9. Which is the best estimate?

    15,835 ÷ 2

    A. 9,000   **C.** 7,000

    B. 8,000   **D.** 6,000

10. 800 ÷ 20 = ☐

    F. 4,000   **H.** 40

    G. 400   **J.** 4

GO ON ➡

11. $3,557 \div 6 =$

   A. 600   **C.** 592 R5

   B. 593 R5   **D.** 590

---

12. Which is the best estimate?

   $3,477 \div 7$

   F. 500   **H.** 400

   G. 450   **J.** 350

---

13. $500,000 \div 500 =$

   A. 10   **C.** 1,000

   B. 100   **D.** 10,000

---

14. Which is the best estimate?

   $482,312 \div 4$

   F. 100,000   **H.** 140,000

   G. 120,000   **J.** 160,000

---

15. $13,753 \div 7 =$

   A. 2,000   **C.** 1,964

   B. 1,974 R5   **D.** 1,964 R5

---

16. A group of 80 students arrive at Marla's Restaurant. If each table at the restaurant seats 6 people, how many tables will the group need?

   F. 12 tables   **H.** 14 tables

   G. 13 tables   **J.** 15 tables

17. Each day a tourist group travels 5 hours by bus. If the group covers 600 miles in 3 days, how many miles does the group travel each day?

   A. 300 miles   **C.** 150 miles

   B. 200 miles   **D.** 120 miles

---

18. Doreen plans to share her stickers with 4 friends. If she has 55 stickers, how many stickers will each friend receive?

   F. 14 stickers   **H.** 12 stickers

   G. 13 stickers   **J.** 11 stickers

---

19. On a field trip, there is 1 adult for every 8 students. If 8 adults go on the field trip, about how many students are going on the field trip?

   A. 72 students

   B. 65 students

   C. 64 students

   D 56 students

---

20. Mark has a 794-page book. If he reads 35 pages an evening, about how many days will it take him to finish reading the book?

   F. 23 days   **H.** 21 days

   G. 22 days   **J.** 20 days

STOP

Read each question carefully. Fill in the correct answer in the space provided.

1. $400 \div 80 =$ _____

_____

2. $6\overline{)371} =$ _____

_____

3. Estimate.

$730 \div 8$

_____

4. If $420 \div 60 = 7$, what is $4,200 \div 60$?

_____

_____

5. $4\overline{)423} =$ _____

6. Estimate.

$3,289 \div 6$

_____

7. If $63 \div 7 = 9$, what is $630,000 \div 700$?

_____

_____

8. $5\overline{)4,766} =$ _____

_____

9. What is the best estimate?

$3,469 \div 7$

_____

10. If $90 \div 30 = 3$, what is $900 \div 30$?

_____

GO ON ▶

11. What is 3,938 ÷ 7?

_____

12. What is the best estimate?

4,666 ÷ 8

_____

13. If 420,000 ÷ 7,000 = 60,
what is 4,200 ÷ 700?

_____

14. Estimate.

199,256 ÷ 314

_____

15. 17,395 ÷ 4 = _____

16. Francesca's Restaurant seats 72 people.
If each table has 6 seats, how many
tables does Francesca's Restaurant have?

_____

17. A tourist group travels 200 miles a
day. If the bus goes 50 miles per hour,
how many hours does the group
spend traveling?

_____

18. Josh has a collection of 165 baseball
cards. If he shares the cards with
4 friends, how many cards will each
friend receive?

_____

19. Fifty-seven students visit a whaling
museum. If there is 1 adult for every
6 students, how many adults go on
the field trip?

_____

20. Dena reads 40 pages every evening.
If her book has 632 pages, about
how many days will it take her to read
her book?

_____

STOP

Chapter 6 – Teacher Interview

Core Concept: *Dividing Whole Numbers and Decimals*

Student Activity: Students demonstrate an understanding of how to divide whole numbers and decimals. Assign problems such as 1,296.4 ÷ 27 or 25.04 ÷ 6.3. The examples below apply to the first problem.

Teacher Question 1:

• What steps did you use to find the quotient and remainder?

Understanding Student Response	Practice and Improvement
Students who try dividing several numbers before determining the first digit in the quotient.	Review Chapter 5, lesson 2 to help students recall how to estimate in order to determine the first digit when dividing.
Students who divide as with whole numbers and then guess the placement of the decimal point.	Review lesson 4 to reinforce steps for dividing numbers with decimals.

Teacher Question 2:

• How can you estimate to check whether your answer is reasonable?

Understanding Student Response	Practice and Improvement
Students who estimate by dividing 1,000 by 20.	Review Chapter 5, lesson 2 to help students recall guidelines for estimating.
Students who estimate by dividing 1,000 by 207.	Review lesson 1 to help reinforce estimating with compatible numbers.

Teacher Question 3:

• How can you prove that your answer is right?

Understanding Student Response	Practice and Improvement
Students who estimate by dividing 1,200 by 30.	Review Chapter 5, lesson 1 to help students recall how to check quotients by multiplying.
Students who redo the problem several times to check correctness.	Review Chapter 5, lesson 1 to reinforce the relationship between multiplication and division.

Chapter 6 – Journal Writing

Encourage students to generate their own journal entries related to math ideas in general or to concepts in this chapter. For students requiring guidance, present the following journal prompt:

- When you are problem solving, why is it important to categorize the information? What are some tools you can use to categorize the information in a word problem?

  (Responses should include references to necessary vs. unnecessary information. Some ways to organize information are to use a table, chart, or a graphic organizer.)

JOURNAL WRITING/PROBLEM SOLVING

In a 50-square mile reserve, there are approximately 820 deer, 2,120 birds, 6,500 squirrels, and 950 raccoons. About how many birds per square mile are in the reserve?

Read

Have students find the answer to the problem. Then ask them to write a few sentences telling—

- which information they used to find the answer

- what they did with that information.

Have students make up another problem with different information for which they would have to follow the same procedure. Then have students solve the problem and supply the correct answer.

Plan

Students must recognize that the problem involves dividing, knowing how to divide by a 2-digit number, and how to round decimals to whole numbers.

Solve

The correct response to the assigned problem is about 42 birds per square mile. Students had to know the number of birds and the miles in the reserve. Then they had to divide the number of birds by the number of miles, computing correctly and rounding to the nearest whole number.

Look Back

A correct response demonstrates the ability to discriminate between necessary vs. unnecessary information and apply the appropriate operation to solve the problem. (See scoring rubric on page 7.)

Chapter 6 – Monitoring Student Progress

☐ Form A   ☐ Form B

Name _____ Date _____

Directions: For each item that is answered incorrectly, cross out the item number. Then record the number of correct responses in the appropriate Student Score column. If the student has not met the Criterion Score for an objective, circle the student's score. Recommended assignments are listed in the Prescription Table on the next page.

Objective	Item Numbers	Criterion Score	Student Score
A. Divide whole numbers by 2-digit numbers.	1, 5, 8, 11, 15	4/5	/5
B. Divide whole numbers and decimals.	2, 4, 7, 10, 13	4/5	/5
C. Estimate quotients of whole numbers and decimals.	3, 6, 9, 12, 14	4/5	/5
D. Use skills and strategies to solve problems.	16, 17, 18, 19, 20	4/5	/5
Total Test Score		16/20	/20
Total Percent Correct			%

Chapter 6 – Prescription Table

The following chart correlates the tested objectives for this chapter to supplementary materials that meet the individual needs of the students. The Reteach and Practice pages are designed for students who need further instruction in the math concepts taught in this chapter. The Enrich pages are designed for students who need advanced challenges.

Objective	Reteach	Practice	Enrich
A. Divide whole numbers by 2-digit numbers.	94, 97	95, 98	96, 99
B. Divide whole numbers and decimals.	100	101	102
C. Estimate quotients of whole numbers and decimals.	91	92	93
D. Use skills and strategies to solve problems.	103, 104	105	

Name_____

Read each question carefully. Darken the circle on your answer sheet for the correct answer.

1. 4,397 ÷ 11 =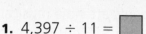

   A. 400   **C.** 399

   B. 399 R8   **D** 390 R8

2. Round to the nearest tenth.

   32.9 ÷ 5 =

   F. 658   **H.** 6.6

   G. 65.8   **J.** 6.58

3. Which is the best estimate?

   855 ÷ 29

   A. 20   **C.** 40

   B. 30   **D.** 50

4. Round to the nearest hundredth.

   262 ÷ 6.2 =

   F. 42.26   **H.** 4.23

   G. 42.2   **J.** 4.2

5. 6,296 ÷ 35 =

   A. 178 R29   **C.** 179 R29

   B. 178 R31   **D.** 179 R31

6. Which is the best estimate?

   739 ÷ 68

   F. 100   **H.** 10

   G. 50   **J.** 7

7. Round to the nearest tenth.

   65.08 ÷ 9 =

   A. 7.2

   B. 7.23

   C. 72

   D. 72.3

8. 52)‾2,984

   F. 5.52   **H.** 55R20

   G. 5.72   **J.** 57 R20

9. Which is the best estimate?

   5,724 ÷ 27

   A. 300   **C.** 30

   B. 200   **D.** 20

10. 4.68 ÷ 13 =

   F. 36   **H.** 0.36

   G. 3.6   **J.** 0.336

GO ON

11. $29\overline{)6,578}$

A. 227   **C.** 226 R24

B. 227 R14   **D.** 226

12. Which is the best estimate?

6,277 ÷ 75

F. 70   **H.** 700

G. 80   **J.** 800

13. Round to the nearest hundredth.

337 ÷ 4.4 =

A. 76.59   **C.** 85

B. 76.5   **D.** 85.59

14. Which is the best estimate?

46,771 ÷ 52

F. 70   **H.** 700

G. 80   **J.** 900

15. 3,335 ÷ 99 =

A. 30   **C.** 34

B. 33 R68   **D.** 34 R68

16. The music group needs $500. Adult tickets cost $5 and student tickets cost $2. If 60 adult tickets are sold, how many students need to buy tickets to reach $500?

F. 40 tickets   **H.** 100 tickets

G. 50 tickets   **J.** 200 tickets

17. Twenty-five students attend a musical concert. Tickets cost $15 but they receive a group discount of $45. How much did the concert cost for all twenty-five students?

A. $330   **C.** $675

B. $375   **D.** $1,125

18. A plumber charges a flat fee of $40 per repair, plus an hourly rate. If the plumber charges $120 for a repair that takes 4 hours, what is the hourly rate?

F. $80   **H.** $30

G. $40   **J.** $20

19. The school computer class raised money to buy computers for the school. They spent $200 on flyers. They spent half of the remaining money on printing raffle tickets. The class still has $350. How much money did they raise?

A. $1,000   **C.** $550

B. $900   **D.** $450

20. A running club has 112 members who are either coaches or runners. There are 8 coaches. Of the runners, $\frac{1}{2}$ are sprinters. How many sprinters does the club have?

F. 64 sprinters   **H.** 56 sprinters

G. 60 sprinters   **J.** 52 sprinters

STOP

Name _____

Read each question carefully. Fill in the correct answer in the space provided.

1. $2,879 \div 13 =$ _____

_____

2. Round to the nearest tenth.

$52.8 \div 6 =$ _____

_____

3. Estimate.

$658 \div 14$

_____

4. Round to the nearest hundredth.

$375 \div 8.8 =$ _____

_____

5. $4,849 \div 22 =$ _____

6. Estimate.

$924 \div 85$

_____

7. Round to the nearest tenth.

$57.5 \div 7 =$ _____

_____

8. $63\overline{)3,433} =$ _____

_____

9. Estimate.

$3,842 \div 48$

_____

10. $7.56 \div 42 =$ _____

GO ON

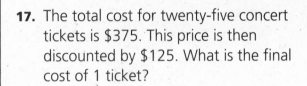

11. $37\overline{)7,463}$ = _____

12. Estimate.

1,762 ÷ 46

_____

_____

13. Round to the nearest hundredth.

668 ÷ 5.5 = _____

_____

14. Estimate.

71,062 ÷ 82

_____

_____

15 5,119 ÷ 88 = _____

_____

16. The French club raised $600 selling concert tickets. Adult tickets cost $12 and student tickets cost $2. If 40 adult tickets were sold, how many students bought tickets?

_____

17. The total cost for twenty-five concert tickets is $375. This price is then discounted by $125. What is the final cost of 1 ticket?

_____

_____

18. A plumber charges a flat fee of $25 per repair, plus an hourly rate. If the plumber charges $85 for a repair that takes 2 hours, what is the hourly rate?

_____

19. The computer class raised $1,200 to buy computers for the school. They spent $300 on advertising and half of the remaining money on renting a booth. How much did the club spend on renting the booth?

_____

20. A running club has 135 members who are either coaches or runners. There are 15 coaches. Of the runners, $\frac{1}{3}$ are sprinters. How many sprinters does the club have?

_____

STOP

Unit 3 Performance Assessment

Road Trip

- *Target Skill:*   Divide whole numbers and decimals.
- *Additional Skills:*   Multiply whole numbers and interpret remainders.

**Task
Description:** This task requires students to select between planned trips, based on miles traveled per day. The students are then asked to compute the cost of gas. Both tasks involve division of decimals.

Preparing: You may wish to have the students review multiplication of whole numbers and decimals.

Materials	Group Size	Time on Task
Calculator (optional)	1 to 2 students	1 day

Guiding: Remind students that this is a round trip, and the mileage should reflect that.

Tell students that the family buys one tank of gas for every full (and partial) day of the trip.

**Observing/
Monitoring:** As you move among the students, pose the following questions:

Which remainders are part of the solution, and which are not?

How can you calculate how many gallons of gas they will buy on the trip?

Unit 3 Performance Assessment Scoring Rubric

Road Trip

Score	Explanation
3	Students demonstrate an efficient strategy and a thorough approach that enables them to solve the problem completely. A satisfactory answer: • demonstrates correct division; • calculates the proper destination and cost of gas; • shows all work. Students are able to complete the problem quickly and have all of the above correct solutions.
2	Students demonstrate a strategy that enables them to solve most of the problem correctly. The strategy is somewhat disorganized, making it less efficient. A solution is found, but errors are contained. Students may: • decide on the correct destination; • not have divided all numbers correctly. Students may have some difficulty determining all solutions correctly but demonstrate an understanding of general concepts.
1	Students demonstrate a confused strategy, which leads to difficulty solving the problem. Most answers are incorrect, but students demonstrate knowledge of at least one concept being assessed, such as division of dividends with decimals or interpretation of remainders.

Unit 3 Performance Assessment Student Activity

Road Trip

You will need
- Calculator (optional)

Connie and her family are planning to spend part of their summer vacation visiting parts of America they've never seen.

They want to drive across the country to either San Diego, which is 1,847.6 miles away, or to Seattle which is 1,635.1 miles away. Use the following information:

- The family car gets 25 miles per gallon, and the tank holds 12 gallons.
- Connie's parents want to fill the tank once a day, at most.
- They must return in time for Aunt Mamie's visit, 12 days after they leave.

Complete the chart to help them decide which trip is possible. Then answer the question below the chart.

Destination	Miles (round-trip)	How far we can go on one tank?	Number of days needed for trip	Home in time?
San Diego				
Seattle				

If the family spends $223.08 on gas, what would be the average cost of gas per gallon on the trip?

Unit 3 – Monitoring Student Progress

☐ **Form A**   ☐ **Form B**

Name _____ Date _____

Directions: This test targets selected objectives. For each item that is answered incorrectly, cross out the item number. Then record the number of correct responses in the column labeled **Number of Correct Responses.** Add to find the **Total Number of Correct Responses** and record the total. Use this total to determine the **Total Test Score** and the **Total Percent Correct.**

Strand • Objective(s)	Item Numbers	Number of Correct Responses
Number Sense, Concepts, and Operations • Divide whole numbers by 1-digit numbers. • Divide whole numbers by 2-digit numbers. • Divide by 10, 100, and 1,000. • Estimate quotients of whole numbers and decimals. • Divide whole numbers and decimals. • Use skills and strategies to solve problems.	1–40	/40
Total Number of Correct Responses		
Total Test Score		/40
Total Percent Correct		%

Read each question carefully. Darken the circle on your answer sheet for the correct answer.

1. $418 \div 22 =$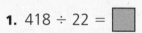

A. 240   C. 24

B. 190   D. 19

---

2. Round to the nearest tenth.

5)6.5

F. 1.1   H. 1.5

G. 1.3   J. 1.7

---

3. 4)10.4

A. 2.2   C. 2.6

B. 2.4   D. 2.1

---

4. $452 \div 24 =$

F. 18 R2   H. 19

G. 18 R20   J. 19.4

---

5. $23.2 \div 8 =$

A. 2.2   C. 3.1

B. 2.9   D. 3.7

---

6. $4.8 \div 10 =$

F. 48   H. 0.048

G. 0.48   J. 0.0048

---

7. Which is the best estimate?

$316 \div 8$

A. 45   C. 31

B. 40   D. 30

---

8. 100)954

F. 95.4   H. 0.954

G. 9.54   J. 0.0954

---

9. $77.3 \div 100 =$

A. 773   C. 0.773

B. 7.73   D. 0.073

---

10. Which is the best estimate?

$5,746 \div 72$

F. 65   H. 500

G. 80   J. 800

---

11. $6.21 \div 1,000 =$

A. 6.21   C. 0.00621

B. 0.0621   D. 0.000621

---

12. Which is the best estimate?

$8,696 \div 92$

F. 9   H. 900

G. 90   J. 1,000

---

13. $83.002 \div 1,000 =$

A. 830.02   C. 0.83002

B. 8.3002   D. 0.083002

---

14. Which is the best estimate?

$27,504 \div 32$

F. 90   H. 9,000

G. 900   J. 90,000

GO ON

15. Which is the best estimate?

48,030 ÷ 23

A. 100   **C.** 1,000

B. 200   **D.** 2,000

16. Ben took a one-week train trip through Mexico. The train covered 1,489 miles. About how far did the train average each day?

F. 20 mi

G. 40 mi

H. 50 mi

J. 60 mi

17. The archaeological museum collected $2,448 in ticket fees one day. If each ticket cost $8, how many people bought tickets?

A. 301 people

B. 306 people

C. 316 people

D. 3,100 people

18. Each table at the Sea Land Café seats 6 people. How many tables will a group of 98 students need if they eat at the same time?

F. 6 tables

G. 7 tables

H. 16 tables

J. 17 tables

19. The smallest hummingbird weighs about 0.1 pound. The largest ostrich weighs about 300 pounds. Compare the weights of the largest and smallest birds.

A. 300 times heavier

B. 3,000 times heavier

C. 4,800 times heavier

D. 48,000 times heavier

20. A group of students visit a zoo. They pay $5.50 for each student, but receive a $12.50 group discount. They pay $37 for the group's admission. How many students are in the group?

F. 6 students

G. 7 students

H. 9 students

J. 10 students

GO ON

21. 2,842 ÷ 49 = ▢

   A. 54   **C.** 58

   B. 55 R3   **D.** 59

22. 8.5 ÷ 100 = ▢

   F. 8500   **H.** 0.85

   G. 85   **J.** 0.085

23. 6)11.4

   A. 19   **C.** 2.4

   B. 9   **D.** 1.9

24. 32.9 ÷ 7 = ▢

   F. 3.5   **H.** 4.7

   G. 3.8   **J.** 4.9

25. 27,904 ÷ 32 = ▢

   A. 802   **C.** 827

   B. 817   **D.** 872

26. 9.86 ÷ 10 = ▢

   F. 98.6   **H.** 0.0986

   G. 0.986   **J.** 0.00986

27. Which is the best estimate?

    573 ÷ 18

   A. 3   **C.** 30

   B. 5   **D.** 300

28. 887 ÷ 100 = ▢

   F. 88.7   **H.** 0.887

   G. 8.87   **J.** 0.0887

29. 475.22 ÷ 100 = ▢

   A. 47.522   **C.** 0.47522

   B. 4.7522   **D.** 0.047522

30. Which is the best estimate?

    3,895 ÷ 62

   F. 6   **H.** 600

   G. 60   **J.** 6,000

31. 1.643 ÷ 1,000 = ▢

   A. 16.43   **C.** 0.01643

   B. 0.1643   **D.** 0.001643

32. Which is the best estimate?

    43,799 ÷ 71

   F. 60   **H.** 600

   G. 70   **J.** 6,000

GO ON

33. 395.0081 ÷ 1,000 = ☐

   A. 39.50081   **C.** 0.3950081

   B. 3.950081   **D.** 0.03950081

---

34. Which is the best estimate?

   36,881 ÷ 39

   F. 90   **H.** 900

   G. 100   **J.** 9,000

---

35. Which is the best estimate?

   8,221 ÷ 420

   A. 20   **C.** 200

   B. 100   **D.** 2,000

---

36. Terri was sightseeing in the Brazilian rain forest. During 6 days, she traveled 53.4 miles. How far did she average each day?

   F. 8.2 mi

   G. 8.7 mi

   H. 8.9 mi

   J. 89 mi

---

37. The tropical zoo collected $2,884 in ticket fees one day. If each ticket cost $7, how many people bought tickets?

   A. 402 people

   B. 412 people

   C. 512 people

   D. 522 people

38. A group of 145 tourists wants to take a boat trip on the Amazon River. Each boat holds 28 people. How many boats will they need for all of the tourists?

   F. 4 boats

   G. 5 boats

   H. 5.2 boats

   J. 6 boats

---

39. Galapagos turtles can reach up to 500 pounds. Galapagos turtles can gain 45 pounds a year. About how long does it take for a 180 pound turtle to reach the maximum weight?

   A. 4 years

   B. 5 years

   C. 7 years

   D. 11 years

---

40. A group of friends visit a museum that usually charges $9.50 for each person; but they receive a $6.50 group discount. They pay $41 for the group's admission. How many friends are in the group?

   F. 4 friends

   G. 5 friends

   H. 6 friends

   J. 7 friends

STOP

Read each question carefully. Fill in the correct answer in the space provided.

1. $368 \div 16 =$ _____

_____

2. Round to the nearest tenth.

$88\overline{)5,284}$

_____

3. $9\overline{)25.2}$

_____

4. $54\overline{)4,226}$

_____

_____

5. $725 \div 38 =$ _____

6. $84 \div 1,000 =$ _____

_____

7. Estimate.

$861 \div 9$

_____

8. $10\overline{)4.59}$

_____

_____

9. $37.5 \div 100 =$ _____

_____

10. Estimate.

$3,764 \div 75$

_____

GO ON

11. 0.126 ÷ 10 = _____

_____

12. Estimate.

2,969 ÷ 51

_____

_____

13. 2,308 ÷ 100 = _____

_____

14. Estimate.

23,405 ÷ 72

_____

_____

15. Estimate.

32,030 ÷ 84

_____

_____

16. Marcia flew from New York to San Francisco in six hours. The plane traveled 3,158 miles. How far did the plane average per hour? Round to the nearest tenth.

_____

17. The aquarium collected $7,608 in ticket fees one day. If each ticket cost $12, how many people bought tickets?

_____

_____

18. Each table at Jeannie's seats 4 people. How many tables will a group of 11 teachers need if they eat at the same time?

_____

_____

19. A poem has 20 words. A novel has 30,000 words. Compare the lengths of the novel and poem.

_____

_____

20. A group of students visit an amusement park. They pay $9 for each student, but receive a $15 group discount. They pay $57 for the group's admission. How many students are in the group?

_____

GO ON

21. 4,592 ÷ 82 = _____

_____

22. 100)526.3

_____

_____

23. 37)2,113

_____

_____

24. 557 ÷ 100

_____

_____

25. 9)24.3

_____

26. 68.9 ÷ 1,000 = _____

_____

27. Estimate.

813 ÷ 75

_____

_____

28. 78.8 ÷ 10 = _____

_____

29. 225.7 ÷ 1,000 = _____

_____

30. Estimate.

3,159 ÷ 83

_____

GO ON

31. 3,461 ÷ 100 = _____

_____

32. Estimate.

17,997 ÷ 34

_____

_____

33. 1,859.3 ÷ 100 = _____

_____

34. Estimate.

93,168 ÷ 98

_____

_____

35. Estimate.

2,421 ÷ 28

_____

_____

36. A copier made 16,710 copies in the month of April. How many pages were printed per day? Round to the nearest page.

_____

37. The high school collected $1,265 in ticket fees for a football game. If each ticket was $11, how many people bought tickets?

_____

_____

38. Mark wants to place 75 baseball cards in protective sleeves. If each sleeve holds 9 cards, how many sleeves does he need?

_____

_____

39. Tara reads about 70 pages an hour. About how long would it take her to read a 757-page novel?

_____

_____

40. A group of friends attend a concert that offers a $20 group discount. Each ticket costs $14. They pay $78 for the group's admission. How many friends are in the group?

_____

STOP

Chapter 7 – Teacher Interview

Core Concept: *Range, Mean, Median, and Mode*

Student Activity: Students demonstrate an understanding of how to use range, mean, median, and mode for understanding and displaying data. Assign problems such as: A group of students compare the money they earn baby sitting during a week. Ben earns $20, Lisa $35, Jackie $20, Sam $42, Barry $55, and Sue $28. What are the range, mean, median, and mode?

Teacher Question 1:

• How did you find the range of the data? The mean? The median? The mode?

Understanding Student Response	Practice and Improvement
Students who say the median is the number that appears most often (or the mode is the middle number).	Review lesson 2 to reinforce how to find median, range, mode, and mean.
Students who say the range is the average of the numbers (or the mean is the difference between the largest and smallest numbers).	Review lesson 2 to reinforce how to find median, range, mode, and mean.

Teacher Question 2:

• How would you display the data in a line plot?

Understanding Student Response	Practice and Improvement
Students who put the students' names on the bottom and money on the side (or the names in one column and money in another column).	Review lesson 1 to help students recall line plots (and tables) and how they are different.
Students who put a picture of each student on the side and dollar signs for each dollar in a row next to each picture.	Review lessons 1 and 3 to help students recall line plots and pictographs and how they are different.

Teacher Question 3:

• What other kind of table or graph might you use to display this data? Why?

Understanding Student Response	Practice and Improvement
Students who would use a double bar graph because there is more than one student.	Review lesson 4 to help students understand situations for using different graphs.
Students who would use a pictograph because you can make a picture of a person.	Review lesson 3 to help students understand situations for using different graphs.

Chapter 7 – Journal Writing

Encourage students to generate their own journal entries related to math ideas in general or to concepts in this chapter. Present the following journal prompt and have students share their drawing/writing with a partner:

- What steps do you follow to make a line graph?

  (Responses should indicate drawing and labeling the vertical and horizontal axes, deciding on the intervals, plotting the points, connecting the points with a straight line, and giving the graph a title.)

JOURNAL WRITING/PROBLEM SOLVING

Kneepad sales from March through July at the In-line Skate Shop are 45, 60, 52, 48, and 39. Which type of a graph will best display the data? Make a graph of the data. What is the range, mean, median, and mode?

Read

Have students find the answer to the problem. Then ask them to write a few sentences telling——

- which information they used to find the answer

- what they did with the information

Have students make up another problem with different information for which they could have followed the same procedure. Then have students solve the problem and supply the correct response.

Plan

Students must decide on a graph that will best display the data, and make a graph. Students must also use the data to find the range, mean, median, and mode.

Solve

The correct response to the assigned problem is a correctly drawn and labeled line graph. The range is 21, the mean is 48.8, the median is 48, and there is no mode.

Look Back

A correct response demonstrates the ability to use key words in the problem to determine the kind of graph to show the best way to display the data and then use the data to find the range, mean, median, and mode. (See scoring rubric on page 7.)

Chapter 7 – Monitoring Student Progress

☐ Form A   ☐ Form B

Name _____ Date _____

Directions: For each item that is answered incorrectly, cross out the item number. Then record the number of correct responses in the appropriate Student Score column. If the student has not met the Criterion Score for an objective, circle the student's score. Recommended assignments are listed in the Prescription Table on the next page.

Objective	Item Numbers	Criterion Score	Student Score
A. Read and interpret data in line plots, pictographs, bar graphs, and line graphs.	1, 7, 10, 12, 15	4/5	/5
B. Organize and display data in line plots, pictographs, bar graphs, and line graphs.	6, 11, 16	2/3	/3
C. Find range, mean, median, and mode.	2, 3, 4, 5, 8, 9, 13, 14	7/8	/8
D. Use skills and strategies to solve problems.	17, 18, 19, 20	3/4	/4
Total Test Score		16/20	/20
Total Percent Correct			%

Chapter 7 – Prescription Table

The following chart correlates the tested objectives for this chapter to supplementary materials that meet the individual needs of the students. The Reteach and Practice pages are designed for students who need further instruction in the math concepts taught in this chapter. The Enrich pages are designed for students who need advanced challenges.

Objective	Reteach	Practice	Enrich
A. Read and interpret data in line plots, pictographs, bar graphs, and line graphs.	113, 116 119	114, 117 120	115, 118 121
B. Organize and display data in line plots, pictographs, bar graphs, and line graphs.	107	108	109
C. Find range, mean, median, and mode.	110	111	112
D. Use skills and strategies to solve problems.	122	123	124

Name _____

Read each question carefully. Darken the circle on your answer sheet for the correct answer.

Use the line plot for problems 1–6.

Students Who Own CDs

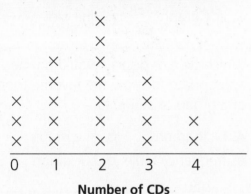

Number of CDs

1. How many students own CDs?

   A. 3   **B.** 10   **C.** 18   **D.** 21

2. What is the range of the number of CDs?

   F. 7   **G.** 5   **H.** 4   **J.** 3

3. What is the median number of CDs?

   A. 5   **B.** 4   **C.** 3   **D.** 2

4. What is the mean of the number of CDs to the nearest tenth?

   F. 1.9   **H.** 3.2
   G. 4   **J.** 2.2

5. What is the mode of the number of CDs?

   A. 4   **C.** 2
   B. 3   **D.** 1

6. Which other kind of graph would best show the data?

   F. histogram

   G. stem-and-leaf plot

   H. frequency table

   J. double-bar graph

Use the line graph for problems 7–11.

7. How much money does Mike save during the 6-week period?

   A. $210 **B.** $200 **C.** $100 **D.** $50

8. What is the range of money saved in dollar amounts?

   F. $50   **G.** $40   **H.** $20   **J.** $10

9. What is the mode for the set of data?

   A. $10   **B.** $20   **C.** $40   **D.** $50

10. In which week does Mike save the least amount of money?

   F. Week 2   **H.** Week 4
   G. Week 3   **J.** Week 6

GO ON

11. Suppose a pictograph of this set of data shows $$ for week 2. What would the graph show for Week 6?

A. $$$$$$ **C.** $$$

B. $$$$ **D.** $$

Use the pictograph for problems 12–16.

Favorite After School Sports	
Sport	**Number of Students**
Soccer	🧍🧍🧍🧍🧍🧍🧍
Basketball	🧍🧍🧍🧍🧍🧍
Football	🧍🧍🧍🧍🧍🧍🧍🧍🧍
Baseball	🧍🧍🧍🧍🧍🧍🧍🧍
Swimming	🧍🧍🧍🧍🧍

Key: each 🧍 = 5 students

12. How many students participate in after school sports?

F. 40   **G.** 80   **H.** 100   **J.** 200

13. What is the median for the set of data?

A. 50   **B.** 45   **C.** 40   **D.** 35

14. What is the mean for this set of data?

F. 35   **G.** 40   **H.** 45   **J.** 50

15. Which two sports represent 70 students?

A. Soccer and Basketball

B. Basketball and Football

C. Baseball and Football

D. Swimming and Soccer

16. What other type of graph would best display the data?

F. bar graph   **H.** double bar graph

G. line graph   **J.** line plot

17. Which type of display would not be appropriate to show the favorite foods of a group of students?

A. pictograph   **C.** line graph

B. frequency table **D.** bar graph

18. A puppy weighed 2 lb at birth and weighed 18 pounds after 4 months. You keep track of the weight on a line graph. Which intervals are most appropriate for the axis showing the number of pounds?

F. intervals of 2 pounds

G. intervals of 5 pounds

H. intervals of 10 pounds

J. intervals of 18 pounds

19. Which type of graph could you use to best display the number of inches of rainfall during a 12-month period?

A. double bar graph   **C.** bar graph

B. line graph   **D.** pictograph

20. Which type of display is best for comparing the costs of four bicycles?

F. double bar graph

G. line graph

H. frequency table

J. bar graph

STOP

Name _____

Read each question carefully. Fill in the correct answer in the space provided.

Use the line plot for problems 1–6.

Museum Visits in a Month

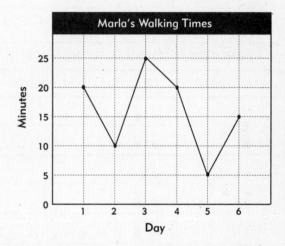

```
                ×
        ×       ×       ×
×               ×   ×   ×
×       ×       ×   ×   ×
──────────────────────────
0       1       2   3   4
```

Number of Visits

1. How many students visited the museum?

_____

2. What is the range of the number of visits to the museum?

_____

3. What is the median number of visits?

_____

4. What is the mean of the number of visits to the nearest tenth?

_____

5. What is the mode of the number of visits?

_____

6. Which other kind of graph would best show the data?

_____

_____

Use the line graph for problems 7–11.

Marla's Walking Times

(line graph: Minutes vs. Day; points at Day 1 = 20, Day 2 = 10, Day 3 = 25, Day 4 = 20, Day 5 = 5, Day 6 = 15)

7. How many minutes does Marla walk during the 6-day period?

_____

8. What is the range of minutes walked?

_____

9. What is the mode for the set of data?

_____

10. On which day does Marla walk the least number of minutes?

_____

GO ON

11. Suppose you use a pictograph to display this set of data. You use a picture of one shoe to show a walking distance of 5 minutes. How many shoes would you show for day 6?

_____

Use the pictograph for problems 12–16.

Favorite Musical Instruments	
Instrument	**Number of Students**
Drums	♪♪♪♪♪♪♪
Piano	♪♪♪♪
Trumpet	♪
Violin	♪♪
Guitar	♪♪♪♪♪♪

Key: each ♪ = 5 students

12. How many students play a musical instrument?

_____

13. What is the median for the set of data?

_____

14. What is the mean for this set of data?

_____

15. Which two musical instruments represent 25 students?

_____

16. Write *true* or *false*. A double bar graph could also be used to show the data.

_____

17. Which type of display would **not** be appropriate to show the favorite juice drinks of a group of students?

_____

18. Jerry planted a seed that grew into a 24-inch tall plant after 4 months. Suppose he makes a line graph to show changes in the plant's height over time. Which intervals are most appropriate for the axis showing the number of inches?

_____

19. Which type of graph could you use to best display the number of inches of snowfall during a 6-week period—a double bar graph or a line graph?

_____

20. Which type of graph might you use to convince your teacher that more students want to visit the science museum than the zoo—a line graph or bar graph?

_____

STOP

Chapter 8 – Teacher Interview

Core Concept: *Stem-and-Leaf Plots*

Student Activity: Students demonstrate an understanding of organizing data and are able to make a stem-and-leaf plot. Provide students with the following problem: The list shows the number of movie rentals over a ten-day period: 25, 24, 46, 30, 8, 30, 22, 37, 5, 49, 22, 42. How can a stem-and-leaf-plot be used to organize the data?

Teacher Question 1:

- How will you organize the data?

Understanding Student Response	Practice and Improvement
Students who order the data from greatest to least.	Review lesson 2 to reinforce an understanding of how a stem-and-leaf plot shows data.
Students who say the stems for the plot are the ones digits (or the leaves for the plot are the tens digits).	Review lesson 2 to reinforce an understanding of what each stem shows and what the leaves show.

Teacher Question 2:

- How will you make a stem-and-leaf plot for the data?

Understanding Student Response	Practice and Improvement
Students who label the stem without adding the numbers 0, 1, 2, 3, and 4.	Review lesson 2 to help students learn to write the stems 0, 1, 2, 3, and 4.
Students who do not include a leaf for each data point.	Review lesson 2 to help students learn that each data point has a leaf. Make sure students understand that, for the data set shown, the stem-and-leaf plot should show the stem–and–leaves: 2 │ 2 = 4 5.
Students who do not include a key such as 3 │ 7 = 10.	Review lesson 2 to reinforce an understanding of what the key to a stem–and–leaf plot shows.
Students who do not label the stems and leaves, or do not title their stem-and-leaf plot.	Review lesson 2 to allow students to examine the stem-and-leaf plots. Point out each of the different parts of a plot to the student. You may make a checklist for the students to refer to when practicing.

Chapter 8 – Journal Writing

Encourage students to generate their own journal entries related to math ideas in general or to concepts in this chapter. Present the following journal prompt and have students share their drawing/writing with a partner:

- When you are choosing a type of graph to display data, why is it important to know which type of graph to use?

  (Responses should indicate that certain types of graphs display data better than others and that an appropriate graph presents data accurately and clearly.)

JOURNAL WRITING/PROBLEM SOLVING

The chart shows the number of students by age that attended camp for the years 2001–2005. Present the data in a histogram. Which year had the highest attendance?

Read

Have students find the answer to the problem. Then ask them to write a few sentences telling—

Age of Students

Year	6–7	7–8	9–10	11–12
2001	15	22	25	35
2002	15	20	30	42
2003	17	25	38	45
2004	16	23	40	40
2005	15	25	37	41

- which information they used to find the answer

- what they did with the information

Have students make up another problem with different information for which they could have followed the same procedure. Then have students solve the problem and supply the correct response.

Plan

Students must correctly follow the steps for making a histogram.

Solve

The correct response to the assigned problem is a histogram that shows the number of students attending soccer camp from 2001–2005. In 2003, 125 students attended camp, the highest attendance.

Look Back

A correct response demonstrates the ability to follow the steps in making a histogram from the data in the chart. (See scoring rubric on page 7.)

Chapter 8 – Monitoring Student Progress

☐ Form A   ☐ Form B

Name _____ Date _____

Directions: For each item that is answered incorrectly, cross out the item number. Then record the number of correct responses in the appropriate Student Score column. If the student has not met the Criterion Score for an objective, circle the student's score. Recommended assignments are listed in the Prescription Table on the next page.

Objective	Item Numbers	Criterion Score	Student Score
A. Read and interpret data in histograms and stem-and-leaf plots.	1, 2 ,3 ,4 ,7 ,8 ,9 ,10	7/8	/8
B. Organize and display data in histograms and stem-and-leaf plots.	5,11	1/2	/2
C. Select a random sample.	12, 13, 14, 15, 16	4/5	/5
D. Use skills and strategies to solve problems.	6, 17, 18, 19, 20	4/5	/5
Total Test Score		16/20	/20
Total Percent Correct			%

Chapter 8 – Prescription Table

The following chart correlates the tested objectives for this chapter to supplementary materials that meet the individual needs of the students. The Reteach and Practice pages are designed for students who need further instruction in the math concepts taught in this chapter. The Enrich pages are designed for students who need advanced challenges.

Objective	Reteach	Practice	Enrich
A. Read and interpret data in histograms and stem-and-leaf plots.	125, 128	126, 129	127, 130
B. Organize and display data in histograms and stem-and-leaf plots.	131, 132	133	
C. Select a random sample.	134	135	136
D. Use skills and strategies to solve problems.	131, 132	133	

Read each question carefully. Darken the circle on your answer sheet for the correct answer.

Use the histogram for problems 1-6.

Earnings: Selling Notepads

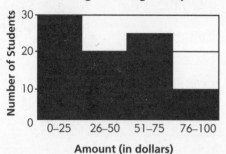

1. How many students sold notepads?

A. 85   **B.** 75   **C.** 50   **D.** 30

2. How many students sold between $26 and $50 worth of notepads?

F. 10   **G.** 20   **H.** 25   **J.** 30

3. What is the greatest number of students that could have earned $17 dollars?

A. 10   **B.** 20   **C.** 25   **D.** 30

4. How many students sold between $51 and $100 worth of notepads?

F. 55   **G.** 45   **H.** 35   **J.** 25

5. Suppose 10 more students earned $115 from selling notepads. Which interval would you add to the histogram?

A. 126–150   **C.** 101–125
B. 101–150   **D.** 101–115

6. What other kind of display would best show this data?

F. double bar graph

G. line graph

H. frequency table

J. pictograph

Use the stem-and-leaf plot for problems 7–11.

Bike Rentals for 2 Weeks

```
2 | 3 3 4 6
3 | 2 3 3 5 6 6    Key: 2|3 = 23
4 | 1 3 5
5 | 4 6
```

7. During how many days did people rent more than 36 bikes

A. 4   **B.** 5   **C.** 6   **D.** 7

8. During how many days did people rent fewer than 35 bikes?

F. 2   **G.** 5   **H.** 7   **J.** 10

9. Each bike rental costs $7. If 50 bikes were rented during 2 days, how much did the rental shop earn?

A. $250   **C.** $300
B. $275   **D.** $350

10. Which stem has the most leaves?

F. 2   **G.** 3   **H.** 4   **J.** 5

GO ON

11. Suppose you use a histogram to display this set of data. Which interval would show a gap?

A. 0–19   **C.** 30–39
B. 20–29   **D.** 40–49

12. In a population of 1,000 people, 150 people are surveyed. What are the people surveyed called?

F. a population   **H.** a representative
G. a sample   **J.** a survey

13. There are 400 students in a school. If you put all their names in a hat, and choose 100 students, which type of a sample would you have?

A. random   **C.** representative
B. biased   **D.** population

14. Suppose 2 friends pick 25 students out of a total of 500 students for a survey. What is the population in this example?

F. 2 friends
G. 25 students chosen
H. 475 students not chosen
J. 500 students

15. A survey asks the 15 youngest members in 3 classes of fifth-graders to name the President of the United States. What kind of a sample is this?

A. population   **C.** representive
B. random   **D.** biased

16. If each member of the school population has the same chance of being chosen for a survey, what kind of a sample is that?

F. random
G. biased
H. population
J. representative

17. Which type of display would best show the average temperatures of 50 cities?

A. line graph
B. stem-and-leaf plot
C. double bar graph
D. bar graph

18. Which type of graph could you use to best display the prices of hardware stock during one year?

F. histogram   **H.** double bar graph
G. line graph   **J.** pictograph

19. Which type of graph could you use to best display the number of boys and girls who attended computer camp each year from 2002–2004?

A. double bar graph   **C.** bar graph
B. line graph   **D.** pictograph

20. Kelly measured the heights of 100 students. She wants to organize her data into 5 groups. Which type of display should she use?

F. double bar graph   **H.** pictograph
G. line graph   **J.** histogram

STOP

Name _____

Read each question carefully. Fill in the correct answer in the space provided.

Use the histogram for problems 1–6.

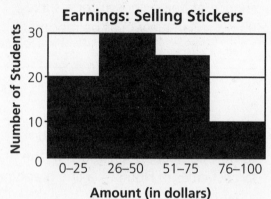

Earnings: Selling Stickers

Amount (in dollars)

1. How many students sold stickers?

_____

2. How many students sold between $26 and $50 worth of stickers?

_____

3. What is the greatest number of students that could have earned $63?

_____

4. How many students sold between $51 and $100 worth of stickers?

_____

5. 10 more students earned $120 from selling stickers. Which interval would you add to the histogram?

_____

6. What other kind of display would best show this data?

_____

Use the stem-and-leaf plot for problems 7–11.

Kayak Rentals for 2 Weeks

```
2 | 3 4 4 5
3 | 2 3 4 5 5 6    Key: 2|3 = 23
4 | 1 3 4
5 | 2 8
```

7. During how many days did people rent more than 25 kayaks?

_____

8. During how many days did people rent fewer than 36 kayaks?

_____

9. Each kayak rental costs $9. If 50 kayaks were rented during 2 days, how much did the rental shop earn?

_____

10. Which stem has the least leaves?

_____

GO ON

11. Suppose you use a bar graph to display this set of data. Which interval would show a gap?

_____

_____

12. At a concert, 6 students survey 500 of the 3,000 people who bought tickets. How many people are in the sample?

_____

13. If you put all the names of students in a hat and choose 200 students of 800 students, which type of a sample would you have?

_____

14. Suppose 50 students of a total of 750 were chosen for a survey. How many students are in the population?

_____

15. A survey asks the 15 oldest members in 3 classes of fifth-graders to name the capital of their state. What kind of a sample is this—representative or biased?

_____

16. Write *true* or *false*. If each member of the school population has the same chance of being chosen for a survey, then the sample would be random.

_____

_____

17. Which type of graph could you use to best compare populations of the largest cities in Florida—a line graph or a bar graph?

_____

18. Which type of graph would be the best display for showing the prices of eggs during one year—a double bar graph or a line graph?

_____

19. Which type of graph could you use to best display the number of boys and girls who attended sports camp each year from 2002–2004—a bar graph or a double bar graph?

_____

20. Which type of graph could you use to best display the number of students in a school and their ages in equal intervals—a line graph or a histogram?

_____

STOP

Unit 4 Performance Assessment

Everyone Talks About the Weather

- *Target Skill:*   Find range, mean, median, and mode.
- *Additional Skills:*   Demonstrate understanding of the concept of mode.

**Task
Description:** This task requires students to research weather facts in a newspaper and then derive statistics from the data.

Preparing: You may wish to have the students review the ideas of and differences between range, mean, median, and mode.

Materials	Group Size	Time on Task
National daily newspaper	2 to 3 students	1 day

Guiding: Tell students that they should work together to collect their data.

Remind students to arrange the data so that each problem is easier to solve.

**Observing/
Monitoring:** As you move among the students, pose the following questions:

To what place does it make sense to round the mean?

What does it mean if there is no mode?

How does the range change with the different seasons?

Unit 4 Performance Assessment Scoring Rubric

Everyone Talks About the Weather

Score	Explanation
3	Students demonstrate an efficient strategy and a thorough approach that enables them to solve the problem completely. A satisfactory answer: • selects the proper data; • calculate the statistics correctly; • interprets the data sensibly. Students are able to complete the problem quickly and have all of the above correct solutions.
2	Students demonstrate a strategy that enables them to solve most of the problem correctly. The strategy is somewhat disorganized, making it less efficient. A solution is found, but errors are contained. Students may: • select the correct data; • confuse the mean, median, or mode with one another. Students have some difficulty determining all solutions correctly but demonstrate an understanding of general concepts.
1	Students demonstrate a confused strategy, which leads to difficulty solving the problem. Most answers are incorrect, but students demonstrate knowledge of at least one concept being assessed. Students may: • find the proper data; OR • correctly calculate 1 or 2 statistics using inappropriate data.

Unit 4 Performance Assessment Student Activity

Everyone Talks About the Weather

You will need
• National newspaper's weather page

Work with a partner. Look in the newspaper together to find yesterday's temperature in these nine U.S. cities. Fill in the chart and answer the questions below:

City	°F
Boston	
Philadelphia	
Atlanta	
Miami	
Phoenix	
Seattle	
Kansas City	
Anchorage	
Denver	

1. What was the mean temperature in the nine cities yesterday?

_____

2. What was the range of temperatures?

_____

3. What was the median temperature?

_____

4. Was there a mode? Are you surprised? Why?

_____

Unit 4 – Monitoring Student Progress

☐ Form A   ☐ Form B

Name _____ Date _____

Directions: This test targets selected objectives. For each item that is answered incorrectly, cross out the item number. Then record the number of correct responses in the column labeled **Number of Correct Responses.** Add to find the **Total Number of Correct Responses** and record the total. Use this total to determine the **Total Test Score** and the **Total Percent Correct.**

Strand • Objective(s)	Item Numbers	Number of Correct Responses
Data Analysis and Probability • Read and interpret data in line plots, pictographs, bar graphs, and line graphs. • Organize and display data in line plots, pictographs, bar graphs, and line graphs. • Find range, mean, median, and mode. • Read and interpret data in histograms and stem-and-leaf plots. • Organize and display data in histograms and stem-and-leaf plots. • Select a random sample. • Use skills and strategies to solve problems.	1, 2, 3, 4, 5, 6, 7, 8, 9, 10, 11, 12, 13, 14, 15, 16, 17, 18, 19, 20, 21, 22, 23, 24, 25, 26, 27, 28, 29, 30, 31, 32, 33, 34, 35, 36, 37, 38, 39, 40	/40
Total Number of Correct Responses		
Total Test Score		/40
Total Percent Correct		%

Read each question carefully. Darken the circle on your answer sheet for the correct answer.

Use the line plot for exercises 1–6.

Library Visits in a Month

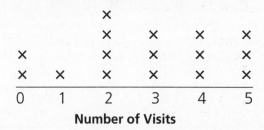

Number of Visits

1. How many students were surveyed?

A. 10   **B.** 12   **C.** 16   **D.** Not Here

2. What is the median of the number of visits?

F. 2   **G.** 3   **H.** 4   **J.** 5

3. What is the mode of the number of visits?

A. 2   **B.** 3   **C.** 4   **D.** 5

4. What is the mean of the number of visits to the nearest tenth?

F. 2   **G.** 2.8   **H.** 3   **J.** 3.2

5. What is the range of the number of visits?

A. 1   **B.** 2   **C.** 3   **D.** 5

6. What other kind of display would best show the data?

F. histogram

G. stem-and-leaf plot

H. frequency table

J. double-bar graph

Use the bar graph for exercises 7–11.

Favorite Juices

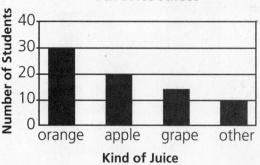

Kind of Juice

7. How many more students chose orange juice than apple juice?

A. 5   **B.** 10   **C.** 20   **D.** 50

8. What other type of graph would best display the data?

F. line graph

G. stem-and-leaf plot

H. pictograph

J. double-bar graph

9. How many students chose apple juice and grape juice altogether?

A. 10   **C.** 25

B. 20   **D.** 35

10. Which is the most popular juice?

F. apple   **H.** grape

G. orange   **J.** other

11. How many fewer students chose grape juice than orange juice?

A. 5   **B.** 10   **C.** 15   **D.** 30

GO ON

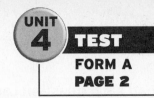
Use the histogram for exercises 12–14.

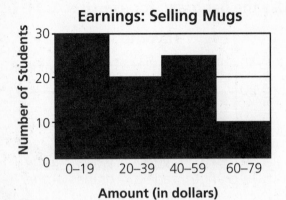

12. The fewest number of students earned which amount?

F. $0–$19   **H.** $40–$59

G. $20–$39   **J.** $60–$79

---

13. How many students sold 0–19 dollars worth of mugs?

A. 25   **B.** 30   **C.** 35   **D.** 55

---

14. How many students sold mugs?

F. 30   **G.** 50   **H.** 75   **J.** 85

Use the stem-and-leaf plot for exercises 15–17.

Canoes Rented Over Two Weeks

```
2 | 4 4 5 6
3 | 3 4 4 5 6
4 | 2 3 4        Key: 2|4 means 24
5 | 1 3
```

15. During how many days did people rent more than 35 canoes?

A. 5   **B.** 6   **C.** 7   **D.** 8

16. Each rental costs $5. During how many days did rentals bring in more than $250?

F. 2   **G.** 5   **H.** 10   **J.** 14

---

17. During how many days did people rent fewer than 33 canoes?

A. 4   **B.** 5   **C.** 6   **D.** 8

---

18. Sarah wants to survey bikers to see which bike trails are the most popular in the park. In order to get a random sample, when should she survey the bikers in the park?

F. in the morning

G. in the afternoon

H. in the evening

J. at random times

---

19. The Amoco Cadiz spilled 68 million gallons of oil. The Braer spilled 25 million, and the Torrey Canyon spilled 37 million. If a bar graph is used to display the data, which intervals are most appropriate for the axis showing the number of gallons?

A. intervals of 10 gallons

B. intervals of 100 gallons

C. intervals of 10 million gallons

D. intervals of 100 million gallons

---

20. Which type of graph could you use to best display the daily high and low temperatures for 5 days?

F. double-bar graph

G. stem-and-leaf plot

H. histogram

J. line graph

GO ON

Use the line plot for exercises 21–26.

TV Sets in Houses

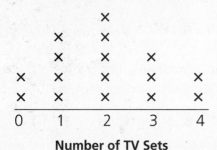

Number of TV Sets

---

21. How many students were surveyed?

A. 4   **B.** 16   **C.** 18   **D.** 122

---

22. What is the median of the number of TV sets?

F. 1   **G.** 2   **H.** 3   **J.** 4

---

23. What is the mode of the number of TV sets?

A. 2   **B.** 3   **C.** 4   **D.** 5

---

24. What is the mean of the number of TV sets to the nearest tenth?

F. 1.9   **H.** 3
G. 2.2   **J.** 3.2

---

25. What is the range of the number of TV sets?

A. 1   **B.** 2   **C.** 3   **D.** 4

---

26. What other kind of display would best show the data?

F. line graph
G. stem-and-leaf plot
H. frequency table
J. double-bar graph

Use the bar graph for exercises 27–31.

Favorite New Movies

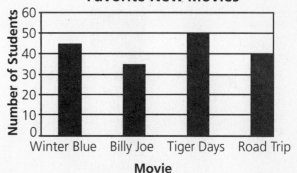

Movie

---

27. How many more students chose "Tiger Days" than "Billy Joe"?

A. 10   **B.** 15   **C.** 20   **D.** 25

---

28. What other type of graph would best display the data?

F. line graph
G. stem-and-leaf plot
H. pictograph
J. double-bar graph

---

29. How many students chose "Winter Blue" and "Tiger Days" altogether?

A. 45   **B.** 80   **C.** 85   **D.** 95

---

30. Which is the most popular movie?

F. "Billy Joe"   **H.** "Tiger Days"
G. "Winter Blue"   **J.** "Road Trip"

---

31. How many fewer students chose "Road Trip" than "Winter Blue"?

A. 5   **B.** 10   **C.** 15   **D.** 35

GO ON

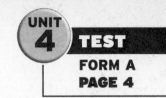

Use the histogram for exercises 32–34.

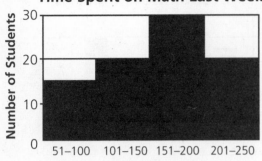

Time Spent on Math Last Week

32. The greatest number of students spent how much time?

F. 51–100 min   **H.** 151–200 min

G. 101–150 min   **J.** 201–250 min

33. How many students spent more than $2\frac{1}{2}$ hours on math homework last week?

A. 30   **B.** 50   **C.** 70   **D.** 85

34. How many students were surveyed?

F. 120   **G.** 85   **H.** 80   **J.** 30

Use the stem-and-leaf plot for exercises 35–37.

Lawn Mowers Rented Over a Year

```
1 | 7 8 9
2 | 7 8 8 8 9     Key: 1|7 means 17
3 | 4 5
4 | 1 1
```

35. During how many months were more than 20 lawn mowers rented?

A. 3   **B.** 5   **C.** 7   **D.** 9

36. Each rental costs $10. During how many months did rentals bring in more than $300?

F. 4   **G.** 6   **H.** 10   **J.** 11

37. During how many months were fewer than 28 lawn mowers rented?

A. 3   **B.** 4   **C.** 6   **D.** 10

Solve.

38. Which type of display would not be appropriate to show your friends' favorite meals?

F. pictograph

G. bar graph

H. histogram

J. frequency table

39. Ace Electronics earned $3 million last year. Game World earned $4.5 million, and Cyber Market earned $3.5 million. If a bar graph is used to display the data, which intervals are appropriate for the axis showing earnings?

A. intervals of $1

B. intervals of $2

C. intervals of 0.5 million dollars

D. intervals of 10 million dollars

40. Which type of graph could you use to best display the number of boys and girls who attended summer school each year from 1997–2000.

F. stem-and-leaf plot

G. histogram

H. double-bar graph

J. bar graph

STOP

Name_____

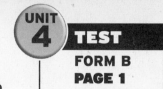

Read each question carefully. Fill in the correct answer in the space provided.

Use the line plot for exercises 1–6.

Video Store Visits In a Week

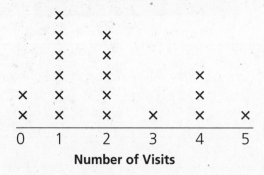

Number of Visits

1. How many students were surveyed?

   _____

2. What is the range of the number of visits?

   _____

3. What is the mean of the number of visits to the nearest tenth?

   _____

4. What is the median of the number of visits?

   _____

5. What is the mode of the number of visits?

   _____

6. What other kind of display would best show the data?

   _____

Use the bar graph for exercises 7–11.

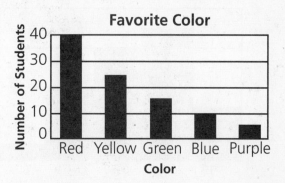

7. How many more students chose yellow than green?

   _____

8. How many students chose red and purple all together?

   _____

9. How many fewer students chose blue than red?

   _____

10. What is the most popular color?

    _____

11. What other type of graph would best display the data?

    _____

GO ON ▶

Use the histogram for exercises 12–14.

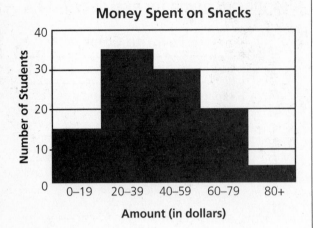

Money Spent on Snacks

12. How many students were surveyed?

_____

13. How many students spent 40–59 dollars on snacks?

_____

14. The least number of students spent what amount?

_____

Use the stem-and-leaf plot for exercises 15–17.

Daily Video Game Rentals

```
0 | 7 8 8 9
1 | 0 0 1 2    Key: 1|0 means 10 games
2 | 5
3 | 3 6 8
4 | 1
```

15. During how many days did people rent more than 13 games?

_____

16. Each rental costs $3. During how many days did rentals bring in more than $100?

_____

_____

17. During how many days did people rent less than 11 games?

_____

_____

18. Matt wants to survey joggers to see which jogging trails are the most popular in the park. In order to get a random sample, when should he survey joggers in the park?

_____

_____

19. Cathy is 1.4 meters tall. Sean is 1.6 meters tall. If a bar graph is used to display the data, what intervals are most appropriate for the axis showing the number of meters?

_____

_____

20. What type of graph could you use to best display the daily high and low temperatures for 5 days?

_____

GO ON

Name_____

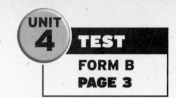
Use the line plot for exercises 21–26.

Computers in Houses

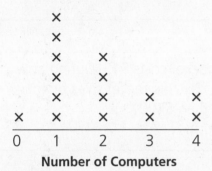

Number of Computers

21. How many students were surveyed?

_____

_____

22. What is the median of the number of computers?

_____

_____

23. What is the mode of the number of computers?

_____

_____

24. What is the mean of the number of computers to the nearest tenth?

_____

_____

25. What is the range of the number of computers?

_____

26. What other kind of display would best show the data?

_____

_____

Use the bar graph for exercises 27–31.

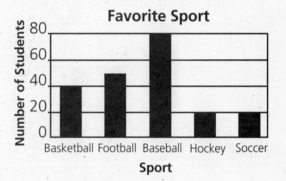

27. How many more students prefer football over hockey?

_____

_____

28. What other type of graph would best display this data?

_____

_____

29. How many students chose baseball and soccer altogether?

_____

_____

30. What is the most popular sport?

_____

GO ON

31. How many fewer students chose basketball than baseball?

_____

_____

Use the histogram for exercises 32–34.

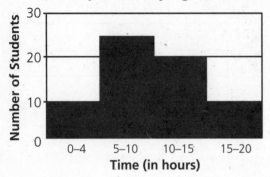

Time Spent Studying Last Week

32. The greatest number of students spent how much time studying?

_____

33. How many students spent more than 10 hours studying last week?

_____

34. How many students were surveyed?

_____

Use the stem-and-leaf plot for exercises 35–37.

Daily Tennis Racket Sales

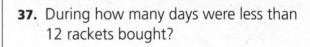

```
0 | 4 5 5 8
1 | 0 0 0 1 3 5 6 7 8
2 | 2
```

Key: 2|2 means 22 rackets

35. During how many days were more than 7 rackets bought?

_____

36. Each racket costs $45. During how many days did racket sales bring in more than $500?

_____

37. During how many days were less than 12 rackets bought?

_____

38. What type of display would be most appropriate for showing the average daily temperatures during July, a frequency table or a line graph?

_____

39. Ophel Industries lost $5.6 million last year. Telestrian Technologies lost $9.3 million, and Rosewood Manufacturing lost $1.7 million. If a bar graph is used to display the data, which intervals are appropriate for the axis showing losses?

_____

40. What type of graph could you use to best display the number of men and women who visited a fitness center each month during 2002?

_____

STOP

Chapter 9 – Teacher Interview

Core Concept: *Find Common Factors and Equivalent Fractions*

Student Activity: Students demonstrate an understanding of how to find common factors, and the GCF. Students also demonstrate an understanding of fractions and equivalent fractions. Present the students with several 2-digit numbers and ask them to find the factors of these numbers, and to identify common factors.

Teacher Question 1:
- List all the factors of 60.

Understanding Student Response	Practice and Improvement
Students cannot find the factors, or cannot find all of the factors.	Review lesson 3 to practice finding factors.
Students list multiples of 60.	Review lessons 1 and 3 to remind students that a number's factors are the numbers by which it can be evenly divided.

Teacher Question 2:
- What are the common factors of 18 and 30? What is their greatest common factor?

Understanding Student Response	Practice and Improvement
Students forget to include 1 and the number itself when finding factors.	Review lesson 2 and lesson 3 to help students identify all factors.
Students cannot identify common factors.	Review lesson 3 to help students compare lists of factors and find common factors.

Teacher Question 3:
- Find two equivalent fractions for $\frac{2}{3}$.

Understanding Student Response	Practice and Improvement
Students cannot find equivalent fractions, or do not understand what the fraction represents.	Review lesson 5 to help students understand equivalent fractions. Review lesson 4 to remind student how a fraction represents a part of a whole.
Students try to find equivalent fractions by adding equal amounts to the numerator and denominator.	Review lesson 5 to remind students to multiply or divide numerator and denominator by equal amounts.

Chapter 9 – Journal Writing

Encourage students to generate their own journal entries related to math ideas in general or to concepts in this chapter. For students requiring guidance, present the following journal prompt:

- When you read a word problem, why is it important to organize the information you find? What are some ways to organize the information in a word problem?

  (Responses should include references to necessary vs. unnecessary information. Some ways to organize information are to use a table, chart, or graphic organizer.)

JOURNAL WRITING/PROBLEM SOLVING

Stacy made 30 bracelets and 42 necklaces while she was at summer camp. She decided to give them to her friends as presents when she got home. She divided them up so that each of her friends would receive the same number of bracelets and the same number of necklaces, with none left over. What is the greatest number of friends to whom Stacy could have given her presents? How many bracelets and how many necklaces would each friend receive?

Read

Have students find the answer to the problem. Then ask them to write a few sentences telling—

- which information they used to find the answer

- what they did with that information

Have students make up another problem with different information.

Plan

Students must identify the situation as a problem relating to the GCF of two numbers and organize the facts as a simple problem. They must then apply the appropriate method to find the solution.

Solve

Stacy could give her gifts to 6 friends. 6 is the GCF of 30 and 42. Each friend would receive 5 bracelets and 7 necklaces.

Look Back

A correct response demonstrates the ability to discriminate between necessary and unnecessary information and apply the appropriate operation to solve the problem. (See scoring rubric on page 7.)

Chapter 9 – Monitoring Student Progress

☐ Form A   ☐ Form B

Name _____ Date _____

Directions: For each item that is answered incorrectly, cross out the item number. Then record the number of correct responses in the appropriate Student Score column. If the student has not met the Criterion Score for an objective, circle the student's score. Recommended assignments are listed in the Prescription Table on the next page.

Objective	Item Numbers	Criterion Score	Student Score
A. Identify prime or composite numbers.	1, 2, 7, 9, 13	4/5	/5
B. Find common factors and greatest common factors.	3, 5, 8, 12, 15	4/5	/5
C. Find equivalent fractions and simplify fractions.	4, 6, 10, 11, 14	4/5	/5
D. Use skills and strategies to solve problems.	16, 17, 18, 19, 20	4/5	/5
Total Test Score		16/20	/20
Total Percent Correct			%

Chapter 9 – Prescription Table

The following chart correlates the tested objectives for this chapter to supplementary materials that meet the individual needs of the students. The Reteach and Practice pages are designed for students who need further instruction in the math concepts taught in this chapter. The Enrich pages are designed for students who need advanced challenges.

Objective	Reteach	Practice	Enrich
A. Identify prime or composite numbers.	139, 142	140, 143	141, 144
B. Find common factors and greatest common factors.	145	146	147
C. Find equivalent fractions and simplify fractions.	148, 151, 154	149, 152, 155	150, 153, 156
D. Use skills and strategies to solve problems.	157	158	159

Read each question carefully. Darken the circle on your answer sheet for the correct answer.

1. Which number is prime?

    A. 14   **B.** 24   **C.** 29   **D.** 26

2. Which number is composite?

    F. 50   **G.** 47   **H.** 43   **J.** 41

3. What is the greatest common factor (GCF) of 24 and 64?

    A. 2   **B.** 4   **C.** 6   **D.** 8

4. Which is the simplest form of $\frac{60}{100}$?

    F. $\frac{4}{15}$ **G.** $\frac{5}{12}$ **H.** $\frac{3}{5}$ **J.** $\frac{1}{2}$

5. What is the greatest common factor (GCF) of 25 and 35?

    A. 15   **B.** 10   **C.** 5   **D.** 3

6. Which fraction is equivalent to $\frac{9}{12}$ and $\frac{18}{24}$?

    F. $\frac{6}{8}$ **G.** $\frac{3}{4}$ **H.** $\frac{5}{8}$ **J.** $\frac{2}{3}$

7. Which of the following numbers is **not** prime?

    A. 11   **B.** 13   **C.** 16   **D.** 17

8. What is the greatest common factor (GCF) of 14, 28, and 35?

    F. 2   **G.** 4   **H.** 5   **J.** 7

9. Which of the following is **not** composite?

    A. 48   **B.** 49   **C.** 50   **D.** 53

10. Which two fractions are equivalent to $\frac{2}{3}$?

    F. $\frac{3}{8}$ and $\frac{9}{18}$

    G. $\frac{9}{12}$ and $\frac{18}{24}$

    H. $\frac{4}{6}$ and $\frac{8}{12}$

    J. $\frac{5}{8}$ and $\frac{10}{16}$

11. Which is the simplest form of $\frac{12}{48}$?

    A. $\frac{1}{4}$ **B.** $\frac{1}{3}$ **C.** $\frac{1}{5}$ **D.** $\frac{1}{2}$

12. Which of the numbers is **not** a common factor of 24?

    F. 8   **G.** 6   **H.** 5   **J.** 4

13. Which number is composite?

    A. 29   **B.** 32   **C.** 37   **D.** 41

GO ON

14. Which is an equivalent fraction for $\frac{18}{36}$?

F. $\frac{1}{6}$ **G.** $\frac{1}{4}$ **H.** $\frac{1}{3}$ **J.** $\frac{1}{2}$

15. What is the greatest common factor (GCF) of 21 and 54?

A. 3   **B.** 4   **C.** 6   **D.** 9

16. Students sold tickets to the annual play. The math club sold $\frac{1}{4}$ of the tickets, the science club sold $\frac{3}{8}$ of the tickets, and the music group sold $\frac{1}{8}$ of the tickets. How many tickets did the math club sell? What information is missing to solve the problem?

F. the number of students attending the play

G. the total number of tickets sold

H. the cost of the tickets

J. the group who sold $\frac{1}{3}$ of the tickets

17. On the first night of the play, one row of seats was empty. The auditorium seats 350 people. How many seats were empty? What information is missing to solve the problem?

A. the number of adults attending the performance

B. the number of tickets sold for each performance

C. the number of seats in a row

D. the number of students attending the performance

18. Over 250 students attended the play. Each student bought a ticket. The runner's club sold $\frac{1}{4}$ of the tickets to adults. Student tickets cost $2. How much did the school collect from the students? What extra information is given?

F. Over 250 students attended.

G. The runner's club sold $\frac{1}{4}$ of the tickets to adults.

H. Student tickets cost $2.

J. Each student bought a ticket.

19. At the performance, 27 school ushers wore armbands. No one wanted to wear green armbands. One-half of the ushers wore yellow armbands. A second group wore red. One-third group wore blue. How many ushers word red armbands? What extra information is given?

A. 27 school ushers wore armbands.

B. No one wanted green armbands.

C. One group wore yellow armbands.

D. A second group wore red.

20. On the first night, 250 students and 100 adults attended the performance. Only one row of seats was empty. How many seats were empty? What information is missing?

F. the number of seats in the auditorium

G. the number of performers

H. the number of rows of seats in the auditorium

J. the number of tickets sold

STOP

Read each question carefully. Fill in the correct answer in the space provided.

1. Which number is prime?

22   32   37   44

_____

2. Which number is composite?

29   31   36   37

_____

3. What is the greatest common factor (GCF) of 18 and 36?

_____

4. What is the simplest form of $\frac{30}{90}$?

_____

5. What is the greatest common factor (GCF) of 20 and 45?

_____

6. What fraction is equivalent to $\frac{8}{12}$ and $\frac{16}{24}$?

_____

7. Which number is **not** prime?

13   16   17   19

_____

8. What is the greatest common factor (GCF) of 27, 36, and 45?

_____

9. Which number is **not** composite?

22   31   36   40

_____

10. Write two equivalent fractions for $\frac{2}{5}$.

_____

GO ON

11. Write $\frac{14}{56}$ in simplest form.

_____

12. Which number is not a common factor of 36?

4   5   6   8

_____

13. Which number is composite?

23   31   37   42

_____

14. Which is an equivalent fraction of $\frac{21}{35}$?

$\frac{1}{2}$ $\frac{3}{5}$ $\frac{2}{3}$ $\frac{3}{4}$

_____

15. What is the greatest common factor (GCF) of 32 and 48?

_____

16. Students sold tickets to the graduation dance. The social committee sold $\frac{3}{8}$ of the tickets, the band sold $\frac{1}{4}$ of the tickets, and the decoration committee sold $\frac{1}{4}$ of the tickets. How many tickets did the band sell? What information is missing to solve the problem?

_____

17. On the night of the dance, only one table was empty. All the other tables were full. If 8 people sat at each table, how many people attended the dance? What information is missing to solve the problem?

_____

18. A total of 175 tickets were sold to a dance. The social club sold $\frac{1}{8}$ of the tickets to adults. Each ticket costs $3. How much did the dance committees collect in ticket sales? What extra information is given in the problem?

_____

19. At the dance, 12 members of the dance committee wore colored bracelets. No one wanted to wear yellow bracelets. One-fourth of the members wore black bracelets. The social committee wore red bracelets. One-third of the members wore blue bracelets. How many members wore red bracelets? What extra information is given in the problem?

_____

20. On the night of the dance, 175 students and 20 adults attended. Only 5 tables were empty. How many tables were full? What information is missing to solve the problem?

_____

STOP

Chapter 10 – Teacher Interview

Core Concept: *Finding GCF, LCM, LCD*

Student Activity: Students demonstrate an understanding of how to find GCF, LCM, and LCD. Assign problems that require students to use GCF, LCM, and/or LCD to compare and order fractions and mixed numbers such as $\frac{2}{3}$, $\frac{5}{9}$ and $\frac{3}{5}$, or $2\frac{7}{8}$, $1\frac{1}{4}$, and $2\frac{4}{5}$.

Teacher Question 1:

• How did you come up with your answer?

Understanding Student Response	Practice and Improvement
Students who estimated how close to $\frac{1}{2}$ each fraction is.	Review lesson 2 to reinforce how to use the LCM and LCD to compare fractions.
Students who made three fraction strips to show each fraction.	Review lesson 2 to help students use the LCM and LCD to compare fractions.

Teacher Question 2:

• How do fractions change when you use their LCD to compare them?

Understanding Student Response	Practice and Improvement
Students who multiply (or change) the denominators only.	Review lesson 1 to help students recognize how the LCD is related to finding equivalent fractions.
Students who multiply the fractions (or their parts) by their LCD.	Review lesson 1 to make sure students understand LCD.

Teacher Question 3:

• How would the problem change if you had to compare a decimal (such as 0.61 or 2.79) with the fractions?

Understanding Student Response	Practice and Improvement
Students who would compare the fractions and then estimate whether the decimal was larger or smaller.	Review lesson 6 to help students recall how to compare and order fractions and decimals.
Students who would change all the numbers to fractions with denominators of 100.	Review lesson 6 to help students recall how to compare and order fraction and decimals.

Chapter 10 – Journal Writing

Encourage students to generate their own journal entries related to math ideas in general or to concepts in this chapter. For students requiring guidance, present the following journal prompt:

• When you are problem solving, why is it important to categorize the information? What are some tools you can use to categorize the information in a word problem?

(Responses should include references to necessary vs. unnecessary information. Some ways to organize information are to use a table, chart, or a graphic organizer.)

JOURNAL WRITING/PROBLEM SOLVING

For homework, Ben, Simone, and Terri have to do 20 math problems, answer 30 questions for French, and study a 2-page map. They also have to finish reading a book. After 2 days, Ben had read $\frac{7}{8}$ of the book. Simone had read $\frac{3}{4}$. Terri had read $\frac{6}{7}$. Who had read the most?

Read

Have students find the answer to the problem. Then ask them to write a few sentences telling—

• which information they used to find the answer

• what they did with that information

Have students make up another problem with different information for which they would have to follow the same procedure. Then have students solve the problem and supply the correct response.

Plan

Students must know how to find a common denominator, compute equivalent fractions, and compare fractions accurately.

Solve

The correct response to the assigned problem is Ben ($\frac{7}{8}$). Students had to find a common multiple of the denominators for all fractions (such as 56, the LCM) and use it to rewrite the fractions with a common denominator. Then they had to compare the fractions to determine which is the largest.

Look Back

A correct response demonstrates the ability to discriminate between necessary and unnecessary information and apply the appropriate operation to solve the problem. (See scoring rubric on page 7.)

Chapter 10 – Monitoring Student Progress

☐ Form A   ☐ Form B

Name _____ Date _____

Directions: For each item that is answered incorrectly, cross out the item number. Then record the number of correct responses in the appropriate Student Score column. If the student has not met the Criterion Score for an objective, circle the student's score. Recommended assignments are listed in the Prescription Table on the next page.

Objective	Item Numbers	Criterion Score	Student Score
A. Find common multiples, least common multiple, and least common denominator.	1, 2, 3, 9, 10, 11, 15	6/7	/7
B. Change a fraction to a decimal and a decimal to a fraction.	4, 7, 12, 13, 16	4/5	/5
C. Compare and order fractions, mixed numbers, and decimals.	5, 6, 8, 14	3/4	/4
D. Use skills and strategies to solve problems.	17, 18, 19, 20	3/4	/4
Total Test Score		16/20	/20
Total Percent Correct			%

Chapter 10 – Prescription Table

The following chart correlates the tested objectives for this chapter to supplementary materials that meet the individual needs of the students. The Reteach and Practice pages are designed for students who need further instruction in the math concepts taught in this chapter. The Enrich pages are designed for students who need advanced challenges.

Objective	Reteach	Practice	Enrich
A. Find common multiples, least common multiple, and least common denominator.	160	161	162
B. Change a fraction to a decimal and a decimal to a fraction.	166	167	168
C. Compare and order fractions, mixed numbers, and decimals.	163, 172, 175	164, 173, 176	165, 174, 177
D. Use skills and strategies to solve problems.	169, 170	171	

Read each question carefully. Darken the circle on your answer sheet for the correct answer.

1. What is the least common multiple (LCM) of 3 and 8?

   A. 16   **C.** 24

   B. 20   **D.** 32

2. What is the least common denominator (LCD) for $\frac{1}{2}$ and $\frac{3}{4}$?

   F. 4   **H.** 12

   G. 8   **J.** 16

3. Using the least common denominator (LCD), what are equivalent fractions for $\frac{2}{5}$ and $\frac{2}{3}$?

   A. $\frac{4}{10}$ and $\frac{4}{9}$ **C.** $\frac{8}{20}$ and $\frac{4}{9}$

   B. $\frac{6}{15}$ and $\frac{10}{15}$ **D.** $\frac{5}{15}$ and $\frac{9}{15}$

4. What is the fraction in simplest form for 0.3?

   F. $\frac{3}{1,000}$ **G.** $\frac{3}{100}$ **H.** $\frac{31}{100}$ **J.** $\frac{3}{10}$

5. Order $\frac{1}{3}$, $\frac{3}{10}$, $\frac{4}{15}$, and $\frac{1}{4}$ from least to greatest.

   A. $\frac{1}{3}$, $\frac{3}{10}$, $\frac{4}{15}$, $\frac{1}{4}$ **C.** $\frac{1}{4}$, $\frac{4}{15}$, $\frac{3}{10}$, $\frac{1}{3}$

   B. $\frac{1}{4}$, $\frac{3}{10}$, $\frac{4}{15}$, $\frac{1}{3}$ **D.** $\frac{1}{3}$, $\frac{4}{15}$, $\frac{3}{10}$, $\frac{1}{4}$

6. Write $\frac{44}{7}$ as a mixed number in simplest form.

   F. $6\frac{1}{7}$ **H.** $7\frac{1}{6}$

   G. $6\frac{2}{7}$ **J.** $7\frac{2}{7}$

7. Write $3\frac{3}{8}$ as a decimal.

   A. 0.338   **C.** 3.38

   B. 0.375   **D.** 3.375

8. Order $5\frac{5}{8}$, 5.07, $5\frac{7}{8}$, and 5.7 from greatest to least.

   F. $5\frac{5}{8}$, 5.07, $5\frac{7}{8}$, 5.7

   G. $5\frac{7}{8}$, 5.7, $5\frac{5}{8}$, 5.07

   H. 5.7, 5.07, $5\frac{7}{8}$, $5\frac{5}{8}$

   J. 5.07, $5\frac{5}{8}$, $5\frac{7}{8}$, and 5.7

9. What is the least common multiple (LCM) of 6 and 18?

   A. 42   **C.** 18

   B. 24   **D.** 6

10. What is the least common denominator (LCD) for $\frac{1}{3}$ and $\frac{5}{8}$?

   F. 32   **H.** 15

   G. 24   **J.** 8

GO ON

11. Using the least common denominator (LCD), what are equivalent fractions for $\frac{1}{3}$ and $\frac{5}{12}$?

A. $\frac{4}{12}$ and $\frac{5}{12}$ **C.** $\frac{12}{15}$ and $\frac{10}{24}$

B. $\frac{5}{15}$ and $\frac{5}{12}$ **D.** $\frac{3}{24}$ and $\frac{10}{24}$

12. What is the fraction in simplest form for 0.75?

F. $\frac{1}{4}$ **H.** $\frac{3}{4}$

G. $\frac{2}{3}$ **J.** $\frac{7}{8}$

13. Write 0.07 as a fraction.

A. $\frac{7}{1,000}$ **C.** $\frac{17}{100}$

B. $\frac{7}{100}$ **D.** $\frac{7}{10}$

14. Order $\frac{1}{3}$, $\frac{1}{2}$, $\frac{1}{5}$, and $\frac{1}{4}$ from greatest to least.

F. $\frac{1}{3}, \frac{1}{2}, \frac{1}{5}, \frac{1}{4}$ **H.** $\frac{1}{2}, \frac{1}{3}, \frac{1}{4}, \frac{1}{5}$

G. $\frac{1}{4}, \frac{1}{2}, \frac{1}{5}, \frac{1}{3}$ **J.** $\frac{1}{5}, \frac{1}{4}, \frac{1}{3}, \frac{1}{2}$

15. Write $6\frac{6}{9}$ as a mixed number in simplest form.

A. $7\frac{1}{3}$ **C.** $8\frac{1}{3}$

B. $6\frac{2}{3}$ **D.** $8\frac{2}{9}$

16. Write $12\frac{9}{10}$ as a decimal.

F. 12.009   **H.** 12.9

G. 12.09   **J.** 129

Use the table for problems 17–20.

Favorite Apples	Number of Students
Granny Smith	25
Delicious	20
Gala	15
Cortland	22
Empire	18

17. Which fraction, in simplest form, names the part of the group of students who like Granny Smith apples?

A. $\frac{1}{2}$ **C.** $\frac{1}{4}$

B. $\frac{1}{3}$ **D.** $\frac{1}{5}$

18. Which fraction, in simplest form, names the part of the group of students who like Cortland and Empire apples?

F. $\frac{2}{3}$ **H.** $\frac{1}{2}$

G. $\frac{2}{5}$ **J.** $\frac{1}{3}$

19. Which decimal names the part of the group of students who like Delicious apples?

A. 0.18   **C.** 0.22

B. 0.20   **D.** 0.25

20. Which decimal represents the group of students who like Granny Smith, Cortland, and Empire apples?

F. 0.45   **H.** 0.60

G. 0.50   **J.** 0.65

STOP

1. What is the least common multiple (LCM) of 5 and 8?

_____

_____

2. What is the least common denominator (LCD) for $\frac{1}{3}$ and $\frac{3}{5}$?

_____

_____

3. Using the least common denominator (LCD), what are equivalent fractions for $\frac{5}{6}$ and $\frac{3}{4}$?

_____

_____

4. What is the fraction in simplest form for 0.6?

_____

_____

5. Order $\frac{1}{4}$, $\frac{4}{10}$, $\frac{3}{8}$, and $\frac{1}{3}$ from least to greatest.

_____

6. Write $\frac{58}{9}$ as a mixed number in simplest form.

_____

_____

7. Write $5\frac{7}{8}$ as a decimal.

_____

_____

8. Order $4\frac{5}{6}$, 4.06, $4\frac{1}{6}$, and 4.6 from greatest to least.

_____

_____

9. What is the least common multiple (LCM) of 7 and 21?

_____

_____

10. What is the least common denominator (LCD) for $\frac{1}{4}$ and $\frac{5}{6}$?

_____

GO ON

11. Using the least common denominator (LCD), what are equivalent fractions for $\frac{1}{5}$ and $\frac{3}{8}$?

_____

_____

12. What is the fraction in simplest form for 0.67?

_____

_____

13. Write 0.03 as a fraction.

_____

_____

14. Order $\frac{1}{6}$, $\frac{4}{5}$, $\frac{3}{4}$, and $\frac{2}{3}$ from greatest to least.

_____

_____

15. Write $\frac{68}{8}$ as a mixed number in simplest form.

_____

_____

16. Write $23\frac{7}{10}$ as a decimal.

_____

Use the table for problems 17–20.

Favorite Vegetable	Number of Students
peas	35
string beans	20
corn	25
broccoli	12
squash	8

17. Which fraction, in simplest form, names the part of the group of students that likes corn?

_____

_____

18. Which fraction, in simplest form, names the part of the group that likes string beans, broccoli, and squash?

_____

_____

19. Which decimal names the part of the group that likes peas and squash?

_____

_____

20. Which decimal represents the group of students that likes peas and string beans?

_____

STOP

Unit 5 Performance Assessment

Put Me In, Coach!

- *Target Skill:*   Calculating decimals from fractions.
- *Additional Skills:*   Ordering fractions and decimals.

Task Description: This task requires students to calculate and order a set of fractions.

Preparing: You may wish to have the students review how to calculate a decimal from a fraction. You may also want to discuss what a batting average is.

Materials	Group Size	Time on Task
Calculator (optional)	1 to 2 students	1 day

Guiding: Tell students that they should calculate the decimals to three places.

Observing/ Monitoring: As you move among the students, pose the following questions:

Can you simplify the fractions to make computing easier?

What should you do if there is no remainder after the tenths place?

What should you do if the decimal repeats?

Unit 5 Performance Assessment Scoring Rubric

Put Me In, Coach!

Score	Explanation
3	Students demonstrate an efficient strategy and a thorough approach that enables them to solve the problem completely. A satisfactory answer: • calculates decimals from fractions correctly; • simplifies the fractions to make computing easier; • orders the decimals properly. Students are able to complete the problem quickly and have all of the above correct solutions.
2	Students demonstrate a strategy that enables them to solve most of the problem correctly. The strategy is somewhat disorganized, making it less efficient. A solution is found, but errors are contained. Students may: • correctly calculate most decimals; • order the decimals from greatest to least. Students may have some difficulty determining all solutions correctly but demonstrate an understanding of general concepts.
1	Students demonstrate a confused strategy, which leads to difficulty solving the problem. Most answers are incorrect, but students demonstrate knowledge of at least one concept being assessed. Students may: • calculate some decimals correctly; OR • order decimals from greatest to least.

Unit 5 Performance Assessment Student Activity

Put Me In, Coach!

You will need
- Calculator (optional)

You have volunteered to help Mr. Milch, the coach of the junior high baseball team, keep track of stats. Mr. Milch hasn't had much help, and his statistics aren't up to date. The big game with Lincoln is two days away, and the coach wants to order his hitters from best batting average to lowest. He hands you the following information.

$$\text{Batting Average} = \frac{\text{Hits}}{\text{At-Bats}}$$

Name	Hits/At-Bats	Batting Average
Roger	$\frac{15}{48}$	
Kiki	$\frac{12}{45}$	
Ed	$\frac{12}{48}$	
Tyrone	$\frac{16}{44}$	
Suzette	$\frac{12}{40}$	
Shampa	$\frac{22}{44}$	
Mickey	$\frac{15}{42}$	
Eduardo	$\frac{11}{44}$	
Rachel	$\frac{12}{36}$	

Find each player's average.

Then, order the averages for him, from highest batting average to lowest. Round each batting average to the nearest thousandth.

What is the batting order that Mr. Milch should use based on the batting averages?

Unit 5 – Monitoring Student Progress

☐ Form A   ☐ Form B

Name _____ Date _____

Directions: This test targets selected objectives. For each item that is answered incorrectly, cross out the item number. Then record the number of correct responses in the column labeled **Number of Correct Responses.** Add to find the **Total Number of Correct Responses** and record the total. Use this total to determine the **Total Test Score** and the **Total Percent Correct.**

Strand • Objective(s)	Item Numbers	Number of Correct Responses
Number Sense, Concepts, and Operations • Identify prime or composite numbers. • Find common factors and greatest common factors. • Find equivalent fractions and simplify fractions. • Find common multiples, least common multiple, and least common denominator. • Convert a fraction to a decimal and a decimal to a fraction. • Compare and order fractions, mixed numbers, and decimals. • Use skills and strategies to solve problems.	1, 2, 3, 4, 5, 6, 7, 8, 9, 10, 11, 12, 13, 14, 15, 16, 17, 18, 19, 20, 21, 22, 23, 24, 25, 26, 27, 28, 29, 30, 31, 32, 33, 34, 35, 36, 37, 38, 39, 40	/40
Total Number of Correct Responses		
Total Test Score		/40
Total Percent Correct		%

Read each question carefully. Darken the circle on your answer sheet for the correct answer.

1. Which number is prime?

   A. 51   **B.** 76   **C.** 87   **D.** 97

2. Which number is composite?

   F. 43   **G.** 61   **H.** 81   **J.** 83

3. Which is the simplest form of $\frac{40}{56}$?

   A. $\frac{10}{14}$ **B.** $\frac{5}{7}$ **C.** $\frac{11}{16}$ **D.** $\frac{5}{8}$

4. What is the decimal form of $\frac{3}{8}$?

   F. 0.38   **H.** 0.83

   G. 0.24   **J.** 0.375

5. Order $3\frac{7}{9}$, $\frac{29}{8}$, and 3.7 from least to greatest.

   A. 3.7, $3\frac{7}{9}$, $\frac{29}{8}$ **C.** $3\frac{7}{9}$, 3.7, $\frac{29}{8}$

   B. $\frac{29}{8}$, 3.7, $3\frac{7}{9}$ **D.** $3\frac{7}{9}$, $\frac{29}{8}$, 3.7

6. What is the least common multiple (LCM) of 8 and 15?

   F. 40   **G.** 80   **H.** 90   **J.** 120

7. Rewrite $\frac{1}{6}$, $\frac{4}{15}$, and $\frac{3}{4}$ using their least common denominator.

   A. $\frac{5}{30}$, $\frac{8}{30}$, $\frac{21}{30}$ **C.** $\frac{15}{90}$, $\frac{24}{90}$, $\frac{60}{90}$

   B. $\frac{10}{60}$, $\frac{16}{60}$, $\frac{45}{60}$ **D.** $\frac{20}{120}$, $\frac{32}{120}$, $\frac{90}{120}$

8. Which is the simplest form of $\frac{12}{54}$?

   F. $\frac{1}{6}$ **G.** $\frac{4}{18}$ **H.** $\frac{6}{27}$ **J.** $\frac{2}{9}$

9. Order $\frac{1}{3}$, 0.24, and $\frac{2}{7}$ from least to greatest.

   A. 0.24, $\frac{2}{7}$, $\frac{1}{3}$ **C.** $\frac{2}{7}$, 0.24, $\frac{1}{3}$

   B. 0.24, $\frac{1}{3}$, $\frac{2}{7}$ **D.** $\frac{2}{7}$, $\frac{1}{3}$, 0.24

10. Rewrite $\frac{3}{7}$, $\frac{1}{2}$, and $\frac{2}{3}$ using their least common denominator.

   F. $\frac{6}{14}$, $\frac{7}{14}$, $\frac{8}{14}$ **H.** $\frac{18}{42}$, $\frac{21}{42}$, $\frac{28}{42}$

   G. $\frac{12}{28}$, $\frac{14}{28}$, $\frac{18}{28}$ **J.** $\frac{36}{84}$, $\frac{42}{84}$, $\frac{56}{84}$

11. Write $\frac{46}{6}$ as a mixed number in simplest form.

   A. $6\frac{5}{6}$ **B.** $7\frac{1}{3}$ **C.** $7\frac{2}{3}$ **D.** 8

12. Write $\frac{42}{8}$ as a mixed number in simplest form.

   F. $5\frac{1}{21}$ **G.** $5\frac{1}{4}$ **H.** 6   **J.** $6\frac{2}{3}$

13. What is the prime factorization of 75?

   A. 5×3^2 **C.** 5×3^5

   B. 5×3^3 **D.** 3×5^2

14. What is the greatest common factor (GCF) of 18 and 81?

   F. 3   **G.** 6   **H.** 9   **J.** 18

GO ON

15. Order $\frac{9}{5}$, 1.2, and $1\frac{2}{5}$ from least to greatest on a number line.

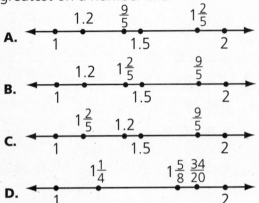

A.

B.

C.

D.

16. Order $1\frac{3}{10}$, $\frac{9}{4}$, and 1.85 from least to greatest.

F. $1\frac{3}{10}$, $\frac{9}{4}$, 1.85   **H.** 1.85, $\frac{9}{4}$, $1\frac{3}{10}$

G. $1\frac{3}{10}$, 1.85, $\frac{9}{4}$ **J.** $\frac{9}{4}$, 1.85, $1\frac{3}{10}$

Use the table for problems 17–18.

Favorite Sport	Number of Students
indoor swimming	3
basketball	12
skiing	6
skating	3
volleyball	8

17. Which fraction, in simplest form, names the part of the group of students who like basketball best?

A. $\frac{1}{8}$ **B.** $\frac{1}{4}$ **C.** $\frac{5}{16}$ **D.** $\frac{3}{8}$

18. Which fraction, in simplest form, names the part of the group of students who like volleyball best?

F. $\frac{1}{8}$ **G.** $\frac{1}{4}$ **H.** $\frac{5}{16}$ **J.** $\frac{3}{4}$

19. Three students agreed to sell tickets. Lisa sold $\frac{2}{7}$ of her tickets. Kelly sold $\frac{3}{14}$. Frank sold $\frac{1}{4}$.

What information is needed to find the number of tickets they each sold?

A. the number of students who attended the play

B. the cost of the ticket

C. the number of days the play will be running

D. the total number of tickets they each agreed to sell

20. Three students agreed to sell tickets. Lila sold 0.5 of her tickets. Terry sold 0.25. Vance sold 0.125. Who sold exactly $\frac{1}{8}$ of his or her tickets?

F. Lila   **H.** Vance

G. Terry

21. Which number is prime?

   A. 21   **B.** 49   **C.** 52   **D.** 73

---

22. Which number is composite?

   F. 24   **G.** 37   **H.** 61   **J.** 79

---

23. Which is the simplest form of $\frac{21}{56}$?

   A. $\frac{3}{8}$ **B.** $\frac{3}{7}$ **C.** $\frac{5}{16}$ **D.** $\frac{11}{28}$

---

24. What is the fractional form of 0.55?

   F. $\frac{11}{20}$ **H.** $\frac{1}{55}$

   G. $\frac{3}{20}$ **J.** $\frac{13}{20}$

---

25. Order $2\frac{3}{4}$, $\frac{25}{9}$, and 2.76 from least to greatest.

   A. $2\frac{3}{4}$, $\frac{25}{9}$, 2.76   **C.** 2.76, $2\frac{3}{4}$, $\frac{25}{9}$

   B. $2\frac{3}{4}$, 2.76, $\frac{25}{9}$ **D.** Not Here

---

26. What is the least common multiple (LCM) of 5, 6, and 8?

   F. 40   **G.** 60   **H.** 120   **J.** 240

---

27. Rewrite $\frac{1}{8}$, $\frac{1}{3}$, and $\frac{5}{12}$ using their least common denominator.

   A. $\frac{2}{12}$, $\frac{4}{12}$, $\frac{5}{12}$ **C.** $\frac{6}{48}$, $\frac{16}{48}$, $\frac{20}{48}$

   B. $\frac{3}{24}$, $\frac{8}{24}$, $\frac{10}{24}$ **D.** $\frac{7}{60}$, $\frac{20}{60}$, $\frac{5}{60}$

---

28. Which is the simplest form of $\frac{58}{12}$?

   F. $4\frac{2}{3}$ **G.** $4\frac{5}{6}$ **H.** 5   **J.** $5\frac{1}{2}$

---

29. Order $\frac{1}{6}$, 0.15, and $\frac{2}{11}$ from least to greatest.

   A. $\frac{1}{6}$, 0.15, $\frac{2}{11}$ **C.** 0.15, $\frac{2}{11}$, $\frac{1}{6}$

   B. $\frac{1}{6}$, $\frac{2}{11}$, 0.15   **D.** 0.15, $\frac{1}{6}$, $\frac{2}{11}$

---

30. Rewrite $\frac{2}{9}$, $\frac{4}{7}$, and $\frac{10}{21}$ using their least common denominator.

   F. $\frac{5}{21}$, $\frac{4}{21}$, $\frac{10}{21}$ **H.** $\frac{28}{126}$, $\frac{72}{126}$, $\frac{60}{126}$

   G. $\frac{14}{63}$, $\frac{36}{63}$, $\frac{30}{63}$ **J.** $\frac{41}{147}$, $\frac{84}{147}$, $\frac{70}{147}$

---

31. Write $\frac{75}{9}$ as a mixed number in simplest form.

   A. $7\frac{8}{9}$ **B.** $8\frac{1}{9}$ **C.** $8\frac{1}{3}$ **D.** $8\frac{2}{3}$

---

32. Write $\frac{374}{121}$ as a mixed number in simplest form.

   F. 3   **G.** $3\frac{1}{11}$ **H.** $3\frac{1}{4}$ **J.** $3\frac{1}{3}$

---

33. What is the prime factorization of 72?

   A. 7×3^2 **C.** 3^4

   B. $3^2 \times 2^3$ **D.** 2^5

GO ON

34. What is the greatest common factor (GCF) of 12 and 60?

F. 2　　**G.** 4　　**H.** 6　　**J.** 12

35. Order $1\frac{5}{8}$, $1\frac{1}{4}$, and $\frac{34}{20}$ from least to greatest on a number line.

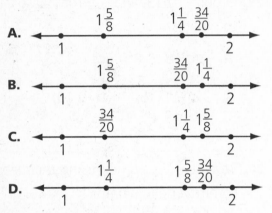

36. Order $4\frac{2}{3}$, 4.59, and $\frac{24}{5}$ from least to greatest.

F. 4.59, $4\frac{2}{3}$, $\frac{24}{5}$　　**H.** $4\frac{2}{3}$, $\frac{24}{5}$, 4.59

G. 4.59, $\frac{24}{5}$, $4\frac{2}{3}$　　**J.** $\frac{24}{5}$, 4.59, $4\frac{2}{3}$

Use the table for problems 37–38.

Type of Tree	Number of Trees
apple	12
chestnut	14
maple	25
oak	37
pine	12

37. Which fraction, in simplest form, names the part of the trees that are maple?

A. $\frac{3}{18}$　**B.** $\frac{1}{4}$　**C.** $\frac{1}{3}$　**D.** $\frac{5}{12}$

38. Which fraction, in simplest form, names the part of the trees that are chestnut?

F. $\frac{7}{50}$　　　　**H.** $\frac{7}{10}$

G. $\frac{7}{100}$　　　　**J.** $\frac{7}{25}$

39. Four students agreed to sell cookies. Ben sold $\frac{1}{4}$ of his cookies. Tom sold $\frac{1}{5}$. Nicki sold $\frac{1}{5}$. Lee sold $\frac{1}{2}$. What information is needed to find the number of cookies they each sold?

A. the number of students who attended the fair

B. the cost of a cookie

C. the total number of cookies they each agreed to sell

D. the number of teachers who attended the fair

40. Brenda did 0.11 of an assignment. Todd did 0.25. Joe did 0.17. Bill did 0.14. Who did about $\frac{1}{7}$ of the job?

F. Brenda　　　　**H.** Joe

G. Todd　　　　**J.** Bill

STOP

Name _____

Read each question carefully. Fill in the correct answer in the space provided.

1. Which number is prime?

63, 77, 79, or 81

_____

2. Which number is composite?

53, 61, 83, or 91

_____

3. What is the simplest form of $\frac{56}{64}$?

_____

4. What is the decimal form of $\frac{3}{20}$?

_____

5. Order $\frac{18}{7}$, 2.5, $\frac{19}{8}$ from greatest to least.

_____

6. What is the least common multiple (LCM) of 12 and 16?

_____

7. Rewrite $\frac{1}{5}$, $\frac{3}{4}$, and $\frac{5}{6}$ using their least common denominator.

_____

8. What is the simplest form of $\frac{8}{36}$?

_____

9. Order 0.4, $\frac{3}{8}$, and $\frac{7}{19}$ from least to greatest.

_____

10. Rewrite $\frac{1}{2}$, $\frac{2}{3}$, and $\frac{5}{8}$ using their least common denominator.

_____

GO ON

11. Write $\frac{33}{7}$ as a mixed number in simplest form.

_____

_____

12. Write $\frac{34}{9}$ as a mixed number in simplest form.

_____

_____

13. What is the prime factorization of 84?

_____

_____

14. What is the greatest common factor of 72 and 96?

_____

_____

15. Order 0.75, $\frac{7}{4}$, and $2\frac{1}{2}$ from least to greatest on a number line.

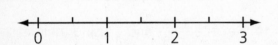

_____

16. Order $\frac{8}{7}$, $1\frac{3}{10}$, and 1.25 from greatest to least.

_____

Use the table for problems 17–18.

Favorite Movie Genre	Number of People
Action	37
Comedy	18
Drama	8
Horror	12
Suspense	25

17. What fraction, in simplest form, represents the part of the group of people who like suspense best?

_____

_____

18. What fraction, in simplest form, represents the part of the group of people who like comedy best?

_____

_____

19. Four students agreed to sell tickets. Jamal sold $\frac{3}{4}$ of his tickets. Marian sold $\frac{3}{5}$ of her tickets. Gina sold $\frac{7}{8}$ of her tickets, and Julius sold $\frac{1}{2}$ of his tickets. What information is required to determine the total number of tickets they each agreed to sell?

_____

_____

20. Three students agreed to sell tickets. Moira sold 0.8 of her tickets. Nina sold 0.55. Tim sold 0.7. Who sold exactly $\frac{11}{20}$ of his or her tickets?

_____

GO ON

21. Which number is prime?

27, 51, 63, or 79

_____

_____

22. Which number is composite?

41, 43, 45, or 47

_____

_____

23. What is the simplest form of $\frac{28}{49}$?

_____

_____

24. What is the fractional form of 0.625?

_____

_____

25. Order 5.6, $\frac{53}{9}$, and $5\frac{3}{4}$ from greatest to least.

_____

26. What is the least common multiple (LCM) of 8, 12, and 18?

_____

_____

27. Rewrite $\frac{1}{5}$, $\frac{2}{9}$, and $\frac{7}{30}$ using their least common denominator.

_____

_____

28. What is the simplest form of $\frac{75}{18}$?

_____

_____

29. Order $4\frac{1}{7}$, 4.25, and $\frac{21}{5}$ from least to greatest.

_____

_____

30. Rewrite $\frac{3}{4}$, $\frac{5}{9}$, and $\frac{13}{18}$ using their least common denominator.

_____

_____

GO ON

31. Write $\frac{66}{8}$ as a mixed number in simplest form.

_____

32. Write $\frac{343}{21}$ as a mixed number in simplest form.

_____

33. What is the prime factorization of 90?

_____

34. What is the greatest common factor of 91 and 65?

_____

35. Order $1\frac{3}{5}$, $\frac{31}{20}$, and 1.5 from least to greatest on a number line.

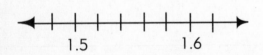

1.5   1.6

36. Order 5.01, $\frac{46}{9}$, and $4\frac{7}{8}$ from least to greatest.

_____

Use the table for problems 37–38.

Color of Pen	Number of Pens
Red	10
Green	23
Blue	29
Black	35
Violet	1
Orange	2

37. What fraction, in simplest form, represents the part of the pens that are black?

_____

38. What fraction, in simplest form, represents the part of the pens that are either red or orange?

_____

39. Three students work at a fast-food place. Madeleine served $\frac{1}{8}$ of the customers. Miranda served $\frac{1}{3}$. Antoine served $\frac{2}{7}$. What information is needed to find the number of customers they each served?

_____

40. Josh did 0.3 of his homework. Scott did 0.72. Caryn did 0.65. Jessica did 0.9. Who did about $\frac{2}{3}$ of his or her homework?

_____

STOP

Chapter 11 – Teacher Interview

Core Concept: *Add Fractions*

Student Activity: Students demonstrate an understanding of how to calculate and estimate sums of mixed numbers with like and unlike denominators.

Assign addition problems with fractions, such as $1\frac{5}{7} + 3\frac{4}{7}$

Teacher Question 1:

• What steps did you use to find your answer?

Understanding Student Response	Practice and Improvement
Students who first added both numerators and denominators	Review lesson 1 to help student recall how to add fractions with like denominators.
Students who did not add to the whole number after regrouping.	Review lesson 1 to help students remember how to regroup with mixed numbers.

Teacher Question 2:

• How would you add $1\frac{1}{3} + 2\frac{1}{2}$?

Understanding Student Response	Practice and Improvement
Students who try to regroup.	Review lesson 3 to show students that regrouping is only necessary when the sum of the fraction part is greater than 1.
Students who cannot find the LCD.	Review lessons 3–5 to help students practice finding the LCD.

Teacher Question 3:

• Would the problem be different if both fractions had the same denominator? The same numerator?

Understanding Student Response	Practice and Improvement
Students who say the problem would be exactly the same if the fractions had the same denominator.	Review lesson 4 to reinforce the need to find an LCD only if denominators are different.
Students who say the problem would be different if the fractions had the same numerator.	Review lesson 4 to help students recognize that only the denominators determine the need for using an LCD.

Chapter 11 – Journal Writing

Encourage students to generate their own journal entries related to math ideas in general or to concepts in this chapter. For students requiring guidance, present the following journal prompt:

- When you are problem solving, why is it important to categorize the information? What are some tools you can use to categorize the information in a word problem?

    (Responses should include references to necessary vs. unnecessary information. Some ways to organize information are to use a table, chart, or a graphic organizer.)

JOURNAL WRITING/PROBLEM SOLVING

Rachel and Leanna worked on a puzzle for $1\frac{1}{2}$ hours and played a board game for another $\frac{3}{4}$ of an hour. Then they went outside. They rode their bikes for $2\frac{3}{5}$ hours and then used sidewalk chalk for $\frac{2}{3}$ of an hour. How long did they play inside? How long did they play outside?

Read

Have students find the answer to the problem. Then ask them to write a few sentences telling—

- which information they used to find the answer

- what they did with that information

Have students make up another problem with different information for which they would have to follow the same procedure. Then have students solve the problem and supply the correct response.

Plan

Students must recognize that the operation is addition, find the LCD to determine equivalent fractions, and compute accurately.

Solve

The correct response to the assigned problem is $2\frac{1}{4}$ hours inside and $3\frac{4}{15}$ hours outside. Students had to know the amount of time spent doing each activity, and whether that activity took place inside or outside. Then they had to add the appropriate mixed numbers, find the correct LCD, and compute accurately.

Look Back

A correct response demonstrates the ability to discriminate between necessary and unnecessary information and apply the appropriate operation to solve the problem. (See scoring rubric on page 7.)

Chapter 11 – Monitoring Student Progress

☐ Form A   ☐ Form B

Name _____ Date _____

Directions: For each item that is answered incorrectly, cross out the item number. Then record the number of correct responses in the appropriate Student Score column. If the student has not met the Criterion Score for an objective, circle the student's score. Recommended assignments are listed in the Prescription Table on the next page.

Objective	Item Numbers	Criterion Score	Student Score
A. Add fractions.	1, 4, 8, 10, 12, 15	5/6	/6
B. Add mixed numbers.	2, 5, 9, 13, 16	4/5	/5
C. Identify and use addition properties with fractions.	3, 6, 7, 11, 14	4/5	/5
D. Use skills and strategies to solve problems.	17, 18, 19, 20	3/4	/4
Total Test Score		16/20	/20
Total Percent Correct			%

Chapter 11 – Prescription Table

The following chart correlates the tested objectives for this chapter to supplementary materials that meet the individual needs of the students. The Reteach and Practice pages are designed for students who need further instruction in the math concepts taught in this chapter. The Enrich pages are designed for students who need advanced challenges.

Objective	Reteach	Practice	Enrich
A. Add fractions.	185, 188	186, 189	187, 190
B. Add mixed numbers.	179, 191	180, 192	181, 193
C. Identify and use addition properties with fractions.	194	195	196
D. Use skills and strategies to solve problems.	182	183	184

Read each question carefully. Darken the circle on your answer sheet for the correct answer.

1. $\frac{7}{10} + \frac{3}{5} = \square$

  A. $\frac{4}{10}$ **C.** $\frac{10}{15}$

  B. $1\frac{1}{10}$ **D.** $1\frac{3}{10}$

2. $2\frac{1}{4} + 7\frac{5}{6} = \square$

  F. $10\frac{1}{12}$ **H.** $10\frac{1}{6}$

  G. $10\frac{1}{4}$ **J.** $9\frac{11}{12}$

3. Identify the property used.

  $\frac{3}{4} + 0 = \frac{3}{4}$

  A. Associative Property

  B. Commutative Property

  C. Identity Property

  D. Addition

4. $\frac{1}{10} + \frac{3}{8} = \square$

  F. $\frac{19}{80}$ **H.** $\frac{19}{40}$

  G. $\frac{9}{10}$ **J.** $\frac{19}{30}$

5. $3\frac{5}{8} + 9\frac{2}{3} = \square$

  A. $12\frac{7}{11}$ **C.** $13\frac{1}{4}$

  B. $12\frac{7}{8}$ **D.** $13\frac{7}{24}$

6. Find the missing number and identify the property used.

  $\square + \frac{1}{7} = \frac{1}{7} + \frac{1}{3}$

  F. $\frac{1}{3}$, Associative Property

  G. $\frac{1}{7}$, Associative Property

  H. $\frac{1}{7}$, Commutative Property

  J. $\frac{1}{3}$, Commutative Property

7. Find the missing number and identify the property used.

  $\frac{1}{3} + (\square + \frac{1}{4}) = (\frac{1}{3} + \frac{1}{6}) + \frac{1}{4}$

  A. $\frac{1}{6}$, Associative Property

  B. $\frac{1}{3}$, Associative Property

  C. $\frac{1}{6}$, Commutative Property

  D. $\frac{1}{4}$, Commutative Property

8. $\frac{1}{3} + \frac{8}{9} = \square$

  F. $\frac{5}{9}$ **G.** $1\frac{1}{12}$ **H.** $1\frac{2}{9}$ **J.** $1\frac{1}{3}$

9. $42\frac{1}{10} + 16\frac{2}{5} = \square$

  A. $58\frac{3}{5}$ **C.** $57\frac{1}{2}$

  B. $58\frac{1}{2}$ **D.** $57\frac{3}{10}$

10. $\frac{2}{3} + \frac{4}{5} = \square$

  F. $1\frac{7}{15}$ **H.** $1\frac{1}{5}$

  G. $1\frac{1}{3}$ **J.** $\frac{3}{4}$

GO ON

11. Find the missing number and identify the property used.

$$2\frac{2}{3} + \boxed{} = \frac{1}{5} + 2\frac{2}{3}$$

A. $\frac{1}{5}$, Multiplication Property

B. $\frac{1}{5}$, Identity Property

C. $\frac{1}{5}$, Associative Property

D. $\frac{1}{5}$, Commutative Property

12. $\frac{5}{8} + \frac{1}{6} = \boxed{}$

F. $1\frac{1}{2}$ **H.** $\frac{19}{24}$

G. $1\frac{5}{12}$ **J.** $\frac{6}{14}$

13. $31\frac{1}{2} + 9\frac{1}{6} = \boxed{}$

A. $41\frac{1}{3}$ **C.** $40\frac{1}{3}$

B. $40\frac{2}{3}$ **D.** $39\frac{2}{3}$

14. Find the missing number and identify the property used.

$$\left(2\frac{1}{10} + 1\frac{1}{8}\right) + \boxed{} = 2\frac{1}{10} + \left(1\frac{1}{8} + 3\frac{1}{4}\right)$$

F. $3\frac{1}{4}$, Associative Property

G. $2\frac{1}{10}$, Commutative Property

H. $1\frac{1}{8}$, Identity Property

J. $3\frac{1}{4}$, Commutative Property

15. $\frac{7}{8} + \frac{3}{16} = \boxed{}$

A. $\frac{15}{16}$ **C.** $1\frac{1}{8}$

B. 1 **D.** $1\frac{1}{16}$

16. $8\frac{2}{3} + 6\frac{7}{15} = \boxed{}$

F. $15\frac{1}{15}$ **G.** $15\frac{2}{15}$ **H.** $15\frac{1}{5}$ **J.** $15\frac{1}{3}$

17. Janice spent $\frac{1}{3}$ of her savings on an outfit. The next week Janice spent another $\frac{1}{4}$ of her savings on a CD. How much of her total savings does she spend?

A. $\frac{1}{7}$ **B.** $\frac{5}{12}$ **C.** $\frac{1}{2}$ **D.** $\frac{7}{12}$

18. Janice's brother, Steve, spent $\frac{1}{3}$ of his weekly allowance of \$12 in May. In June, he spent $\frac{1}{2}$ of his weekly allowance on repairing his bike. How much more of his allowance in dollars does he spend in June than in May?

F. \$2.00 **H.** \$4.00

G. \$3.00 **J.** \$10.00

19. On Tuesday, Rachel made $3\frac{1}{2}$ pounds of meatloaf for her family. On Saturday, she made $5\frac{1}{3}$ pounds for the soccer team. How many pounds of meatloaf does she make in all?

A. $9\frac{1}{3}$ lb **B.** $8\frac{5}{6}$ lb **C.** $8\frac{1}{6}$ lb **D.** $1\frac{5}{6}$ lb

20. In Rachel's recipe, she used $\frac{1}{2}$ cup breadcrumbs, $1\frac{3}{4}$ cup tomato sauce, and $\frac{1}{4}$ cup onions. How many cups of the ingredients does she use all together?

F. 2 cups **H.** $2\frac{1}{2}$ cups

G. $2\frac{1}{4}$ cups **J.** $2\frac{3}{4}$ cups

STOP

Name_____

Read each question carefully. Fill in the correct answer in the space provided.

1. $\dfrac{2}{5} + \dfrac{2}{3} =$ _____

_____

2. $3\dfrac{3}{8} + 6\dfrac{3}{4} =$ _____

_____

3. Identify the property used.

$\dfrac{5}{6} + 0 = \dfrac{5}{6}$

_____

_____

4. $\dfrac{3}{5} + \dfrac{3}{10} =$ _____

_____

5. $5\dfrac{3}{8} + 7\dfrac{3}{4} =$ _____

6. Find the missing number and identify the property used.

$\dfrac{5}{9} + \boxed{} = \dfrac{1}{3} + \dfrac{5}{9}$

_____

_____

7. Find the missing number and identify the property used.

$\left(\dfrac{5}{8} + \boxed{}\right) + \dfrac{1}{2} = \dfrac{5}{8} + \left(\dfrac{2}{3} + \dfrac{1}{2}\right)$

_____

8. $\dfrac{2}{7} + \dfrac{11}{14} =$ _____

_____

9. $24\dfrac{4}{5} + 18\dfrac{1}{2} =$ _____

_____

10. $\dfrac{1}{4} + \dfrac{4}{5} =$ _____

GO ON ▶

11. Find the missing number and identify the property used.

$$3\frac{1}{2} + \boxed{} = \frac{1}{3} + 3\frac{1}{2}$$

_____

_____

12. $\frac{3}{8} + \frac{5}{6} = $ _____

_____

13. $46\frac{1}{3} + 5\frac{1}{6} = $ _____

_____

14. Find the missing number and identify the property used.

$$\left(3\frac{3}{10} + 2\frac{3}{8}\right) + \boxed{} = 3\frac{3}{10} + \left(2\frac{3}{8} + 1\frac{1}{5}\right)$$

_____

_____

15. $\frac{3}{4} + \frac{5}{16} = $ _____

_____

16. $6\frac{11}{15} + 5\frac{1}{3} = $ _____

17. Tom spent $\frac{1}{4}$ of his allowance on a bike tire. The next week Tom spent another $\frac{2}{3}$ of his allowance on new bike brakes. How much of his total allowance for the two weeks does he spend?

_____

_____

18. Sara used her allowance to buy school supplies. In August, she spent $\frac{1}{5}$ of her weekly allowance of $20 on a notepad. She spent $\frac{1}{4}$ of her allowance on rulers and pens in September. How much more of her allowance in dollars does she spend in September than in August?

_____

_____

19. Paulo cooked $2\frac{3}{4}$ pounds of chicken for a hiking trip. He also made $3\frac{1}{8}$ pounds of meatballs. How many pounds of food does Paulo cook in all?

_____

_____

20. The recipe for meatballs calls for $\frac{3}{4}$ cups breadcrumbs, $2\frac{1}{4}$ cups tomato sauce, and $\frac{1}{2}$ cup tomato paste. How many cups of the ingredients are used altogether in the recipe?

_____

STOP

Chapter 12 – Teacher Interview

Core Concept: *Subtract Fractions*

Student Activity: Students demonstrate an understanding of how to calculate and estimate differences of mixed numbers with like and unlike denominators.

Assign subtraction problems with fractions, such as $9\frac{5}{6} - 5\frac{3}{4}$.

Teacher Question 1:

• What steps did you use to find your answer?

Understanding Student Response	Practice and Improvement
Students who first subtracted both numerators and denominators.	Review lesson 2 to help the student recall how to subtract fractions with unlike denominators.
Students who subtracted the whole numbers first.	Review lesson 4 to help the student remember how to regroup with mixed numbers.

Teacher Question 2:

• How can you use estimating to show that your answer is reasonable?

Understanding Student Response	Practice and Improvement
Students who estimated that $9\frac{5}{6} - 5\frac{3}{4}$ is 3.	Review lesson 6 to help the student remember when to round up or down.
Students who estimated that $9\frac{5}{6} - 5\frac{3}{4}$ is 5.	Review lesson 6 to help the student remember when to round up or down.

Teacher Question 3:

• Would the problem be different if both fractions had the same denominator? The same numerator?

Understanding Student Response	Practice and Improvement
Students who say the problem would be exactly the same if the fractions had the same denominator.	Review lesson 1 to reinforce the need to find an LCD only if denominators are different.
Students who say the problem would be different if the fractions had the same numerator.	Review lesson 2 to help the student recognize that only the denominators determine the need for using an LCD.

Chapter 12 – Journal Writing

Encourage students to generate their own journal entries related to math ideas in general or to concepts in this chapter. For students requiring guidance, present the following journal prompt:

- When you are problem solving, why is it important to categorize the information? What are some tools you can use to categorize the information in a word problem?

  (Responses should include references to necessary vs. unnecessary information. Some ways to organize information are to use a table, chart, or a graphic organizer.)

JOURNAL WRITING/PROBLEM SOLVING

Jack buys $3\frac{1}{2}$ pounds of apples, $1\frac{3}{4}$ pounds of bananas, $4\frac{2}{3}$ pounds of grapes, $1\frac{1}{8}$ pounds of oranges, and $2\frac{4}{5}$ pounds of pears. How many more pounds of grapes than pears does Jack buy?

Read

Have students find the answer to the problem. Then ask them to write a few sentences telling—

- which information they used to find the answer

- what they did with that information

Have students make up another problem with different information for which they would have to follow the same procedure. Then have students solve the problem and supply the correct response.

Plan

Students must recognize that the operation is subtraction, find LCD to determine equivalent fractions, and compute accurately.

Solve

The correct response to the assigned problem is $1\frac{3}{15}$ pounds. Students had to know the amount of grapes and the amount of pears. Then they had to subtract the amount of pears ($2\frac{4}{5}$ pounds) from the amount of grapes ($4\frac{2}{3}$ pounds), finding the correct LCD and computing accurately.

Look Back

A correct response demonstrates the ability to discriminate between necessary and unnecessary information and apply the appropriate operation to solve the problem. (See scoring rubric on page 7.)

Chapter 12 – Monitoring Student Progress

☐ **Form A**   ☐ **Form B**

Name _____ Date _____

Directions: For each item that is answered incorrectly, cross out the item number. Then record the number of correct responses in the appropriate Student Score column. If the student has not met the Criterion Score for an objective, circle the student's score. Recommended assignments are listed in the Prescription Table on the next page.

Objective	Item Numbers	Criterion Score	Student Score
A. Subtract fractions.	1, 4, 7, 10, 14	4/5	/5
B. Subtract mixed numbers.	2, 5, 9, 13, 15	4/5	/5
C. Estimate sums and differences of mixed numbers.	3, 6, 8, 11, 12	4/5	/5
D. Use skills and strategies to solve problems.	16, 17, 18, 19, 20	4/5	/5
Total Test Score		16/20	/20
Total Percent Correct			%

Chapter 12 – Prescription Table

The following chart correlates the tested objectives for this chapter to supplementary materials that meet the individual needs of the students. The Reteach and Practice pages are designed for students who need further instruction in the math concepts taught in this chapter. The Enrich pages are designed for students who need advanced challenges.

Objective	Reteach	Practice	Enrich
A. Subtract fractions.	200	201	202
B. Subtract mixed numbers.	197, 203, 206	198, 204, 207	199, 205, 208
C. Estimate sums and differences of mixed numbers.	212	213	214
D. Use skills and strategies to solve problems.	209, 210	211	

Name _____

Read each question carefully. Darken the circle on your answer sheet for the correct answer.

1. $\frac{5}{8} - \frac{1}{8} = \square$

   A. $\frac{3}{4}$ **C.** $\frac{3}{8}$

   B. $\frac{1}{2}$ **D.** $\frac{1}{4}$

2. $15\frac{13}{16} - 3 = \square$

   F. $18\frac{13}{16}$ **H.** $12\frac{13}{16}$

   G. $18\frac{5}{8}$ **J.** $12\frac{3}{16}$

3. Which is the best estimate?

$3\frac{4}{5} + 1\frac{3}{10}$

   A. 6   **C.** 4

   B. 5   **D.** 3

4. $\frac{9}{10} - \frac{2}{10} = \square$

   F. $\frac{2}{5}$ **H.** $\frac{7}{10}$

   G. $\frac{1}{2}$ **J.** $1\frac{1}{10}$

5. $25\frac{3}{8} - 23\frac{1}{4} = \square$

   A. $2\frac{1}{8}$ **C.** $1\frac{7}{8}$

   B. $2\frac{1}{2}$ **D.** $1\frac{1}{2}$

6. Which is the best estimate?

$8\frac{2}{3} + 6\frac{3}{5}$

   F. 14   **H.** 16

   G. 15   **J.** 17

7. $\frac{3}{4} - \frac{1}{6} = \square$

   A. $\frac{7}{12}$ **C.** $\frac{1}{2}$

   B. $\frac{5}{12}$ **D.** $\frac{1}{3}$

8. Which is the best estimate?

$4\frac{1}{5} - 1\frac{7}{10}$

   F. 1   **H.** 3

   G. 2   **J.** 5

9. $19\frac{1}{6} - 6\frac{1}{2} = \square$

   A. $12\frac{1}{2}$ **C.** $13\frac{1}{2}$

   B. $12\frac{2}{3}$ **D.** $13\frac{2}{3}$

10. $\frac{13}{20} - \frac{3}{10} = \square$

   F. $\frac{9}{10}$ **H.** $\frac{1}{2}$

   G. $\frac{7}{10}$ **J.** $\frac{7}{20}$

GO ON

11. Which is the best estimate?

$$57\frac{5}{6} - 21\frac{1}{6}$$

A. 80   **C.** 40

B. 70   **D.** 30

12. Which is the best estimate?

$$78\frac{11}{12} - 49\frac{7}{12}$$

F. 45   **H.** 35

G. 40   **J.** 30

13. $19\frac{9}{10} - 10\frac{1}{4} = \square$

A. $10\frac{3}{20}$ **C.** $9\frac{13}{20}$

B. $9\frac{7}{10}$ **D.** $9\frac{1}{4}$

14. $\frac{11}{12} - \frac{2}{3} = \square$

F. $\frac{1}{4}$ **G.** $\frac{1}{3}$ **H.** $\frac{2}{3}$ **J.** $\frac{3}{4}$

15. $51\frac{1}{2} - 13\frac{3}{4} = \square$

A. $38\frac{3}{4}$ **C.** $37\frac{3}{4}$

B. $38\frac{1}{2}$ **D.** $37\frac{1}{2}$

16. Gavin circles his age on a calendar, doubles it, and then adds 5. The result is 23. Which equation shows his age?

F. $\square \times 2 - 5 = 23$

G. $\square \times 2 + 5 = 23$

H. $\square + 2 \times 5 = 23$

J. $\square + 2 + 5 = 23$

17. Marlene circles her age on a calendar, divides her age by 2, and then adds 10. The result is 15. Which equation shows her age?

A. $\square \div 2 + 10 = 15$

B. $\square + 2 - 10 = 15$

C. $\square - {}^-2 + 10 = 15$

D. $\square \div 2 - 10 = 15$

18. A 20-pound bag of nails has $7\frac{1}{4}$ pounds left. How many nails have been removed?

F. $13\frac{1}{4}$ lb   **H.** $12\frac{3}{4}$ lb

G. $13\frac{1}{8}$ lb   **J.** $12\frac{1}{4}$ lb

19. Luisa has $1\frac{3}{4}$ pound of nails in a large jar. She puts $\frac{1}{2}$ pound into a small jar. How many pounds of nails are left in the large jar?

A. $1\frac{3}{4}$ lb   **C.** $\frac{3}{4}$ lb

B. $1\frac{1}{4}$ lb   **D.** $\frac{1}{2}$ lb

20. At a hardware store Marcy buys 5 gallons of white paint and 2 gallons of blue paint. She uses $3\frac{3}{4}$ gallons of white paint on her bedroom walls. How many gallons of white and blue paint does she have left?

F. 7 gal   **H.** $3\frac{1}{4}$ gal

G. $3\frac{3}{4}$ gal   **J.** 2 gal

STOP

Read each question carefully. Fill in the correct answer in the space provided.

1. $\frac{5}{6} - \frac{1}{6} =$ _____

2. $13\frac{7}{8} - 2 =$ _____

3. Which is the best estimate?

$2\frac{5}{8} + 1\frac{1}{3}$

_____

4. $\frac{11}{12} - \frac{5}{12} =$ _____

5. $37\frac{5}{8} - 35\frac{1}{4} =$ _____

6. Which is the best estimate?

$9\frac{5}{6} + 3\frac{2}{3}$

_____

7. $\frac{2}{3} - \frac{1}{4} =$ _____

8. Which is the best estimate?

$6\frac{1}{6} - 1\frac{11}{12}$

_____

9. $17\frac{1}{8} - 5\frac{3}{4} =$ _____

10. $\frac{15}{21} - \frac{3}{7} =$ _____

GO ON

11. Which is the best estimate?

$$48\frac{5}{8} - 23\frac{1}{8}$$

_____

_____

12. Which is the best estimate?

$$67\frac{9}{10} - 49\frac{3}{10}$$

_____

_____

13. $45\frac{7}{10} - 10\frac{1}{3} =$ _____

_____

14. $\frac{7}{12} - \frac{1}{3} =$ _____

_____

15. $62\frac{1}{4} - 23\frac{2}{3} =$ _____

16. Gail circles her age on a calendar, doubles it, and then adds 7. The result is 31. Write an equation that shows her age.

_____

_____

17. Rich circles his age on a calendar, divides his age by 2, and then adds 12. The result is 27. Write an equation that shows his age.

_____

_____

18. A 30-pound bag of shells has $12\frac{1}{2}$ pounds left. How many shells have been removed?

_____

_____

19. Dora has $2\frac{1}{2}$ pounds of shells in a large bottle. She puts $\frac{3}{4}$ pound into a small bottle. How many pounds of shells are left in the large bottle?

_____

_____

20. Marco buys 4 gallons of cherry stain and 3 gallons of clear stain. He uses $1\frac{1}{3}$ gallons of cherry stain on woodwork. How many gallons of cherry and clear stain does he have left?

_____

STOP

Unit 6 Performance Assessment

Training for the Marathon

- *Target Skill:*   Add and subtract mixed numbers.
- *Additional Skills:*   Find equivalent fractions and simplify fractions.

Task Description: This task requires students to keep a log of a runner's schedule. The students will be asked to add and subtract to find how many miles a runner has to run.

Preparing: You may wish to discuss with students the distances runners run. Review with students how to use the LCD to add and subtract fractions.

Materials	Group Size	Time on Task
Pencil Paper	1 to 2 students	1 day

Guiding: Tell students that they will be adding and subtracting mixed numbers. Remind students to regroup when subtracting mixed numbers if the fraction part of the second number is larger than that of the first number.

Observing/ Monitoring: As you move among the students, pose the following questions:

How does the chart help you to organize your data?

Which common denominators can you use to add and subtract the mixed numbers?

Unit 6 Performance Assessment Scoring Rubric

Training for the Marathon

Score	Explanation
3	Students demonstrate an efficient strategy and a thorough approach that enables them to solve the problem completely. A satisfactory answer: • shows organized and correct mileage totals; • keeps Mona on a 20-mile schedule; • shows all work. Students are able to complete the problem quickly and have all of the above correct solutions.
2	Students demonstrate a strategy that enables them to solve most of the problem correctly. The strategy is somewhat disorganized, making it less efficient. A solution is found, but errors are contained. Students may: • add most of the numbers correctly; • have a correct schedule. Students have some difficulty determining all solutions correctly but demonstrate an understanding of general concepts.
1	Students demonstrate a confused strategy, which leads to difficulty solving the problem. Most answers are incorrect, but students demonstrate knowledge of at least one concept being assessed such as adding or subtracting mixed numbers.

Name _____

Unit 6 Performance Assessment Student Activity

Training for the Marathon

You will need
• Paper

Mona is training for the Summitville Mini Marathon. She wants to run 20 miles each week to get ready. On Monday, she runs $3\frac{1}{2}$ miles, and on Tuesday she runs $2\frac{3}{4}$ miles. On Wednesday and Thursday, Mona only has time to run $2\frac{7}{8}$ miles each day.

Make a chart of how many miles Mona has run each day to help you answer the questions.

Day	Miles Run	Total Miles Run
Monday		
Tuesday		
Wednesday		
Thursday		
Friday		
Saturday		
Sunday		

1. How many miles will Mona have to run the rest of the week to stay on her schedule?

_____

2. If Mona runs $4\frac{1}{2}$ miles on Friday, how many miles will she have left to do over the weekend?

_____

3. If Mona doesn't want to run more than 5 miles on any day, can she take a day off and still make her goal this week?

_____

4. Schedule Mona's runs for the weekend.

_____

Unit 6 – Monitoring Student Progress

☐ Form A   ☐ Form B

Name _____ Date _____

Directions: This test targets selected objectives. For each item that is answered incorrectly, cross out the item number. Then record the number of correct responses in the column labeled **Number of Correct Responses.** Add to find the **Total Number of Correct Responses** and record the total. Use this total to determine the **Total Test Score** and the **Total Percent Correct.**

Strand • Objective(s)	Item Numbers	Number of Correct Responses
Number Sense, Concepts, and Operations • Add fractions. • Add mixed numbers. • Identify and use addition properties with fractions. • Subtract fractions. • Subtract mixed numbers. • Estimate sums and differences of mixed numbers. • Use skills and strategies to solve problems.	1, 2, 3, 4, 5, 6, 7, 8, 9, 10, 11, 12, 13, 14, 15, 16, 17, 18, 19, 20, 21, 22, 23, 24, 25, 26, 27, 28, 29, 30, 31, 32, 33, 34, 35, 36, 37, 38, 39, 40	/40
Total Number of Correct Responses		
Total Test Score		/40
Total Percent Correct		%

Read each question carefully. Darken the circle on your answer sheet for the correct answer.

1. $1\frac{13}{25} + 2\frac{17}{25} = \square$

A. $3\frac{23}{25}$ **C.** $4\frac{6}{25}$

B. $4\frac{1}{5}$ **D.** 5

2. $5\frac{7}{8} - 2\frac{3}{8} = \square$

F. $3\frac{1}{4}$ **H.** $3\frac{1}{2}$

G. $3\frac{3}{8}$ **J.** $3\frac{3}{4}$

3. Identify the property used.

$\frac{7}{9} + \frac{3}{8} = \frac{3}{8} + \frac{7}{9}$

A. Associative Property
B. Commutative Property
C. Identity Property
D. Distributive Property

4. Which is the best estimate?

$4\frac{2}{3} + 5\frac{11}{13}$

F. 4   **G.** 5   **H.** 11   **J.** 20

5. $\frac{4}{5} + \frac{3}{4} = \square$

A. $\frac{19}{20}$ **C.** $1\frac{11}{20}$

B. $1\frac{1}{2}$ **D.** $1\frac{3}{5}$

6. $4\frac{2}{3} + \frac{5}{6} = \square$

F. $5\frac{1}{2}$ **G.** $5\frac{5}{6}$ **H.** $6\frac{1}{6}$ **J.** $6\frac{2}{3}$

7. $\frac{9}{11} - \frac{3}{7} = \square$

A. $\frac{4}{11}$ **B.** $\frac{3}{7}$ **C.** $\frac{30}{77}$ **D.** $\frac{6}{11}$

8. Identify the property used.

$\frac{5}{7} + (\frac{1}{7} + \frac{3}{4}) = (\frac{5}{7} + \frac{1}{7}) + \frac{3}{4}$

F. Associative Property
G. Commutative Property
H. Identity Property
J. Distributive Property

9. Which is the best estimate?

$7\frac{2}{9} + 11\frac{4}{7}$

A. 7   **B.** 11   **C.** 19   **D.** 77

10. $2\frac{3}{7} + 4\frac{10}{21} = \square$

F. $5\frac{2}{3}$ **H.** $6\frac{6}{7}$

G. $6\frac{19}{21}$ **J.** $5\frac{13}{21}$

11. $12\frac{5}{8} - \frac{3}{4} = \square$

A. $11\frac{1}{2}$ **C.** $12\frac{1}{8}$

B. $11\frac{7}{8}$ **D.** $12\frac{7}{8}$

12. Which is the best estimate?

$9\frac{7}{10} - 4\frac{1}{8}$

F. 6   **G.** 9   **H.** 13   **J.** 94

GO ON

Grade 5   **193**

13. Identify the property used.

$$4\frac{11}{12} + 0 = 4\frac{11}{12}$$

A. Associative Property

B. Commutative Property

C. Identity Property

D. Distributive Property

14. $16\frac{2}{3} - 4\frac{1}{4} = \blacksquare$

F. $12\frac{5}{12}$ H. $12\frac{3}{7}$

G. $12\frac{2}{7}$ J. $12\frac{1}{2}$

15. Evaluate.

$$8\frac{2}{3} + (6\frac{4}{5} + 2\frac{1}{5}) = \blacksquare$$

A. $16\frac{2}{3}$ C. $17\frac{1}{5}$

B. $16\frac{14}{15}$ D. $17\frac{2}{3}$

16. Which is the best estimate?

$$16\frac{1}{8} - 7\frac{5}{6}$$

F. 8   H. 23

G. 16   J. 167

17. Dave bought two loaves of bread. One loaf weighed $2\frac{3}{8}$ pounds. The other loaf weighed $1\frac{3}{4}$ pounds. What was the total weight?

A. $3\frac{1}{2}$ lb   C. $4\frac{1}{8}$ lb

B. 4 lb   D. $4\frac{1}{2}$ lb

18. Liz made a loaf of banana bread that weighed $1\frac{5}{8}$ pounds. She gave Tim $\frac{4}{5}$ pound of the bread. How much was left?

F. $\frac{1}{8}$ lb   H. $\frac{33}{40}$ lb

G. $\frac{3}{40}$ lb   J. $\frac{3}{5}$ lb

19. Ginny's family ate $6\frac{1}{4}$ pounds of bread in March. They ate $7\frac{2}{5}$ pounds in April. How much did they eat in those two months?

A. $13\frac{1}{3}$ lb   C. $13\frac{2}{3}$ lb

B. $13\frac{13}{20}$ lb   D. $13\frac{3}{4}$ lb

20. John's family buys $2\frac{2}{9}$ pounds of whole wheat bread each month. They buy $1\frac{4}{5}$ pounds of oat bread. How much more whole wheat than oat bread do they buy?

F. $\frac{1}{5}$ lb   H. $\frac{4}{9}$ lb

G. $\frac{19}{45}$ lb   J. $1\frac{1}{2}$ lb

GO ON

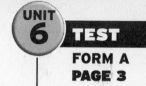
21. $3\frac{7}{18} + 2\frac{13}{18} = \blacksquare$

   A. $6\frac{1}{18}$ **B.** $6\frac{1}{9}$ **C.** $6\frac{1}{3}$ **D.** $6\frac{1}{2}$

22. $4\frac{1}{10} - 2\frac{3}{10} = \blacksquare$

  F. $1\frac{1}{2}$ **H.** $1\frac{4}{5}$

  G. $1\frac{7}{10}$ **J.** $1\frac{9}{10}$

23. Identify the property used.

$$16\frac{3}{8} + \frac{1}{4} + 0 = 16\frac{3}{8} + \frac{1}{4}$$

  A. Associative Property
  B. Commutative Property
  C. Identity Property
  D. Distributive Property

24. Which is the best estimate?

$$12\frac{5}{9} + 4\frac{1}{18}$$

  F. 12   **H.** 28
  G. 17   **J.** 124

25. $\frac{7}{8} + \frac{1}{6} = \blacksquare$

  A. $1\frac{1}{24}$ **C.** $1\frac{1}{8}$

  B. $1\frac{1}{12}$ **D.** $1\frac{1}{4}$

26. $5\frac{1}{9} + \frac{12}{27} = \blacksquare$

  F. $5\frac{13}{36}$ **H.** $5\frac{5}{9}$

  G. $5\frac{13}{27}$ **J.** $5\frac{2}{3}$

27. $\frac{12}{17} - \frac{7}{34} = \blacksquare$

  A. $\frac{5}{34}$ **B.** $\frac{1}{2}$ **C.** $\frac{9}{17}$ **D.** $\frac{3}{34}$

28. Identify the property used.

$$\frac{2}{5} + \frac{8}{9} = \frac{8}{9} + \frac{2}{5}$$

  F. Associative Property
  G. Commutative Property
  H. Identity Property
  J. Distributive Property

29. Which is the best estimate?

$$1\frac{9}{10} + 5\frac{11}{22}$$

  A. 5   **B.** 8   **C.** 15   **D.** 51

30. $11\frac{7}{18} + 5\frac{4}{9} = \blacksquare$

  F. $16\frac{5}{6}$ **H.** $17\frac{1}{18}$

  G. $16\frac{17}{18}$ **J.** $17\frac{5}{6}$

31. $9\frac{2}{3} - \frac{5}{8} = \blacksquare$

  A. $8\frac{7}{8}$ **C.** $9\frac{1}{12}$

  B. $9\frac{1}{24}$ **D.** $9\frac{1}{8}$

32. Which is the best estimate?

$$10\frac{7}{12} - 6\frac{1}{6}$$

  F. 5   **H.** 16
  G. 10   **J.** 60

GO ON

33. Identify the property used.

$(\frac{4}{5} + \frac{5}{9}) + \frac{4}{9} = \frac{4}{5} + (\frac{5}{9} + \frac{4}{9})$

A. Associative Property

B. Commutative Property

C. Identity Property

D. Distributive Property

34. $18\frac{3}{5} - 2\frac{3}{4} = $ ▢

F. $15\frac{17}{20}$ **H.** $15\frac{19}{20}$

G. $15\frac{3}{4}$ **J.** $16\frac{1}{5}$

35. Evaluate.

$(9\frac{3}{8} + 5\frac{1}{8}) + 4\frac{1}{4} = $ ▢

A. $18\frac{1}{2}$ **C.** $18\frac{3}{4}$

B. $18\frac{5}{8}$ **D.** 19

36. Which is the best estimate?

$21\frac{1}{7} - 12\frac{9}{14}$

F. 8   **H.** 21

G. 12   **J.** 33

37. Trent picked two bags of apples. One bag weighed $5\frac{4}{5}$ pounds. The other weighed $7\frac{3}{10}$ pounds. What was the total weight?

A. $12\frac{9}{10}$ lb   **C.** $13\frac{1}{5}$ lb

B. $13\frac{1}{10}$ lb   **D.** $13\frac{2}{5}$ lb

38. Tony bought an $8\frac{1}{2}$-pound bag of apples. He gave $2\frac{1}{7}$ pounds to his friend. How many pounds were left?

F. $6\frac{1}{7}$ lb   **H.** $6\frac{2}{7}$ lb

G. $6\frac{3}{14}$ lb   **J.** $6\frac{5}{14}$ lb

39. Sara made two pies. She used $3\frac{2}{3}$ pounds of apples in one and $3\frac{5}{8}$ pounds in the other. How many pounds did she use in all?

A. $7\frac{1}{3}$ lb   **C.** $7\frac{7}{24}$ lb

B. $7\frac{3}{8}$ lb   **D.** $7\frac{2}{3}$ lb

40. Nadja's family ate $15\frac{1}{8}$ pounds of apples in September. They ate $4\frac{1}{2}$ pounds of pears. How many more pounds of apples than pears did they eat?

F. $10\frac{1}{2}$ lb   **H.** $10\frac{3}{4}$ lb

G. $10\frac{5}{8}$ lb   **J.** $10\frac{7}{16}$ lb

STOP

Name _____

Read each question carefully. Fill in the correct answer in the space provided.

1. $2\frac{8}{15} + 4\frac{13}{15} =$ _____

6. $5\frac{3}{7} + \frac{4}{5} =$ _____

_____

2. $4\frac{7}{9} - 3\frac{5}{9} =$ _____

7. $\frac{7}{8} - \frac{5}{7} =$ _____

_____

3. Identify the property used.

$\frac{2}{3} + \frac{7}{8} = \frac{7}{8} + \frac{2}{3}$

_____

8. Identify the property used.

$\frac{2}{9} + (\frac{3}{8} + \frac{4}{5}) = (\frac{2}{9} + \frac{3}{8}) + \frac{4}{5}$

_____

4. Estimate.

$3\frac{7}{9} + 2\frac{11}{12}$

_____

9. Estimate.

$\frac{2}{7} + 17\frac{4}{11}$

_____

_____

10. $3\frac{1}{6} + 2\frac{3}{4} =$ _____

5. $\frac{7}{10} + \frac{3}{8} =$ _____

11. $11\frac{3}{8} - \frac{2}{3} =$ _____

12. Estimate.

$10\frac{7}{9} - 8\frac{1}{4}$

_____

13. Identify the property used.

$5\frac{9}{10} + 0 = 5\frac{9}{10}$

_____

14. $7\frac{1}{2} - 5\frac{4}{9} =$ _____

15. Evaluate.

$4\frac{3}{4} + (3\frac{5}{6} + 1\frac{1}{3}) =$ _____

16. Estimate.

$12\frac{1}{10} - 6\frac{5}{7}$

17. Sasha bought two pies. One pie weighed $17\frac{1}{2}$ ounces. The other weighed $21\frac{2}{3}$ ounces. What was the total weight?

_____

_____

18. Jason bought a bag of oranges that weighed $9\frac{1}{4}$ pounds. He gave away $2\frac{5}{6}$ pounds of oranges. How much was left?

_____

_____

19. Casey's family ate $12\frac{2}{5}$ pounds of salad in June. They ate $14\frac{1}{4}$ pounds in July. How much did they eat in those two months?

_____

_____

20. Karen's family buys $3\frac{3}{7}$ pounds of apples each month. They buy $2\frac{5}{8}$ pounds of grapes. How much more apples than grapes do they buy?

_____

GO ON

21. $4\frac{5}{12} + 6\frac{7}{12} =$ _____

_____

22. $3\frac{1}{8} - 1\frac{5}{8} =$ _____

_____

23. Identify the property used.

$8\frac{1}{2} + 0 = 8\frac{1}{2}$

_____

24. Estimate.

$9\frac{5}{12} + 18\frac{1}{4}$

_____

25. $\frac{5}{8} + \frac{2}{3} =$ _____

26. $4\frac{1}{12} + \frac{7}{30} =$ _____

_____

27. $\frac{13}{15} - \frac{11}{30} =$ _____

_____

28. Identify the property being used.

$\frac{1}{4} + \frac{9}{10} = \frac{9}{10} + \frac{1}{4}$

_____

29. Estimate.

$10\frac{7}{8} + 5\frac{2}{3}$

_____

30. $8\frac{3}{5} + 9\frac{1}{4} =$ _____

GO ON

31. $3\frac{2}{9} - \frac{2}{3} =$ _____

_____

32. Estimate.

$12\frac{7}{10} - 5\frac{1}{8}$

_____

33. Identify the property used.

$(\frac{2}{3} + \frac{4}{7}) + \frac{2}{7} = \frac{2}{3} + (\frac{4}{7} + \frac{2}{7})$

_____

34. $8\frac{2}{5} - 4\frac{2}{3} =$ _____

_____

35. Evaluate.

$(7\frac{1}{3} + 8\frac{1}{5}) + 3\frac{1}{2} =$ _____

36. Estimate.

$17\frac{1}{11} - 14\frac{3}{4}$

_____

37. Calvin bought two bags of groceries. One bag weighed $3\frac{1}{3}$ pounds. The other bag weighed $7\frac{4}{5}$ pounds. What was the total weight?

_____

_____

38. Meredith bought a $31\frac{1}{2}$-ounce bag of chocolate. She gave $17\frac{8}{9}$ ounces to her friends. How many ounces were left?

_____

_____

39. Patrick made two sculptures. He used $7\frac{2}{9}$ pounds of marble for one and $9\frac{3}{14}$ for the other. How many pounds did he use in all?

_____

_____

40. Yvonne's family ate $12\frac{1}{4}$ pounds of oranges in October. They ate $4\frac{6}{7}$ pounds of cherries. How many more pounds of oranges than cherries did they eat?

_____

_____

STOP

Chapter 13 – Teacher Interview

Core Concept: *Estimate Products of Fractions and Whole Numbers*

Student Activity: Students demonstrate an understanding of fractions and mixed numbers and are able to estimate products using rounding and compatible numbers. Ask students to estimate products for $7 \times 2\frac{2}{3}$, $\frac{1}{3} \times 8\frac{7}{12}$, and $\frac{2}{5} \times 44$.

Teacher Question 1:

- How can you use rounding to estimate the product of $7 \times 2\frac{2}{3}$?

Understanding Student Response	Practice and Improvement
Students who round $2\frac{2}{3}$ to 2.	Review lesson 5 to reinforce an understanding of rounding a mixed number to the nearest whole number.
Students who say the estimated product is 14.	Review lesson 5 to help students recognize that $2\frac{2}{3}$ rounds to 3 and $7 \times 3 = 21$.

Teacher Question 2:

- How can you use compatible numbers to estimate the product of $\frac{1}{3} \times 8\frac{7}{12}$?

Understanding Student Response	Practice and Improvement
Students who round $\frac{1}{3}$ to the nearest 10 as a compatible number.	Review lesson 5 to help students learn to use a compatible number for the mixed number.
Students who say the estimated product is about 6.	Review lesson 1 to help students learn how to multiply a whole number by a fraction.

Teacher Question 3:

- How can you use compatible numbers to estimate the product of $\frac{2}{5}$ and 44?

Understanding Student Response	Practice and Improvement
Students who round down to the nearest 10 or 40.	Review lesson 5 to reinforce an understanding of recognizing compatible numbers.

Chapter 13 – Journal Writing

Encourage students to generate their own journal entries related to math ideas in general or to concepts in this chapter. Present the following journal prompt and have students share their drawing/writing with a partner:

- When you are problem solving, why is it important to carefully read the problem to determine if it involves more than one step to solve?

  (Responses should indicate that when more than one step is involved, you need to decide how to solve each step and in which order to solve.)

JOURNAL WRITING/PROBLEM SOLVING

Jeff has 42 feet of lumber. He uses $\frac{1}{3}$ of it to build shelves and the rest to build a frame for a bookcase. How much lumber did he use on the frame for the bookcase?

Read

Have students find the answer to the problem. Then ask them to write a few sentences telling—

- which information they used to find the answer

- what they did with the information

Have students make up another problem with different information for which they could have followed the same procedure. Then have students solve the problem and supply the correct response.

Plan

Students must correctly determine the product of 42 and $\frac{1}{3}$ and then subtract to find the solution.

Solve

The correct response to the assigned problem is 28 feet of lumber.

Look Back

A correct response demonstrates the ability to solve a multi-step problem and multiply a whole number by a fraction. (See scoring rubric on page 7.)

Chapter 13 – Monitoring Student Progress

☐ Form A   ☐ Form B

Name _____ Date _____

Directions: For each item that is answered incorrectly, cross out the item number. Then record the number of correct responses in the appropriate Student Score column. If the student has not met the Criterion Score for an objective, circle the student's score. Recommended assignments are listed in the Prescription Table on the next page.

Objective	Item Numbers	Criterion Score	Student Score
A. Multiply fractions and whole numbers.	1, 2, 5,10,12	4/5	/5
B. Multiply fractions.	3, 4, 7, 11, 13, 15	5/6	/6
C. Estimate products of fractions and whole numbers.	6, 8, 9, 14, 16	4/5	/5
D. Use skills and strategies to solve problems.	17, 18, 19, 20	3/4	/4
Total Test Score		16/20	/20
Total Percent Correct			%

Chapter 13 – Prescription Table

The following chart correlates the tested objectives for this chapter to supplementary materials that meet the individual needs of the students. The Reteach and Practice pages are designed for students who need further instruction in the math concepts taught in this chapter. The Enrich pages are designed for students who need advanced challenges.

Objective	Reteach	Practice	Enrich
A. Multiply fractions and whole numbers.	217	218	219
B. Multiply fractions.	220, 223	221, 224	222, 225
C. Estimate products of fractions and whole numbers.	229	230	231
D. Use skills and strategies to solve problems.	226	227	228

Read each question carefully. Darken the circle on your answer sheet for the correct answer.

1. $\frac{3}{5}$ of $35 = \square$

   A. 21   C. $\frac{7}{35}$

   B. 14   D. $\frac{21}{35}$

2. $\frac{7}{12} \times 48 = \square$

   F. 35   H. 24
   G. 28   J. 12

3. $\frac{1}{3} \times \frac{1}{5} = \square$

   A. $\frac{3}{5}$ C. $\frac{3}{15}$

   B. $\frac{2}{5}$ D. $\frac{1}{15}$

4. $\frac{1}{9} \times \frac{1}{2} = \square$

   F. $\frac{1}{18}$ H. $\frac{1}{3}$

   G. $\frac{1}{8}$ J. $\frac{1}{2}$

5. $\frac{2}{3}$ of $36 = \square$

   A. 18   C. 24
   B. 21   D. 28

6. Which is the best estimate?

   $\frac{1}{6} \times 56$

   F. about 7
   G. about 8
   H. about 9
   J. about 12

7. $\frac{1}{2} \times \frac{2}{5} = \square$

   A. $\frac{1}{10}$ C. $\frac{1}{4}$

   B. $\frac{1}{5}$ D. $\frac{3}{4}$

8. Estimate and compare.

   $4 \times \frac{2}{3} \bigcirc 5 \times \frac{3}{4}$

   F. $>$
   G. $<$
   H. $=$

9. Which is the best estimate?

   $8\frac{1}{6} \times \frac{3}{4}$

   A. about 6   C. about 4
   B. about 5   D. about 3

10. $\frac{10}{3}$ of $\frac{27}{5} = \square$

    F. 36   H. 18
    G 27   J. 9

GO ON

11. $\frac{3}{5} \times \frac{5}{8} =$ ▨

   A. $\frac{1}{4}$ **C.** $\frac{3}{8}$

   B. $\frac{2}{5}$ **D.** $\frac{7}{8}$

12. $\frac{5}{8} \times 64 =$ ▨

   F. 56   **H.** 44

   G. 48   **J.** 40

13. $\frac{5}{11} \times \frac{11}{20} =$ ▨

   A. $\frac{1}{10}$ **C.** $\frac{1}{5}$

   B. $\frac{1}{4}$ **D.** $\frac{1}{2}$

14. Which is the best estimate?

$$9\frac{1}{5} \times 3\frac{5}{6}$$

   F. about 45   **H.** about 25

   G. about 36   **J.** about 18

15. $\frac{7}{15} \times \frac{5}{14} =$ ▨

   A. $\frac{5}{6}$ **C.** $\frac{1}{3}$

   B. $\frac{2}{3}$ **D.** $\frac{1}{6}$

16. Estimate and compare.

$$\frac{5}{6} \times 26 \bigcirc \frac{1}{3} \times 43$$

   F. $>$

   G. $<$

   H. $=$

17. Amelia is reading a 750-page book. If she has $\frac{3}{5}$ of the book left to read, how many pages has she read so far?

   A. 450 pages

   B. 350 pages

   C. 300 pages

   D. 250 pages

18. Josh is building a model airplane that has 125 pieces. He has put together $\frac{2}{5}$ of the pieces. How many more pieces does Josh need to put together?

   F. 25 pieces   **H.** 75 pieces

   G. 50 pieces   **J.** 100 pieces

19. Danny wants to make 3 shelves from a 4-foot-long piece of lumber. He wants each shelf to be 15 inches long. How much lumber will be left over?

   A. 3 inches   **C.** 5 inches

   B. 4 inches   **D.** 6 inches

20. Darlene gets an allowance of $24. She saves $\frac{1}{3}$ of it in the bank and is allowed to spend the rest. She spends $\frac{1}{4}$ of it on a book. How much of her allowance does Darlene have left to spend?

   F. $12.00   **H.** $8.00

   G. $10.00   **J.** $6.00

STOP

Name_____

Read each question carefully. Fill in the correct answer in the space provided.

1. $\frac{3}{7}$ of 42 = _____

_____

2. $\frac{7}{12} \times 60 =$ _____

_____

3. $\frac{1}{5} \times \frac{2}{3} =$ _____

_____

4. $\frac{1}{8} \times \frac{1}{2} =$ _____

_____

5. $\frac{3}{4}$ of 52 = _____

6. Estimate.

$\frac{1}{8} \times 50$

_____

7. $\frac{6}{12} \times \frac{5}{6} =$ _____

_____

8. Estimate and compare. Write >, <, or =.

$7 \times \frac{1}{3} \quad \bigcirc \quad 5 \times \frac{3}{4}$

_____

9. Estimate.

$11\frac{1}{8} \times \frac{5}{6}$

_____

10. $\frac{7}{10}$ of 70 = _____

GO ON

11. $\frac{2}{5} \times \frac{7}{8} =$ _____

12. $\frac{3}{7} \times 56$ _____

13. $\frac{3}{11} \times \frac{11}{12} =$ _____

14. Estimate.

$8\frac{1}{3} \times 2\frac{7}{9}$

_____

15. $\frac{7}{15} \times \frac{3}{14} =$ _____

16. Estimate and compare. Write >, <, or =.

$\frac{5}{8} \times 30 \bigcirc \frac{1}{7} \times 67$

_____

17. Gavin is reading a 720-page book. If he has $\frac{1}{3}$ of the book left to read, how many pages has he read so far?

_____

18. June is knitting squares for a quilt that has 120 squares. She has $\frac{2}{5}$ of the squares done. How many more squares does June need to knit?

_____

19. Kevin wants to make 4 shelves from a 5-foot-long piece of lumber. He wants each shelf to be 14 inches long. How much lumber will be left over?

_____

20. Kayla gets an allowance of $18. She puts $\frac{1}{3}$ of it into her savings account and is allowed to spend the rest. She spends $\frac{1}{6}$ of it on a magazine. How much of her allowance does Kayla have left?

_____

STOP

Chapter 14 – Teacher Interview

Core Concept: *Divide Fractions and Mixed Numbers*

Student Activity: Students demonstrate an understanding of relating multiplication and division to dividing fractions and mixed numbers and dividing using reciprocals. Ask students to solve $\frac{1}{2} \div 2\frac{3}{4}$.

Teacher Question 1:

- Which operation is related to division? Give an example.

Understanding Student Response	Practice and Improvement
Students who say multiplication and subtraction are related.	Review lesson 6 to reinforce an understanding that multiplication and division are related operations.
Students who say $3 \div \frac{1}{2} = \frac{1}{3} \times \frac{2}{1} = \frac{2}{3}$ or a similar example.	Review lesson 6 to help students recognize that they need to multiply the reciprocal of the divisor: $3 \times \frac{2}{1} = 6$.

Teacher Question 2:

- How do you use the reciprocal of $2\frac{3}{4}$ to solve $\frac{1}{2} \div 2\frac{3}{4}$?

Understanding Student Response	Practice and Improvement
Students who say $\frac{1}{2} \times \frac{11}{4}$.	Review lesson 6 to reinforce what a reciprocal is.

Teacher Question 3:

- What is $\frac{1}{2} \div 2\frac{3}{4}$?

Understanding Student Response	Practice and Improvement
Students who say $\frac{2}{1} \times \frac{11}{4} = 5\frac{1}{2}$.	Review lesson 6 to reinforce an understanding of using the reciprocal of the divisor to multiply $\frac{1}{2} \times \frac{4}{11} = \frac{2}{11}$.
Students who say $\frac{1}{2} \times \frac{11}{4} = \frac{11}{8}$.	Review lesson 6 to help students learn how to divide a fraction by a mixed number.

Chapter 14 – Journal Writing

Encourage students to generate their own journal entries related to math ideas in general or to concepts in this chapter. Present the following journal prompt and have students share their drawing/writing with a partner:

- When you have combinations or patterns in a word problem, how does making an organized list help you solve the problem?

  (Responses should indicate that making an organized list can help you see the combinations or patterns and check the answer.)

JOURNAL WRITING/PROBLEM SOLVING

Martha has 6 hours of movie videos. If each video is $1\frac{1}{2}$ hours long, how many movies does she have?

Read

Have students find the answer to the problem. Then ask them to write a few sentences telling—

- which information they used to find the answer

- what they did with the information

Have students make up another problem with different information for which they could have followed the same procedure. Then have students solve the problem and supply the correct response.

Plan

Students must correctly determine how many movies Martha has by dividing the total hours by the length of each video. Students must also remember to multiply by the reciprocal of $1\frac{1}{2}$ to find the answer.

Solve

The correct response to the assigned problem is 4 movies.

Look Back

A correct response demonstrates the ability to divide a whole number by a mixed number. (See scoring rubric on page 7.)

Chapter 14 – Monitoring Student Progress

☐ Form A   ☐ Form B

Name _____ Date _____

Directions: For each item that is answered incorrectly, cross out the item number. Then record the number of correct responses in the appropriate Student Score column. If the student has not met the Criterion Score for an objective, circle the student's score. Recommended assignments are listed in the Prescription Table on the next page.

Objective	Item Numbers	Criterion Score	Student Score
A. Multiply mixed numbers and whole numbers.	1, 3, 6, 10, 14	4/5	/5
B. Multiply fractions and mixed numbers.	2, 4, 8, 12, 16	4/5	/5
C. Divide fractions, mixed numbers, and whole numbers.	5, 7, 9, 11, 13, 15	5/6	/6
D. Use skills and strategies to solve problems.	17, 18, 19, 20	3/4	/4
Total Test Score		16/20	/20
Total Percent Correct			%

Chapter 14 – Prescription Table

The following chart correlates the tested objectives for this chapter to supplementary materials that meet the individual needs of the students. The Reteach and Practice pages are designed for students who need further instruction in the math concepts taught in this chapter. The Enrich pages are designed for students who need advanced challenges.

Objective	Reteach	Practice	Enrich
A. Multiply mixed numbers and whole numbers.	235	236	237
B. Multiply fractions and mixed numbers.	238, 241	239, 242	240, 243
C. Divide fractions, mixed numbers, and whole numbers.	247, 250	248, 251	249, 252
D. Use skills and strategies to solve problems.	244, 245	246	

Read each question carefully. Darken the circle on your answer sheet for the correct answer.

1. $3 \times 4\frac{1}{6} = \boxed{}$

A. $12\frac{1}{2}$ **C.** 12

B. $12\frac{1}{6}$ **D.** $7\frac{1}{6}$

6. $45 \times 3\frac{3}{4} = \boxed{}$

F. $135\frac{3}{4}$ **H.** $165\frac{1}{6}$

G. $137\frac{1}{4}$ **J.** $168\frac{3}{4}$

2. $3\frac{1}{5} \times \frac{1}{10} = \boxed{}$

F. $\frac{31}{50}$ **H.** $\frac{8}{25}$

G. $\frac{17}{50}$ **J.** $\frac{1}{3}$

7. $\frac{3}{4} \div \frac{1}{3} = \boxed{}$

A. $2\frac{1}{2}$ **C.** $1\frac{1}{2}$

B. $2\frac{1}{4}$ **D.** $\frac{1}{4}$

3. $28 \times 4\frac{3}{8} = \boxed{}$

A. $112\frac{3}{8}$ **C.** $122\frac{1}{2}$

B. $122\frac{3}{8}$ **D.** $122\frac{3}{4}$

8. $1\frac{7}{9} \times \frac{1}{12} = \boxed{}$

F. $\frac{1}{3}$ **H.** $\frac{6}{27}$

G. $\frac{4}{27}$ **J.** $\frac{5}{6}$

4. $\frac{3}{7} \times 1\frac{1}{3} = \boxed{}$

F. $\frac{4}{7}$ **H.** $\frac{2}{3}$

G. $\frac{1}{2}$ **J.** $2\frac{1}{3}$

9. $\frac{4}{5} \div 1\frac{1}{2} = \boxed{}$

A. $\frac{1}{3}$ **C.** $\frac{8}{15}$

B. $\frac{2}{5}$ **D.** $\frac{1}{2}$

5. $\frac{5}{6} \div \frac{5}{12} = \boxed{}$

A. $\frac{1}{2}$ **C.** $1\frac{5}{6}$

B. $1\frac{1}{2}$ **D.** 2

10. $9 \times 3\frac{2}{3} = \boxed{}$

F. $27\frac{2}{3}$ **H.** 33

G. 30 **J.** 35

GO ON

11. $\frac{7}{12} \div \frac{1}{12} = $ ▨

   A. $\frac{1}{2}$ **B.** $\frac{2}{3}$ **C.** 6   **D.** 7

12. $4\frac{2}{3} \times \frac{2}{5} = $ ▨

   F. $1\frac{3}{15}$ **G.** $1\frac{3}{5}$ **H.** $1\frac{13}{15}$ **J.** $1\frac{4}{5}$

13. $7\frac{1}{2} \div 2\frac{5}{8} = $ ▨

   A. $2\frac{5}{7}$ **B.** $2\frac{6}{7}$ **C.** $3\frac{5}{7}$ **D.** $3\frac{6}{7}$

14. $2\frac{5}{8} \times 32 = $ ▨

   F. $64\frac{5}{8}$ **G.** $65\frac{1}{4}$ **H.** 84   **J.** $85\frac{1}{2}$

15. $\frac{5}{6} \div 3\frac{1}{3} = $ ▨

   A. $\frac{1}{4}$ **C.** $1\frac{1}{3}$

   B. $\frac{1}{2}$ **D.** $2\frac{7}{9}$

16. $5\frac{1}{2} \times \frac{1}{8} = $ ▨

   F. $\frac{11}{16}$ **H.** $\frac{1}{2}$

   G. $\frac{5}{8}$ **J.** $\frac{7}{16}$

17. Wanda makes scarves. She can make a scarf with a solid color, a plaid, or a pattern. She can also cut the material into a square or a rectangle. In how many ways can Wanda make a scarf?

   A. 3   **B.** 4   **C.** 5   **D.** 6

18. George likes to design board games. He draws the board in a zigzag pattern, in a straight line, or in a large circle. He also fills the squares with a solid color, a stripe, or a dotted-line pattern. In how many ways does he design board games?

   F. 9   **G.** 8   **H.** 7   **J.** 6

19. Christine has two fraction spinners. On one she can spin $\frac{1}{6}$, $\frac{1}{5}$, and $\frac{1}{4}$. On the other she can spin $\frac{1}{3}$ and $\frac{1}{2}$. If she spins both, which products can she find?

   A. $\frac{1}{30}$, $\frac{1}{24}$, $\frac{1}{24}$, $\frac{1}{12}$, $\frac{1}{10}$

   B. $\frac{1}{18}$, $\frac{1}{15}$, $\frac{1}{12}$, $\frac{1}{10}$, $\frac{1}{8}$

   C. $\frac{1}{36}$, $\frac{1}{30}$, $\frac{1}{24}$, $\frac{1}{16}$, $\frac{1}{8}$

   D. $\frac{1}{18}$, $\frac{1}{9}$, $\frac{1}{5}$, $\frac{1}{7}$, $\frac{1}{6}$

20. Carl has four tiles: a red triangle, a blue square, a yellow rectangle, and a gray rhombus. Jean has an orange triangle, a green square, a purple rectangle, and a white rhombus. If each person uses one tile, how many different pairs of tiles can they make?

   F. 20

   G. 16

   H. 8

   J. 4

STOP

Read each question carefully. Fill in the correct answer in the space provided.

1. $2 \times 5\frac{1}{3} =$ _____

2. $5\frac{2}{3} \times \frac{1}{2} =$ _____

3. $48 \times 2\frac{1}{6} =$ _____

4. $\frac{5}{6} \times \frac{1}{12} =$ _____

5. $\frac{2}{5} \div \frac{1}{5} =$ _____

6. $32 \times 2\frac{1}{8} =$ _____

7. $\frac{2}{3} \div \frac{1}{4} =$ _____

8. $1\frac{4}{9} \times \frac{1}{16} =$ _____

9. $\frac{1}{8} \div 2\frac{1}{6} =$ _____

10. $6 \times 2\frac{5}{8} =$ _____

GO ON

11. $\frac{5}{12} \div \frac{1}{6} =$ _____

12. $3\frac{3}{5} \times \frac{1}{3} =$ _____

13. $5\frac{1}{3} \div 3\frac{5}{6} =$ _____

14. $4\frac{3}{8} \times 24 =$ _____

15. $\frac{7}{12} \div 4\frac{1}{2} =$ _____

16. $7\frac{1}{3} \times \frac{1}{6} =$ _____

17. Will makes kites. He can make a kite with a solid color, a plaid, or a pattern. He can also cut the paper into a square or a rectangle. In how many ways can Will make a kite?

_____

18. Jerry likes to design patterns on wood. He draws wavy lines, straight lines, or circles. He also uses markers to fill the patterns with a solid color, a stripe, or a dotted-line pattern. In how many ways does he design patterns?

_____

_____

19. Karen has two fraction spinners. On one she can spin $\frac{1}{4}$, $\frac{1}{3}$, and $\frac{1}{2}$. On the other she can spin $\frac{1}{5}$ and $\frac{1}{6}$. If she spins both, which products can she find?

_____

_____

20. Juan has four tiles: a triangle, a square, a rectangle, and a rhombus. Sal has an octagon, a hexagon, and a pentagon. If each person uses one tile, how many different pairs of tiles can they make?

_____

STOP

Unit 7 Performance Assessment

Cliff's Colossal Salad

- *Target Skill:* Multiply fractions and mixed numbers.
- *Additional Skills:* Add and subtract fractions and mixed numbers; divide by 2-digit divisors; simplify fractions.

Task Description: This task requires students to multiply a fraction or mixed number by a mixed number to find the weight of a fruit salad. The students will be asked to compare the weight of the fruit salad with the weight of one of the ingredients.

Preparing: You may wish to have the students discuss their favorite fruits. Review with students the relative sizes of fruit.

Materials	Group Size	Time on Task
Calculator (optional)	1 to 2 students	1 day

Guiding: Remind students that to multiply with mixed numbers, it is necessary to first convert the mixed number to an improper fraction.

Observing/ Monitoring: As you move among the students, pose the following questions:

How do you multiply a fraction by a mixed number?

How does simplifying the fraction before multiplying make computing easier?

Unit 7 Performance Assessment Scoring Rubric

Cliff's Colossal Salad

Score	Explanation
3	Students demonstrate an efficient strategy and a thorough approach that enables them to solve the problem completely. A satisfactory answer: • correctly finds the weight of each fruit; • states how much melon to use; • states how much salad is left over. Students are able to complete the problem quickly and have all of the above correct solutions.
2	Students demonstrate a strategy that enables them to solve most of the problem correctly. The strategy is somewhat disorganized, making it less efficient. A solution is found, but errors are contained. Students may: • multiply most of the products correctly; • accurately compare the salad with the melon. Students have some difficulty determining all solutions correctly but demonstrate an understanding of general concepts.
1	Students demonstrate a confused strategy, which leads to difficulty solving the problem. Most answers are incorrect, but students demonstrate knowledge of at least one concept being assessed. Students may: • multiply some of the products correctly; OR • correctly apply some other operation.

Unit 7 Performance Assessment Student Activity

Cliff's Colossal Salad

You will need
- Calculator (optional)

It's finally spring — time for the Skene School Kite-Flyers Club annual picnic! The club president has asked Cliff to prepare a fruit salad for the 27 people expected at the party. Here is a recipe for Cliff's special fruit salad:

Serves 10:
Strawberries – $\frac{7}{8}$ lb
Melon – $2\frac{1}{2}$ lb
Blueberries – $\frac{3}{4}$ lb
Sliced apples – $1\frac{1}{8}$ lb
Kiwis – $\frac{1}{2}$ lb

1. Cliff will make enough salad to serve 30 people. How much of each fruit does he need?

_____

_____

_____

2. If 15 people each eat an equal amount of salad, how much can each person have?

_____

3. If each person eats $\frac{1}{2}$ pound of salad, how many pounds of salad will be left over?

_____

4. If you modify Cliff's recipe so that $\frac{1}{3}$ of the fruit is melon, how much melon will you use to make 10 servings?

_____

Unit 7 – Monitoring Student Progress

☐ Form A   ☐ Form B

Name _____ Date _____

Directions: This test targets selected objectives. For each item that is answered incorrectly, cross out the item number. Then record the number of correct responses in the column labeled **Number of Correct Responses.** Add to find the **Total Number of Correct Responses** and record the total. Use this total to determine the **Total Test Score** and the **Total Percent Correct.**

Strand • Objective(s)	Item Numbers	Number of Correct Responses
Number Sense, Concepts, and Operations • Multiply fractions and whole numbers. • Multiply fractions. • Estimate products of fractions and whole numbers. • Multiply mixed numbers and whole numbers. • Multiply fractions and mixed numbers. • Divide fractions, mixed numbers, and whole numbers. • Use skills and strategies to solve problems.	1, 2, 3, 4, 5, 6, 7, 8, 9, 10, 11, 12, 13, 14, 15, 16, 17, 18, 19, 20, 21, 22, 23, 24, 25, 26, 27, 28, 29, 30, 31, 32, 33, 34, 35, 36, 37, 38, 39, 40	/40
Total Number of Correct Responses		
Total Test Score		/40
Total Percent Correct		%

Read each question carefully. Darken the circle on your answer sheet for the correct answer.

1. $121 \times \frac{4}{11} = \square$

   A. 51   **C.** 44

   B. $48\frac{1}{11}$ **D.** 40

2. $\frac{3}{4} \div \frac{5}{9} = \square$

   F. $1\frac{2}{5}$ **H.** $\frac{5}{12}$

   G. $1\frac{7}{20}$ **J.** $\frac{1}{3}$

3. $9 \times 5\frac{2}{5} = \square$

   A. 45   **C.** $48\frac{3}{5}$

   B. $45\frac{2}{5}$ **D.** $49\frac{2}{5}$

4. Which is the best estimate?

   $\frac{4}{7} \times 44$

   F. 1   **G.** 4   **H.** 22   **J.** 44

5. $\frac{7}{15} \times \frac{3}{14} = \square$

   A. $\frac{10}{29}$ **C.** $\frac{7}{60}$

   B. $\frac{1}{7}$ **D.** $\frac{1}{10}$

6. $48 \div \frac{5}{12} = \square$

   F. 20   **H.** $111\frac{1}{5}$

   G. 22   **J.** $115\frac{1}{5}$

7. $6\frac{3}{8} \times \frac{1}{4} = \square$

   A. $1\frac{1}{2}$ **C.** $6\frac{5}{8}$

   B. $1\frac{19}{32}$ **D.** $7\frac{1}{2}$

8. Which is the best estimate?

   $19\frac{2}{3} \times \frac{3}{10}$

   F. 21   **H.** 6

   G. 20   **J.** 1

9. $5\frac{2}{3} \times 15 = \square$

   A. 75   **C.** 85

   B. $75\frac{2}{3}$ **D.** $86\frac{1}{3}$

10. $4\frac{3}{8} \times 7\frac{5}{7} = \square$

   F. 35   **H.** $33\frac{3}{4}$

   G. $34\frac{5}{8}$ **J.** $33\frac{1}{4}$

11. $23\frac{1}{5} \div 7\frac{1}{2} = \square$

   A. 174   **C.** $3\frac{1}{5}$

   B. 154   **D.** $3\frac{7}{75}$

12. $29\frac{2}{3} \times 1\frac{3}{4} = \square$

   F. $29\frac{1}{2}$ **H.** $51\frac{11}{12}$

   G. $31\frac{5}{12}$ **J.** $52\frac{3}{4}$

GO ON

13. Which is the best estimate?

$$37\frac{1}{6} \times \frac{5}{8}$$

A. 40   **B.** 10   **C.** 25   **D.** 1

---

14. $15\frac{1}{6} \div 2\frac{1}{3} = \blacksquare$

F. $19\frac{1}{2}$ **G.** 13   **H.** $6\frac{1}{2}$ **J.** $2\frac{11}{14}$

---

15. Which is the best estimate?

$$4\frac{7}{8} \times 16\frac{3}{5}$$

A. 64   **C.** 80

B. 68   **D.** 85

---

16. Which is the best estimate?

$$32\frac{1}{8} \times 49\frac{4}{5}$$

F. 15   **H.** 1,500

G. 150   **J.** 15,000

---

17. Troy had $\frac{2}{3}$ can of brown paint. He used $\frac{2}{7}$ of the paint for a science project. How much of the can did he use?

A. $\frac{2}{5}$ can   **C.** $\frac{1}{5}$ can

B. $\frac{4}{21}$ can   **D.** $\frac{2}{21}$ can

---

18. Rosa bought $7\frac{1}{4}$ yards of cloth. She used $\frac{3}{5}$ of it. How much is left?

F. $\frac{1}{10}$ yd   **H.** $2\frac{13}{20}$ yd

G. $2\frac{9}{10}$ yd   **J.** Not Here

---

19. Gerry cuts 64 feet of rope into jump ropes. If each jump rope is $3\frac{5}{9}$ feet, how many jump ropes does he cut?

A. 228 jump ropes

B. 227 jump ropes

C. 25 jump ropes

D. 18 jump ropes

---

20. Ben has two spinners. On one he can spin $\frac{1}{7}$, $\frac{1}{8}$, and $\frac{1}{9}$. On the other he can spin $\frac{1}{5}$ or $\frac{1}{6}$. He spins both and finds the product. Which products can he find?

F. $\frac{1}{35}$, $\frac{1}{40}$, $\frac{1}{41}$, $\frac{1}{42}$, $\frac{1}{46}$, $\frac{1}{60}$

G. $\frac{1}{35}$, $\frac{1}{40}$, $\frac{1}{42}$, $\frac{1}{45}$, $\frac{1}{48}$, $\frac{1}{54}$

H. $\frac{1}{24}$, $\frac{1}{26}$, $\frac{1}{28}$, $\frac{1}{30}$

J. $\frac{1}{12}$, $\frac{1}{13}$, $\frac{1}{14}$, $\frac{1}{15}$

GO ON

21. $42 \times \frac{6}{7} =$ ▢

    A. 49   **C.** 36

    B. 42   **D.** 30

22. $\frac{12}{17} \div \frac{9}{34} =$ ▢

    F. $2\frac{2}{3}$ **H.** $\frac{27}{119}$

    G. $2\frac{1}{2}$ **J.** $\frac{9}{40}$

23. $16 \times 9\frac{1}{3} =$ ▢

    A. 144   **C.** $150\frac{1}{3}$

    B. $149\frac{1}{3}$ **D.** $169\frac{1}{3}$

24. Which is the best estimate?

    $\frac{5}{8} \times 49$

    F. 2   **H.** 48

    G. 30   **J.** 100

25. $\frac{3}{4} \times \frac{8}{9} =$ ▢

    A. $\frac{5}{6}$ **C.** $\frac{11}{13}$

    B. $\frac{2}{3}$ **D.** $\frac{11}{36}$

26. $144 \div \frac{3}{8} =$ ▢

    F. 384   **H.** 192

    G. 376   **J.** 54

27. $15 \times 4\frac{1}{3} =$ ▢

    A. $19\frac{1}{3}$ **C.** $61\frac{2}{3}$

    B. 60   **D.** 65

28. Which is the best estimate?

    $\frac{7}{9} \times 25\frac{4}{5}$

    F. 37   **H.** 29

    G. 30   **J.** 21

29. $17\frac{2}{3} \times 21 =$ ▢

    A. 371   **C.** 357

    B. $367\frac{1}{3}$ **D.** $373\frac{2}{3}$

30. $19\frac{1}{8} \times 12\frac{2}{3} =$ ▢

    F. $242\frac{1}{4}$ **H.** $161\frac{1}{2}$

    G. 204   **J.** $80\frac{3}{4}$

31. $18\frac{6}{7} \div 4\frac{2}{3} =$ ▢

    A. 88   **C.** $4\frac{1}{2}$

    B. 44   **D.** $4\frac{2}{49}$

GO ON ➤

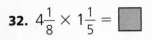
32. $4\frac{1}{8} \times 1\frac{1}{5} = $ ▢

F. $4\frac{5}{88}$ **H.** $5\frac{3}{4}$

G. $5\frac{51}{88}$ **J.** $4\frac{19}{20}$

33. Which is the best estimate?

$$123\frac{1}{8} \times \frac{7}{10}$$

A. 140   **B.** 130   **C.** 84   **D.** 20

34. $32\frac{2}{5} \div \frac{3}{4} = $ ▢

F. $86\frac{2}{5}$ **G.** $48\frac{2}{5}$ **H.** $43\frac{1}{5}$ **J.** $24\frac{3}{10}$

35. Which is the best estimate?

$$7 \times 2\frac{4}{7}$$

A. 14   **C.** 21

B. 16   **D.** 24

36. Which is the best estimate?

$$54\frac{6}{11} \times 21\frac{3}{22}$$

F. 70   **H.** 540

G. 100   **J.** 1,000

37. Dean had $\frac{7}{8}$ carton of juice. He drank $\frac{2}{3}$ of that amount. How much of the carton did he drink?

A. $\frac{3}{4}$ carton   **C.** $\frac{7}{12}$ carton

B. $\frac{9}{11}$ carton   **D.** $\frac{1}{2}$ carton

38. Jim bought $21\frac{2}{3}$ yards of canvas. He used $\frac{3}{4}$ of it. How much was left?

F. $11\frac{3}{4}$ yd   **H.** $5\frac{5}{12}$ yd

G. $5\frac{5}{8}$ yd   **J.** $11\frac{1}{4}$ yd

39. Elly cuts a 52-foot roll of plastic into strips. If each strip is $4\frac{1}{3}$ feet long, how many strips does she cut?

A. 5 strips   **C.** 12 strips

B. 9 strips   **D.** 20 strips

40. June has two spinners. On one she can spin $\frac{1}{2}$ or $\frac{1}{3}$. On the other she can spin $\frac{2}{3}$ or $\frac{3}{4}$. She spins both and finds the product. Which products can she find?

F. $\frac{5}{8}, \frac{2}{9}, \frac{1}{3}, \frac{3}{8}$

G. $\frac{2}{9}, \frac{1}{4}, \frac{1}{3}, \frac{5}{8}$

H. $\frac{2}{3}, \frac{5}{9}, \frac{1}{4}, \frac{4}{5}$

J. $\frac{1}{3}, \frac{3}{8}, \frac{2}{9}, \frac{1}{4}$

STOP

Name _____

Read each question carefully. Fill in the correct answer in the space provided.

1. $132 \times \frac{5}{12} =$ _____

2. $\frac{3}{5} \div \frac{4}{9} =$ _____

3. $8 \times 6\frac{3}{5} =$ _____

4. Estimate.

$\frac{5}{9} \times 48$

_____

5. $\frac{7}{8} \times \frac{5}{14} =$ _____

6. $64 \div \frac{9}{16} =$ _____

7. $7\frac{3}{10} \times \frac{1}{5} =$ _____

8. Estimate.

$17\frac{4}{5} \times \frac{2}{6}$

_____

9. $4\frac{3}{4} \times 12 =$ _____

10. $4\frac{4}{7} \times 5\frac{9}{8} =$ _____

11. $21\frac{2}{5} \div 4\frac{1}{2} =$ _____

_____

12. $10\frac{2}{3} \times 1\frac{1}{4} =$ _____

_____

13. Estimate.

$41\frac{5}{8} \times \frac{5}{6} =$

_____

14. $16\frac{5}{6} \div 3\frac{2}{3} =$ _____

_____

15. Estimate.

$3\frac{7}{8} \times 18\frac{2}{5}$

_____

16. Estimate.

$45\frac{1}{4} \times 52\frac{2}{3}$

_____

17. Leah has $\frac{3}{4}$ can of red paint. She used $\frac{2}{5}$ of the paint for a social studies project. How much of the can did she use?

_____

18. John is running $8\frac{1}{2}$ miles. He has run $\frac{3}{5}$ of the course so far. How far has he run?

_____

19. Betsy cuts 75 feet of rope into jump rope. If each jump rope is $6\frac{1}{4}$ feet, how many jump ropes does she cut?

_____

20. Matt has two spinners. On one he can spin $\frac{1}{6}$, $\frac{1}{7}$, and $\frac{1}{9}$. On the other he can spin $\frac{1}{3}$ or $\frac{1}{4}$. If he spins both, what are the possible products he could find?

_____

GO ON

21. $35 \times \frac{5}{7} =$ _____

_____

22. $\frac{6}{19} \div \frac{21}{38} =$ _____

_____

23. $18 \times 7\frac{1}{4} =$ _____

_____

24. Estimate.

$\frac{3}{8} \times 38$

_____

25. $\frac{2}{5} \times \frac{7}{9} =$ _____

26. $162 \div \frac{3}{7} =$ _____

_____

27. $21 \times 3\frac{2}{3} =$ _____

_____

28. Estimate.

$\frac{5}{8} \times 41$

_____

29. $18\frac{1}{4} \times 22 =$ _____

_____

30. $17\frac{3}{8} \times 14\frac{1}{3} =$ _____

GO ON

31. $11\frac{5}{7} \div 5\frac{1}{3} =$ _____

32. $5\frac{2}{6} \times 1\frac{2}{5} =$ _____

33. Estimate.

$115\frac{2}{3} \times \frac{4}{5}$

34. $34\frac{3}{5} \div \frac{1}{4} =$ _____

35. Estimate.

$8 \times 2\frac{5}{7}$

36. Estimate.

$51\frac{5}{9} \times 22\frac{1}{19}$

37. Dwayne had $\frac{9}{10}$ liter of sports drink. He drank $\frac{4}{5}$ of that amount. How much of the sports drink did he drink?

38. Melissa bought $16\frac{1}{4}$ yards of yarn. She used $\frac{4}{5}$ of it. How much was left?

39. Laz cut a 68-foot-long piece of steel into strips. If each strip is $5\frac{2}{3}$ feet long, how many strips does she cut?

40. Elyssia has two spinners. On one she can spin $\frac{3}{4}$ or $\frac{2}{5}$. On the other she can spin $\frac{1}{3}$ and $\frac{1}{4}$. What products can she find if she spins both spinners?

STOP

Chapter 15 – Teacher Interview

Core Concept: *Choosing Appropriate Customary Measurement*

Student Activity: Students demonstrate an understanding of customary measurements and are able to change and compare units of length, weight, and capacity. Ask students to use customary measurements to solve the problems.

Teacher Question 1:

- Which unit of measurement would you use to weigh tomatoes?

Understanding Student Response	Practice and Improvement
Students who say customary units of capacity such as pints or gallons.	Review lesson 4 to reinforce an understanding of customary weight.
Students who say customary units of length such as inches or feet.	Review lesson 3 to help students recognize that inches and feet are customary units of length.

Teacher Question 2:

- How many gallons and quarts does 7 quarts equal?

Understanding Student Response	Practice and Improvement
Students who change quarts to fluid ounces, cups, and pints.	Review lesson 4 to help students visualize customary units of capacity.
Students who say the answer is 1 gallon 2 pints.	Review lesson 4 to help students learn that if 1 gallon = 4 quarts, the answer is 1 gallon 3 quarts.

Teacher Question 3:

- A poster measures 18 inches × 22 inches and a painting measures 1 foot 5 inches × 2 feet. Which is larger? By how much is the object larger?

Understanding Student Response	Practice and Improvement
Students who say the poster is larger.	Review lesson 3 to reinforce an understanding of customary length.
Students who say the painting is larger by 1 foot × 2 inches.	Review lesson 3 to help students learn to change feet to inches and then subtract to find that the painting is larger by 1 inch × 2 inches.

Chapter 15 – Journal Writing

Encourage students to generate their own journal entries related to math ideas in general or to concepts in this chapter. Present the following journal prompt and have students share their drawing/writing with a partner:

- When you are problem solving, why is it important to check for reasonableness?

    (Responses should indicate that problem solving requires you to think about what you already know about the problem so that when you solve it, the answer makes sense.)

JOURNAL WRITING/PROBLEM SOLVING

Janice plans to paint and decorate her bedroom furniture. She buys 1 gallon of green paint, two 8-ounce jars of yellow paint, and 5 pints of red paint. How many ounces of paint does she buy in all?

Read

Have students find the answer to the problem. Then ask them to write a few sentences telling—

- which information they used to find the answer

- what they did with the information

Have students make up another problem with different information for which they have to follow the same procedure. Then have students solve the problem and supply the correct response.

Plan

Students must correctly convert gallons and pints to ounces. Students must then add all the volumes to find the total number of ounces of paint.

Solve

The correct response to the assigned problem is 224 ounces.

Look Back

A correct response demonstrates the ability to recognize and convert customary units of capacity. (See scoring rubric on page 7.)

Chapter 15 – Monitoring Student Progress

☐ Form A   ☐ Form B

Name _____ Date _____

Directions: For each item that is answered incorrectly, cross out the item number. Then record the number of correct responses in the appropriate Student Score column. If the student has not met the Criterion Score for an objective, circle the student's score. Recommended assignments are listed in the Prescription Table on the next page.

Objective	Item Numbers	Criterion Score	Student Score
A. Convert and compute with units of time and find elapsed time.	1, 3, 7, 11, 14	4/5	/5
B. Choose appropriate units and estimate length, weight/mass, and capacity, and measure length.	2, 4, 8, 12, 15	4/5	/5
C. Convert units of measurements.	5, 6, 9, 10, 13, 16	5/6	/6
D. Use skills and strategies to solve problems.	17, 18, 19, 20	3/4	/4
Total Test Score		16/20	/20
Total Percent Correct			%

Chapter 15 – Prescription Table

The following chart correlates the tested objectives for this chapter to supplementary materials that meet the individual needs of the students. The Reteach and Practice pages are designed for students who need further instruction in the math concepts taught in this chapter. The Enrich pages are designed for students who need advanced challenges.

Objective	Reteach	Practice	Enrich
A. Convert and compute with units of time and find elapsed time.	254	255	256
B. Choose appropriate units and estimate length, weight/mass, and capacity, and measure length.	257, 260	258, 261	259, 262
C. Convert units of measurement.	263	264	265
D. Use skills and strategies to solve problems.	266	267	268

Read each question carefully. Darken the circle on your answer sheet for the correct answer.

1. 50 d = ☐ w ☐ d

    A. 6 w 1 d   **C.** 7 w 1 d

    B. 6 w 6 d   **D.** 7 w 6 d

2. Choose the most reasonable unit for measuring the height of a flagpole.

    F. in.   **H.** gal

    G. ft   **J.** mi

3. 700 min = ☐ h ☐ min

    A. 10 h 40 min   **C.** 11 h 40 min

    B. 11 h 20 min   **D.** 12 h

4. Choose the most reasonable unit for measuring the distance from Florida to Kentucky.

    F. mi   **H.** ft

    G. yd   **J.** in.

5. 46 fl oz = ☐ c ☐ fl oz

    A. 6 c 6 fl oz   **C.** 5 c 6 fl oz

    B. 6 c 4 fl oz   **D.** 5 c 4 fl oz

6. 67 oz = ☐ lb ☐ oz

    F. 3 lb 13 oz   **H.** 4 lb 13 oz

    G. 3 lb 3 oz   **J.** 4 lb 3 oz

7. Find the time.

3 hours 45 minutes after 4:46 P.M.

    A. 8:46 P.M.   **C.** 7:46 P.M.

    B. 8:31 P.M.   **D.** 7:31 P.M.

8. Choose the most reasonable unit for measuring the weight of a trailer tractor.

    F. T   **H.** in.

    G. mi   **J.** oz

9. 192 oz = ☐ lb

    A. 24 lb   **C.** 12 lb

    B. 22 lb   **D.** 6 lb

10. $1\frac{1}{2}$ T = ☐ lb

    F. 3,500 lb   **H.** 2,750 lb

    G. 3,000 lb   **J.** 2,500 lb

GO ON

11. Find the elapsed time.

7:14 A.M. to 4:22 P.M.

A. 9 h 8 min   **C.** 10 h 8 min

B. 9 h 18 min   **D.** 10 h 18 min

---

12. Choose the most reasonable unit for measuring the length of a twin bed.

F. c   **H.** in.

G. oz   **J.** mi

---

13. 24 c = ▢ qt ▢ pt

A. 4 qt 2 pt   **C.** 6 qt 2 pt

B. 5 qt 2 pt   **D.** 7 qt 2 pt

---

14. Find the elapsed time.

4:20 A.M. to 2:45 P.M.

F. 12 h 45 min

G. 11 h 45 min

H. 11 h 25 min

J. 10 h 25 min

---

15. Choose the most reasonable unit for measuring the weight of a chair.

A. oz   **C.** T

B. lb   **D.** qt

---

16. 125 ft = ▢ yd ▢ ft

F. 42 yd 1 ft   **H.** 41 yd 1 ft

G. 41 yd 2 ft   **J.** 40 yd 2 ft

---

17. Calvin estimates that he can use a 12-fl oz container to fill with 2 cups of water. Does his answer seem reasonable? If not, how many cups of water can he pour in to fill the container?

A. yes   **C.** no, $1\frac{1}{3}$ c

B. no, $1\frac{1}{2}$ c   **D.** no, $1\frac{1}{4}$ c

---

18. Marla's dog weighs 160 ounces. What is an appropriate number of pounds for the dog to weigh?

F. 10   **H.** 16

G. 12   **J.** 20

---

19. Mr. Smith measured the length of the bases on the baseball field. They are 90 feet apart from each other. What is an appropriate number of yards for the same distance?

A. 10   **C.** 90

B. 30   **D.** 270

---

20. After a rain storm, a birdbath had about 5 cups of water in it. About how many quarts and cups do 5 cups of water equal?

F. 2 qt 1 cup   **H.** 1 qt 1 cup

G. 1 qt 2 cups   **J.** 1 qt 0 cups

STOP

Read each question carefully. Fill in the correct answer in the space provided.

1. 57 d = _____ w _____ d

6. 78 oz = _____ lb _____ oz

2. Choose the most reasonable unit for measuring the height of a building.

Write in., ft, or mi

_____

7. Find the time.

4 hours 15 minutes after 3:26 P.M.

_____

3. 645 min = _____ h _____ min

8. Choose the most reasonable unit for measuring the weight of a mobile home.

Write oz, lb, or T.

_____

4. Choose the most reasonable unit for measuring the distance from Texas to Kansas.

Write in., ft, or mi

_____

9. 272 oz = _____ lb

_____

10. $1\frac{3}{4}$ T = _____ lb

5. 59 fl oz = _____ c _____ fl oz

11. Find the elapsed time.

5:13 A.M. to 2:32 P.M.

_____

12. Choose the most reasonable unit for measuring the width of a king-size bed.

Write in., yd, or mi.

_____

13. 33 qt = _____ gal _____ qt

_____

14. Find the elapsed time.

3:05 A.M. to 1:35 P.M.

_____

15. Choose the most reasonable unit for measuring the weight of a dining room table.

Write oz, lb, or T.

_____

16. 133 ft = _____ yd _____ ft

_____

17. Todd estimates that he can use a 20-oz container to fill $3\frac{1}{2}$ cups of water. Does his answer seem reasonable? Explain.

_____

18. Vicky's German shepherd weighs 90 pounds. She says that her dog Fred weighs about 14,000 ounces. Is her estimate reasonable? Explain.

_____

19. A football field is 360 feet from end zone to end zone. Mrs. Jones says that a football field is 1,080 yards long. Is her estimate reasonable? Explain.

_____

20. When the snow melted, a wagon had about 7 cups of water in it. About how many quarts and cups do 7 cups of water equal?

_____

STOP

Chapter 16 – Teacher Interview

Core Concept: *Choosing Appropriate Metric Measurement*

Student Activity: Students demonstrate an understanding of metric measurement and are able to convert and compare units of length, capacity, and mass. Ask students to use metric measurements to solve the problems.

Teacher Question 1:

- Which unit would you use to tell how heavy a cat is?

Understanding Student Response	Practice and Improvement
Students who say gram (milligram).	Review lesson 2 to reinforce an understanding of relating mass to objects.
Students who say Liter (milliliter)	Review lesson 2 to help students recognize that mass measures weight and capacity measures the volume of the inside of a container.

Teacher Question 2:

- How will you change centimeters to meters?

Understanding Student Response	Practice and Improvement
Students who multiply by 100 or 10.	Review lesson 3 to help students learn how to convert centimeters to meters.
Students who divide by 1,000 or 10.	Review lesson 3 to help students learn how to convert centimeters to meters, and that the prefix centi means 100.

Teacher Question 3:

- How many grams does 1.56 kilograms equal?

Understanding Student Response	Practice and Improvement
Students who divide by 1,000 or 10.	Review lesson 2 to reinforce an understanding of units of mass and relating mg to g to kg.
Students who multiply by 100 or 10.	Review lesson 3 to help students learn how to convert from a larger to smaller unit.

Chapter 16 – Journal Writing

Encourage students to generate their own journal entries related to math ideas in general or to concepts in this chapter. Present the following journal prompt and have student share their drawing/writing with a partner:

- What are some situations that drawing a diagram helps you to problem solve?

  (Responses should indicate that drawing a diagram helps with problems involving a pattern or an order. Drawing a diagram helps to think about the problem, visualize the situation, and solve the problem.)

JOURNAL WRITING/PROBLEM SOLVING

When Joseph left for school, the temperature was 8°C. When he returned home, the temperature was ⁻1°C. How many degrees Celsius did the temperature fall?

Read

Have students find the answer to the problem. Then ask them to write a few sentences telling—

- which information they used to find the answer

- what they did with the information

Have students make up another problem for which they have to follow the same procedure. Then have students solve the problem and supply the correct response.

Plan

Students must recognize that the new temperature is a negative number, and then subtract correctly, or draw a number line to find the answer.

Solve

The correct response to the assigned problem is 9°C.

Look Back

A correct response demonstrates the ability to read and understand problems and to draw diagrams to solve problems. (See scoring rubric on page 7.)

Chapter 16 – Monitoring Student Progress

☐ Form A   ☐ Form B

Name _____ Date _____

Directions: For each item that is answered incorrectly, cross out the item number. Then record the number of correct responses in the appropriate Student Score column. If the student has not met the Criterion Score for an objective, circle the student's score. Recommended assignments are listed in the Prescription Table on the next page.

Objective	Item Numbers	Criterion Score	Student Score
A. Choose appropriate units and estimate length, weight/mass, capacity, and temperature and measure length.	1, 2, 7, 9, 13, 16	5/6	/6
B. Convert between units of measurement.	3, 4, 8, 10, 14	4/5	/5
C. Compare and order integers.	5, 6, 11, 12, 15	4/5	/5
D. Use skills and strategies to solve problems.	17, 18, 19, 20	3/4	/4
Total Test Score		16/20	/20
Total Percent Correct			%

Chapter 16 – Prescription Table

The following chart correlates the tested objectives for this chapter to supplementary materials that meet the individual needs of the students. The Reteach and Practice pages are designed for students who need further instruction in the math concepts taught in this chapter. The Enrich pages are designed for students who need advanced challenges.

Objective	Reteach	Practice	Enrich
A. Choose appropriate units and estimate length, weight/mass, capacity, and temperature and measure length.	269, 272	270, 273	271, 274
B. Convert between units of measurement.	275, 284	276, 285	277, 286
C. Compare and order integers.	281	282	283
D. Use skills and strategies to solve problems.	278, 279	280	

Read each question carefully. Darken the circle on your answer sheet for the correct answer.

1. Which is the most reasonable metric unit of length to measure the distance from New York to Chicago, Illinois?

   A. mm   **C.** m

   B. cm   **D.** km

2. Which is the most reasonable metric unit to measure the thickness of your notepad?

   F. mm

   G. kg

   H. m

   J. km

3. 5.5 m = ☐ cm

   A. 550

   B. 55

   C. 0.55

   D. 0.055

4. 320 mL = ☐ L

   F. 0.032

   G. 0.32

   H. 3.2

   J. 32

5. 6 ◯ ⁻3

   A. >

   B. <

   C. =

6. Compare and order from least to greatest.

   5, ⁻6, ⁻5, 6

   F. ⁻5, ⁻6, 5, 6   **H.** ⁻6, ⁻5, 6, 5

   G. ⁻6, ⁻5, 5, 6   **J.** 6, 5, ⁻5, ⁻6

7. Estimate.

   2°C = ☐ °F

   A. about 16

   B. about 26

   C. about 36

   D. about 46

8. 18 kg = ☐ g

   F. 18,000

   G. 1,800

   H. 180

   J. 1.8

9. Which is the most reasonable metric unit of mass to measure a horse?

   A. mg

   B. cg

   C. g

   D. kg

10. 45.6 mg = ☐ g

   F. 4.56   **H.** 0.0456

   G. 0.456   **J.** 0.00456

GO ON ➡

Name _____

11. 0 ◯ ⁻8

  A. >

  B. <

  C. =

12. ⁻12 ◯ ⁻12

  F. >

  G. <

  H. =

13. Which is the most reasonable metric unit of mass to measure the capacity of a glass of juice?

  A. mL   **C.** metric cup

  B. cL   **D.** L

14. 24.3 mm = ☐ cm

  F. 0.243   **H.** 24.03

  G. 2.43   **J.** 243

15. Which situation best represents ⁻$45?

  A. owing money

  B. a loss in driving time

  C. earning money

  D. a gain in weight

16. Estimate.

40°C = ☐ °F

  F. about 0   **H.** about 80

  G. about 70   **J.** about 100

17. Paula draws a 3 by 3 grid. She writes the letters of the alphabet A through I in order on the grid, starting with the top left square. What are three letters in the middle column of the grid?

  A. D, E, F   **C.** B, E, H

  B. C, E, G   **D.** A, B, C

18. A desk 5 feet wide and 4 feet long has a peg at every foot on each side and one at each corner. How many pegs are there on the desk?

  F. 14 pegs   **H.** 18 pegs

  G. 16 pegs   **J.** 20 pegs

19. Along a garden that is 16 feet by 20 feet are candles. Candles are placed every four feet. If one candle is placed in each corner, how many candles are along both of the two 20-foot sides?

  A. 9 candles

  B. 12 candles

  C. 14 candles

  D. 15 candles

20. Brian is building a fence. He plans to put a post at the beginning and then every 6 feet. If the yard measures 24 feet by 48 feet, how many posts will he use along the sides that measure 48 feet?

  F. 12 posts

  G. 14 posts

  H. 16 posts

  J. 18 posts

STOP

Name _____

Read each question carefully. Fill in the correct answer in the space provided.

1. Which is the most reasonable metric unit of length to measure the distance from California to Texas?

_____

2. Which is the most reasonable metric unit to measure the thickness of your mattress?

_____

3. 6.6 cm = _____ m

_____

4. 530 mL = _____ L

_____

5. Compare. Use >, <, or =.

8 ◯ ⁻5

_____

6. Order from least to greatest

9, ⁻7, 7, ⁻9

_____

7. Estimate.

4°C = _____ °F

_____

8. 22 kg = _____ g

_____

9. Which is the most reasonable metric unit of mass to measure a pig?

_____

10. 24.5 g = _____ kg

Grade 5 **243**

11. Compare. Use >, <, or =.

0 ⁻4

_____

12. Compare. Use >, <, or =.

⁻15 ⬤ ⁻15

_____

13. Which is the most reasonable metric unit of mass to measure the capacity of a fish tank?

_____

_____

14. 44.6 cm = _____ mm

_____

15. Write a situation that represents ⁻$25.

_____

_____

16. Estimate.

25°C = _____ °F

17. Linda draws a 3 by 3 grid. She writes the letters of the alphabet L through T in order on the grid, starting with the top left square. What are the letters in the middle column of the grid?

_____

18. A desk 4 feet wide and 6 feet long has a peg at every foot on each side and one at each corner. How many pegs are there on the desk?

_____

19. Along a walkway that is 12 feet by 24 feet are candles. Candles are placed every four feet. If one candle is placed in each corner, how many candles are along each of the two 24-foot sides?

_____

20. Dave is building a fence. He plans to put a post at the beginning and then every 5 feet. If the yard measures 20 feet by 40 feet, how many posts will he use along the one side that measures 40 feet?

_____

STOP

Unit 8 Performance Assessment

I Hear That Whistle Blowing

- **Target Skill:** Find elapsed time.
- **Additional Skills:** Compute with units of time.

Task Description: This task requires students to plan a trip based on a train schedule. The students will be asked to determine how they can be on time under different circumstances.

Preparing: You may wish to discuss different modes of transportation with students. Explain to students that trains were integral in the U.S. Industrial Revolution and they still remain an important means of transportation in large cities.

Materials	Group Size	Time on Task
Pencil and paper	1 to 2 students	1 day

Guiding: Tell students that they will plan the debate team's trip to the regional championship, based on a train schedule and the timing of the event.

Tell students that on a train schedule, the place of departure is on the left and the destination is on the right.

Observing/ Monitoring: As you move among the students, pose the following questions:

What elapsed times do you need to consider to get to the debate on time?

What trains can you take to return on?

Unit 8 Performance Assessment Scoring Rubric

I Hear That Whistle Blowing

Score	Explanation
3	Students demonstrate an efficient strategy and a thorough approach that enables them to solve the problem completely. A satisfactory answer: • selects the proper segments involved in each trip; • adds the elapsed times correctly; • selects the right trains for all scenarios. Students are able to complete the problem quickly and have all of the above correct solutions.
2	Students demonstrate a strategy that enables them to solve most of the problem correctly. The strategy is somewhat disorganized, making it less efficient. A solution is found, but errors are contained. Students may: • add elapsed times correctly; • mismatch train numbers with times. Students have some difficulty determining all solutions correctly but demonstrate an understanding of general concepts.
1	Students demonstrate a confused strategy, which leads to difficulty solving the problem. Most answers are incorrect, but students demonstrate knowledge of at least one concept being assessed such as: • selecting some of the proper trip segments; OR • adding elapsed times.

Name _____

Unit 8 Performance Assessment
Student Activity

I Hear That Whistle Blowing

You will need:
- Paper
- Pencil

The Lincoln School debate team is traveling to the regional championships in Springfield by train. Answer the questions below based on this train schedule:

	Lincoln	Douglaston	Springfield
Train # 41	9:20 A.M.	9:40 A.M.	10:30 A.M.
# 42	10:05 A.M.	(express →)	10:55 A.M.
# 43	10:15 A.M.	10:40 A.M.	11:30 A.M.
# 44	10:45 A.M.	11:05 A.M.	11:55 A.M.
# 45	11:00 A.M.	(express →)	12:00 P.M.

	Springfield	Douglaston	Lincoln
Train # 71	3:50 P.M.	4:25 P.M.	4:45 P.M.
# 72	4:30 P.M.	5:05 P.M.	5:25 P.M.
# 73	4:50 P.M.	5:25 P.M.	5:45 P.M.
# 74	5:05 P.M.	(express →)	5:55 P.M.
# 75	5:20 P.M.	5:55 P.M.	6:20 P.M.

1. If the debate team meets at the train station in Lincoln at 10 A.M., and the travel time from the Springfield station to the school is 10 minutes, which trains can the Lincoln team take to register by the noon deadline?

_____

2. If the debate team wants to ride with the Douglaston School debate team, which train should they take to arrive on time?

_____

3. If the debate program lasts 4 hours 30 minutes and begins at 12:30 P.M., which train is the earliest they can take back to Lincoln after the debate finishes?

_____

4. When will they arrive?

_____

Unit 8 – Monitoring Student Progress

☐ **Form A**   ☐ **Form B**

Name _____ Date _____

Directions: This test targets selected objectives. For each item that is answered incorrectly, cross out the item number. Then record the number of correct responses in the column labeled **Number of Correct Responses.** Add to find the **Total Number of Correct Responses** and record the total. Use this total to determine the **Total Test Score** and the **Total Percent Correct.**

Strand • Objective(s)	Item Numbers	Number of Correct Responses
Measurement • Convert and compute with units of time and find elapsed time. • Choose appropriate units and estimate length, weight/mass, capacity, temperature, and measure length. • Convert units of measurement. • Compare and order integers. • Use skills and strategies to solve problems.	1, 2, 3, 4, 5, 6, 7, 8, 9, 10, 11, 12, 13, 14, 15, 16, 17, 18, 19, 20, 21, 22, 23, 24, 25, 26, 27, 28, 29, 30, 31, 32, 33, 34, 35, 36, 37, 38, 39, 40	/40
Total Number of Correct Responses		
Total Test Score		/40
Total Percent Correct		%

Read each question carefully. Darken the circle on your answer sheet for the correct answer.

1. 32 h = ⬜ min

   A. 3,200   **C.** 768

   B. 1,920   **D.** 224

2. Choose the most appropriate unit for measuring the weight of a television set.

   F. kilogram   **H.** centimeter

   G. gram   **J.** milligram

3. Choose the most appropriate unit for measuring the length of a full-size bed.

   A. inch   **C.** yard

   B. ounce   **D.** mile

4. 4.5 lb = ⬜ oz

   F. 9,000   **H.** 72

   G. 450   **J.** 45

5. Estimate the temperature of a glass of ice water.

   A. ⁻20°C   **C.** 20°C

   B. 5°C   **D.** 37°C

6. Find the elapsed time.

7:25 P.M. to 11:05 P.M.

   F. 4 h 30 min   **H.** 3 h 40 min

   G. 4 h 20 min   **J.** 3 h 30 min

7. 5 km = ⬜ m

   A. 50,000   **C.** 500

   B. 5,000   **D.** 50

8. Choose the most appropriate unit for measuring the capacity of a swimming pool.

   F. ounce   **H.** pound

   G. inch   **J.** gallon

9. 24 qt = ⬜ gal

   A. 18   **C.** 6

   B. 12   **D.** 2.4

10. Find the time.

2 h 15 min after 6:55 A.M.

   F. 9:30 A.M.   **H.** 8:20 A.M.

   G. 9:10 A.M.   **J.** 9:15 A.M.

11. Measure the length of the line segment to the nearest centimeter.

   A. 4 cm   **C.** 6 cm

   B. 5 cm   **D.** 52 cm

GO ON

Name_____

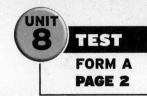

UNIT 8 TEST
FORM A
PAGE 2

12. 7.5 L = ⬜ cL

   F. 75,000   **H.** 750

   G. 7,500   **J.** 75

13. Measure the length of the line segment to the nearest quarter inch.

   A. $2\frac{1}{4}$ in.   **C.** $2\frac{3}{4}$ in.

   B. $2\frac{1}{2}$ in.   **D.** $3\frac{3}{4}$ in.

14. Estimate the capacity of a fish bowl.

   F. 2.5 cL   **H.** 25 mL

   G. 25 L   **J.** 2.5 L

15. What is a reasonable estimate of the length of a peanut?

   A. 4 m   **C.** 4 cm

   B. 40 cm   **D.** 4 mm

16. Estimate the weight of an apple.

   F. 50 lb   **H.** 10 oz

   G. 5 lb   **J.** 1 oz

17. Bob goes to work at 8:45 A.M. He returns home at 6:15 P.M. For how many hours is Bob gone?

   A. 10 h 50 min   **C.** 9 h 50 min

   B. 10 h 15 min   **D.** 9 h 30 min

18. Fran's journal has a mass of 0.9 kilogram. What is that mass in grams?

   F. 90,000 g   **H.** 90 g

   G. 900 g   **J.** 9 g

19. Ed measured the height of his room. Which is the most reasonable unit to use?

   A. inch   **C.** yard

   B. quart   **D.** mile

20. A rectangular garden 12 yards wide and 18 yards long has poles on each side every 2 yards apart and one at each corner. How many poles are there in the garden?

   F. 82 poles   **H.** 32 poles

   G. 35 poles   **J.** 30 poles

GO ON

21. 11 min 35 s = ▢ s

    A. 1,135   **C.** 598

    B. 695   **D.** 299

22. Choose the most appropriate unit for measuring the capacity of a glass.

    F. pound   **H.** ton

    G. fluid ounce   **J.** inch

23. Choose the most appropriate unit for measuring the length of a football field.

    A. mile   **C.** gallon

    B. yard   **D.** inch

24. 2,400 g = ▢ kg

    F. 2,400   **H.** 24

    G. 240   **J.** 2.4

25. Estimate the temperature of a pot of boiling water.

    A. 0°F   **C.** 200°F

    B. 100°F   **D.** 250°F

26. Find the elapsed time.

    5:45 P.M. to 9:10 P.M.

    F. 4 h 55 min   **H.** 3 h 25 min

    G. 4 h 35 min   **J.** 3 h 15 min

27. 36 yd = ▢ ft

    A. 360   **C.** 108

    B. 180   **D.** 12

28. Choose the most appropriate unit for measuring the capacity of a kitchen sink.

    F. milliliter   **H.** meter

    G. liter   **J.** kilometer

29. 15 pt = ▢ c

    A. 60   **C.** 30

    B. 45   **D.** 7.5

30. Find the time.

    5 h 35 min after 10:10 P.M.

    F. 5:35 A.M.   **H.** 3:45 A.M.

    G. 4:35 A.M.   **J.** 4:45 A.M.

31. Measure the length of the line segment to the nearest centimeter.

    A. 3 cm   **C.** 5 cm

    B. 4 cm   **D.** 37 cm

GO ON ▶

32. 28 cm = ☐ mm

    F. 28,000   **H.** 280

    G. 2,800   **J.** 2.8

33. Measure the length of the line segment to the nearest quarter inch.

    A. $1\frac{1}{4}$ in.   **C.** $1\frac{3}{4}$ in.

    B. $1\frac{1}{2}$ in.   **D.** $2\frac{1}{2}$ in.

34. Estimate the capacity of a kitchen sink.

    F. 10 c   **H.** 400 gal

    G. 10 pt   **J.** 10 gal

35. What is a reasonable estimate of the length of a bicycle?

    A. 4 yd   **C.** 5 ft

    B. 40 ft   **D.** 400 in.

36. Estimate the mass of your math book.

    F. 500 g   **H.** 2 kg

    G. 50 g   **J.** 20 kg

37. Denise goes to camp at 10:15 A.M. She gets home at 2:30 P.M. For how long was she gone?

    A. 4 h 45 min   **C.** 3 h 55 min

    B. 4 h 35 min   **D.** 4 h 15 min

38. Lee's dog has a mass of 6,500 grams. What is that mass in kilograms?

    F. 6,500 kg   **H.** 65 kg

    G. 650 kg   **J.** 6.5 kg

39. Barbara measured the distance between two houses. Which is the most reasonable unit to use?

    A. millimeter   **C.** meter

    B. liter   **D.** kilogram

40. A rectangular garden 15 yards wide and 21 yards long has poles on each side every 3 yards apart and one at each corner. How many poles are there in the garden?

    F. 24 poles   **H.** 32 poles

    G. 28 poles   **J.** 36 poles

STOP

Name _____

Read each question carefully. Fill in the correct answer in the space provided.

1. 36 h = _____ min

2. What is the most appropriate metric unit for measuring the mass of a television set?

_____

3. What is the most appropriate customary unit for measuring the height of your school?

_____

4. 5.5 lb = _____ oz

_____

5. Estimate the temperature in °C of a glass of cold milk.

_____

6. Find the elapsed time.

6:35 P.M. to 10:15 P.M.

_____

_____

7. 4 km = _____ m

_____

8. What is the most appropriate customary unit for measuring the capacity of a bathtub?

_____

_____

9. 28 qt = _____ gal

_____

10. Find the time.

2 h 25 min after 7:50 A.M.

_____

GO ON

11. Measure the length of the line segment to the nearest centimeter.

_____

_____

12. 6.8 L = _____ cL

_____

13. Measure the length of the line segment to the nearest quarter inch.

_____

_____

_____

14. The metric capacity of a can of soup is about 0.5 _____.

_____

_____

15. The metric length of a pencil is about 16 _____.

_____

16. The customary weight of an orange is about 6 _____.

_____

_____

17. Marcus goes to work at 7:15 A.M. He returns home at 6:00 P.M. For how long is Marcus gone?

_____

_____

18. Carol's book has a mass of 0.8 kilogram. What is that mass in grams?

_____

_____

19. What is the most appropriate customary unit for measuring the height of a room?

_____

_____

20. A rectangular garden 15 yards wide and 20 yards long has poles on each side every 5 yards apart and one at each corner. How many poles are there in the garden?

_____

GO ON

21. 12 min 25 s = _____ s

22. What is the most appropriate customary unit for measuring the capacity of a coffee mug?

23. What is the most appropriate customary unit for measuring the length of a hole on a golf course?

24. 3,500 g = _____ kg

25. 457 min = _____ h

26. Find the elapsed time.

3:45 P.M. to 7:20 P.M.

27. 42 yd = _____ ft

28. What is the most appropriate metric unit for measuring the capacity of a large milk carton?

29. 20 pt = _____ c

30. Find the time.

6 h 25 min after 9:30 P.M.

GO ON

31. Measure the length of the line segment to the nearest centimeter.

_____

_____

32. 34 cm = _____ mm

_____

33. Measure the length of the line segment to the nearest quarter inch.

_____

_____

34. The customary capacity of a bathroom sink is about 8 _____.

_____

35. The customary length of a car is about 15 _____.

_____

36. The mass of a dictionary is about 3 _____.

_____

_____

37. Rachel goes to the mall at 11:35 A.M. She gets home at 4:25 P.M. For how long was she gone?

_____

_____

38. Jo's cat has a mass of 5,700 grams. What is that mass in kilograms?

_____

_____

39. Petra wants to measure the distance between two telephone poles. Which metric unit should she use?

_____

_____

40. A rectangular garden 12 yards wide by 16 yards wide has fence posts on each side every 4 yards apart and one at each corner. How many fence posts are there?

_____

STOP

Chapter 17 – Teacher Interview

Core Concept: *Write and Evaluate Algebraic Expressions*

Student Activity: Students demonstrate an understanding of algebraic expressions and are able to evaluate expressions, given a variable. Provide student with algebraic expressions to solve, given a variable.

Teacher Question 1:

- How will you evaluate $n - 9$, if $n = 34.5$?

Understanding Student Response	Practice and Improvement
Students who add 9 and 34.5 and say the answer is 43.5.	Review lesson 1 to reinforce an understanding of expressions and variables.
Students who do not substitute the value of n in expression, $n - 9$.	Review lesson 1 to help students look for and describe a relationship.

Teacher Question 2:

- How will you evaluate $4 \times c$, if $c = 22$?

Understanding Student Response	Practice and Improvement
Students who add (subtract) 4 and 22.	Review lesson 2 to help students learn to use the variable to multiply.
Students who say the answer is 66.	Review lesson 2 to help students learn how to use counters to model the expression.

Teacher Question 3:

- How can you write an expression for this situation?
  Each year students plant 30 tulips around the front door of the school.
  How many tulips will they plant in y years?

Understanding Student Response	Practice and Improvement
Students who say 30 divided by y.	Review lesson 2 to reinforce an understanding of writing an expression for a situation.
Students who say $y + 30$ or $30 - y$.	Review lesson 2 to help students learn how to make a connection and model the situation.

Chapter 17 – Journal Writing

Encourage students to generate their own journal entries related to math ideas in general or to concepts in this chapter. Present the following journal prompt and have students share their drawing/writing with a partner:

- When you are problem solving using graphs, how does the slant of the line help you to identify a change or a relationship? Give an example of a change?

  (Responses should indicate that the slant of the line in a line graph shows how a change in one quantity affects the other quantity. For example, the steeper the slant of a line, the greater the change.)

JOURNAL WRITING/PROBLEM SOLVING

Malcolm has to read a 240-page book. He reads p pages each day. Use the expression $\frac{240}{p}$ to find out how many days it will take Malcolm to finish his book if he reads for 2 hours each day and reads 40 pages each day.

Read

Have students find the answer to the problem. Then ask them to write a few sentences telling—

- which information they used to find the answer

- what they did with the information

Have students make up another problem for which they could have followed the same procedure. Then have students solve the problem and supply the correct response.

Plan

Students must understand how the expression relates to the question and correctly evaluate the expression.

Solve

The correct response to the assigned problem is 6 days. Students had to substitute the correct value into the expression and evaluate.

Look Back

A correct response demonstrates the ability to relate an expression to a situation and to evaluate expressions for a given variable. (See scoring rubric on page 7.)

Chapter 17 – Monitoring Student Progress

☐ **Form A**   ☐ **Form B**

Name _____   Date _____

Directions: For each item that is answered incorrectly, cross out the item number. Then record the number of correct responses in the appropriate Student Score column. If the student has not met the Criterion Score for an objective, circle the student's score. Recommended assignments are listed in the Prescription Table on the next page.

Objective	Item Numbers	Criterion Score	Student Score
A. Write and evaluate algebraic expressions.	1, 2, 5, 10, 15	4/5	/5
B. Use order of operations.	3, 4, 6, 11, 16	4/5	/5
C. Represent and solve problems with tables, graphs, and functions.	7, 8, 9, 12, 13, 14	5/6	/6
D. Use skills and strategies to solve problems.	17, 18, 19, 20	3/4	/4
Total Test Score		16/20	/20
Total Percent Correct			%

Chapter 17 – Prescription Table

The following chart correlates the tested objectives for this chapter to supplementary materials that meet the individual needs of the students. The Reteach and Practice pages are designed for students who need further instruction in the math concepts taught in this chapter. The Enrich pages are designed for students who need advanced challenges.

Objective	Reteach	Practice	Enrich
A. Write and evaluate algebraic expressions.	289, 292	290, 293	291, 294
B. Use order of operations.	295	296	297
C. Represent and solve problems with tables, graphs, and functions.	298, 301	299, 302	300, 303
D. Use skills and strategies to solve problems.	304	305	306

Read each question carefully. Darken the circle on your answer sheet for the correct answer.

1. Evaluate $\frac{a}{6}$, for $a = 420$.

   A. 6   **C.** 60

   B. 7   **D.** 70

2. Evaluate $7 \times k$, for $k = 63$.

   F. 441   **H.** 341

   G. 420   **J.** 320

3. Evaluate. Use the order of operations.

$4 \times (3 + 9) - 3 \times 5$

   A. 30   **C.** 90

   B. 33   **D.** 93

4. Evaluate. Use the order of operations.

$9 - 24 \div 8 + (6 \times 5)$

   F. 3   **H.** 17

   G. 13   **J.** 36

5. Evaluate $\frac{1}{3}p$, for $p = 21$.

   A. 18   **C.** 7

   B. 16   **D.** 6

6. Evaluate. Use the order of operations.

$6 + 45 \times (4 \times 2) - 3$

   F. 405   **H.** 231

   G. 363   **J.** 93

Use the table for problems 7–9.

t	2	4	6
s			

7. Complete the table, if $s = 4t - 2$.

   A. 6, 14, 22   **C.** 4, 14, 22

   B. 6, 12, 20   **D.** 4, 12, 20

8. Which ordered pairs match $s = 4t - 2$?

   F. (1, 2), (2, 6), (3, 10)

   G. (1, 2), (2, 10), (3, 14)

   H. (2, 6), (3, 6), (4, 10)

   J. (2, 6), (4, 16), (5, 18)

9. Which ordered pairs match $s = 4t + 2$?

   A. (1, 4), (2, 6), (4, 18)

   B. (1, 6), (2, 8), (5, 18)

   C. (2, 10), (4, 18), (5, 22)

   D. (2, 6), (4, 14), (5, 22)

10. Evaluate $n - 8$, for $n = 17.8$.

   F. 25.8   **H.** 9.2

   G. 9.8   **J.** 9

GO ON ➡

11. Evaluate. Use the order of operations.

$(20 - 8) \div 3 + 9$

A. 13   **B.** 18   **C.** 27   **D.** 45

Use data from the graph for problems 12–14.

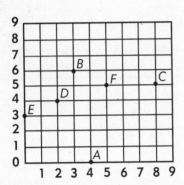

12. Find the coordinates for *B*.

F. (1, 3)   **H.** (3, 6)
G. (2, 4)   **J.** (7, 3)

13. Find the point for (8, 5).

A. *F*   **B.** *E*   **C.** *C*   **D.** *B*

14. Find the coordinates for *D* and *F*.

F. (2, 4) and (5, 5)   **H.** (5, 5) and (6, 3)
G. (2, 4) and (8, 5)   **J.** (5, 5) and (3, 6)

15. Find an expression for this situation.

Miguel read 10 more pages than Bob. Miguel read *p* pages. How many pages did Bob read?

A. $10 + p$ **C.** $10 \times p$
B. $10 - p$ **D.** $10 \div p$

16. Evaluate. Use the order of operations.

$30 - 12 \div 3 - 4$

F. 30   **G.** 22   **H.** 3   **J.** 2

Use data from the graph for problems 17–20.

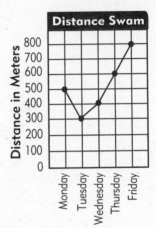

17. On which day did the swim team swim 400 meters?

A. Monday   **C.** Wednesday
B. Tuesday   **D.** Thursday

18. What change occurred in the distance swam between Wednesday and Thursday?

F. increased by 400 meters
G. decreased by 400 meters
H. increased by 200 meters
J. decreased by 200 meters

19. How many meters did the swim team swim from Monday through Friday?

A. 2,400 meters   **C.** 2,800 meters
B. 2,600 meters   **D.** 3,000 meters

20. On which two days did the swim team swim Friday's total distance?

F. Monday and Wednesday
G. Tuesday and Thursday
H. Monday and Tuesday
J. Tuesday and Thursday

STOP

Read each question carefully. Fill in the correct answer in the space provided.

1. Evaluate $\frac{a}{7}$, for $a = 490$.

_____

_____

2. Evaluate $9 \times k$, for $k = 33$.

_____

_____

3. Evaluate. Use the order of operations.

$3 \times (5 + 7) - 4 \times 6$

_____

_____

4. Evaluate. Use the order of operations.

$7 - 36 \div 9 + (4 \times 7)$

_____

_____

5. Evaluate $\frac{1}{5}p$, for $p = 40$.

_____

6. Evaluate. Use the order of operations.

$8 + 54 \times (5 \times 2) - 4$

_____

_____

7. Complete the table, if $s = 5t - 1$.

t	2	4	6
s			

_____

8. Find the ordered pairs for the missing numbers if $s = 5t - 1$, for $t = 1, 2,$ and 3.

_____

_____

9. Complete the table, if $s = 5t + 1$.

t	2	4	6
s			

_____

_____

10. Evaluate $n - 4$, for $n = 14.6$.

_____

GO ON

11. Evaluate. Use the order of operations.

$24 - 6 \div 2 + 5$

_____

Use data from the graph for problems 12–14.

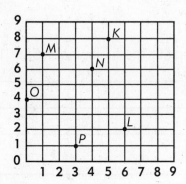

12. Find the coordinates for *K*.

_____

13. Find the point for (6, 2).

_____

14. Find the coordinates for *M* and *N*.

_____

15. Write an expression for this situation.

Gina ran 2 more miles than Ellen. Gina ran *r* miles. How many miles did Ellen run?

_____

16. Evaluate. Use the order of operations.

$36 - 12 \div (6 - 3) + 4$

_____

Use data from the graph for problems 17–20.

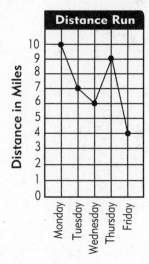

17. On which day did the running club run 6 miles?

_____

18. What change occurred in the running distance between Wednesday and Thursday?

_____

19. How many miles did the running club run from Monday through Friday?

_____

20. On which two days did the running club run Monday's total distance?

_____

STOP

Chapter 18 – Teacher Interview

Core Concept: *Two-Step Equations*

Student Activity: Students demonstrate an understanding of using inverse operations to solve two-step equations. Ask students to solve problems that involve using inverse operations and two steps.

Teacher Question 1:

- Solve $3y + 8 = 28$.

Understanding Student Response	Practice and Improvement
Students who add 8 to both sides of the equation.	Review lesson 6 to reinforce an understanding of using inverse operations to isolate the unknown.
Students who say $y = 21$.	Review lesson 4 to help students learn how to divide to find the variable.

Teacher Question 2:

- Solve $\frac{m}{3} - 2 = 13$.

Understanding Student Response	Practice and Improvement
Students who subtract 2 from both sides of the equation.	Review lesson 6 to reinforce an understanding of using inverse operations to isolate the unknown.
Students who say $m = 5$.	Review lesson 4 to help students learn to find the variable.

Teacher Question 3:

- Suppose your friend tells you that, for the equation $2b + 3 = 11$, $b = 4$. How can you check your answer?

Understanding Student Response	Practice and Improvement
Students who are unable to solve the equation and get the same result.	Review lesson 6 to reinforce an understanding of using inverse operations to isolate the unknown.
Students who are able to solve for b.	Review lesson 6 to help students understand that it may be easier to substitute the value of b in the equation, then see if the two sides of the equation are equal.

Chapter 18 – Journal Writing

Encourage students to generate their own journal entries related to math ideas in general or to concepts in this chapter. Present the following journal prompt and have students share their drawing/writing with a partner:

- When you are problem solving, how does making a graph help you in solving a problem?

  (Responses should indicate that making a graph helps you to visualize the information from the problem and then use the graph to solve the problem.)

JOURNAL WRITING/PROBLEM SOLVING

The temperature is 64°F. The television announcer forecasts that the temperature will be 52°F in 6 hours. By how many degrees Fahrenheit per hour does the temperature fall? Write an equation and solve it.

Read

Have students find the answer to the problem. Then ask them to write a few sentences telling—

- which information they used to find the answer

- what they did with the information

Have students make up another problem with different information for which they would have to follow the same procedure. Then have students solve the problem and supply the correct response.

Plan

Students must correctly use the information in the problem to write an equation. Students must also solve the equation to find out the rate at which the temperature falls.

Solve

The correct response to the assigned problem is 2°F per hour. The equation is $\frac{64 - 52}{6} = r$. Students have to determine that they need to find the change in temperature and divide by the number of hours.

Look Back

A correct response demonstrates the ability to write an equation and solve it. (See scoring rubric on page 7.)

Chapter 18 – Monitoring Student Progress

☐ Form A   ☐ Form B

Name _____ Date _____

Directions: For each item that is answered incorrectly, cross out the item number. Then record the number of correct responses in the appropriate Student Score column. If the student has not met the Criterion Score for an objective, circle the student's score. Recommended assignments are listed in the Prescription Table on the next page.

Objective	Item Numbers	Criterion Score	Student Score
A. Solve addition and subtraction equations.	1, 2, 5, 6, 9, 11	5/6	/6
B. Solve multiplication and division equations.	3, 4, 7, 8, 10, 14	5/6	/6
C. Solve two-step equations.	12, 13, 15, 16	3/4	/4
D. Use skills and strategies to solve problems.	17, 18, 19, 20	3/4	/4
Total Test Score		16/20	/20
Total Percent Correct			%

Chapter 18 – Prescription Table

The following chart correlates the tested objectives for this chapter to supplementary materials that meet the individual needs of the students. The Reteach and Practice pages are designed for students who need further instruction in the math concepts taught in this chapter. The Enrich pages are designed for students who need advanced challenges.

Objective	Reteach	Practice	Enrich
A. Solve addition and subtraction equations.	307, 310, 313	308, 311, 314	309, 312, 315
B. Solve multiplication and division equations.	316	317	318
C. Solve two-step equations.	322	323	324
D. Use skills and strategies to solve problems.	319, 320	321	

Read each question carefully. Darken the circle on your answer sheet for the correct answer.

1. $b + 26 = 35$

   A. 9
   B. 19
   C. 51
   D. 61

2. $v - 4.5 = 8.9$

   F. 40.05
   G. 13.4
   H. 12.4
   J. 4.4

3. $9k = 72$

   A. 10
   B. 9
   C. 8
   D. 7

4. $m \div 4 = 13$

   F. 52
   G. 42
   H. 17
   J. 9

5. $p + 4\frac{3}{5} = 17$

   A. $21\frac{3}{5}$
   B. $20\frac{3}{5}$
   C. $12\frac{2}{5}$
   D. $11\frac{2}{5}$

6. $h - \frac{7}{8} = 9$

   F. $7\frac{7}{8}$
   G. $9\frac{7}{8}$
   H. $9\frac{1}{8}$
   J. $10\frac{1}{8}$

7. $w \times 3.8 = 22.8$

   A. 5.2
   B. 6
   C. 7.2
   D. 8

8. $\frac{g}{7} = 8$

   F. 72
   G. 64
   H. 56
   J. 48

9. $e - 4.68 = 0.87$

   A. 5.55
   B. 4.55
   C. 3.81
   D. 2.81

10. $\frac{49.7}{c} = 7.1$

   F. 6.1
   G. 6.7
   H. 7
   J. 7.7

GO ON

11. $50 = j - 4$

    A. 8   **C.** 46

    B. 9   **D.** 54

12. $10f - 20 = 120$

    F. 10   **H.** 14

    G. 12   **J.** 15

13. $3d + 5 = 29$

    A. 8   **C.** 10

    B. 9   **D.** 11

14. $s \times 3 = 139$

    F. $46\frac{1}{3}$ **H.** $43\frac{1}{3}$

    G. 46   **J.** 43

15. $\frac{n}{5} - 20 = 15$

    A. 35   **C.** 175

    B. 100   **D.** 195

16. $3m + 35 = 62$

    F. 6   **H.** 27

    G. 9   **J.** 97

Use data from the graph for problems 17–20.

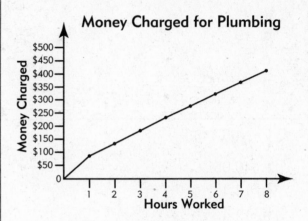

17. If Ed earned $275 on a job, how many hours did he work?

    A. 3 hours   **C.** 5 hours

    B. 4 hours   **D.** 6 hours

18. If Ed worked 7 hours on a job, how much money did he earn?

    F. $410   **H.** $320

    G. $365   **J.** $275

19. What equation represents the money Ed earns per job?

    A. $C = 45h - 50$ **C.** $C = 50h - 45$

    B. $C = 45h + 50$ **D.** $C = 50h + 45$

20. How much would Ed earn for a 12-hour job?

    F. $590   **H.** $495

    G. $540   **J.** $450

STOP

Read each question carefully. Fill in the correct answer in the space provided.

1. $d + 16 = 45$

_____

2. $n - 5.4 = 9.8$

_____

3. $8h = 72$

_____

4. $z \div 6 = 16$

_____

5. $q + 7\frac{1}{5} = 17$

_____

6. $j - \frac{7}{10} = 8$

_____

7. $e \times 8.3 = 66.4$

_____

8. $\frac{d}{8} = 6$

_____

9. $c - 8.46 = 0.78$

_____

10. $\frac{48.8}{c} = 6.1$

_____

GO ON

Name _____

11. $70 = j - 6$

_____

_____

12. $10a - 40 = 110$

_____

_____

13. $5d + 3 = 48$

_____

_____

14. $s \times 4 = 183$

_____

_____

15. $\frac{n}{6} - 15 = 20$

_____

_____

16. $3p + 35 = 59$

_____

Use data from the graph for problems 17–20.

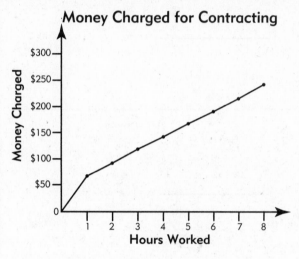

Money Charged for Contracting

17. If Deb earned $190 on a job, how many hours did she work?

_____

_____

18. If Deb worked 4 hours on a job, how much money did she earn?

_____

_____

19. Write an equation to represent the money Deb earns per job. Let M represent the money earned in dollars and h represent the number of hours worked.

_____

_____

20. How much would Deb earn for a 12-hour job?

_____

STOP

Unit 9 Performance Assessment

Keep My Cocoa Warm

- ***Target Skill:*** Plotting functions and equation writing.
- ***Additional Skills:*** Evaluate algebraic expressions.

Task Description: This task requires students to plot ordered pairs on a graph, and write an equation expressing the relationship between the number of people on a ski trip and the cost. The students will be asked to calculate other values for the expression.

Preparing: You may wish to have the students review ordered pairs.

Materials	Group Size	Time on Task
Graph paper	1 to 2 students	1 day

Guiding: Remind students of the difference between an expression and an equation.

Tell students that they can then calculate any other ordered pair in the relationship by substitution.

Observing/ Monitoring: As you move among the students, pose the following questions:

What is the lift ticket price per person?

How does knowing the cost of the lift ticket help you to write the equation?

How can you find the cost for any number of people?

Unit 9 Performance Assessment Scoring Rubric

Keep My Cocoa Warm

Score	Explanation
3	Students demonstrate an efficient strategy and a thorough approach that enables them to solve the problem completely. A satisfactory answer: • creates the ordered pairs and plots the points correctly; • writes the correct equations; • evaluates the expression for all values correctly. Students are able to complete the problem quickly and have all of the above correct solutions.
2	Students demonstrate a strategy that enables them to solve most of the problem correctly. The strategy is somewhat disorganized, making it less efficient. A solution is found, but errors are contained. Students may: • plot the ordered pairs correctly; • evaluate most of the equations properly. Students may have some difficulty determining all solutions correctly but demonstrate an understanding of general concepts.
1	Students demonstrate a confused strategy, which leads to difficulty solving the problem. Most answers are incorrect, but students demonstrate knowledge of at least one concept being assessed such as solving problems using a graph or table.

Name _____

Unit 9 Performance Assessment
Student Activity

Keep My Cocoa Warm

You will need
- Graph Paper

The Cutting Edge Ski Club is planning their winter break ski trip. The table below shows the relation between the number of members taking the trip to Mogul Mountain, and the price of lift tickets.

People	10	20	30	50
Price	$150	$300	$450	$750

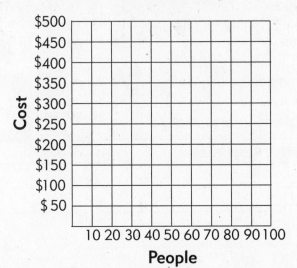

Cost of Ski Trip

1. Plot the ordered pairs and write an equation expressing the relation between the number of people and the cost.

   _____

2. What would be the cost if 40 members attend?

   _____

3. What would be the cost if 75 members attend?

   _____

Unit 9 – Monitoring Student Progress

☐ Form A   ☐ Form B

Name _____ Date _____

Directions: This test targets selected objectives. For each item that is answered incorrectly, cross out the item number. Then record the number of correct responses in the column labeled **Number of Correct Responses.** Add to find the **Total Number of Correct Responses** and record the total. Use this total to determine the **Total Test Score** and the **Total Percent Correct.**

Strand • Objective(s)	Item Numbers	Number of Correct Responses
Algebraic Thinking • Write and evaluate algebraic expressions. • Use order of operations. • Represent and solve problems with tables, graphs, and functions. • Solve addition and subtraction equations. • Solve multiplication and division equations. • Solve two-step equations. • Use skills and strategies to solve problems.	1, 2, 3, 4, 5, 6, 7, 8, 9, 10, 11, 12, 13, 14, 15, 16, 17, 18, 19, 20, 21, 22, 23, 24, 25, 26, 27, 28, 29, 30, 31, 32, 33, 34, 35, 36, 37, 38, 39, 40	/40
Total Number of Correct Responses		
Total Test Score		/40
Total Percent Correct		%

Read each question carefully. Darken the circle on your answer sheet for the correct answer.

1. Simplify using order of operations.

$$5 - 15 \div 5 + (7 \times 3) = \boxed{}$$

A. 23   **C.** 19

B. 21   **D.** 15

2. Evaluate $2x + 18 \div 3$ for $x = 8$.

F. 22.66   **H.** 14

G. 22   **J.** 11.333

3. Simplify using order of operations.

$$9 - 54 \div 6 + 5 \times (4 - 2) = \boxed{}$$

A. 48   **C.** 10

B. 18   **D.** ⁻12

4. Simplify using order of operations.

$$15 + 24 \times (6 \div 3) - 9 = \boxed{}$$

F. 84   **H.** 27

G. 54   **J.** 23

5. Evaluate $t + 4^2 - 42 \div 7$ for $t = 3$.

A. 25   **C.** 13

B. 15   **D.** 27

6. Write an expression for the situation.

7 less than eight times a number n

F. $8n + 7$ **H.** $8n \div 7$

G. $7(8n)$ **J.** $8n - 7$

7. Simplify using order of operations.

$$4 \times (6 + 5) - 8 \times 5 = \boxed{}$$

A. 160   **B.** 105   **C.** 26   **D.** 4

8. Write an expression for the situation.

Jannell can read 15 pages in an hour. At that rate, how many pages can she read in h hours?

F. $15 + h$ **H.** $15h$

G. $h - 15$ **J.** $15 \div h$

Use the information below for exercises 9–12.

Ms. Gonzales took 5 children to the movies. She spent t dollars for each child's ticket and $8 for her tickets.

9. Which expression represents the total amount, in dollars, that Ms. Gonzales paid for tickets?

A. $8t + 5$ **C.** $5t - 8$

B. $5t + 8$ **D.** $5 \times (t + 8)$

10. If Ms. Gonzales paid a total of $28 for tickets, how much did each child's ticket cost?

F. $5.60   **H.** $4.00

G. $5.00   **J.** $3.00

GO ON

11. Suppose each child's ticket cost $6. Which table shows how to find the price of admission for 1, 2, 3, or 4 children?

A.

Number of children	1	2	3	4
Price	$4	$8	$12	$16

B.

Number of children	1	2	3	4
Price	$6	$12	$18	$2

C.

Number of children	1	2	3	4
Price	$5	$10	$15	$20

D.

Number of children	1	2	3	4
Price	$14	$20	$28	$32

12. Suppose each child's ticket cost $6 and Ms. Gonzales bought $9 worth of popcorn. How much did she spend for popcorn and the tickets for herself and the 5 children?

F. $48   **H.** $39

G. $47   **J.** $38

13. Solve for x. $5x - 10 = 45$

A. 55   **B.** 22   **C.** 11   **D.** 7

14. Solve for t. $9 + 3t = 81$

F. 30   **G.** 24   **H.** 12   **J.** 9

15. Solve for a. $4a = 12$

A. 48   **B.** 3   **C.** 16   **D.** 8

16. Solve for p. $p \div 30 = 5$

F. 350   **G.** 150   **H.** $\frac{1}{6}$ **J.** $\frac{1}{5}$

Use the following graph for exercises 17–18.

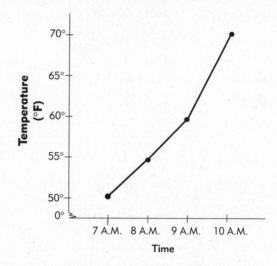

17. Which change in the temperature occurred between 9 A.M. and 10 A.M.?

A. Increase of 5 degrees

B. Decrease of 5 degrees

C. Increase of 10 degrees

D. Decrease of 10 degrees

18. As time passes, what happens to the temperature?

F. It increases.

G. It stays the same.

H. It decreases.

19. Terri charges $12 to rake a yard. How much did she earn from raking 7 yards?

A. $84   **B.** $42   **C.** $38   **D.** $19

20. The beach is 15 miles from Lisa's house. She took a bus 10 miles of this distance. Then she walked the rest of the way at the rate of 2.5 miles per hour. How long did it take her to walk to the beach?

F. 5 h   **G.** 3 h   **H.** 2 h   **J.** 1 h

GO ON

21. Simplify using order of operations.

$22 + 21 \div 7 - (3 \times 4) = \boxed{}$

A. 88   **C.** $12\frac{4}{7}$

B. 13   **D.** $^-6\frac{5}{7}$

22. Evaluate $42 + 3x$ for $x = 5$.

F. 57   **H.** 22

G. 27   **J.** 15

23. Simplify using order of operations.

$3^3 + 18 \times (5 + 1) - 11 = \boxed{}$

A. 259   **C.** 106

B. 124   **D.** 89

24. Write an expression for the situation.

Three times a number n, increased by 44.

F. $3n + 44$ **H.** $3 + n + 44$

G. $3 \div n + 44$ **J.** $3n - 44$

25. Evaluate $20 - 3b + 9b^3$ for $b = 2$.

A. 98   **C.** 68

B. 86   **D.** 89

26. Write an expression for the situation.

Cal can bike 5 miles in an hour. At that rate, how far can he bike in h hours?

F. $5 \div h$ **H.** $h - 5$

G. $5 + h$ **J.** $5h$

27. Simplify using order of operations.

$81 \div 9 - 4 + 8(6 + 1) + 7 = \boxed{}$

A. $176\frac{2}{5}$ **C.** 61

B. 68   **D.** 52

28. Simplify using order of operations.

$15 \times (9 - 7) + 6 \times 2 = \boxed{}$

F. 268   **H.** 72

G. 150   **J.** 42

Use the information below for exercises 29–32.

Tim had read 32 pages of a book by Monday. He can read 18 pages in an hour.

29. Tim read for h hours on Monday. Which expression represents the number of pages he read?

A. $18 \div h + 32$ **C.** $18 - h + 32$

B. $h + 18 + 32$ **D.** $18h + 32$

30. Suppose Tim had read 150 pages by the end of Tuesday and he read h hours on Wednesday. Write a new expression that shows how much he read by the end of Wednesday.

F. $18h - 150$ **H.** $18h + 150$

G. $18h \div 150$ **J.** $18h(150)$

GO ON

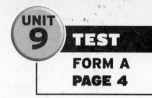
31. Suppose Tim read 5 hours each day for 5 days. Which table shows how to find the number of pages he could have read?

A.

Days	1	2	3	4	5
Total Number of Pages	5	25	30	35	40

B.

Days	1	2	3	4	5
Total Number of Pages	45	90	150	185	500

C.

Days	1	2	3	4	5
Total Number of Pages	90	180	270	360	450

D.

Days	1	2	3	4	5
Total Number of Pages	90	180	360	720	1,440

32. Suppose Tim read 122 pages by the end of Monday. For how many hours did he read?

F. 7 h   **G.** 6 h   **H.** 5 h   **J.** 4 h

33. Solve for *a*. $12 + 22a = 78$

A. $6\frac{1}{2}$ **B.** 5   **C.** $4\frac{1}{11}$ **D.** 3

34. Solve for *t*. $18t - 6 = 156$

F. 14   **G.** 11   **H.** 9   **J.** $8\frac{1}{3}$

35. Solve for *m*. $3m = 15$

A. 45   **B.** 5   **C.** 18   **D.** 12

36. Solve for *r*. $r \div 9 = 18$

F. 0.5   **G.** 2   **H.** 9   **J.** 162

Use the following graph for exercises 37–38.

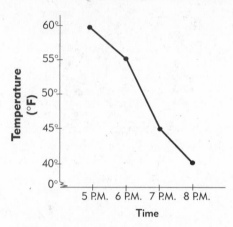

37. Which change in the temperature occurred between 7 P.M. and 8 P.M.?

A. Increase of 5 degrees

B. Decrease of 5 degrees

C. Increase of 10 degrees

D. Decrease of 10 degrees

38. As time passes, what happens to the temperature?

F. It increases.

G. It stays the same.

H. It decreases.

39. Ben washed cars for $15 each. How much did he earn from washing 11 cars?

A. $300.00   **C.** $85.00

B. $165.00   **D.** $82.50

40. Erin earned $3 per hour babysitting. In addition, she got $4 allowance each week. How much did she get altogether during a week when she babysat for 8 hours?

F. $70.00   **H.** $35.00

G. $64.00   **J.** $28.00

STOP

Read each question carefully. Fill in the correct answer in the space provided.

1. Simplify using the order of operations.

   $9 - 24 \div 8 + (5 \times 6) =$ _____

   _____

2. Evaluate $3x + 28 \div 4$ for $x = 7$

   _____

3. Simplify using the order of operations.

   $8 - 48 \div 6 + 2 \times (7 - 4) =$ _____

   _____

4. Simplify using the order of operations.

   $12 + 36 \times (12 \div 4) - 8 =$ _____

   _____

5. Evaluate $m + 5^2 - 56 \div 7$ for $m = 4$.

   _____

6. Write an expression for the situation.

   8 more than seven times a number g

   _____

7. Simplify using the order of operations.

   $5 \times (4 + 8) - 7 \times 6 =$ ☐

   _____

   _____

8. Write an expression for the situation.

   Harold can type 75 words in a minute. At that rate, how many words can he type in t minutes?

   _____

Use the information below for exercises 9–12.

Mr. Costanza took 4 of his children to the amusement park. He spent a dollars for each child's ticket and $25 for his ticket.

9. Write an expression that represents the total amount, in dollars, that Mr. Costanza paid for the tickets.

   _____

10. If Mr. Costanza paid a total of $85 for tickets, how much did each child's ticket cost?

    _____

GO ON

11. Suppose each child's ticket cost $8. Complete the table to show the price of admission for 1, 2, 3, or 4 children.

Number of children	1	2	3	4
Price				

12. Suppose each child's ticket cost $8 and Mr. Costanza spent $25 at lunch. How much did he spend for lunch and the tickets for himself and his 4 children?

_____

_____

13. Solve for p. $6p - 8 = 64$

_____

_____

14. Solve for w. $7 + 3w = 52$

_____

_____

15. Solve for b. $4b = 24$

_____

_____

16. Solve for v. $v \div 40 = 7$

_____

Use the following graph for exercises 17–18.

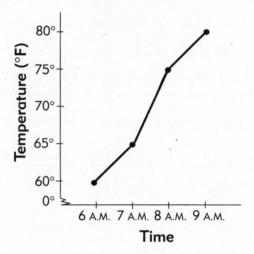

17. How much did the temperature increase between 6 A.M. and 7 A.M.?

_____

_____

18. What happens to the temperature as time passes?

_____

_____

19. Laura charges $15 to mow the lawn. How much did she earn from mowing 6 lawns?

_____

_____

20. Rick earns $5 per hour baby-sitting and he gets $9 allowance each week. How much does he get in a week when he baby-sat for 7 hours?

_____

GO ON

21. Simplify using the order of operations.

$28 + 27 \div 9 - (5 \times 2) =$ _____

_____

22. Evaluate $51 + 4x$ for $x = 4$.

_____

_____

23. Simplify using the order of operations.

$4^3 + 15 \times (4 + 3) - 12 =$ _____

_____

24. Write an expression for the situation.

Four times a number z, increased by 37.

_____

_____

25. Evaluate $22 - 4y + 8y^3$, for $y = 2$.

_____

26. Write an expression for the situation. Kellie can walk 4 miles in an hour. At that rate how far can she walk in h hours?

_____

_____

27. Simplify using the order of operations.

$72 \div 9 - 6 + 7(5 + 2) + 8 =$ _____

_____

28. Simplify using the order of operations.

$12 \times (8 - 5) + 5 \times 8 =$ _____

_____

Use the information below for exercises 29–32.

Nia had read 28 pages of a book by Friday. She can read 22 pages in an hour.

29. Nia read for h hours on Friday. Write an expression that represents the number of pages she read.

_____

_____

30. Suppose Nia had read 176 pages by the end of Saturday and she read h hours on Sunday. Write a new expression that shows how much she read by the end of Sunday.

_____

GO ON

31. Suppose Nia read 4 hours each day. Complete the table to show how many pages she read for 1, 2, 3, or 4 days.

Number of Days	1	2	3	4
Total Number of Pages				

_____

32. Suppose Nia read 138 pages by the end of Friday. For how many hours did she read?

_____

_____

33. Solve for q. $15 + 18q = 87$

_____

_____

34. Solve for p. $25p - 12 = 188$

_____

_____

35. Solve for u. $5u = 45$

_____

_____

36. Solve for s. $s \div 8 = 19$.

_____

Use the following graph for exercises 37–38.

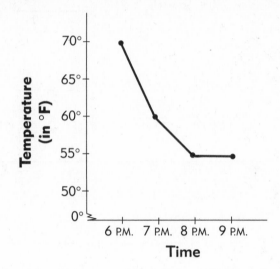

37. What was the change in temperature between 6 P.M. and 7 P.M.?

_____

38. As time passes, what happens to the temperature?

_____

_____

39. Barry washed cars for $16 each. How much did he get for washing 14 cars?

_____

_____

40. Lynn earned $7 per hour baby-sitting. In addition she earns $10 allowance each week. How much did she get during a week when she baby-sat 9 hours?

_____

STOP

Chapter 19 – Teacher Interview

Core Concept: *Identifying, classifying, and calculating with lines, angles, and shapes.*

Student Activity: Students demonstrate an understanding of how to identify and classify lines, angles, triangles, and quadrilaterals and how to calculate the missing angle(s) of the triangle or quadrilateral.

Assign geometry problems such as: Use a protractor and ruler to draw a right triangle *ABC* with two sides the same length.

Teacher Question 1:

- How did you know how to draw the right angle?

Understanding Student Response	Practice and Improvement
Students who say that a right angle is less than 90°.	Review lesson 3 to help the students with measuring and identifying angles.
Students who say that a right angle is greater than 90°.	Review lesson 3 to help the students with measuring and identifying angles.

Teacher Question 2:

- Suppose you connect points A and B of ∠ABC to form a triangle. How would you classify this triangle? Give two classifications.

Understanding Student Response	Practice and Improvement
Students who say the triangle is acute or obtuse.	Review lesson 4 to reinforce classification of triangles.
Students who say the triangle is equilateral or scalene.	Review lesson 4 to reinforce classification of triangles.

Teacher Question 3:

- How could you figure out the measurement of the three angles of this triangle?

Understanding Student Response	Practice and Improvement
Students who say you need to know another angle to figure out these measurements.	Review lesson 4 to help the students recall calculating missing angles.
Students who say all three angles are different.	Review lesson 4 to help the students recall the classification of an isosceles right triangle.

Chapter 19 – Journal Writing

Encourage students to generate their own journal entries related to math ideas in general or to concepts in this chapter. For students requiring guidance, present the following journal prompt:

- When you are problem solving, why is it important to categorize the information? What are some tools you can use to categorize the information in a word problem?

  (Responses should include references to necessary vs. unnecessary information. Some ways to organize information are to use a table, chart, or a graphic organizer.)

JOURNAL WRITING/PROBLEM SOLVING

The sides of a trapezoid measure 3 cm by 6 cm by 7 cm by 7 cm. Three of its angles measure 90°, 90°, and 122°. What is the measure of the fourth angle?

Read

Have students find the answer to the problem. Then ask them to write a few sentences telling—

- which information they used to find the answer

- what they did with that information

Have students make up another problem with different information for which they would have to follow the same procedure. Then have the students solve the problem and supply the correct response.

Plan

Students must know the total number of degrees in a quadrilateral and use this information to calculate an unknown angle.

Solve

The correct response to the assigned problem is 58°. Students had to know the sum of three of the four angles (90° + 90° + 122° = 302°). They had to know that the sum of four angles of a quadrilateral is always 360°. Then they had to use this information to calculate the fourth angle (360° − 302° = 58°).

Look Back

A correct response demonstrates the ability to discriminate between necessary and unnecessary information and apply the appropriate operation to solve the problem. (See scoring rubric on page 7.)

Chapter 19 – Monitoring Student Progress

☐ Form A ☐ Form B

Name _____ Date _____

Directions: For each item that is answered incorrectly, cross out the item number. Then record the number of correct responses in the appropriate Student Score column. If the student has not met the Criterion Score for an objective, circle the student's score. Recommended assignments are listed in the Prescription Table on the next page.

Objective	Item Numbers	Criterion Score	Student Score
A. Measure, draw, and classify angles.	1, 4, 6, 10, 13	4/5	/5
B. Describe and classify geometric figures.	2, 3, 5, 7, 8, 9, 15	6/7	/7
C. Find the unknown angles of a figure.	11, 12, 14, 16	3/4	/4
D. Use skills and strategies to solve problems.	17, 18, 19, 20	3/4	/4
Total Test Score		16/20	/20
Total Percent Correct			%

Chapter 19 – Prescription Table

The following chart correlates the tested objectives for this chapter to supplementary materials that meet the individual needs of the students. The Reteach and Practice pages are designed for students who need further instruction in the math concepts taught in this chapter. The Enrich pages are designed for students who need advanced challenges.

Objective	Reteach	Practice	Enrich
A. Measure, draw, and classify angles.	329, 332	330, 333	331, 334
B. Describe and classify geometric figures.	326	327	328
C. Find the unknown angles of a figure.	335, 338	336, 339	337, 340
D. Use skills and strategies to solve problems.	341	342	343

Read each question carefully. Darken the circle on your answer sheet for the correct answer.

1. Classify the angle.

A. acute

B. obtuse

C. right

D. straight

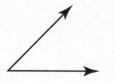

2. Classify the polygon.

F. hexagon

G. pentagon

H. rhombus

J. trapezoid

3. Classify the triangle.

A. equilateral

B. isosceles

C. right

D. scalene

4. Classify the angle.

F. acute

G. obtuse

H. right

J. straight

5. Classify the polygon.

A. hexagon   C. rhombus

B. pentagon   D. trapezoid

6. Measure the angle.

F. 180°

H. 90°

G. 137°

J. 20°

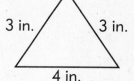

7. Classify the triangle.

A. equilateral

B. isosceles

C. right

D. scalene

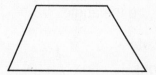

3 in.   3 in.

4 in.

8. Classify the polygon.

F hexagon   H. rhombus

G. pentagon   J. trapezoid

9. Classify the triangle.

A. equilateral

B. isosceles

C. right

D. scalene

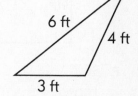

6 ft   4 ft

3 ft

10. Find the measure of the angle.

F. 45°   H. 180°

G. 90°   J. 360°

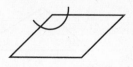
GO ON

11. Find the measure of the unknown angle.

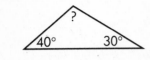

A. 110° **C.** 70°

B. 88° **D.** 40°

12. Find the measure of the unknown angle.

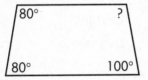

F. 180°

H. 80°

G. 100°

J. 75°

13. Measure the angle.

A. acute

B. right

C. obtuse

D. straight

14. Find the measure of the unknown angle.

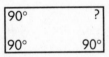

F. 360° **H.** 90°

G. 180° **J.** 45°

15. Classify the pair of lines.

A. intersecting

B. parallel

C. perpendicular

D. straight

16. Find the measure of the unknown angle.

F. 60°

H. 105°

G. 75°

J. 120°

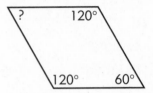

17. Al needs to pack his laptop computer in a box. The computer measures 9 inches by 12 inches. Which type of box will best store the computer?

A. rectangular **C.** pentagonal

B. square **D.** trapezoidal

18. Sue draws a diagram of her garden in the shape of a triangle. Each side is 5 inches. What kind of a triangle does she draw?

F. scalene **H.** isosceles

G. obtuse **J.** equilateral

19. Tonya places an $8\frac{1}{2}$ by 10 book in a box. Which size box would be the best choice?

A. 11 by 11 box **C.** 9 by 11 box

B. 10 by 12 box **D.** 8 by 12 box

20. Ray measures his bedroom and then draws a diagram of it. Three of the four sides of his bedroom measure 12 feet, 12 feet, and 10 feet. Which shape is his bedroom?

F. triangle **H.** rectangle

G. square **J.** rhombus

STOP

Name_____

Read each question carefully. Fill in the correct answer in the space provided.

1. Classify the angle.

_____

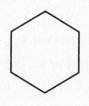

_____

2. Classify the polygon.

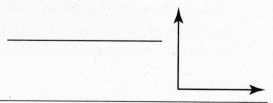

_____

3. Classify the triangle.

_____

4. Measure the angle.

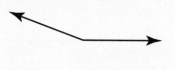

_____

5. Classify the polygon.

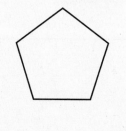

_____

6. Classify the angle.

_____

7. Classify the triangle.

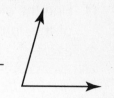

_____

8. Classify the triangle.

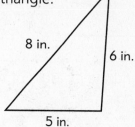

8 in.

6 in.

5 in.

_____

9. Classify the polygon.

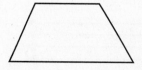

_____

10. Measure the angle.

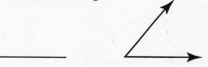

_____

GO ON

11. Find the measure of the unknown angle.

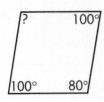

_____

12. Find the measure of the unknown angle.

_____

13. Find the measure of the angle.

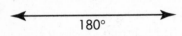

180°

_____

14. Find the measure of the unknown angle.

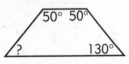

50° 50°
? 130°

_____

15. Classify the lines.

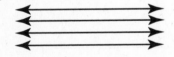

_____

16. Find the measure of the unknown angle.

?
35°   25°

_____

17. Karla measures her bedroom and then draws a diagram of it. Three of the four sides of her bedroom measure 11 feet, 11 feet, and $9\frac{1}{2}$ feet. What shape is her bedroom?

_____

18. Tony places a CD that measures $5\frac{1}{2}$ inches by $5\frac{1}{2}$ inches in a 7-inch square envelope. Which size envelope would be the best choice: a 6-inch square or a 6-inch by 9-inch envelope?

_____

19. Brenda draws a diagram of her garden in the shape of a triangle. It measures 4 yards by 6 yards by 6 yards. What kind of a triangle does she draw: an equilateral, an isosceles, or a scalene triangle?

_____

20. Tim places a 12-inch by 18-inch keyboard into a box. Which type of box will best store the keyboard: square or rectangular?

_____

STOP

Chapter 20 – Teacher Interview

Core Concept: *Similar Shapes, Congruent Shapes, and Transformations*

Student Activity: Students demonstrate an understanding of similarity and congruency by identifying and constructing similar and congruent shapes. Students also identify and illustrate basic transformations on shapes and objects. Provide students with compass, ruler, and protractor. Draw or describe various triangles and other polygons, and prompt the students to construct similar or congruent shapes.

Teacher Question 1:

- Construct a right triangle. Now construct another similar triangle. How do you know the two shapes are similar?

Understanding Student Response	Practice and Improvement
Students say the sides of the two shapes must have equal lengths.	Review lesson 2 to help students understand similarity.
Students say larger shape has larger angles.	Review lesson 2 to help students understand similarity.

Teacher Question 2:

- Construct a trapezoid. Now construct another congruent trapezoid. How do you know the two figures are congruent?

Understanding Student Response	Practice and Improvement
Students construct two shapes of unequal size.	Review lesson 2 to help students understand congruency.
Students construct two shapes with different angles.	Review lesson 2 to help students understand congruency.

Teacher Question 3:

- Construct another trapezoid to show what would happen if you rotated your original trapezoid 90 degrees to the left and reflected it across a vertical line. Is the new trapezoid congruent to the first one?

Understanding Student Response	Practice and Improvement
Students say the new trapezoid is not congruent.	Review lesson 3 to show students that a transformation does not change a shape's size or form.
Students cannot perform transformation.	Review lesson 3 to help students understand transformations.

Chapter 20 – Journal Writing

Encourage students to generate their own journal entries related to math ideas in general or to concepts in this chapter. For students requiring guidance, present the following journal prompt:

- What does it mean for two shapes to be similar? What does it mean for two shapes to be congruent?

  (Responses should indicate that similar shapes have the same form whereas congruent shapes have the same size and form.)

JOURNAL WRITING/PROBLEM SOLVING

Use graph paper to solve.

John and Debbie are in the marching band. They both stand in the center of the field at the beginning of the half-time show. Debbie marches 20 yards toward the home team's end zone. She turns 90 degrees to her left and marches 10 yards. Then she marches straight back to the point where she started. John marches 10 yards toward the opposing team's end zone. He turns 90 degrees to his left and marches 5 yards. Then he marches straight back to his starting point. Draw shapes to represent their marching patterns. Are the shapes similar? Are they congruent?

Read

Have students find the answer to the problem. Then ask them to write a few sentences telling—

- which information they used to find the answer

- what they did with that information

Have students make up another problem with different information.

Plan

Students must represent the information in the problem in graphical form. They must then apply test of similarity and congruency to the shapes they construct.

Solve

Students should draw two right triangles on graph paper. The first measures 20 units in the horizontal direction and 10 units in the vertical. The second measures 10 units in the horizontal and 5 units in the vertical. The triangles are similar but are not congruent.

Look Back

A correct response demonstrates the ability to recognize and discriminate between similarity and congruence. (See scoring rubric on page 7.)

Chapter 20 – Monitoring Student Progress

☐ **Form A**   ☐ **Form B**

Name _____ Date _____

Directions: For each item that is answered incorrectly, cross out the item number. Then record the number of correct responses in the appropriate Student Score column. If the student has not met the Criterion Score for an objective, circle the student's score. Recommended assignments are listed in the Prescription Table on the next page.

Objective	Item Numbers	Criterion Score	Student Score
A. Identify the center, diameter, and radius of a circle.	1, 2, 3, 4, 5	4/5	/5
B. Identify congruent and similar shapes.	6, 7, 10, 11, 14	4/5	/5
C. Identify transformations.	8, 9, 12, 13, 15	4/5	/5
D. Use skills and strategies to solve problems.	16, 17, 18, 19, 20	4/5	/5
Total Test Score		16/20	/20
Total Percent Correct			%

Chapter 20 – Prescription Table

The following chart correlates the tested objectives for this chapter to supplementary materials that meet the individual needs of the students. The Reteach and Practice pages are designed for students who need further instruction in the math concepts taught in this chapter. The Enrich pages are designed for students who need advanced challenges.

Objective	Reteach	Practice	Enrich
A. Identify the center, diameter, and radius of a circle.	344	345	346
B. Identify congruent and similar shapes.	347	348	349
C. Identify transformations.	350	351	352
D. Use skills and strategies to solve problems.	353	354	355

Read each question carefully. Darken the circle on your answer sheet for the correct answer.

Use the figure below to answer questions 1–5.

1. Identify $\overline{DE}$ on the circle.

   A. center   **C.** diameter

   B. chord   **D.** radius

2. Identify E on the circle.

   F. center   **H.** diameter

   G. chord   **J.** radius

3. Identify $\overline{BC}$ on the circle.

   A. center   **C.** diameter

   B. chord   **D.** radius

4. Identify $\overline{DF}$ on the circle.

   F. center   **H.** diameter

   G. chord   **J.** radius

5. Identify two radii on the circle.

   A. $\overline{AF}$ and $\overline{EF}$ **C.** $\overline{DE}$ and $\overline{EF}$

   B. $\overline{AF}$ and $\overline{DE}$ **D.** $\overline{EF}$ and $\overline{BC}$

6. Identify how the figures appear to be.

   F. congruent

   G. similar

   H. neither

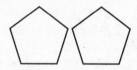

7. Identify how the figures appear to be.

   A. congruent

   B. similar

   C. neither

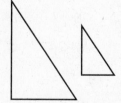

8. Identify the transformation.

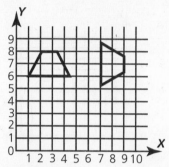

   F. glide reflection

   G. reflection

   H. rotation

   J. translation

9. Identify the transformation.

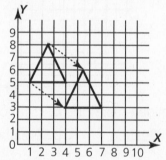

   A. glide reflection   **C.** rotation

   B. reflection   **D.** translation

10. Identify how the figures appear to be.

   F. congruent

   G. similar

   H. neither

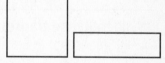

11. Identify how the figures appear to be.

   F. congruent

   G. similar

   H. neither

GO ON

12. Identify the transformation.

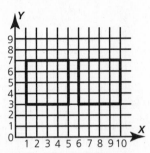

A. glide reflection   **C.** rotation

B. reflection   **D.** translation

13. Identify the transformation.

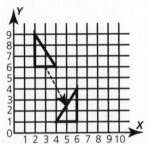

A. glide reflection   **C.** rotation

B. reflection   **D.** translation

14. Identify how the figures appear to be.

F. congruent

G. similar

H. neither

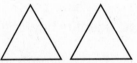

15. Identify the transformation.

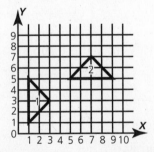

A. glide reflection   **C.** rotation

B. reflection   **D.** translation

16. In a row are four triangles. A green triangle is to the left of a red triangle. A blue triangle is in between the green and red triangle. A yellow triangle is first. What color is the last triangle?

F. blue   **H.** red

G. green   **J.** yellow

17. If you repeat the four-triangle pattern above three times, what color will the seventh triangle be?

A. blue   **C.** red

B. green   **D.** yellow

18. A shape pattern begins with a rectangle, pentagon, square, hexagon, octagon, and square. If this pattern continues, what is the thirtieth shape likely to be?

F. hexagon   **H.** pentagon

G. octagon   **J.** square

19. A shape pattern has a right triangle, rectangle, equilateral triangle, square, and a scalene triangle. If you repeat the pattern six times, what is the twentieth shape?

A. scalene triangle   **C.** equilateral triangle

B. right triangle   **D.** rectangle

20. In a row of three circles, the second circle is white. If there are eight rows, how many circles will not be white?

F. 24   **G.** 21   **H.** 16   **J.** 8

STOP

Name _____

Read each question carefully. Fill in the correct answer in the space provided.

Use the figure below to answer questions 1–5.

1. Identify *N* on the circle.

_____

_____

2. Identify $\overline{KL}$ on the circle.

_____

_____

3. Identify $\overline{JN}$ on the circle.

_____

_____

4. Identify two radii on the circle.

_____

_____

5. Identify $\overline{MO}$ on the circle.

_____

_____

6. Are the figures congruent, similar, or neither?

_____

_____

7. Are the figures congruent, similar, or neither?

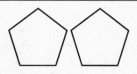

_____

8. Which kind of transformation was made?

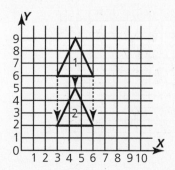

_____

_____

9. Which kind of transformation was made?

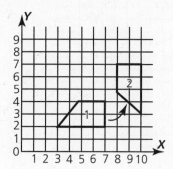

_____

_____

10. Are the figures congruent, similar, or neither?

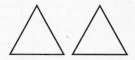

_____

_____

11. Do the figures appear to be congruent, similar, or neither?

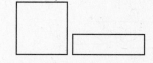

_____

12. Identify the transformation for exercises 12–14.

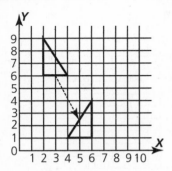

_____

13.

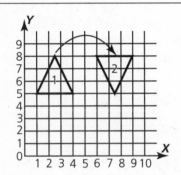

_____

14.

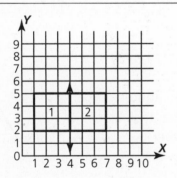

_____

15. Do the figures appear to be congruent, similar, or neither?

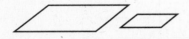

_____

16. In a row are 4 triangles. A green triangle is to the left of a red triangle. A blue triangle is in between the green and red triangle. A yellow triangle is first. What color is the third triangle?

_____

17. If you repeat the four-triangle pattern above five times, what color will the tenth triangle be?

_____

18. A shape pattern begins with a rectangle, pentagon, square, hexagon, octagon, and square. If this pattern continues, what is the twentieth shape likely to be?

_____

19. A shape pattern has a right triangle, rectangle, equilateral triangle, square, and a scalene triangle. If you repeat the pattern four times, what is the fourteenth shape?

_____

20. In a row of three circles, the second circle is purple. If there are nine rows, how many circles will not be purple?

_____

STOP

Unit 10 Performance Assessment

Dancing Triangle

- *Target Skill:*   Identify transformations.
- *Additional Skills:*   Identify congruent and similar figures.

Task
Description: This task requires students to use transformations to move a triangle from one location to another. The student will be asked to give ordered pairs for each transformation.

Preparing: Review the three transformations taught in the unit. Show the students how each transformation is used in a grid.

Materials	Group Size	Time on Task
Graph paper Work chart	2 students	1 to 2 days

Guiding: Remind students that the first coordinate is the number to the right of 0.

Remind students that the second coordinate is the number above 0.

Observing/
Monitoring: As you move among the students, pose the following questions:

Which transformations are you using?

How do you know which transformation to use?

What happens to the triangle when you transform it?

Unit 10 Performance Assessment Scoring Rubric

Dancing Triangle

Score	Explanation
3	Students demonstrate an efficient strategy and a thorough approach that enables them to solve the problem completely. A satisfactory answer: • indicates that it takes 1 translation, 1 rotation, and 1 reflection to move the figure; • writes the correct ordered pairs and plots the points after each transformation; • indicates that the triangle remains congruent after each transformation. Students are able to complete the problem quickly and have all of the above correct solutions.
2	Students demonstrate a strategy that enables them to solve most of the problem correctly. The strategy is somewhat disorganized, making it less efficient. A solution is found, but errors are contained. Students may: • plot the ordered pairs correctly; • know two of the transformations needed to move the triangle. Students have some difficulty determining all solutions correctly but demonstrate an understanding of general concepts.
1	Students demonstrate a confused strategy, which leads to difficulty solving the problem. Most answers are incorrect, but students demonstrate knowledge of at least one concept being assessed such as writing ordered pairs or transforming figures.

Unit 10 Performance Assessment Student Activity

Dancing Triangle

You will need
• graph paper

On the grid, draw a triangle with vertices of A at (5,3), B at (3,5), and C at (3,1). Write down the transformations needed so that the triangle ends up with vertices of D at (2, 2), E at (4, 0), and F at (0, 0).

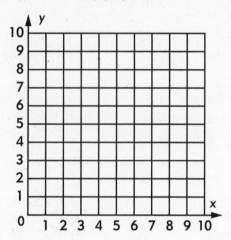

1. For each transformation, write down the ordered pairs for each vertex.

Transformation	A to D	B to E	C to F
Start	(5,3)	(3,5)	(3,1)
	(,)	(,)	(,)
	(,)	(,)	(,)
	(,)	(,)	(,)
	(,)	(,)	(,)

2. How many steps did it take to move the triangle into position?

_____

_____

3. Does the triangle remain congruent after each transformation? Explain.

_____

_____

Unit 10 – Monitoring Student Progress

☐ Form A   ☐ Form B

Name _____ Date _____

Directions: This test targets selected objectives. For each item that is answered incorrectly, cross out the item number. Then record the number of correct responses in the column labeled **Number of Correct Responses.** Add to find the **Total Number of Correct Responses** and record the total. Use this total to determine the **Total Test Score** and the **Total Percent Correct.**

Strand • Objective(s)	Item Numbers	Number of Correct Responses
Geometry and Spatial Sense • Measure, draw, and classify angles. • Describe and classify geometric figures. • Find the unknown angles of a figure. • Identify the center, diameter, and radius of a circle. • Identify congruent and similar figures. • Identify transformations. • Use skills and strategies to solve problems.	1, 2, 3, 4, 5, 6, 7, 8, 9, 10, 11, 12, 13, 14, 15, 16, 17, 18, 19, 20, 21, 22, 23, 24, 25, 26, 27, 28, 29, 30, 31, 32, 33, 34, 35, 36, 37, 38, 39, 40	/40
Total Number of Correct Responses		
Total Test Score		/40
Total Percent Correct		%

Read each question carefully. Darken the circle on your answer sheet for the correct answer.

1. Classify the angle.

A. acute

B. right

C. obtuse

D. congruent

2. Classify the polygon.

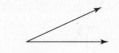

F. trapezoid   **H.** pentagon

G. rhombus   **J.** hexagon

3. Measure the angle.

A. 155°   **C.** 24°

B. 45°   **D.** 10°

4. Measure the angle.

F. 178°   **H.** 20°

G. 162°   **J.** 15°

5. Classify the angle.

A. acute

B. right

C. obtuse

D. similar

6. Classify the triangle.

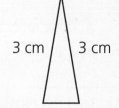

F. scalene

G. isosceles

H. right

J. equilateral

3 cm   3 cm

7. Classify the pair of lines.

A. intersecting   **C.** perpendicular

B. parallel   **D.** right

8. The center of the circle is *D*. Name the radius.

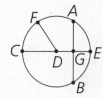

F. $\overline{AB}$

G. $\overline{AG}$

H. $\overline{DE}$

J. ∠*CDF*

9. Do the figures appear to be congruent, similar, or both?

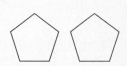

A. congruent

B. similar

C. both

10. Are the figures congruent, similar, or neither?

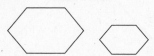

F. congruent   **H.** neither

G. similar

GO ON

11. Which kind of transformation was made?

A. glide reflection   **C.** rotation

B. translation   **D.** reflection

12. Find the missing angle measure.

F. 120°   **H.** 48°

G. 58°   **J.** 32°

13. Find the missing angle measure.

A. 125°   **C.** 50°

B. 60°   **D.** 35°

14. Which kind of transformation was made?

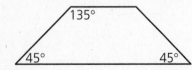

F. glide reflection   **H.** rotation

G. translation   **J.** reflection

15. Find the missing angle measure.

A. 135°   **C.** 90°

B. 100°   **D.** 45°

16. What is the missing shape in the pattern?

F. ▢

G. ◯

H. ⬡

J. ⯃

Solve.

17. Nan looks at a shape and says, "I see a parallelogram with four congruent sides and four right angles." Which shape does she see?

A. hexagon   **C.** square

B. trapezoid   **D.** right triangle

18. Rob measures the angles of a triangle as 40°, 90°, and 50°. Which kind of a triangle is it?

F. acute   **H.** right

G. obtuse

19. Sue measures two angles of a trapezoid as 70° and 70°. Which is the sum of the measures of the other two angles?

A. 280°   **C.** 240°

B. 260°   **D.** 220°

20. Frank cuts a board to make a figure. The sides of the figure are 8 inches by 8 inches by 8 inches. Which kind of triangle is it?

F. isosceles   **H.** equilateral

G. right   **J.** scalene

21. Classify the angle.

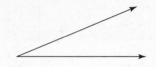

A. acute   **C.** obtuse

B. right   **D.** neither

22. Classify the polygon.

F. trapezoid   **H.** pentagon

G. rhombus   **J.** hexagon

23. Measure the angle.

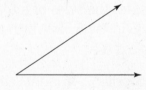

A. 63°   **C.** 45°

B. 53°   **D.** 33°

24. Measure the angle.

F. 90°   **H.** 75°

G. 85°   **J.** 60°

25. Classify the angle.

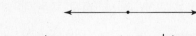

A. acute   **C.** obtuse

B. right   **D.** straight

26. Classify the triangle.

F. scalene   **H.** right

G. isosceles   **J.** equilateral

27. Classify the pair of lines.

A. intersecting   **C.** perpendicular

B. parallel   **D.** right

28. Name the arc.

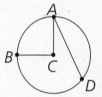

F. $\overarc{AD}$

G. $\overarc{AC}$

H. $\angle CAD$

J. $\angle ACB$

29. Do the figures appear to be congruent, similar, or neither?

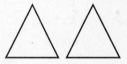

A. congruent

B. similar

C. neither

30. Are the figures congruent, similar, or neither?

F. congruent   **H.** neither

G. similar

GO ON

31. Which kind of transformation was made?

A. glide reflection   C. rotation

B. translation   D. reflection

32. Find the missing angle measure.

F. 110°   H. 80°

G. 100°   J. 70°

33. Find the missing angle measure.

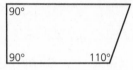

A. 107°   C. 83°

B. 97°   D. 92°

34. Which kind of transformation was made?

P q

F. reflection   H. rotation

G. translation   J. glide reflection

35. Find the missing angle measure.

A. 90°   C. 70°

B. 80°   D. 60°

36. What is the missing figure in the pattern?

○△□○ _ □

F. ○

G. △

H. □

Solve.

37. Jim looks at a shape and says, "I see a quadrilateral with exactly one pair of parallel sides." Which shape does he see?

A. rectangle   C. square

B. trapezoid   D. right triangle

38. Beth measures the sides of a triangle as 6 in. by 6 in. by 6 in. Which kind of a triangle is it?

F. right isosceles   H. right scalene

G. obtuse isosceles   J. equilateral

39. Rikki measures two angles of a trapezoid as 108° and 108°. What is the sum of the measures of the other two angles?

A. 216°   C. 108°

B. 144°   D. 90°

40. Dennis cuts a board to make a figure. The sides of the figure are 9 in. by 13 in. by 9 in. Which kind of triangle is it?

F. isosceles   H. equilateral

G. right   J. scalene

STOP

Read each question carefully. Fill in the correct answer in the space provided.

1. Classify the angle.

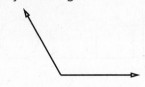

_____

_____

2. Classify the polygon.

_____

_____

3. Measure the angle.

_____

_____

4. Measure the angle.

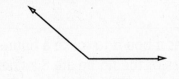

_____

_____

5. Classify the angle.

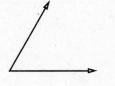

_____

6. Classify the triangle.

_____

_____

7. Classify the pair of lines.

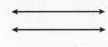

_____

_____

8. The center of a circle is *D*. Name the diameter.

_____

_____

9. Do the figures appear to be congruent, similar, or both?

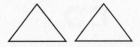

_____

_____

10. Do the figures appear to be congruent, similar, or neither?

_____

GO ON

11. Which kind of transformation was made?

_____

_____

12. Find the missing angle measure.

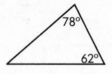

_____

_____

13. Find the missing angle measure.

_____

_____

14. Which kind of transformation was made?

_____

_____

15. What is the missing angle measure?

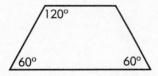

_____

16. Which is the missing shape in the pattern?

_____

_____

17. Cindy looks at a shape and says, "I see a quadrilateral with exactly one pair of parallel sides." Which shape does she see?

_____

_____

18. Brian measures the angles of a triangle as 50°, 30°, and 100°. Which kind of triangle is it?

_____

_____

19. Linda measures two angles of a trapezoid as 55° and 55°. What is the sum of the other two angles?

_____

_____

20. Deb cuts a board to make a figure. The sides of the figure are 8 inches by 8 inches by 6 inches. Which kind of triangle is it?

_____

_____

21. Classify the angle.

_____

22. Classify the polygon.

_____

23. Measure the angle.

_____

24. Measure the angle.

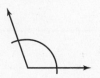

_____

25. Classify the angle.

_____

26. Classify the triangle.

_____

27. Classify the
pair of lines.

_____

28. Name a radius.

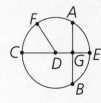

_____

29. Do the figures appear to be congruent,
similar, or both?

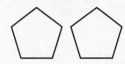

_____

30. Do the figures
appear to be
congruent, similar,
or neither?

_____

GO ON

31. Which kind of transformation was made?

_____

32. Find the missing angle measure.

_____

33. Find the missing angle measure.

_____

34. Which kind of transformation was made?

_____

35. Find the missing angle measure.

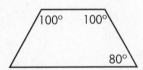

_____

36. What is the missing shape in the pattern?

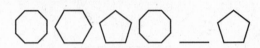

_____

37. Dez looks at a shape and says, "I see a parallelogram with all sides and angles congruent." Which shape does she see?

_____

38. Roberto measures the sides of a triangle as 8 in. by 6 in. by 7 in. What kind of a triangle is it?

_____

39. Louisa measures two angles of a trapezoid as 132°, and 132°. What is the sum of the measures of the other two angles?

_____

40. Ryan cuts a board to make a figure. The sides of the figure are 8 in. by 8 in. by 8 in. What kind of triangle is it?

_____

STOP

Chapter 21 – Teacher Interview

Core Concept: *Area of Parallelograms*

Student Activity: Ask students to draw a parallelogram that has a height of 6 inches and a base of 8 inches, then find the area.

Teacher Question 1:

- Draw a parallelogram with a height of 6 inches and a base of 8 inches.

Understanding Student Response	Practice and Improvement
Students who label the sides as 6 inches and 8 inches.	Review lesson 5 to reinforce the concept of the height of a parallelogram. Draw several parallelograms and allow the student to practice drawing the height of each.
Students who confuse the base and height.	Review lesson 5 to reinforce the concept of the base and height of a parallelogram.

Teacher Question 2:

- Show how you can divide a parallelogram into 2 pieces that you can rearrange to form a rectangle.

Understanding Student Response	Practice and Improvement
Students who are unable to divide a parallelogram into two appropriate pieces.	Review the diagrams in lesson 5. Practice cutting paper models of parallelograms into 2 appropriate pieces.
Students who cannot rearrange the pieces to form a rectangle.	Practice cutting and rearranging paper models of parallelograms to form rectangles.

Teacher Question 3:

- What is the area of the parallelogram?

Understanding Student Response	Practice and Improvement
Students who do not know how to calculate the area.	Review lesson 5 to reinforce the formula for the area of a parallelogram. Encourage the student to relate this formula to the area of the rectangle they made in question 2.

Chapter 21 – Journal Writing

Encourage students to generate their own journal entries related to math ideas in general or to concepts in this chapter. Present the following journal prompt and have students share their drawing/writing with a partner:

• When you are problem solving, why is it important to read what is asked in the problem and often solve a simpler problem in order to solve the overall problem?

(Responses should indicate that breaking down a problem into parts and solving them will make the overall problem simpler and easier to solve.)

JOURNAL WRITING/PROBLEM SOLVING

The floor of a rectangular room measures 15 feet × 14 feet. Geena places a rectangular carpet that measures 8 feet × 12 feet in the corner of the floor. What is the area of the floor that is uncarpeted? Will this area change if Geena moves the carpet to the middle of the floor?

Read

Have students find the answer to the problem. Then ask them to write a few sentences telling—

• which information they used to find the answer

• what they did with the information

Have students make up another problem with different information for which they could have followed the same procedure. Then have students solve the problem and supply the correct response.

Plan

Students must know how to calculate the area of the rectangles. They must also recognize that the uncarpeted area is equal to the difference of the areas of the rectangles, which are fixed.

Solve

The correct response to the assigned problem is 114 square feet. This area will not change if the carpet is moved.

Look Back

A correct response demonstrates the ability to use the formula for finding the area of a rectangle and the ability to apply this formula to solve problems. (See scoring rubric on page 7.)

Chapter 21 – Monitoring Student Progress

☐ **Form A**   ☐ **Form B**

Name _____ Date _____

Directions: For each item that is answered incorrectly, cross out the item number. Then record the number of correct responses in the appropriate Student Score column. If the student has not met the Criterion Score for an objective, circle the student's score. Recommended assignments are listed in the Prescription Table on the next page.

Objective	Item Numbers	Criterion Score	Student Score
A. Find perimeter.	1, 2, 4, 8, 10	4/5	/5
B. Find area of rectangles.	3, 5, 6, 11, 14, 16	5/6	/6
C. Find area of parallelograms.	7, 9, 12, 13, 15	4/5	/5
D. Use skills and strategies to solve problems.	17, 18, 19, 20	3/4	/4
Total Test Score		16/20	/20
Total Percent Correct			%

Chapter 21 – Prescription Table

The following chart correlates the tested objectives for this chapter to supplementary materials that meet the individual needs of the students. The Reteach and Practice pages are designed for students who need further instruction in the math concepts taught in this chapter. The Enrich pages are designed for students who need advanced challenges.

Objective	Reteach	Practice	Enrich
A. Find perimeter.	358, 364	359, 365	360, 366
B. Find area of rectangles.	361, 364	362, 365	363, 366
C. Find area of parallelograms.	370	371	372
D. Use skills and strategies to solve problems.	367	368	369

Name _____

Read each question carefully. Darken the circle on your answer sheet for the correct answer.

1. Find the perimeter.

6 m

6 m

A. 12 m **C.** 36 m

B. 24 m **D.** 48 m

2. Find the perimeter.

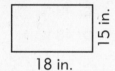

15 in.

18 in.

F. 23 in. **H.** 66 in.

G. 33 in. **J.** 90 in.

3. Find the area.

A. 38 m^2

B. 50 m^2

C. 84 m^2

D. 96 m^2

12 m

7 m

4. Find the perimeter.

F. 180 cm

G. 68 cm

H. 34 cm

J. 17 cm

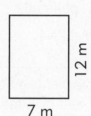

6 cm 6 cm

5 cm

5. Find the area.

A. 36 yd^2

B. 32 yd^2

C. 18 yd^2

D. 13 yd^2

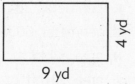

4 yd

9 yd

6. Find the area.

F. 9 in.^{2}

G. 17.25 in.^{2}

H. 19.25 in.^{2}

J. 23.5 in.^{2}

3.5 in.

5.5 in.

7. Find the area.

A. 9 ft^2

B. 18 ft^2

C. 27 ft^2

D. 36 ft^2

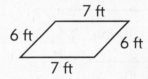

3 ft

6 ft

8. Find the perimeter.

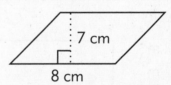

7 ft

6 ft 6 ft

7 ft

F. 84 ft **G.** 56 ft **H.** 26 ft **J.** 14 ft

9. Find the area.

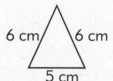

7 cm

8 cm

A. 56 cm^2 **C.** 30 cm^2

B. 54 cm^2 **D.** 28 cm^2

10. Find the perimeter.

F. 51.6 m

G. 86 m

H. 68 m

J. 103.2 m

17.2 m 17.2 m

17.2 m 17.2 m

17.2 m

GO ON

11. Find the area.

A. 350 cm²
B. 300 cm²
C. 200 cm²
D. 150 cm²

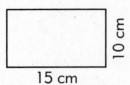

10 cm
15 cm

12. Find the area.

F. 29.9 in.²
G. 27.9 in.²
H. 24.7 in.²
J. 14.6 in.²

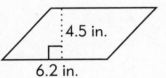

4.5 in.
6.2 in.

13. Find the area.

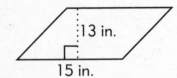

13 in.
15 in.

A. 95 in.²
B. 125 in.²
C. 150 in.²
D. 195 in.²

14. Find the area.

F. 41.82 m²
G. 40.82 m²
H. 28.3 m²
J. 24.3 m²

4.1 m
10.2 m

15. Find the area.

A. 22 yd²
B. 28 yd²
C. 32 yd²
D. 56 yd²

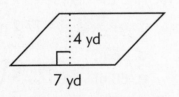

4 yd
7 yd

16. Find the area.

F. 24 in.²
G. 48 in.²
H. 96 in.²
J. 144 in.²

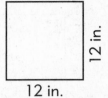

12 in.
12 in.

17. Jose is building a 6 feet by 8 feet platform to use as a tree fort. What is the area of the platform?

A. 20 ft
B. 28 ft²
C. 48 ft
D. 48 ft²

18. Jose decides to put a railing around the platform. What does he need to measure to know how much railing to buy?

F. perimeter
G. area
H. width
J. volume

19. Eve plants a flower garden in a 9 feet by 6 feet area. She decides to double each side of the garden. What is the area of the new garden?

A. 54 ft²
B. 108 ft²
C. 216 ft²
D. 240 ft²

20. Eve wants to plant shrubs around the four sides of her new garden. Which will help her decide how many shrubs to buy—perimeter or area? What is it?

F. perimeter, 30 ft
G. perimeter, 60 ft
H. area, 54 ft²
J. area, 216 ft²

STOP

Name _____

Read each question carefully. Fill in the correct answer in the space provided.

1. Find the perimeter.

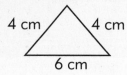

4 cm   4 cm

6 cm

_____

2. Find the perimeter.

_____

7 in.

7 in.

3. Find the area.

2.7 yd

7.2 yd

_____

4. Find the perimeter.

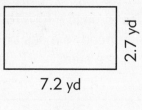

6 yd

16 yd

_____

5. Find the area.

5.2 yd

12.3 yd

_____

6. Find the area.

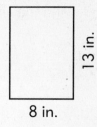

13 in.

8 in.

_____

7. Find the area.

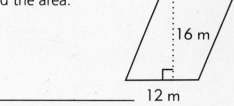

16 m

12 m

_____

8. Find the perimeter.

12.7 m   12.7 m

12.7 m   12.7 m

12.7 m

_____

9. Find the area.

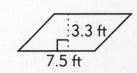

3.3 ft

7.5 ft

_____

10. Find the perimeter.

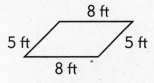

8 ft

5 ft   5 ft

8 ft

_____

11. Find the area.

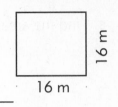

16 m

16 m

_____

12. Find the area.

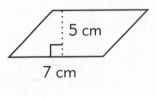

5 cm

7 cm

_____

13. Find the area.

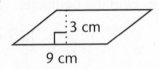

3 cm

9 cm

_____

14. Find the area.

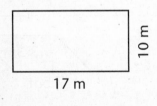

10 m

17 m

_____

15. Find the area.

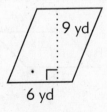

9 yd

6 yd

_____

16. Find the area.

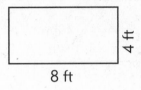

4 ft

8 ft

_____

17. Tom is building a 10 inch by 8 inch raft. What is the area of the raft?

_____

18. Tom decides to build a roof for his raft. Does he need to measure the perimeter or the area?

_____

19. Ella plants a vegetable garden in an 8 feet by 8 feet area. She decides to double the sides of the garden. What is the area of the new garden?

_____

20. In her new garden, Ella decides to fence in her new garden. Which does Ella need to know to decide how much fence to buy—the perimeter or the area? What is it?

_____

STOP

Chapter 22 – Teacher Interview

Core Concept: *Area of Trapezoids*

Student Activity: Students demonstrate an understanding of using the formula for finding the area of a parallelogram and applying it to write a formula and find the area of a trapezoid. Ask students to draw a trapezoid that has a height of 4 feet and base lengths of 3 feet and 7 feet. Then have them find the area of the trapezoid.

Teacher Question 1:

- How can you make a parallelogram from two trapezoids?

Understanding Student Response	Practice and Improvement
Students who draw a rhombus (or a rectangle).	Review lesson 2 to reinforce an understanding that a trapezoid is a polygon with four sides, exactly two of which are parallel.
Students who draw two trapezoids side by side.	Review lesson 2 to help students visualize how two trapezoids form a parallelogram.

Teacher Question 2:

- How can you use the formula for finding the area of a parallelogram to write a formula for the area of the trapezoid?

Understanding Student Response	Practice and Improvement
Students who say the formula for the area of a parallelogram is $l \times w$.	Review lesson 2 to review the formula for the area of a parallelogram as $b \times h$.
Students who label the height of the trapezoid as a base.	Review lesson 2 to help students visualize that one of the trapezoids is $\frac{1}{2}$ of a parallelogram.

Teacher Question 3:

- What is the area of the trapezoid?

Understanding Student Response	Practice and Improvement
Students who use the dimensions for the parallelogram.	Review lesson 2 to reinforce an understanding of the formula for finding the area of a trapezoid.
Students who incorrectly substitute the numbers for the variables.	Review lesson 2 to help students substitute the numbers in the formula, $A = \frac{1}{2} \times 4 (3 + 7)$, or 20 feet^2.

Chapter 22 – Journal Writing

Encourage students to generate their own journal entries related to math ideas in general or to concepts in this chapter. Present the following journal prompt and have students share their drawing/writing with a partner:

- When you are problem solving, why is it important to read what is asked in the problem and often solve a simpler problem before solving the overall problem?

  (Responses should indicate that breaking down a problem into parts and solving them will make the overall problem simpler and easier to solve.)

JOURNAL WRITING/PROBLEM SOLVING

The diameter of a circle is 42 inches. What is the circumference of the circle? Use $\pi \approx 3.14$. Round to the nearest tenth, if necessary.

Read

Have students find the answer to the problem. Then ask them to write a few sentences telling—

- which information they used to find the answer

- what they did with the information

Have students make up another problem with different information for which they could have followed the same procedure. Then have students solve the problem and supply the correct response.

Plan

Students must know that the circumference is the distance around the outside of a circle and must correctly use the circumference formula with the diameter given. Students must also round the circumference to the nearest tenth.

Solve

The correct response to the assigned problem is $C = 131.9$ inches rounded to the nearest tenth.

Look Back

A correct response demonstrates the ability to use the formula for finding the circumference of a circle and round the circumference to the nearest tenth.
(See scoring rubric on page 7.)

Chapter 22 – Monitoring Student Progress

☐ **Form A**   ☐ **Form B**

Name _____ Date _____

Directions: For each item that is answered incorrectly, cross out the item number. Then record the number of correct responses in the appropriate Student Score column. If the student has not met the Criterion Score for an objective, circle the student's score. Recommended assignments are listed in the Prescription Table on the next page.

Objective	Item Numbers	Criterion Score	Student Score
A. Find area of triangles and trapezoids.	1, 2, 5, 6, 13, 14	5/6	/6
B. Find perimeter and area of irregular figures.	3, 7, 9, 11, 15	4/5	/5
C. Find circumference of circles.	4, 8, 10, 12, 16	4/5	/5
D. Use skills and strategies to solve problems.	17, 18, 19, 20	3/4	/4
Total Test Score		16/20	/20
Total Percent Correct			%

Chapter 22 – Prescription Table

The following chart correlates the tested objectives for this chapter to supplementary materials that meet the individual needs of the students. The Reteach and Practice pages are designed for students who need further instruction in the math concepts taught in this chapter. The Enrich pages are designed for students who need advanced challenges.

Objective	Reteach	Practice	Enrich
A. Find area of triangles and trapezoids.	373, 376	374, 377	375, 378
B. Find perimeter and area of irregular figures.	382	383	384
C. Find circumference of circles.	385	386	387
D. Use skills and strategies to solve problems.	379, 380	381	

Name_____

Read each question carefully. Darken the circle on your answer sheet for the correct answer.

1. Find the area.

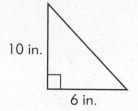

A. 20 in.^{2}

B. 30 in.^{2}

C. 45 in.^{2}

D. 60 in.^{2}

2. Find the area.

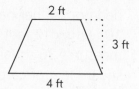

F. 36 ft^2

G. 18 ft^2

H. 9 ft^2

J. 6 ft^2

3. Estimate to find the area. Each square = 1 in.^{2}.

A. 8 in.^{2}

B. 7 in.^{2}

C. 6 in.^{2}

D. 5 in.^{2}

4. Find the approximate circumference of the circle. Use $\pi \approx 3.14$. Round to the nearest hundredth if necessary.

F. 36.68 cm

G. 37.68 cm

H. 75.36 cm

J. 150.72 cm

5. Find the area.

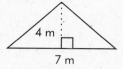

A. 14 m^2

B. 28 m^2

C. 42 m^2

D. 56 m^2

6. Find the area.

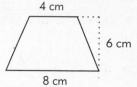

F. 108 cm^2

G. 72 cm^2

H. 54 cm^2

J. 36 cm^2

7. Find the area. Each square = 1 cm^2.

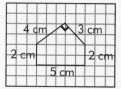

A. 15 cm^2

B. 16 cm^2

C. 17 cm^2

D. 18 cm^2

8. Find the approximate circumference of the circle. Use $\pi \approx 3.14$. Round to the nearest tenth if necessary.

F. 150.2 in.

G. 100.2 in.

H. 50.2 in.

J. 25.5 in.

9. Estimate to find the area. Each square = 1 cm^2.

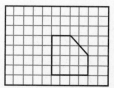

A. 12 cm^2

B. 13 cm^2

C. 14 cm^2

D. 15 cm^2

10. Find the approximate circumference of the circle. Use $\pi \approx 3.14$. Round to the nearest hundredth if necessary.

F. 14.13 m

G. 28.26 m

H. 56.52 m

J. 113.04 m

GO ON

11. Find the area. Each square = 1 cm².

A. 38 cm²

B. 40 cm²

C. 41 cm²

D. 43 cm²

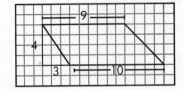

12. Find the approximate circumference of the circle. Use π ≈ 3.14. Round to the nearest tenth if necessary.

F. 94.2 ft

G. 47.1 ft

H. 31.4 ft

J. 23.5 ft

15 ft

13. Find the area.

A. 80 ft²

B. 60 ft²

C. 40 ft²

D. 20 ft²

8 ft

10 ft

14. Find the area.

F. 25.25 m²

G. 26.25 m²

H. 52.5 m²

J. 105 m²

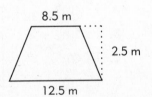

8.5 m

2.5 m

12.5 m

15. Find the area. Each square = 1 in.².

A. 60 in.²

B. 64 in.²

C. 68 in.²

D. 72 in.²

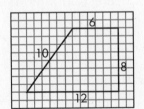

16. Find the approximate circumference of the circle. Use π ≈ 3.14. Round to the nearest tenth if necessary.

F. 200.8 m

G. 100.5 m

H. 75.2 m

J. 25.1 m

8 m

17. Marla is putting new carpeting in her bedroom. If her bedroom measures 10 feet by 12 feet with an alcove that measures 36 square feet, how many square feet of carpet will she need?

A. 156 ft²   C. 126 ft²

B. 140 ft²   D. 120 ft²

18. The total area of a floor plan is 320 ft². If the kitchen measures 5 feet by 9 feet, what is the area of the rest of the floor plan?

F. 595 ft²   H. 275 ft²

G. 298 ft²   J. 45 ft²

19. Saul's front yard measures 50 feet by 20 feet. His driveway takes up 350 ft² of the front yard, and the rest is grass. How much grass is in Saul's front yard?

A. 1,000 ft²   C. 550 ft²

B. 650 ft²   D. 350 ft²

20. Saul's back yard is rectangular and has a perimeter of 180 feet. The two sides of his yard have a total length of 80 feet. If Saul puts a fence along the back of his yard and along one side, how much fence will he need to buy?

F. 180 ft   H. 100 ft

G. 160 ft   J. 90 ft

STOP

Read each question carefully. Fill in the correct answer in the space provided.

1. Find the area.

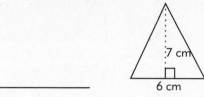

_____

2. Find the area.

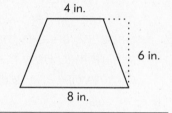

_____

3. Estimate to find the area. Each square = 1 in.^{2}.

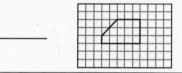

_____

4. Find the approximate circumference of the circle. Use $\pi \approx 3.14$. Round to the nearest hundredth if necessary.

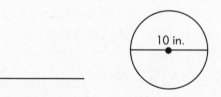

_____

5. Find the area.

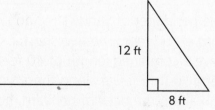

_____

6. Find the area.

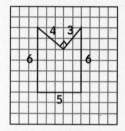

_____

7. Find the area. Each square = 1 cm^2.

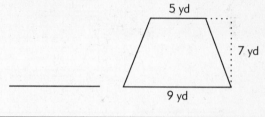

_____

8. Find the approximate circumference of the circle. Use $\pi \approx 3.14$. Round to the nearest tenth if necessary.

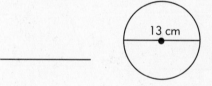

_____

9. Estimate to find the area. Each square = 1 cm^2.

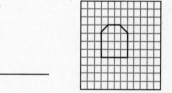

_____

10. Find the approximate circumference of the circle. Use $\pi \approx 3.14$. Round to the nearest tenth if necessary.

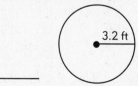

_____

GO ON

11. Find the area. Each square = 1 cm².

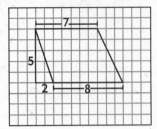

_____

12. Find the approximate circumference of the circle. Use π ≈ 3.14. Round to the nearest hundredth if necessary.

14 m

_____

13. Find the area.

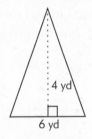

4 yd

6 yd

_____

14. Find the area.

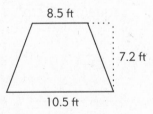

8.5 ft

7.2 ft

10.5 ft

_____

15. Find the area. Each square = 1 in.².

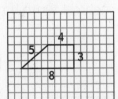

4

5

3

8

_____

16. Find the approximate circumference of the circle. Use π ≈ 3.14. Round to the nearest hundredth if necessary.

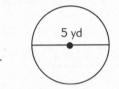

5 yd

_____

17. Carla is replacing a carpet that measures 12 feet × 9 feet. She is also carpeting an area that measures 42 square feet. How many square feet of carpet will Carla need?

_____

18. The total area of a floor plan is 450 ft². If the dining room measures 10 feet × 14 feet, what is the area of the rest of the floor plan?

_____

19. Sandy's back yard measures 60 feet × 20 feet. Her garden takes up 250 square feet, and the rest is grass. How many square feet of grass are in Sandy's back yard?

_____

20. The perimeter of Sandy's rectangular yard is 160 feet. The two shorter sides have a combined length of 40 feet. If Sandy puts a fence along these sides and along the back of her yard, how much fence will she need to buy?

_____

STOP

Unit 11 Performance Assessment

Tanya at the Gymkhana

- **Target Skill:**   Find area of rectangles.
- **Additional Skills:**   Find perimeter, find circumference of circles, find perimeter and area of irregular figures.

Task
Description: This task requires students to find the perimeter and area of a horse show ring. The students will be asked to find the perimeter and area of the rectangular part of the ring and the circumference and the approximate area of the part that are half circles.

Preparing: You may wish to have the students review the formulas for finding perimeter, circumference, and area of triangles. Review with students how to estimate the area of an irregular figure.

Materials	Group Size	Time on Task
Calculator (optional)	1 to 2 students	1 day

Guiding: Remind students that perimeter is found in units and area is found in square units.

Remind them that the circumference of the two half-circles adds up to the circumference of a whole circle.

Observing/
Monitoring: As you move among the students, pose the following questions:

How does knowing the distance between the two straight sides of the ring help you find the perimeter around curved sides?

What would happen if you could remove the rectangle and push the two curved sides together?

How do you estimate the area of an irregular figure?

Unit 11 Performance Assessment Scoring Rubric

Tanya at the Gymkhana

Score	Explanation
3	Students demonstrate an efficient strategy and a thorough approach that enables them to solve the problem completely. A satisfactory answer: • calculates the perimeter and area of the rectangle; • gives a reasonable estimate for the area of the half circles; • labels the perimeter and circumference in meters and the area in square meters. Students are able to complete the problem quickly and have all of the above correct solutions.
2	Students demonstrate a strategy that enables them to solve most of the problem correctly. The strategy is somewhat disorganized, making it less efficient. A solution is found, but errors are contained. Students may: • find the perimeter and area of the rectangle; • give a reasonable estimate for either the circumference or approximate area of the half circles. Students have some difficulty determining all solutions correctly but demonstrate an understanding of general concepts.
1	Students demonstrate a confused strategy, which leads to difficulty solving the problem. Most answers are incorrect, but students demonstrate knowledge of at least one concept being assessed. Students may: • find the perimeter of the rectangle; OR • find the area of the rectangle.

Unit II Performance Assessment
Student Activity

Tanya at the Gymkhana

You will need
• Calculator (optional)

Tanya and her horse Belle are taking part in the Gymkhana (horse show) at the Clinton County Fair. Tanya especially wants to show off Belle's prance around the big show ring.

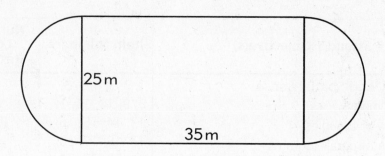

1. How can you find the perimeter of the big show ring?

_____

2. What is the perimeter of the rectangle? _____

3. What is the circumference of the half-circles? _____

4. What is the approximate perimeter of the big show ring? _____

5. What is the area of the rectangle? _____

6. How can you estimate the area of a half circle? What is the approximate area of the half circles?

_____

7. What is the approximate area of the big show ring? _____

Unit 11 – Monitoring Student Progress

☐ Form A   ☐ Form B

Name _____ Date _____

Directions: This test targets selected objectives. For each item that is answered incorrectly, cross out the item number. Then record the number of correct responses in the column labeled **Number of Correct Responses.** Add to find the **Total Number of Correct Responses** and record the total. Use this total to determine the **Total Test Score** and the **Total Percent Correct.**

Strand • Objective(s)	Item Numbers	Number of Correct Responses
Geometry and Spatial Sense • Find perimeter. • Find area of triangles. • Find area of parallelograms. • Find area of triangles and trapezoids. • Find perimeter and area of irregular figures. • Find circumference of circles. • Use skills and strategies to solve problems.	1, 2, 3, 4, 5, 6, 7, 8, 9, 10, 11, 12, 13, 14, 15, 16, 17, 18, 19, 20, 21, 22, 23, 24, 25, 26, 27, 28, 29, 30, 31, 32, 33, 34, 35, 36, 37, 38, 39, 40	/40
Total Number of Correct Responses		
Total Test Score		/40
Total Percent Correct		%

Name_____

Read each question carefully. Darken the circle on your answer sheet for the correct answer.

1. Find the perimeter.

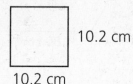

10.2 cm

10.2 cm

A. 104.04 cm   **C.** 30.6 cm

B. 40.8 cm   **D.** 20.4 cm

2. Find the perimeter.

F. 360 ft

G. 180 ft

H. 56 ft

J. 36 ft

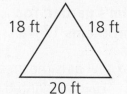

18 ft   18 ft

20 ft

3. Find the approximate circumference.
Use $\pi \approx 3.14$.

27 in.

A. 572.3 in.   **C.** 169.6 in.

B. 286.15 in.   **D.** 84.8 in.

4. Find the approximate circumference.
Use $\pi \approx 3.14$.

9 m

F. 254 m   **H.** 57 m

G. 113 m   **J.** 28 m

5. Find the area.

6 mi

8 mi

A. 96 mi^2 **C.** 28 mi^2

B. 48 mi^2 **D.** 14 mi^2

6. Find the area.

25 ft

25 ft

F. 625 ft^2 **H.** 50 ft^2

G. 100 ft^2 **J.** Not Here

7. Find the area.

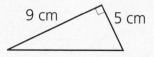

9 cm   5 cm

A. 45 cm^2 **C.** 24 cm^2

B. 25 cm^2 **D.** 22.5 cm^2

8. Find the approximate circumference.
Use $\pi \approx 3.14$.

16 m

F. 50 m^2 **H.** 16 m^2

G. 25 m^2 **J.** 8 m^2

9. Find the area.

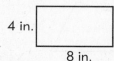

4 in.

8 in.

A. 64 in.^{2} **C.** 16 in.^{2}

B. 32 in.^{2} **D.** 8 in.^{2}

10. Find the area.

F. 48 cm^2

G. 72 cm^2

H. 120 cm^2

J. 144 cm^2

12 cm

GO ON

11. Find the area.

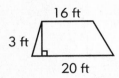

16 ft
3 ft
20 ft

A. 42 ft^2 **C.** 54 ft^2
B. 48 ft^2 **D.** 60 ft^2

12. Find the area.

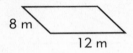

8 m
12 m

F. 12 m^2 **H.** 48 m^2
G. 40 m^2 **J.** 96 m^2

13. Find the area.

A. 11 square units
B. 12 square units
C. 13 square units
D. 14 square units

14. Find the perimeter.

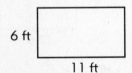

8 cm
5 cm
4 cm
7 cm

F. 18 cm   **H.** 24 cm
G. 23 cm   **J.** 30 cm

15. Find the area.

6 ft
11 ft

A. 17 ft^2 **C.** 36 ft^2
B. 34 ft^2 **D.** 66 ft^2

16. Find the area.

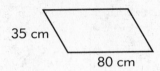

35 cm
80 cm

F. 6400 cm^2 **H.** 1400 cm^2
G. 2800 cm^2 **J.** 230 cm^2

Solve.

Use the diagram of Jim's garden for problems 17–18.

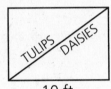

TULIPS DAISIES 7 ft
10 ft

17. What is the area of the part of the garden planted with daisies?

A. 100 ft^2 **C.** 35 ft^2
B. 70 ft^2 **D.** 17 ft^2

18. If Jim puts a fence around the perimeter of the entire garden, how many feet of fencing does he need?

F. 70 ft   **G.** 68 ft   **H.** 34 ft   **J.** 17 ft

19. Samantha walks around a rectangular park that measures 1 mile by 2 miles. How far does she walk?

A. 2 miles   **C.** 4 miles
B. 3 miles   **D.** 6 miles

20. Eve cut a circle out of felt. She wants to sew ribbon around its circumference. The radius is 1 yard. How many yards of ribbon does she need?

F. 6.28 yd   **H.** 4.1 yd
G. 5.14 yd   **J.** 3.14 yd

GO ON

21. Find the perimeter.

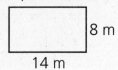
8 m
14 m

A. 672 m **C.** 44 m

B. 112 m **D.** 22 m

22. Find the perimeter.

F. 64 in.
G. 40 in.
H. 32 in.
J. 16 in.

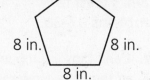
8 in. 8 in.
8 in. 8 in.
8 in.

23. Find the approximate circumference.
Use π ≈ 3.14.

A. 2,826 ft
B. 706 ft
C. 94 ft
D. 47 ft

15 ft

24. Find the approximate circumference.
Use π ≈ 3.14.

22 cm

F. 1,520 cm **H.** 138 cm

G. 380 cm **J.** 69 cm

25. Find the area.

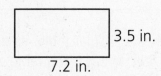
3.5 in.
7.2 in.

A. 151.2 in.^{2} **C.** 25.2 in.^{2}

B. 100.8 in.^{2} **D.** 21.4 in.^{2}

26. Find the area.

F. 40 ft^2
G. 24 ft^2
H. 20 ft^2
J. 16 ft^2

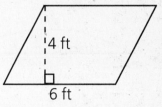
4 ft
6 ft

27. Find the area.

A. 414 cm^2
B. 207 cm^2
C. 164 cm^2
D. 82 cm^2

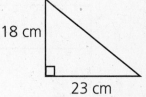
18 cm
23 cm

28. Find the approximate circumference.
Use π ≈ 3.14.

8 m

F. 4 m^2 **H.** 13 m^2

G. 8 m^2 **J.** 25 m^2

29. Find the area.

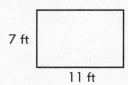
7 ft
11 ft

A. 121 ft^2 **C.** 49 ft^2

B. 77 ft^2 **D.** 36 ft^2

30. Find the area.

F. 225 cm^2
G. 150 cm^2
H. 60 cm^2
J. 30 cm^2

15 cm

GO ON

31. Find the area.

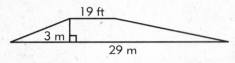

A. 64 m^2 **C.** 192 m^2

B. 152 m^2 **D.** 232 m^2

32. Find the area.

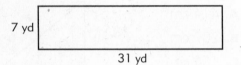

F. 317 m^2 **H.** 76 m^2

G. 217 m^2 **J.** 49 m^2

33. Find the area.

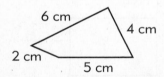

A. 16 square units

B. 15 square units

C. 14 square units

D. 13 square units

34. Find the perimeter.

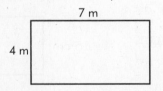

F. 15 cm   **H.** 24 cm

G. 17 cm   **J.** 30 cm

35. Find the area.

7 m

4 m

A. 28 m^2 **C.** 11 m^2

B. 22 m^2 **D.** 14 m^2

36. Find the area.

F 66 in.^{2}

G. 242 in.^{2}

H. 252 in.^{2}

J. 330 in.^{2}

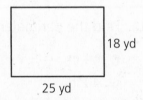

Solve.

**Use the diagram of
Cami's yard for
problems 37–38.**

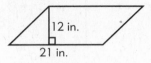

37. Cami digs a ditch around the perimeter
of the yard. How many yards long is
the ditch?

A. 450 yd   **C.** 172 yd

B. 225 yd   **D.** 86 yd

38. Cami covers the yard with grass seed.
What is the area she covers?

F. 450 yd^2 **H.** 172 yd^2

G. 225 yd^2 **J.** 86 yd^2

39. Charlie walks around a rectangular
park that is an equilateral triangle that
measures 2 miles on a side. How far
does he walk?

A. 2 miles   **C.** 6 miles

B. 4 miles   **D.** 8 miles

40. May has a circular table. Its diameter
is 10 feet. What is the table's
approximate circumference?

F. 62 ft   **H.** 16 ft

G. 31 ft   **J.** 10 ft

STOP

Read each question carefully. Fill in the correct answer in the space provided.

1. Find the perimeter.

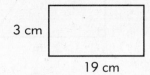

5.1 cm

10.3 cm

_____

2. Find the perimeter.

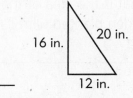

16 in. 20 in.

12 in.

_____

3. Find the approximate circumference. Use π ≈ 3.14.

24 ft

_____

4. Find the approximate circumference. Use π ≈ 3.14.

7 m

_____

5. Find the area.

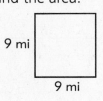

9 mi

9 mi

_____

6. Find the area.

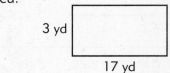

3 cm

19 cm

_____

7. Find the area.

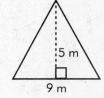

5 m

9 m

_____

8. Find the approximate circumference. Use π ≈ 3.14.

9 in.

_____

_____

9. Find the area.

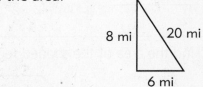

3 yd

17 yd

_____

10. Find the area.

8 mi 20 mi

6 mi

_____

GO ON

11. Find the area.

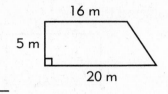

16 m

5 m

20 m

_____

12. Find the area.

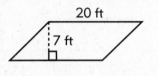

20 ft

7 ft

_____

13. Find the area.

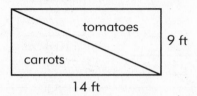

_____

14. Find the perimeter.

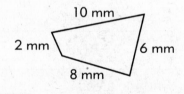

10 mm

2 mm

6 mm

8 mm

_____

15. Find the area.

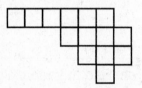

7 ft

7 ft

_____

16. Find the area of the shaded region.

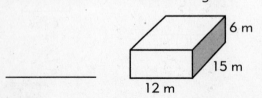

6 m

15 m

12 m

_____

Use the diagram of Harriet's garden for problems 17–18.

tomatoes

9 ft

carrots

14 ft

17. What is the area of the part of the garden planted with carrots?

_____

18. If Harriet puts a fence around the perimeter of the garden, how many feet of fencing does she need?

_____

19. Samuel walks around a circular merry-go-round that measures 10 yards in diameter. About how far did he walk?

_____

20. Simone wants to sew a ribbon around the edge of a rectangular napkin. The napkin measures 7 inches by 8 inches. How many inches of ribbon does she need?

_____

GO ON

Name _____

21. Find the perimeter.

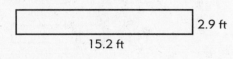

2.9 ft
15.2 ft

_____

22. Find the perimeter.

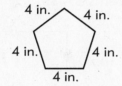

4 in.   4 in.
4 in.   4 in.
4 in.

_____

23. Find the approximate circumference.
Use π ≈ 3.14.

11 in.

_____

24. Find the approximate circumference.
Use π ≈ 3.14.

30 m

_____

25. Find the area.

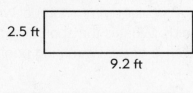

2.5 ft
9.2 ft

_____

26. Find the area.

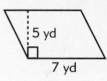

5 yd
7 yd

_____

27. Find the area.

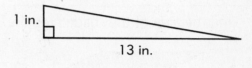

1 in.
13 in.

_____

28. Find the approximate circumference.
Use π ≈ 3.14.

4.5 in.

_____

29. Find the area.

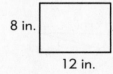

8 in.
12 in.

_____

30. Find the area.

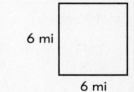

6 mi
6 mi

_____

GO ON

31. Find the area.

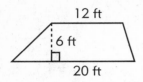

_____

_____

32. Find the area of the shaded region.

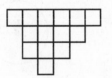

_____

33. Find the area.

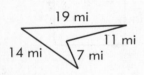

_____

34. Find the perimeter.

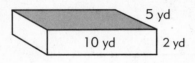

_____

35. Find the area.

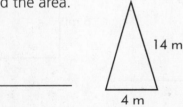

_____

36. Find the area of the shaded region.

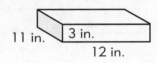

_____

Use the diagram of Camille's yard for problems 37–38.

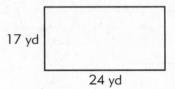

37. Camille digs a ditch around the perimeter of her yard. How many yards long is the ditch?

_____

38. Camille then covers the yard with grass seed. What is the area she covers?

_____

39. Felipe jogs around a parking garage that is shaped like an equilateral triangle that measures 200 yards on each side. How many yards did he jog?

_____

40. Yola has a circular swimming pool with a 6-ft radius. What is the approximate circumference of the swimming pool?

_____

STOP

Chapter 23 – Teacher Interview

Core Concept: *Finding Surface Area and Volume*

Student Activity: Students demonstrate an understanding of rectangular prisms and an ability to find surface area and volume. Have boxes or blocks of various size and shape available to use as models. Describe the dimensions of various rectangular prisms and ask the students to calculate their surface area and volume.

Teacher Question 1:

- A rectangular prism measures 3 in. × 7 in. × 12 in. What is its surface area?

Understanding Student Response	Practice and Improvement
Students find the area of one side only.	Review lesson 3 to practice finding surface area.
Students do not understand the concept of a rectangular prism.	Review lesson 1 to help students understand 3-dimensional figures.

Teacher Question 2:

- A box has a base of 10 cm by 8 cm and is 5 cm high. What is the volume of the box?

Understanding Student Response	Practice and Improvement
Students find area of the base only.	Review lesson 4 to practice finding volume.
Students add dimensions instead of multiplying.	Review lesson 4 to practice finding volume.

Teacher Question 3:

- Suppose we take the same box and make it twice as high. What happens to the surface area and the volume?

Understanding Student Response	Practice and Improvement
Students say the surface area doubles.	Review lesson 3. Show students that increasing the height only changes the surface area of the sides; the top and the base do not change.
Students cannot find the volume.	Review lesson 4. Show students that doubling one dimension doubles the volume.

Chapter 23 – Journal Writing

Encourage students to generate their own journal entries related to math ideas in general or to concepts in this chapter. For students requiring guidance, present the following journal prompt:

- What steps do you follow to find the volume of a rectangular prism?

  (Responses should describe finding the area of the base and then multiplying by the height of the prism. Students may also describe multiplying the three dimensions of the prism to find its volume without referring to first finding the area of a side.)

JOURNAL WRITING/PROBLEM SOLVING

Noel keeps tropical fish in an aquarium. The base of his aquarium is a rectangle measuring 10 inches by 20 inches. The aquarium is 12 inches high. Find the volume of Noel's aquarium.

One day the aquarium sprung a leak. When Noel got home, the water in the aquarium was only 8 inches deep. Find the volume of the water that was left in the aquarium and the volume of the water that had leaked out.

Read

Have students find the answer to the problem. Then ask them to write a few sentences telling—

- which information they used to find the answer

- what they did with that information

Have students make up another problem with different information.

Plan

Students must use the dimensions given to find the volume of a rectangular prism. They must also use subtraction to find the volume of the water that leaked out.

Solve

The volume of the aquarium is 2,400 cubic inches. $10 \times 20 \times 12 = 2,400$.
The volume of water in the aquarium after the leak is 1,600 cubic inches.
$10 \times 20 \times 8 = 1,600$. The volume of water that leaked out is 800 cubic inches.
$2,400 - 1,600 = 800$.

Look Back

A correct response demonstrates the ability to calculate the volume of a rectangular prism and to solve problems related to volume. (See scoring rubric on page 7.)

Chapter 23 – Monitoring Student Progress

☐ Form A   ☐ Form B

Name _____ Date _____

Directions: For each item that is answered incorrectly, cross out the item number. Then record the number of correct responses in the appropriate Student Score column. If the student has not met the Criterion Score for an objective, circle the student's score. Recommended assignments are listed in the Prescription Table on the next page.

Objective	Item Numbers	Criterion Score	Student Score
A. Identify 3-dimensional figures and nets.	1, 2, 4, 7, 10	4/5	/5
B. Find the surface area of rectangular prisms.	3, 8, 9, 11, 13	4/5	/5
C. Find the volume of rectangular prisms.	5, 6, 12, 14, 15	4/5	/5
D. Use skills and strategies to solve problems.	16, 17, 18, 19, 20	4/5	/5
Total Test Score		16/20	/20
Total Percent Correct			%

Chapter 23 – Prescription Table

The following chart correlates the tested objectives for this chapter to supplementary materials that meet the individual needs of the students. The Reteach and Practice pages are designed for students who need further instruction in the math concepts taught in this chapter. The Enrich pages are designed for students who need advanced challenges.

Objective	Reteach	Practice	Enrich
A. Identify 3-dimensional figures and nets.	389, 392	390, 393	391, 394
B. Find the surface area of rectangular prisms.	395	396	397
C. Find the volume of rectangular prisms.	398	399	400
D. Use skills and strategies to solve problems.	401	402	403

Read each question carefully. Darken the circle on your answer sheet for the correct answer.

1. Identify the figure.

A. triangular pyramid

B. square pyramid

C. rectangular prism

D. rectangular pyramid

2. If a triangular pyramid has 4 faces and 6 edges, how many vertices does it have?

F. 2   G. 4   H. 6   J. 8

3. Find the surface area.

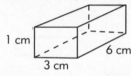

A. 28 cm^2 C. 82 cm^2

B. 54 cm^2 D. 108 cm^2

4. Identify the figure.

F. triangular prism

G. square pyramid

H. rectangular prism

J. rectangular pyramid

5. Find the volume.

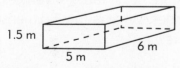

A. 31.5 m^3 C. 90 m^3

B. 45 m^3 D. 135 m^3

6. Find the volume.

$l = 5$ in. $w = 3$ in. $h = 6$ in.

F. 30 in.^{3} H. 60 in.^{3}

G. 45in.^{3} J. 90 in.^{3}

7. If a square pyramid has 5 vertices and 8 edges, how many faces does it have?

A. 8   B. 6   C. 5   D. 4

8. Find the surface area.

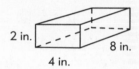

F. 48 in.^{2} H. 96 in.^{2}

G. 60 in.^{2} J. 112 in.^{2}

9. Find the surface area.

A. 300 m^2

B. 150 m^2

C. 100 m^2

D. 50 m^2

10. Identify the figure.

F. triangular prism

G. square pyramid

H. rectangular prism

J. rectangular pyramid

GO ON

11. Find the surface area.

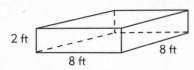

2 ft
8 ft
8 ft

A. 68 ft^2 **C.** 192 ft^2

B. 128 ft^2 **D.** 198 ft^2

12. Find the volume.

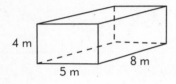

4 m
5 m
8 m

F. 175 m^3 **H.** 80 m^3

G. 160 m^3 **J.** 28 m^3

13. Find the surface area.

A. 10.5 yd^2

B. 24.5 yd^2 3.5 yd

C. 36.75 yd^2 3.5 yd

D. 73.5 yd^2 3.5 yd

14. Find the volume.

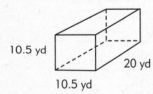

10.5 yd
20 yd
10.5 yd

F. 1,102.5 cm^3 **H.** 2,205 cm^3

G. 1,755 cm^3 **J.** 2,505.5 cm^3

15. Find the volume.

$l = 6$ m $w = 6$ m $h = 6$ m

A. 226 m^3 **C.** 108 m^3

B. 216 m^3 **D.** 72 m^3

16. Al drew a net for a cube. Which one did he draw?

F.

H.

G.

J.

17. In a game, Alicia gives this clue: Which figure has 2 circular bases? Ema replies, "a cone." Which is the correct answer?

A. circle   **C.** cylinder

B. cone   **D.** sphere

18. Lee looks at the top view and side view of the figure. What is the front view?

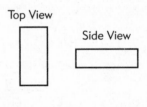

Top View

Side View

F.

H.

G.

J.

19. If the volume of a cube is 64 cubic inches and 2 sides are 4 inches each, what is the dimension of the third side?

A. 2 inches   **C.** 4 inches

B. 3 inches   **D.** 8 inches

20. A figure has 4 faces, 4 vertices, and 6 edges. What is the 3-dimensional figure?

F. triangular prism

G. triangular pyramid

H. square pyramid

J. cube

STOP

Read each question carefully. Fill in the correct answer in the space provided.

1. Identify the figure.

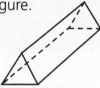

_____

_____

2. If a square pyramid has 5 faces and 5 vertices, how many edges does it have?

_____

_____

3. Find the surface area.

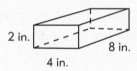

_____

_____

4. Identify the figure.

_____

_____

5. Find the volume.

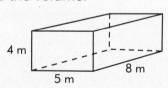

_____

6. Find the volume.

$l = 7$ m $w = 7$ m $h = 7$ m

_____

7. If a triangular pyramid has 6 edges and 6 vertices, how many faces does it have?

_____

8. Find the surface area.

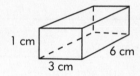

_____

9. Find the surface area.

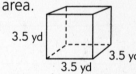

_____

10. Identify the figure from the net.

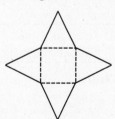

_____

GO ON

11. Find the surface area.

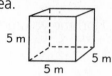

5 m
5 m
5 m

_____

12. Find the volume.

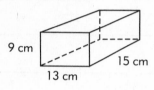

9 cm
15 cm
13 cm

_____

13. Find the surface area.

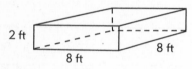

2 ft
8 ft
8 ft

_____

14. Find the volume.

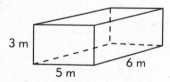

3 m
5 m
6 m

_____

15. Find the volume.

$l = 5$ in. $w = 3$ in. $h = 6$ in.

_____

16. Ella tells Alice how to draw a net of a cube: Draw 6 squares. Then draw a square above and below the second square. Write correct directions for Alice.

_____

_____

17. In a game, Roberto gives this clue: Which figure has 1 circular base and 1 curved surface from base to vertex? Paul replies, "cylinder." What is the correct answer?

_____

_____

18. Look at the front view and side view of a rectangular prism. Draw the top view.

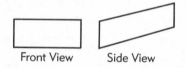

Front View   Side View

_____

19. If the volume of a cube is 125 cubic feet and 2 sides are 5 feet each, what is the dimension of the third side?

_____

_____

20. A figure has 5 faces, 6 vertices, and 9 edges. What is the 3-dimensional figure?

_____

_____

STOP

Chapter 24 – Teacher Interview

Core Concept: *Line Symmetry*

Student Activity: Students demonstrate an understanding of line symmetry. On a separate sheet of drawing paper, have students draw and label each triangle: an equilateral triangle, a scalene triangle, and an isosceles triangle. Ask students to determine whether each triangle has a line of symmetry.

Teacher Question 1:

- How can you tell whether each triangle has a line of symmetry?

Understanding Student Response	Practice and Improvement
Students who show a rotation of the triangle.	Review lesson 1 to reinforce an understanding of line symmetry.
Students who draw smaller triangles within each of the 3 triangles.	Review lesson 1 to help students fold each triangle to find a line of symmetry.

Teacher Question 2:

- How many lines of symmetry does each triangle have?

Understanding Student Response	Practice and Improvement
Students who fold the scalene triangle and find a line of symmetry.	Review lesson 1 to help students visualize why a scalene triangle has no line of symmetry.
Students who say the equilateral triangle has one line of symmetry.	Review lesson 1 to help students visualize why an equilateral triangle has 3 lines of symmetry.

Teacher Question 3:

- How can you prove a line of symmetry?

Understanding Student Response	Practice and Improvement
Students who fold the triangles in thirds (in fourths).	Review lesson 1 to reinforce an understanding of a line of symmetry.
Students who do not see two congruent halves when each triangle is folded in half.	Review lesson 1 to help students learn to fold each triangle in half.

Chapter 24 – Journal Writing

Encourage students to generate their own journal entries related to math ideas in general or to concepts in this chapter. Present the following journal prompt and have students share their drawing/writing with a partner:

- When you are problem solving, how can drawing a diagram help you to solve a problem?

  (Responses should indicate that drawing a diagram helps to visualize the problem and also makes it easier to solve the problem.)

JOURNAL WRITING/PROBLEM SOLVING

On a sheet of paper, draw an uppercase H in block-letter form. Does the figure have line symmetry? Does the figure have rotational symmetry? If so, what is the smallest fraction of a full turn needed for the figure to look the same?

Read

Have students find the answer to the problem. Then ask them to write a few sentences telling—

- which information they used to find the answer

- what they did with the information

Have students make up another problem with different information for which they could have followed the same procedure. Then have students solve the problem and supply the correct response.

Plan

Students must correctly draw an uppercase H in block-letter form. Students must also determine whether the figure has line symmetry and whether the figure has rotational symmetry.

Solve

The correct response to the assigned problem is that an uppercase H has line symmetry and rotational symmetry. A half turn is required for the H to look the same as it did in its original position.

Look Back

A correct response demonstrates an understanding of line symmetry and rotational symmetry. (See scoring rubric on page 7.)

Chapter 24 – Monitoring Student Progress

☐ Form A   ☐ Form B

Name _____ Date _____

Directions: For each item that is answered incorrectly, cross out the item number. Then record the number of correct responses in the appropriate Student Score column. If the student has not met the Criterion Score for an objective, circle the student's score. Recommended assignments are listed in the Prescription Table on the next page.

Objective	Item Numbers	Criterion Score	Student Score
A. Find line symmetry.	1, 2, 4, 7, 8, 11	5/6	/6
B. Find rotational symmetry.	3, 6, 12, 14, 15, 16	5/6	/6
C. Identify tessellations.	5, 9, 10, 13	3/4	/4
D. Use skills and strategies to solve problems.	17, 18, 19, 20	3/4	/4
Total Test Score		16/20	/20
Total Percent Correct			%

Chapter 24 – Prescription Table

The following chart correlates the tested objectives for this chapter to supplementary materials that meet the individual needs of the students. The Reteach and Practice pages are designed for students who need further instruction in the math concepts taught in this chapter. The Enrich pages are designed for students who need advanced challenges.

Objective	Reteach	Practice	Enrich
A. Find line symmetry.	404	405	406
B. Find rotational symmetry.	407	408	409
C. Identify tessellations.	413	414	415
D. Use skills and strategies to solve problems.	410, 411	412	

Read each question carefully. Darken the circle on your answer sheet for the correct answer.

1. Which drawing shows a line of symmetry of the triangle?

1   2   3   4

   A. triangle 1   C. triangle 3
   B. triangle 2   D. triangle 4

2. Which drawing does **not** show a line of symmetry of the square?

1   2   3   4

   F. square 1   H. square 3
   G. square 2   J. square 4

3. Which shape shows a rotational symmetry of 90°?

1   2   3   4

   A. shape 1   C. shape 3
   B. shape 2   D. shape 4

4. Which shape has exactly one line of symmetry?

   F. circle   H. square
   G. rectangle   J. trapezoid

5. Which drawing shows a tessellation of a triangle?

1   2   3

   A. drawing 1   C. drawing 3
   B. drawing 2

6. Which letter looks the same when rotated 180°?

   F. F   G. G   H. H   J. J

7. Does the triangle have line symmetry, rotational symmetry, or both?

   A. line symmetry
   B. rotational symmetry
   C. both

8. How many lines of symmetry does the shape have?

   F. 4   G. 3   H. 2   J. 1

9. Which of these shapes will **not** tessellate?

   A. parallelogram
   B. equilateral triangle
   C. trapezoid
   D. circle

10. Which drawing shows a tessellation of a hexagon?

   F. drawing 1
   G. drawing 2
   H. both
   J. neither

1   2

GO ON

11. How many lines of symmetry does a hexagon have?

A. 6   **B.** 5   **C.** 4   **D.** 2

12. Does the shape have line symmetry, rotational symmetry, or both?

F. line symmetry
G. rotational symmetry
H. both

13. Which drawing shows a tessellation of a pentagon?

1   2

A. figure 1   **C.** both
B. figure 2   **D.** neither

14. Which letter has rotational symmetry?

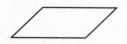

R   S   T   U

F. R   **G.** S   **H.** T   **J.** U

15. How far must this shape turn before it looks the same as it did in its original position?

A. 45°   **B.** 60°   **C.** 72°   **D.** 90°

16. Which shape has line symmetry and rotational symmetry?

F. scalene triangle **H.** right triangle
G. pentagon   **J.** parallelogram

17. Jackie drew a design of 2 squares, 1 circle, 2 rectangles, and 2 triangles. If he repeats the pattern 3 times, which shape is the 17th?

A. square   **C.** rectangle
B. circle   **D.** triangle

18. A diagram shows an arrangement of 24 desks grouped together in fours. If you rearrange the 24 desks so that there are 8 groups, how many desks will be in a group?

F. 3 desks   **H.** 5 desks
G. 4 desks   **J.** 6 desks

19. In making a seat chart, you arrange for a person to sit on each side of a square table. If 3 tables are pushed together, how many people can sit at the larger table?

A. 12 people   **C.** 8 people
B. 10 people   **D.** 6 people

20. Four girls are seated in a row. Katherine is to the left of Marlene. Sara sits between Katherine and Marlene. Beatrice is first. Which girl is seated last in the row?

F. Katherine
G. Marlene
H. Sara
J. Beatrice

STOP

Name _____

Read each question carefully. Fill in the correct answer in the space provided.

1. Which shape has exactly one line of symmetry, a square or a trapezoid?

_____

_____

2. Draw a line of symmetry on the triangle. Name the triangle.

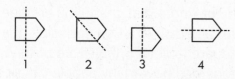

_____

3. Which letter—C, H, T, or A—looks the same when rotated 180°?

_____

_____

4. Which drawing shows a line of symmetry?

1 2 3 4

_____

5. Which drawing shows a tessellation of a hexagon?

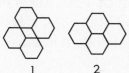

1 2

_____

6. What is the smallest fraction of a full turn needed for this shape to look the same?

_____

_____

7. Does the shape have line symmetry, rotational symmetry, or both?

_____

_____

8. How many lines of symmetry does a hexagon have?

_____

_____

9. Which shape—a circle, a triangle, or a trapezoid will **not** tessellate?

_____

_____

10. Does a pentagon tessellate?

_____

GO ON

11. How many lines of symmetry does an equilateral triangle have?

_____

12. Which shape has line symmetry and rotational symmetry—a right triangle or a pentagon?

_____

13. Which drawing shows a tessellation of a triangle?

1   2

_____

14. Which letter has rotational symmetry?

T   H   L   B

_____

15. Which of these shapes will **not** tessellate—a circle or a trapezoid?

_____

16. How far must this shape turn before it looks the same as it did in its original position?

_____

17. Mark drew a design of 1 square, 2 circles, 2 rectangles, and 1 triangle. If he repeats the pattern 2 times, which shape is the 11th?

_____

18. A diagram shows an arrangement of 24 desks grouped together in fours. If you rearrange the 24 desks so that there are 8 groups, how many desks will be in a group?

_____

19. In making a seat chart, you arrange for a person to sit on each side of a square table. If 5 tables are pushed together, how many people can sit at the larger table?

_____

20. Four boys are seated in a row. Kevin is to the left of Mark. Steve sits between Kevin and Mark. Bart is first. Which boy is seated third in the row?

_____

STOP

Unit 12 Performance Assessment

Music Box

- *Target Skill:*   Finding the volume of a rectangular prism.
- *Additional Skills:*   Finding the volume of a rectangular prism.

**Task
Description:** This task requires students to draw and label a rectangular prism, calculate the surface area and volume of a store carton and a shelf, both rectangular prisms. Students will also be asked to describe the differences between surface area and volume.

Preparing: You may wish to have the students review the formulas for the surface area and volume of rectangular prisms.

Materials	Group Size	Time on Task
Pencil Paper	1–2 students	1 day

Guiding: Tell students that they will need to convert inches to feet, or feet to inches.

Remind students that surface area is measured in square units and volume is measured in cubic units.

**Observing/
Monitoring:** As you move among the students, pose the following questions:
How do you find the volume of a rectangular prism?
How do you find the surface area of a rectangular prism?

Unit 12 Performance Assessment Scoring Rubric

Music Box

Score	Explanation
3	Students demonstrate an efficient strategy and a thorough approach that enables them to solve the problem completely. A satisfactory answer: • includes a correctly drawn and labeled rectangular prism with the dimensions 2 ft × 6 in. × 4 in.; • calculates the volume and surface area of the carton and of the shelf correctly; • describes the differences between surface area and volume. Students are able to complete the problem quickly and have all of the correct solutions.
2	Students demonstrate a strategy that enables them to solve most of the problem correctly. The strategy is somewhat disorganized, making it less efficient. A solution is found, but errors are contained. Students may: • draw a prism without labeling its dimensions; • compute the surface area and volume correctly; • use the incorrect units of measure or not know the difference between surface area and volume. Students have some difficulty determining all solutions correctly but demonstrate an understanding of general concepts.
1	Students demonstrate a confused strategy, which leads to difficulty solving the problem. Most answers are incorrect, but students demonstrate knowledge of at least one concept being assessed, such as finding surface area or volume.

Unit 12 Performance Assessment Student Activity

Music Box

You will need
- Paper
- Pencil

Elliot's In-Sounds has hired George to straighten out its warehouse. Elliot's sells boom boxes that come in cartons which measure 2 feet wide, 6 inches high, and 4 inches deep. George needs to stack them on a shelf that is 2 feet deep, 4 feet high, and 5 feet wide.

In the space below, draw the shape of the boom box carton and label its dimensions.

1. What is the volume of the boom box cartons? _____

2. What is the volume of the shelf? _____

3. What is the surface area of the boom box cartons? _____

4. What is the surface area of the shelf? _____

5. Explain in words how surface area and volume are different.

_____

_____

_____

Unit 12 – Monitoring Student Progress

☐ Form A   ☐ Form B

Name _____ Date _____

Directions: This test targets selected objectives. For each item that is answered incorrectly, cross out the item number. Then record the number of correct responses in the column labeled **Number of Correct Responses.** Add to find the **Total Number of Correct Responses** and record the total. Use this total to determine the **Total Test Score** and the **Total Percent Correct.**

Strand • Objective(s)	Item Numbers	Number of Correct Responses
Geometry and Spatial Sense • Identify 3-dimensional figures and nets. • Find the surface area of rectangular prisms. • Find the volume of rectangular prisms. • Find line symmetry. • Find rotational symmetry. • Identify tessellations. • Use skills and strategies to solve problems.	1, 2, 3, 4, 5, 6, 7, 8, 9, 10, 11, 12, 13, 14, 15, 16, 17, 18, 19, 20, 21, 22, 23, 24, 25, 26, 27, 28, 29, 30, 31, 32, 33, 34, 35, 36, 37, 38, 39, 40	/40
Total Number of Correct Responses		
Total Test Score		/40
Total Percent Correct		%

Read each question carefully. Darken the circle on your answer sheet for the correct answer.

1. How many lines of symmetry does an equilateral triangle have?

A. 0   **C.** 3

B. 1   **D.** 6

2. Which dotted line is not a line of symmetry?

F.   **H.**

G.   **J.**

3. Identify the figure.

A. cylinder   **C.** cone

B. prism   **D.** sphere

4. Identify the figure.

F. cylinder   **H.** cone

G. prism   **J.** sphere

5. Which figure is this a net for?

A. cube

B. cylinder

C. rectangular prism

D. triangular prism

6. Which is the smallest fraction of a turn needed for an equilateral triangle to look the same?

F. $\frac{1}{2}$ **H.** $\frac{1}{4}$

G. $\frac{1}{3}$ **J.** $\frac{1}{6}$

7. Which figure does not tessellate?

A. triangle   **C.** square

B. rectangle   **D.** circle

8. How many lines of symmetry does a regular pentagon have?

F. 0   **H.** 5

G. 1   **J.** 10

9. Find the surface area.

4 in.
4 in.
4 in.

A. 96 in.^{2} **C.** 32 in.^{2}

B. 64 in.^{2} **D.** 16 in.^{2}

10. Find the surface area.

6 cm
6 cm
6 cm

F. 216 cm^2 **H.** 144 cm^2

G. 180 cm^2 **J.** 36 cm^2

GO ON

11. Find the surface area.

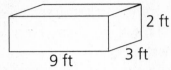

9 ft
2 ft
3 ft

A. 162 ft^2 **C.** 56 ft^2

B. 102 ft^2 **D.** 54 ft^2

12. Find the surface area.

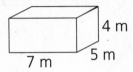

7 m
4 m
5 m

F. 280 m^2 **H.** 110 m^2

G. 166 m^2 **J.** 96 m^2

13. Find the volume.

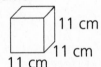

11 cm
11 cm
11 cm

A. 1,331 cm^3 **C.** 484 cm^3

B. 726 cm^3 **D.** 121 cm^3

14. Find the volume.

23 in.
23 in.
23 in.

F. 24,334 in.^{3} **H.** 2,116 in.^{3}

G. 12,167 in.^{3} **J.** 529 in.^{3}

15. Find the volume.

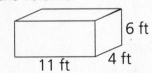

11 ft
6 ft
4 ft

A. 1,584 ft^3 **C.** 264 ft^3

B. 1,056 ft^3 **D.** 66 ft^3

16. Find the volume.

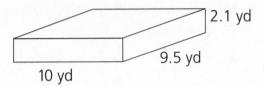

10 yd
2.1 yd
9.5 yd

F. 1,197 yd^3 **H.** 399 yd^3

G. 798 yd^3 **J.** 199.5 yd^3

17. Which 3-dimensional figure is commonly used for wheels?

A. sphere   **C.** cylinder

B. cone   **D.** cube

18. Jim is thinking of a figure that has three sides, one line of symmetry, and no rotational symmetry. What is it?

F. equilateral triangle

G. isosceles triangle

H. right triangle

J. scalene triangle

19. Samantha wraps a box that is 2 ft by 2 ft by 2 ft. What is the surface area of the box?

A. 48 ft^2 **C.** 12 ft^2

B. 24 ft^2 **D.** 6 ft^2

20. Eve has a shoebox that measures 12 in. by 6 in. by 4 in. What is the volume of the box?

F. 288 in.^{3} **H.** 240 in.^{3}

G. 248 in.^{3} **J.** 144 in.^{3}

GO ON

21. How many lines of symmetry does a scalene triangle have?

   A. 3   **C.** 1

   B. 2   **D.** 0

22. Which line is a line of symmetry for the hexagon?

   F. $\overline{AB}$

   G. $\overline{AC}$

   H. $\overline{AD}$

   J. $\overline{AE}$

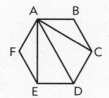

23. Identify the figure.

   A. cube

   B. cylinder

   C. square

   D. rectangular prism

24. Identify the figure.

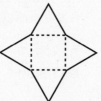

   F. cone

   G. triangular pyramid

   H. rectangular pyramid

   J. triangular prism

25. Which figure is this a net for?

   A. cone

   B. cube

   C. square pyramid

   D. triangular prism

26. Which is the smallest fraction of a turn needed for a rectangle to look the same?

   F. $\frac{1}{6}$ **H.** $\frac{1}{3}$

   G. $\frac{1}{4}$ **J.** $\frac{1}{2}$

27. Which figure does not tessellate?

   A. isosceles triangle

   B. square

   C. parallelogram

   D. rectangle

28. How many lines of symmetry does a hexagon have?

   F. 1   **H.** 3

   G. 2   **J.** 6

29. Find the surface area.

4.4 ft
4.4 ft
4.4 ft

   A. 116.16 ft^2 **C.** 44 ft^2

   B. 77 ft^2 **D.** 19.36 ft^2

30. Find the surface area.

15 in.
15 in.
15 in.

   F. 1,350 in.^{2} **H.** 900 in.^{2}

   G. 1,125 in.^{2} **J.** 225 in.^{2}

GO ON

31. Find the surface area.

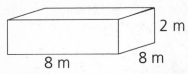

A. 192 m²   **C.** 128 m²

B. 176 m²   **D.** 68 m²

32. Find the surface area.

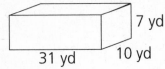

F. 2,170 yd²   **H.** 1,085 yd²

G. 1,194 yd²   **J.** 597 yd²

33. Find the volume.

A. 24,389 ft³   **C.** 1,734 ft³

B. 3,468 ft³   **D.** 289 ft³

34. Find the volume.

F. 4,913 m³   **H.** 1,734 m³

G. 3,468 m³   **J.** 289 m³

35. Find the volume.

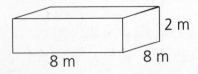

F. 256 cm³   **H.** 128 cm³

G. 176 cm³   **D.** 68 cm³

36. Find the volume.

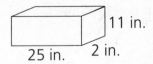

F. 3,300 in.³   **H.** 694 in.³

G. 1,650 in.³   **J.** 550 in.³

37. Which 3-dimensional figure is most likely to be the top of a house?

A. cone   **C.** cube

B. cylinder   **D.** triangular prism

38. Cami is thinking of a figure that has four sides, rotational symmetry, and only needs $\frac{1}{4}$ of a turn to make it look the same. What is it?

F. parallelogram   **H.** square

G. rectangle   **J.** cylinder

39. Charlie is sending some gifts in a box that is 18 in. by 12 in. by 10 in. What is its volume?

A. 2,160 in.³   **C.** 1,080 in.³

B. 2,064 in.³   **D.** 2,060 in.³

40. Eve has a stack of magazines that measures 12 in. by 9 in. by 4 in. What is the surface area of the stack?

F. 436 in.²   **H.** 218 in.²

G. 384 in.²   **J.** 144 in.²

STOP

Read each question carefully. Fill in the correct answer in the space provided.

1. How many lines of symmetry does a rectangle have?

   _____

2. Which is a line of symmetry?

   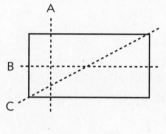

   _____

3. Identify this figure.

   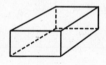

   _____

4. Identify this figure.

   _____

5. What figure is this a net for?

   _____

6. What is the smallest fraction of a turn needed for a square to look the same?

   _____

7. Name a figure that has lines of symmetry but does not tessellate.

   _____

8. How many lines of symmetry does an equilateral triangle have?

   _____

9. Find the surface area of this object.

   5 m
   5 m
   5 m

   _____

10. Find the volume of this object.

    3 in.
    3 in.
    3 in.

    _____

GO ON

11. Calculate the surface area of this object.

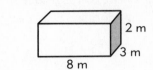

2 m
3 m
8 m

_____

12. Find the volume.

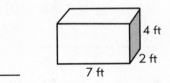

4 ft
2 ft
7 ft

_____

13. Find the surface area of this object.

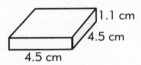

1.1 cm
4.5 cm
4.5 cm

_____

14. Find the volume.

24 yd
24 yd
24 yd

_____

15. Calculate the volume.

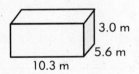

3.0 m
5.6 m
10.3 m

_____

16. Find the surface area.

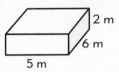

2 m
6 m
5 m

_____

17. Which 3-dimensional figure is commonly used for table tops?

_____

18. Name a figure with 3 lines of symmetry and 3 sides.

_____

19. Brin needs to paint a box 4 ft by 4 ft by 4 ft. What is the surface area of the box?

_____

20. Nathan fills a box with sand. The box is 10 in. by 7 in. by 4 in. What is the volume of the box?

_____

GO ON

21. How many lines of symmetry does a regular octagon have?

_____

22. Which of these lines is not a line of symmetry?

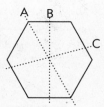

_____

23. Name the figure that this is a net for.

_____

24. Name this figure.

_____

25. Identify this figure.

_____

26. What is the smallest fraction of rotation necessary for an equilateral triangle to look the same?

_____

27. Fran is thinking of a figure that has 4 sides, 0 lines of reflection, and tessellates. Name the figure.

_____

28. How many lines of symmetry does a rectangle have?

_____

29. Find the surface area.

7 in.
7 in.
7 in.

_____

30. Calculate the volume.

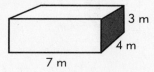

3 m
4 m
7 m

_____

GO ON

31. Calculate the volume.

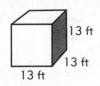

13 ft
13 ft
13 ft

_____

32. Find the surface area.

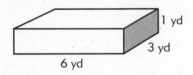

1 yd
3 yd
6 yd

_____

33. Calculate the volume.

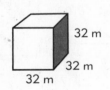

32 m
32 m
32 m

_____

34. Find the surface area.

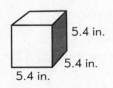

5.4 in.
5.4 in.
5.4 in.

_____

35. Calculate the surface area.

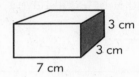

3 cm
3 cm
7 cm

_____

36. Find the volume.

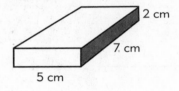

2 cm
7 cm
5 cm

_____

37. Which 3-dimensional shape is commonly used for pens?

_____

38. Name the figure with 4 sides that needs a $\frac{1}{2}$ rotation to look the same.

_____

39. A new television comes packed in a box 2 ft by 2.5 ft by 2.3 ft. What is the volume of the TV box?

_____

40. What is the surface area of a dresser measuring 2 yd by 0.8 yd by 0.5 yd?

_____

STOP

Chapter 25 – Teacher Interview

Core Concept: *Equivalent Ratios*

Student Activity: Students demonstrate an understanding of equivalent fractions and proportions in order to find equivalent ratios. Ask students to determine whether $\frac{2}{3}$ and $\frac{14}{21}$ are equivalent ratios.

Teacher Question 1:

- What are equivalent fractions for $\frac{2}{3}$ and $\frac{14}{21}$?

Understanding Student Response	Practice and Improvement
Students who multiply the numerator but not the denominator by a number (or the denominator and not the numerator).	Review lesson 2 to reinforce how to find equivalent fractions.
Students who do not find a pattern of multiples.	Review lesson 2 to help students recognize that finding a pattern of multiples will help them to find equivalent ratios.

Teacher Question 2:

- Are $\frac{2}{3}$ and $\frac{14}{21}$ equivalent ratios?

Understanding Student Response	Practice and Improvement
Students who say $\frac{2}{3}$ and $\frac{14}{21} = \frac{2}{7}$.	Review lesson 2 to reinforce an understanding of using the least common denominator (LCD) to find equivalent ratios.
Students who say $\frac{2}{3} = \frac{4}{6}, \frac{6}{9}, \frac{8}{12}$.	Review lesson 2 to help students learn that there are many equivalent ratios for a given fraction.

Teacher Question 3:

- How can you use cross products to show that $\frac{2}{3}$ and $\frac{14}{21}$ are equivalent ratios?

Understanding Student Response	Practice and Improvement
Students who say: $2 \times 14 = 3 \times 21$.	Review lesson 2 to help students learn how to find cross products.

Chapter 25 – Journal Writing

Encourage students to generate their own journal entries related to math ideas in general or to concepts in this chapter. Present the following journal prompt and have students share their drawing/writing with a partner:

- When you are problem solving, how can checking for reasonableness help you to solve a problem?

  (Responses should indicate that if an answer fits with the facts within a problem, then the answer would be reasonable.)

JOURNAL WRITING/PROBLEM SOLVING

Ron has a car with a gas tank that holds 16 gallons of gas. If he can drive 352 miles on a full tank, how many miles per gallon does his car get?

Read
Have students find the answer to the problem. Then ask them to write a few sentences telling—

- which information they used to find the answer

- what they did with the information

Have students make up another problem with different information for which they could have followed the same procedure. Then have students solve the problem and supply the correct response.

Plan
Students must correctly find the unit rate by dividing the miles by gallons.

Solve
The correct response to the assigned problem is 22 miles per gallon.

Look Back
A correct response demonstrates the ability to understand and apply unit rate.
(See scoring rubric on page 7.)

Chapter 25 – Monitoring Student Progress

☐ **Form A**   ☐ **Form B**

Name _____ Date _____

Directions: For each item that is answered incorrectly, cross out the item number. Then record the number of correct responses in the appropriate Student Score column. If the student has not met the Criterion Score for an objective, circle the student's score. Recommended assignments are listed in the Prescription Table on the next page.

Objective	Item Numbers	Criterion Score	Student Score
A. Find equivalent ratios.	1, 2, 6, 7, 10, 11	5/6	/6
B. Use scale drawings and maps.	13, 14, 15, 16,	3/4	/4
C. Determine and apply rates and unit prices.	3, 4, 5, 8, 9, 12	5/6	/6
D. Use skills and strategies to solve problems.	17, 18, 19, 20	3/4	/4
Total Test Score		16/20	/20
Total Percent Correct			%

Chapter 25 – Prescription Table

The following chart correlates the tested objectives for this chapter to supplementary materials that meet the individual needs of the students. The Reteach and Practice pages are designed for students who need further instruction in the math concepts taught in this chapter. The Enrich pages are designed for students who need advanced challenges.

Objective	Reteach	Practice	Enrich
A. Find equivalent ratios.	418, 421	419, 422	420, 423
B. Use scale drawings and maps.	433	434	435
C. Determine and apply rates and unit prices.	424, 427	425, 428	426, 429
D. Use skills and strategies to solve problems.	430	431	432

Read each question carefully. Darken the circle on your answer sheet for the correct answer.

1. Which ratio is equivalent to 9 to 15?

A. $\frac{2}{3}$　　　　　**C.** $\frac{2}{5}$

B. $\frac{3}{5}$　　　　　**D.** $\frac{10}{30}$

2. Which number makes the ratio equivalent?

$1:5 = n:20$

F. 4　　　　　**H.** 10

G. 5　　　　　**J.** 15

3. Find the unit rate for $64 in 4 hours.

A. $16 per 1h

B. $20 per 1h

C. $22 per 1h

D. $24 per 1h

4. Find the unit rate for 300 miles in 5 hours.

F. 100 mi per 1 h

G. 60 mi per 1 h

H. 50 mi per 1 h

J. 40 mi per 1 h

5. Find the unit rate for 180 miles on 5 gallons of gas.

A. 60 mi per 1 gal

B. 56 mi per 1 gal

C. 36 mi per 1 gal

D. 30 mi per 1 gal

6. Which number makes the ratios equivalent?

$\frac{n}{10} = \frac{6}{30}$

F. 6　　　　　**H.** 3

G. 5　　　　　**J.** 2

7. Which ratio is equivalent to 5:9?

A. 15:19　　　　**C.** 25:45

B. 30:45　　　　**D.** 45:90

8. Find the unit rate for 72 miles in 8 days.

F. 16 mi per 1 d

G. 12 mi per 1 d

H. 9 mi per 1 d

J. 8 mi per 1 d

9. Find the unit rate for $360 in 12 months.

A. $24 per 1 mo

B. $30 per 1 mo

C. $32 per 1 mo

D. $36 per 1 mo

10. Which two ratios are equivalent to 3:4?

F. $\frac{8}{12}$ and $\frac{12}{16}$　　　**H.** $\frac{9}{12}$ and $\frac{21}{32}$

G. $\frac{9}{12}$ and $\frac{24}{32}$　　　**J.** $\frac{10}{12}$ and $\frac{20}{24}$

GO ON

11. Which ratio is equivalent to $\frac{4}{3}$?

  A. $\frac{1}{2}$ **B.** $\frac{3}{4}$ **C.** $\frac{5}{4}$ **D.** $\frac{8}{6}$

12. Find the unit rate for 90 meters in 5 minutes.

  F. 15 m per 1 min   **H.** 30 m per 1 min
  G. 18 m per 1 min   **J.** 45 m per 1 min

13. Alicia is making a floor plan of a sunroom. She is using the scale 2 in. = 3 feet. One wall is 9 feet. How long should it be on her floor plan?

  A. 3 inches   **C.** 6 inches
  B. 4 inches   **D.** 9 inches

14. Terry makes a map of her neighborhood. She uses a scale of 1 in. = 1 mi. If the neighborhood convenience store is 5 miles away from her house, where will she draw the store on her map?

  F. 2 inches away from her house
  G. 3 inches away from her house
  H. 4 inches away from her house
  J. 5 inches away from her house

15. Randy is making a floor plan of a clubhouse. He is using the scale 2 cm = 1 m. The length of the clubhouse is 4 cm on the plan. How long is the actual length in meters?

  A. 8 cm   **B.** 2 m   **C.** 3 m   **D.** 4 m

16. On a map, Lake Victoria is 1.5 inches long. The actual length of the lake is 15 miles. What is the scale on the map?

  F. 1 inch = 5 miles   **H.** 1 inch = 15 miles
  G. 1 inch = 10 miles   **J.** 1 inch = 20 miles

17. Margo can drive 20 miles in 30 minutes. Is it reasonable to expect that Margo will drive 50 miles in 1 hour? If not, how many miles will she drive in an hour?

  A. yes, 50 miles   **C.** no, 40 miles
  B. no, 30 miles   **D.** no, 60 miles

18. A convenience store sells a package of 12 pocket tissues for $3.00. At the local supermarket, a package of 3 pocket tissues cost $.60. Lane believes that the convenience store is the better buy. Explain why Lane's answer is not reasonable.

  F. convenience store cost $.25 each, supermarket $.20 each
  G. convenience store cost $.30 each, supermarket $.25 each
  H. convenience store cost $.30 each, supermarket $.20 each
  J. convenience store cost $.25 each, supermarket $.25 each

19. Tyler spends $15.75 on a CD. She gives the clerk $20 and expects to receive $5.75 in change. Tyler's answer is not reasonable. What change should she receive?

  A. $4.75 **B.** $4.25 **C.** $3.75 **D.** $3.25

20. Mark can run 5 miles in 50 minutes. Why is it reasonable to expect that Mark will run 2.5 miles in 25 minutes?

  F. $\frac{5}{25} = \frac{2.5}{50}$ **H.** $\frac{50}{25} = \frac{2.5}{5}$

  G. $\frac{25}{5} = \frac{50}{2.5}$ **J.** $\frac{2.5}{5} = \frac{25}{50}$

STOP

Read each question carefully. Fill in the correct answer in the space provided.

1. Find an equivalent ratio to 8 to 24.

_____

2. Find an equivalent ratio.

$1:7 = n:35$

_____

3. Find the unit rate.

$56 in 7 h = _____ per 1 h

4. Find the unit rate.

400 mi in 8 h = _____ mi per 1 h

5. Find the unit rate.

168 mi on 6 gal = _____ mi per 1 gal

6. Find an equivalent ratio.

$$\frac{n}{10} = \frac{24}{60}$$

_____

7. Find an equivalent ratio.

$5:8 = n:40$

_____

8. Find the unit rate.

54 mi in 6 d = _____ mi per 1 d

9. Find the unit rate.

$720 in 1 y = _____ in 1 mo

10. Name two equivalent ratios for 5:6.

_____

GO ON

11. Name an equivalent ratio for $\frac{7}{5}$.

_____

_____

12. Find the unit rate.

105 ft in 3 min = _____ ft per 1 min

_____

13. Alex is making a floor plan of a playroom. He is using the scale 3 in. = 6 feet. One wall is 9 feet. How long should it be on her floor plan?

_____

_____

14. Kerry makes a map of her neighborhood. She uses a scale of 1 in. = 1 mi. If the neighborhood gas station is 3.5 miles away from her house, how far away from her house will the gas station be on her map?

_____

_____

15. Ralph is making a floor plan of a tree house. He is using the scale 3 cm = 1 m. The length of the tree house is 9 cm on the plan. How long is the actual length in meters?

_____

_____

16. On a map, Lake Lorraine is 3.5 inches long. The actual length of the lake is 17.5 miles. What is the scale on the map?

_____

_____

17. Gale can drive 25 miles in 30 minutes. Is it reasonable to expect that Gale will drive 60 miles in 1 hour? If not, how many miles will she drive in an hour?

_____

_____

18. One office supply store sells a package of 12 small note pads for $4.00. Another office supply store has a special of 3 small notepads for $1.05. Selena believes that 3 small notepads for $1.05 is the better buy. Explain why Selena's answer is not reasonable.

_____

_____

_____

19. Amanda spends $35.75 on 2 CDs. She gives the clerk $40 and expects to receive $5.75 in change. Amanda's answer is not reasonable. What change should she receive?

_____

_____

20. Maura can swim 18 laps in 15 minutes. Why is it reasonable to expect that Maura will swim 36 laps in 30 minutes?

_____

_____

STOP

Chapter 26 – Teacher Interview

Core Concept: *Use Probability to Make Predictions*

Student Activity: Students demonstrate an understanding of using probability to make predictions. Ask students to perform an experiment to make a prediction.

Teacher Question 1:

- What is the probability of tossing a 2 on a number cube?

Understanding Student Response	Practice and Improvement
Students who say $\frac{2}{6}$.	Review lesson 1 to reinforce an understanding of the probability of an event.
Students who say a total of 2 possible outcomes.	Review lesson 1 to help students recognize that tossing a 2 is 1 of 6 possible outcomes.

Teacher Question 2:

- What is the probability of tossing an even number on the number cube?

Understanding Student Response	Practice and Improvement
Students who describe the event as *less likely* to happen.	Review lesson 2 to help students learn how to describe probability events and what they mean.
Students who predict $\frac{1}{3}$.	Review lesson 3 to help students learn how to make a prediction about an event.

Teacher Question 3:

- Suppose you toss a number cube 50 times and 10 of those times you toss a 2. What is the probability that your next toss will be a 2?

Understanding Student Response	Practice and Improvement
Students who do not know how to answer the question.	Review lessons 3–4 to reinforce an understanding of making a prediction based on an experiment.
Students who say $\frac{10}{60}$, $\frac{1}{6}$, $\frac{10}{40}$, or $\frac{1}{4}$.	Review lessons 3–4 to reinforce students' understanding of the results of this experiment. Students should be able to explain how these results can be used to make a prediction.

Chapter 26 – Journal Writing

Encourage students to generate their own journal entries related to math ideas in general or to concepts in this chapter. Present the following journal prompt and have students share their drawing/writing with a partner:

- When you are problem solving with probability, how can doing an experiment help you decide whether the result is reasonable?

  (Responses should indicate that doing an experiment can show how likely an event is.)

JOURNAL WRITING/PROBLEM SOLVING

Mark has 30 index cards in a bag. Fifteen of the cards have a blue dot on them and ten of the cards have a red dot on them. Mark chooses 1 card and puts it back in the bag. Then he chooses a second card. What is the probability that 1 card had a blue dot and the other had a red dot?

Read

Have students find the answer to the problem. Then ask them to write a few sentences telling—

- which information they used to find the answer

- what they did with the information

Have students make up another problem with different information for which they would have to follow the same procedure. Then have students solve the problem and supply the correct response.

Plan

Students must correctly find the number of possible outcomes. Students must also find the probability of choosing an index card with a blue dot and then the probability of choosing an index card with a red dot. Finally, students must use the number of possible outcomes to find the probability of choosing an index card with a blue dot and an index card with a red dot.

Solve

The correct response to the assigned problem is $\frac{1}{6}$. Students had to know the probability of each event to find the probability of both events.

Look Back

A correct response demonstrates the ability to find the probability of a compound event. (See scoring rubric on page 7.)

Chapter 26 – Monitoring Student Progress

☐ **Form A**   ☐ **Form B**

Name _____ Date _____

Directions: For each item that is answered incorrectly, cross out the item number. Then record the number of correct responses in the appropriate Student Score column. If the student has not met the Criterion Score for an objective, circle the student's score. Recommended assignments are listed in the Prescription Table on the next page.

Objective	Item Numbers	Criterion Score	Student Score
A. Understand probability.	1, 2	1/2	/2
B. Find the probability of a simple event.	3, 4, 5, 6, 7, 8	5/6	/6
C. Make predictions.	9, 10, 11	2/3	/3
D. Find the probability of a compound event.	12, 13, 14, 15, 16	4/5	/5
E. Use skills and strategies to solve problems.	17, 18, 19, 20	3/4	/4
Total Test Score		15/20	/20
Total Percent Correct			%

Chapter 26 – Prescription Table

The following chart correlates the tested objectives for this chapter to supplementary materials that meet the individual needs of the students. The Reteach and Practice pages are designed for students who need further instruction in the math concepts taught in this chapter. The Enrich pages are designed for students who need advanced challenges.

Objective	Reteach	Practice	Enrich
A. Understand probability.	436	437	438
B. Find the probability of a simple event.	439	440	441
C. Make predictions.	442	443	444
D. Find the probability of a compound event.	448, 451	449, 452	450, 453
E. Use skills and strategies to solve problems.	445, 446	447	

Read each question carefully. Darken the circle on your answer sheet for the correct answer.

Use the spinner for exercises 1–4.

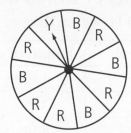

1. Which outcome is most likely?

   A. blue   **C.** yellow

   B. red

2. Which possible outcome is least likely?

   F. blue   **H.** yellow

   G. red

3. What is the probability of spinning a blue?

   A. $\frac{1}{10}$ **B.** $\frac{1}{5}$ **C.** $\frac{2}{5}$ **D.** $\frac{1}{2}$

4. What is the probability of spinning a red or yellow?

   F. $\frac{3}{5}$ **G.** $\frac{1}{2}$ **H.** $\frac{2}{5}$ **J.** $\frac{1}{5}$

Questions 5–11 are about a number cube with the numbers 1, 2, 3, 4, 5, and 6 on the faces.

5. What is the probability of tossing an even number?

   A. $\frac{1}{6}$ **B.** $\frac{1}{3}$ **C.** $\frac{1}{2}$ **D.** $\frac{5}{6}$

6. What is the probability of tossing a number less than 5?

   F. $\frac{1}{6}$ **H.** $\frac{1}{2}$

   G. $\frac{1}{3}$ **J.** $\frac{2}{3}$

7. What is the probability of tossing a 1 or a 4?

   A. $\frac{1}{3}$ **C.** $\frac{2}{3}$

   B. $\frac{1}{2}$ **D.** $\frac{5}{6}$

8. What is the probability of tossing a 0?

   F. certain   **H.** more likely

   G. impossible   **J.** less likely

9. About how many times will you toss an even number in 30 tosses?

   A. about 25 times   **C.** about 15 times

   B. about 20 times   **D.** about 10 times

10. If you toss the number cube 100 times, how many times do you predict you will toss a number greater than 4?

   F. about 22 times   **H.** about 55 times

   G. about 33 times   **J.** about 66 times

11. If you toss the number cube 24 times, how many times do you predict you will toss a 3?

   A. about 12 times   **C.** about 6 times

   B. about 8 times   **D.** about 4 times

GO ON ▶

Questions 12–15, are about 2 number cubes with the numbers 1, 2, 3, 4, 5, and 6 on the faces.

12. How many outcomes are possible if you toss both number cubes?

F. 72   H. 12

G. 36   J. 6

13. What is the probability of tossing a sum of 5?

A. $\frac{1}{9}$ C. $\frac{1}{3}$

B. $\frac{1}{4}$ D. $\frac{1}{2}$

14. Which sum of the two number cubes are you most likely to toss?

F. 9   H. 7

G. 8   J. 6

15. Suppose you add a third number cube, what are the total possible outcomes?

A. 8   C. 216

B. 42   D. 252

16. You pick a marble from a bag filled with marbles that come in 4 colors and 2 patterns. What is the number of possible outcomes?

F. 6   H. 12

G. 8   J. 20

Use the data for problems 17–20.

Frequency of Vowels from 20 Lines of Text

Vowel	Frequency
a	120
e	115
i	114
o	110
u	98

17. Which 2 vowels appear most in print?

A. i, u   B. a, o   C. e, i   D. a, e

18. Which vowel had a frequency of 10 less than vowel *a*?

F. vowel *e*   H. vowel *o*

G. vowel *i*   J. vowel *u*

19. Suppose you added the letter *y* to the experiment. How would the frequencies for the other vowels change?

A. change dramatically

B. more vowel *a*

C. more vowel *u*

D. remain the same

20. If you used 20 different lines of text from the same book, what is the likely outcome?

F. similar frequencies

G. different frequencies

H. more vowel *i* used

J. more vowel *e* used

STOP

Name _____

Read each question carefully. Fill in the correct answer in the space provided.

Use the spinner for exercises 1–4.

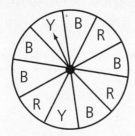

1. Which outcome is least likely?

_____

_____

2. Which outcome is most likely?

_____

_____

3. What is the probability of spinning a red?

_____

_____

4. What is the probability of spinning a blue or a yellow?

_____

_____

Questions 5–11, are about a number cube with the numbers 1, 2, 3, 4, 5, and 6 on the faces.

5. What is the probability of tossing an odd number?

_____

6. What is the probability of tossing a number greater than 4?

_____

_____

7. What is the probability of tossing a 2 or a 5?

_____

_____

8. Is the probability of tossing a 0 *certain* or *impossible*?

_____

_____

9. About how many times will you toss an even number in 60 tosses?

_____

_____

10. If you toss the number cube 100 times, how many times do you predict you will toss a number less than 4?

_____

_____

11. If you toss the number cube 30 times, how many times do you predict you will toss a 5?

_____

GO ON

Questions 12–15, are about 2 number cubes with the numbers 1, 2, 3, 4, 5, and 6 on the faces.

12. How many outcomes are possible if you toss both number cubes?

_____

13. What is the possibility of tossing a sum of 4?

_____

14. Which sum of the two number cubes are you least likely to toss?

_____

15. If there are 1,296 possible outcomes for 4 number cubes, how many outcomes are there for 3 number cubes?

_____

16. If you pick a marble from a bag filled with marbles that come in 5 colors and 3 patterns, what is the number of possible outcomes?

_____

Use the data for problems 17–20.

Frequency of Vowels from 20 Lines of Text

Vowel	Frequency
a	100
e	95
i	94
o	84
u	72

17. Which 2 vowels appear least in print?

_____

18. Which vowel had a frequency of 6 less than vowel *a*?

_____

19. Suppose you added the letter *y* to the experiment. Would the frequencies for the other vowels change?

_____

20. If you used 20 different lines of text from the same book in the experiment, what would the results probably show—frequencies that are *about the same* or *very different*?

_____

STOP

Unit 13 Performance Assessment

Color My World

- *Target Skill:* Find the probability of a simple event.
- *Additional Skills:* Understand probability; make predictions.

Task Description: This task requires students to take turns drawing colored counters and recording the frequency of each color. The students will be asked to identify the probabilities of various events.

Preparing: You may wish to have the students review the concept of compound events.

Materials	Group Size	Time on Task
2 paper bags 9 counters: 4 red, 3 yellow, 2 green.	2 students	1 day

Guiding: Tell students that they will be working in teams to record probabilities by drawing colored counters from opaque bags.

Remind students to sketch out their tally sheets in an orderly way, so they have room to record all their information and are able to refer to it.

Observing/ Monitoring: As you move among the students, pose the following questions:

What results would you expect from the first bag? Why might your results not match expectations?

Would you be surprised to draw a green counter from the second bag?

Would you be surprised if every counter from the second bag were green?

Unit 13 Performance Assessment Scoring Rubric

Color My World

Score	Explanation
3	Students demonstrate an efficient strategy and a thorough approach that enables them to solve the problem completely. A satisfactory answer: • sets up the experiment properly; • records the data thoroughly; • evaluates probabilities accurately; • calculates ratios properly. Students are able to complete the problem quickly and have all of the above correct solutions.
2	Students demonstrate a strategy that enables them to solve most of the problem correctly. The strategy is somewhat disorganized, making it less efficient. A solution is found, but errors are contained. Students may: • tally the outcomes accurately; • calculate most of the probabilities or ratios. Students may have some difficulty determining all solutions correctly but demonstrate an understanding of general concepts.
1	Students demonstrate a confused strategy, which leads to difficulty solving the problem. Most answers are incorrect, but students demonstrate knowledge of at least one concept being assessed. Students may: • tally the outcomes of experiments OR; • calculate some of the probabilities OR; • calculate ratios.

Unit 13 Performance Assessment Student Activity

Color My World

You will need
- 2 paper bags
- nine counters: 4 blue, 3 yellow, 2 green

In the first bag, put one counter of each color. In the second, put all the other counters. One team member draws counters. One keeps a tally. Draw a counter from each bag. Tally the color. Replace the counters in the correct bags. After 30 turns, switch roles.

Compile all your results, and answer these questions.

1. What is the probability of drawing a blue counter from the first bag?

   _____

2. What is the probability of drawing a blue counter from the second bag?

   _____

3. What were your results from each bag for blue counters?

   _____

4. Would you expect the results for green counters to be the same as for blue?

   _____

5. Were your results for green counters the same as for blue?

   _____

6. What was the ratio of green counters you drew to blue counters?

   _____

Unit 13 – Monitoring Student Progress

☐ Form A   ☐ Form B

Name _____ Date _____

Directions: This test targets selected objectives. For each item that is answered incorrectly, cross out the item number. Then record the number of correct responses in the column labeled **Number of Correct Responses.** Add to find the **Total Number of Correct Responses** and record the total. Use this total to determine the **Total Test Score** and the **Total Percent Correct.**

Strand • Objective(s)	Item Numbers	Number of Correct Responses
Number Sense, Concepts, and Operations • Find equivalent ratios. • Determine and apply rates and unit prices. • Use skills and strategies to solve problems.	1, 5, 6, 8, 17, 18, 21, 25, 26, 28, 37, 38	/12
Geometry and Spatial Sense • Use scale drawings and maps. • Understand probability. • Find the probability of a simple event. • Make predictions. • Find the probability of a compound event. • Use skills and strategies to solve problems.	2, 3, 4, 7, 9, 10, 11, 12, 13, 14, 15, 16, 19, 20, 22, 23, 24, 27, 29, 30, 31, 32, 33, 34, 35, 36, 39, 40	/28
Total Number of Correct Responses		
Total Test Score		/40
Total Percent Correct		%

Read each question carefully. Darken the circle on your answer sheet for the correct answer.

1. Find the missing number in the proportion.

$8:12 = 40:$ ▢

  A. 80   **C.** 50

  B. 60   **D.** 40

Questions 2–4 are about tossing a number cube with the numbers 1, 2, 3, 4, 5, and 6 on the faces.

2. What is the probability of tossing a 3?

  F. $\frac{1}{6}$ **H.** $\frac{1}{2}$

  G. $\frac{1}{3}$ **J.** $\frac{2}{3}$

3. What is the probability of tossing a number greater than 4?

  A. $\frac{1}{6}$ **C.** $\frac{1}{2}$

  B. $\frac{1}{3}$ **D.** $\frac{2}{3}$

4. Is tossing a number greater than 3 more likely than, less likely than, or equally likely as tossing an even number?

  F. more likely than

  G. less likely than

  H. equally likely

5. Find the missing number in the proportion.

$15:4 = 75:$ ▢

  A. 25   **B.** 20   **C.** 15   **D.** 10

6. Find the missing number in the proportion.

$7:17 =$ ▢ $:136$

  F. 126   **G.** 70   **H.** 56   **J.** 49

7. If you toss a coin, what is the probability of getting heads?

  A. 0   **B.** $\frac{1}{2}$ **C.** $\frac{3}{4}$ **D.** 1

---

8. Find the missing number in the proportion.

$21:3 =$ ▢ $: 45$

  F. 315   **H.** 140

  G. 168   **J.** 275

Use the spinner for exercises 9–12.

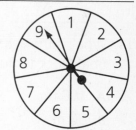

9. Find the probability of spinning a 5.

  A. $\frac{1}{9}$ **B.** $\frac{2}{9}$ **C.** $\frac{3}{9}$ **D.** $\frac{5}{9}$

---

10. Find the probability of spinning an odd number.

  F. $\frac{1}{9}$ **G.** $\frac{4}{9}$ **H.** $\frac{5}{9}$ **J.** $\frac{6}{9}$

---

11. Find the probability of spinning an even number.

  A. $\frac{1}{9}$ **B.** $\frac{4}{9}$ **C.** $\frac{5}{9}$ **D.** $\frac{6}{9}$

---

12. Find the probability of spinning a 1-digit number.

  F. $\frac{4}{9}$ **G.** $\frac{5}{9}$ **H.** $\frac{7}{9}$ **J.** 1

GO ON ➡

Name _____

Use the scale drawing for exercises 13–16.

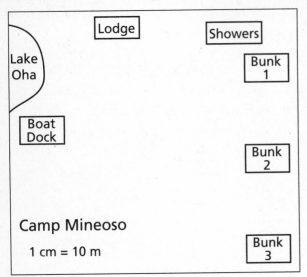

13. What is the actual distance from the Boat Dock to Bunk 1?

A. 100 m   **C.** 45 m

B. 50 m   **D.** 20 m

14. What is the actual distance from the Lake Oha to the Showers?

F. 90 m   **H.** 45 m

G. 50 m   **J.** 40 m

15. What is the actual distance from the Lodge to Bunk 3?

A. 120 m   **C.** 20 m

B. 60 m   **D.** 6 m

16. What is the actual distance from Lake Oha to the Lodge?

F. 150 m   **H.** 30 m

G. 60 m   **J.** 15 m

17. Dave earns $25 baby-sitting for 5 hours. At the same rate, what does he earn for sitting 3 hours?

A. $75   **C.** $15

B. $20   **D.** $10

18. There are 32 students in a classroom, and 8 are wearing blue shirts. There are 192 students in the school. How many students in the school would have to wear blue shirts for the school's ratio of students wearing blue shirts to all students to be the same as the classroom's ratio?

F. 72 students

G. 48 students

H. 24 students

J. 12 students

19. Andrew put 18 cards in a bag. Of the cards, 2 were blue, 3 green, 6 yellow, 3 red, and 4 orange. If he pulls one card from the bag without looking, what is the probability it will be yellow?

A. $\frac{1}{3}$ **C.** $\frac{1}{9}$

B. $\frac{1}{6}$ **D.** $\frac{1}{18}$

20. Malary's town is 18 inches from Royalton on a map. The map scale is 3 in. = 25 mi. How far apart are the two towns?

F. 450 mi   **H.** 150 mi

G. 200 mi   **J.** 100 mi

GO ON

21. Find the missing number in the proportion.

$5:11 = 35:\blacksquare$

A. 77   **C.** 50

B. 55   **D.** 41

Questions 22–24 are about tossing a number cube with the numbers 1, 2, 3, 4, 5, and 6 on the faces.

22. What is the probability of tossing a 2?

F. $\frac{2}{3}$ **H.** $\frac{1}{3}$

G. $\frac{1}{2}$ **J.** $\frac{1}{6}$

23. What is the probability of tossing a number less than 3?

A. $\frac{2}{3}$ **C.** $\frac{1}{3}$

B. $\frac{1}{2}$ **D.** $\frac{1}{6}$

24. Is tossing an odd number more likely than, less likely than, or equally likely as tossing a number greater than 4?

F. more likely than

G. less likely than

H. equally likely

25. Find the missing number in the proportion.

$25:3 = 100:\blacksquare$

A. 78   **C.** 12

B. 30   **D.** 6

26. Find the missing number in the proportion

$9:14 = \blacksquare:126$

F. 121   **G.** 81   **H.** 72   **J.** 36

27. If you toss a coin, what is the probability of getting tails?

A. 1   **B.** $\frac{3}{4}$ **C.** $\frac{1}{2}$ **D.** 0

28. Find the missing number in the proportion.

$40:8 = \blacksquare:32$

F. 160   **G.** 80   **H.** 32   **J.** 22

Use the spinner for exercises 29–32.

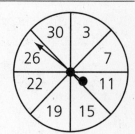

29. Find the probability of spinning a 7.

A. $\frac{3}{8}$ **B.** $\frac{1}{4}$ **C.** $\frac{1}{8}$ **D.** 0

30. Find the probability of spinning an odd number.

F. $\frac{5}{8}$ **G.** $\frac{4}{8}$ **H.** $\frac{3}{8}$ **J.** $\frac{1}{8}$

31. Find the probability of spinning an even number.

A. $\frac{5}{8}$ **B.** $\frac{3}{8}$ **C.** $\frac{1}{8}$ **D.** $\frac{2}{8}$

GO ON

32. Find the probability of spinning a 1–digit number.

F. $\frac{1}{8}$ **G.** $\frac{2}{8}$ **H.** $\frac{3}{8}$ **J.** $\frac{4}{8}$

Use the scale drawing for exercises 33–36.

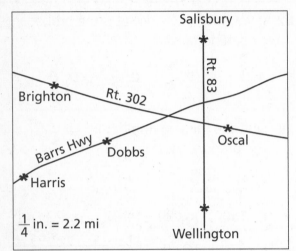

Salisbury
Rt. 83
Brighton   Rt. 302
Barrs Hwy   Dobbs   Oscal
Harris
$\frac{1}{4}$ in. = 2.2 mi
Wellington

33. What is the actual distance from Brighton to Oscal?

A. 17.6 mi   **C.** 4.8 mi

B. 8.8 mi   **D.** 2 mi

---

34. What is the actual distance from Salisbury to Wellington?

F. 25 mi   **H.** 15.4 mi

G. 20 mi   **J.** 4.4 mi

---

35. What is the shortest route from Brighton to Dobbs, if you stay on the roads shown?

A. 19.8 mi   **C.** 11 mi

B. 17.6 mi   **D.** 6.6 mi

---

36. What is the shortest route from Wellington to Harris, if you stay on the roads shown?

F. 26.4 mi   **H.** 11 mi

G. 15.4 mi   **J.** 8.8 mi

Solve.

37. Janet earns $22 for baby-sitting $5\frac{1}{2}$ hours. At the same rate, what does she earn for sitting 4 hours?

A. $24   **C.** $16

B. $20   **D.** $12

---

38. Mr. Dodd has 48 flower bulbs. Six are daffodils. Ms. Evans has 240 bulbs. How many of Ms. Evans's bulbs would have to be daffodils for her ratio of daffodils to bulbs to be the same as Mr. Dodd's ratio?

F. 48 bulbs   **H.** 30 bulbs

G. 40 bulbs   **J.** 24 bulbs

---

39. Daria put 20 marbles in a bag. 5 of the marbles were red, 7 were orange, 4 were green, and 4 were yellow. If she pulls a marble from the bag without looking, what is the probability that it will be orange?

A. $\frac{7}{20}$ **B.** $\frac{1}{4}$ **C.** $\frac{1}{5}$ **D.** $\frac{3}{4}$

---

40. Boylston is 12 inches from Trentown on a map. The map scale is 4 in. = 30 mi. How far apart are the two towns?

F. 360 mi   **H.** 90 mi

G. 150 mi   **J.** 10 mi

STOP

Read each question carefully. Fill in the correct answer in the space provided.

1. Find the missing number in the proportion.

9:15 = 36:☐

_____

Questions 2–4 are about tossing a number cube with the numbers 1, 2, 3, 4, 5, and 6 on the faces.

2. What is the probability of tossing a 4?

_____

3. What is the probability of tossing a number less than 3?

_____

4. Is tossing a number greater than 4 more likely than, less likely than, or equally likely as tossing a 1 or 2?

_____

5. Find the missing number in the proportion.

21:8 = 84:☐

_____

6. Find the missing number in the proportion.

9:22 = ☐:154

_____

7. If you toss a coin, what is the probability of getting tails?

_____

8. Find the missing number in the proportion.

18:3 = ☐:36

_____

Use the spinner for exercises 9–12.

9. Find the probability of spinning a 6.

_____

10. Find the probability of spinning an even number.

_____

GO ON

11. Find the probability of spinning an odd number.

_____

12. Find the probability of spinning a 2-digit number.

_____

Use the scale drawing for exercises 13–16.

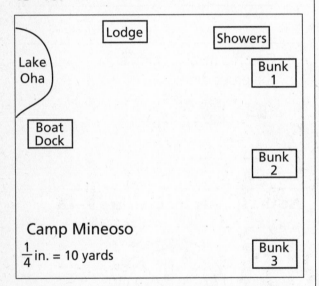

Lodge

Showers

Lake Oha

Bunk 1

Boat Dock

Bunk 2

Camp Mineoso
$\frac{1}{4}$ in. = 10 yards

Bunk 3

13. What is the actual distance from the Showers to Bunk 3?

_____

14. What is the actual distance from Bunk 1 to Bunk 2?

_____

15. What is the actual distance from Bunk 2 to the Boat Dock?

_____

16. What is the actual distance from Lake Oha to Bunk 3?

_____

17. Alissa earns $35 baby-sitting for 7 hours. At the same rate, what does she earn for baby-sitting 4 hours?

_____

18. There are 25 students in a classroom and 7 are wearing the school colors. There are 175 students in the school. How many students in the school would have to wear the school colors for the school's ratio of "students wearing the school colors" to "all students" to be the same as the classroom's ratio?

_____

19. Jen put 24 cards in a bag. Of the cards, 5 were blue, 8 were red, 6 were green, 3 were purple, and 2 were yellow. If she picks a card at random, what is the probability it will be green?

_____

20. Sanjay's town is 15 inches from Mount Hope on a map. The map scale is 3 in. = 35 mi. How far apart are the two towns?

_____

GO ON

21. Find the missing number in the proportion.

$7:13 = 42:$ ▢

_____

Questions 22–24 are about tossing a number cube with the numbers 1, 2, 3, 4, 5, and 6 on the faces.

22. What is the probability of tossing a 5?

_____

23. What is the probability of tossing a number greater than 1?

_____

24. Is tossing a number less than 5 more likely than, less likely than, or equally likely as tossing an odd number?

_____

25. Find the missing number in the proportion.

$75:7 = 300:$ ▢

_____

26. Find the missing number in the proportion.

$11:16 =$ ▢ $:144$

_____

27. If you toss a coin, what is the probability of getting heads or tails?

_____

28. Find the missing number in the proportion.

$35:5 =$ ▢ $:20$

_____

Use the spinner for exercises 29–32.

29. Find the probability of spinning a 9.

_____

30. Find the probability of spinning an even number.

_____

GO ON

31. Find the probability of spinning an odd number.

_____

_____

32. Find the probability of spinning a 2-digit number.

_____

_____

Use the scale drawing for exercises 33–36.

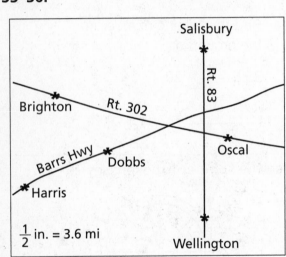

$\frac{1}{2}$ in. = 3.6 mi

33. What is the actual distance from Harris to Dobbs?

_____

34. What is the actual distance from Dobbs to Oscal?

_____

35. What is the actual distance from Oscal to Wellington?

_____

36. What is the shortest route from Salisbury to Brighton, if you stay on the roads shown?

_____

_____

37. Dexter earns $39 for baby-sitting $6\frac{1}{2}$ hours. At the same rate, what does he earn for baby-sitting 5 hours?

_____

_____

38. Mr. Snodgrass has 36 flower bulbs. Eight are tulips. Ms. Flowers has 180 bulbs. How many of Ms. Flowers's bulbs would have to be tulips for her ratio of tulips to bulbs to be the same as Mr. Snodgrass's ratio?

_____

_____

39. Allan put 16 marbles in a bag. Six of the marbles were red, 4 were orange, 5 were blue, and 1 was yellow. If he picks a marble at random, what is the probability that it will be red?

_____

_____

40. Winterville is 16 inches from Suntown on a map. The map scale is 1 in. = 25 mi. How far apart are the two towns?

_____

_____

STOP

Chapter 27 – Teacher Interview

Core Concept: *Percents, Fractions, and Decimals*

Student Activity: Students demonstrate an understanding of fractions, decimals, and percents. Ask students to name the fraction in simplest form, and the fraction and decimal for 60%.

Teacher Question 1:

• How do you show 60% as a fraction in simplest form?

Understanding Student Response	Practice and Improvement
Students who say $\frac{1}{6}$ or $\frac{1}{60}$.	Review lesson 2 and allow students to practice writing percents as fractions.
Students who say $\frac{60}{100}$ or $\frac{6}{10}$.	Review Chapter 9 and lessons 5–6 to reinforce an understanding of renaming fractions in simplest forms.

Teacher Question 2:

• How do you show 60% as a decimal?

Understanding Student Response	Practice and Improvement
Students who say 0.06.	Review lesson 2 to help students learn to divide the number by 100.
Students who say 6.	Review lesson 2 to help students learn how to change a percent to a decimal.

Teacher Question 3:

• How do you show 125% as a fraction and as a decimal?

Understanding Student Response	Practice and Improvement
Students who cannot correctly write 125% as a fraction.	Review lesson 3 to reinforce the concept of dividing a percent by 100 to change it to a fraction.
Students who cannot correctly write 125% as a decimal.	Review lesson 3 to reinforce the concept of dividing a percent by 100 to change it to a decimal.

Chapter 27 – Journal Writing

Encourage students to generate their own journal entries related to math ideas in general or to concepts in this chapter. Present the following journal prompt and have students share their drawing/writing with a partner:

- When you are problem solving and are given numbers as fractions, decimals, and percents, why is it important to represent all the numbers in the same way?

  (Responses should indicate that numbers should be represented in the same way so they can be more easily compared. For example, $\frac{250}{1,000}$ may appear to be greater than 0.30 where as 0.25 is clearly less than 0.30.)

JOURNAL WRITING/PROBLEM SOLVING

This season Danny made 50 percent of his basketball foul shots. Last season he made 50 of 80 foul shots. Did Danny improve his percent over last season? Explain your answer.

Read

Have students find the answer to the problem. Then ask them to write a few sentences telling—

- which information they used to find the answer

- what they did with the information

Have students make up another problem with different information for which they follow the same procedure. Then have students solve the problem and supply the correct response.

Plan

Students must represent both numbers as percents before comparing the foul shots.

Solve

The correct response to the assigned problem is that Danny did not improve his percent because $\frac{50}{80}$ is $\frac{5}{8}$ or 62.5%. 50% is less than 62.5%.

Look Back

A correct response demonstrates the ability to change numbers between fractions and percents, and interpret and compare percents. (See scoring rubric on page 7.)

Chapter 27 – Monitoring Student Progress

☐ Form A   ☐ Form B

Name _____   Date _____

Directions: For each item that is answered incorrectly, cross out the item number. Then record the number of correct responses in the appropriate Student Score column. If the student has not met the Criterion Score for an objective, circle the student's score. Recommended assignments are listed in the Prescription Table on the next page.

Objective	Item Numbers	Criterion Score	Student Score
A. Understand the meaning of percent.	1, 2, 5, 6, 14	4/5	/5
B. Convert numbers between percents, decimals, and fractions.	3, 4, 7, 8, 15	4/5	/5
C. Interpret percents.	9, 10, 11, 12, 13, 16	5/6	/6
D. Use skills and strategies to solve problems.	17, 18, 19, 20	3/4	/4
Total Test Score		16/20	/20
Total Percent Correct			%

Chapter 27 – Prescription Table

The following chart correlates the tested objectives for this chapter to supplementary materials that meet the individual needs of the students. The Reteach and Practice pages are designed for students who need further instruction in the math concepts taught in this chapter. The Enrich pages are designed for students who need advanced challenges.

Objective	Reteach	Practice	Enrich
A. Understand the meaning of percent.	455	456	457
B. Convert numbers between percents, decimals, and fractions.	458	459	460
C. Interpret percents.	461	462	463
D. Use skills and strategies to solve problems.	464	465	466

Read each question carefully. Darken the circle on your answer sheet for the correct answer.

1. Find the fraction to show the shaded part.

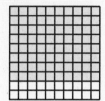

A. $\frac{85}{100}$ **B.** $\frac{80}{100}$ **C.** $\frac{70}{100}$ **D.** $\frac{15}{100}$

2. Find the ratio to show the shaded part.

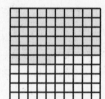

F. $\frac{75}{100}$ **H.** 55:100

G. 6:10   **J.** $\frac{1}{2}$

3. Find 0.15 as a percent.

   A. 0.15%   **B.** 1.5%   **C.** 15%   **D.** 85%

4. Find $\frac{3}{4}$ as a percent.

   F. 0.75%   **G.** 25%   **H.** 70%   **J.** 75%

5. Find the decimal to show the shaded part.

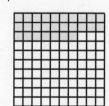

   A. 0.27   **B.** 0.20   **C.** 0.07   **D.** 0.027

6. Find the percent to show the shaded part.

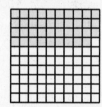

   F. 93%   **H.** 49%

   G. 61%   **J.** 39%

7. Find $\frac{41}{100}$ as a percent.

   A. 41%   **C.** 0.41%

   B. 4.1%   **D.** 0.041%

8. Find 13:100 as a percent.

   F. 0.13%   **H.** 0.31%

   G. 13%   **J.** 31%

9. Find $\frac{300}{100}$ as a percent.

   A. 0.3%   **C.** 30%

   B. 3%   **D.** 300%

10. Find 0.73 as a percent.

   F. 73%   **H.** 7.03%

   G. 7.3%   **J.** 0.73%

GO ON

11. Find 3% as a fraction.

  A. $\frac{3}{1000}$　　　**C.** $\frac{30}{100}$

  B. $\frac{3}{100}$　　　**D.** $\frac{300}{10}$

12. Find 175% as a mixed number.

  F. $1\frac{7}{8}$　　　**H.** $1\frac{1}{3}$

  G. $1\frac{3}{4}$　　　**J.** $1\frac{1}{4}$

13. Find 525% as a mixed number.

  A. $5\frac{1}{4}$　　　**C.** $5\frac{1}{2}$

  B. $5\frac{1}{3}$　　　**D.** $5\frac{3}{4}$

14. Find the percent to show the **unshaded** part.

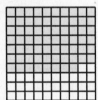

  F. 22%　　　**H.** 68%

  G. 32%　　　**J.** 78%

15. Find 0.92 as a percent.

  A. 9%　　　**C.** 90.2%

  B. 9.2%　　　**D.** 92%

16. Find $\frac{4}{10}$ as a percent.

  F. 0.04%　　　**H.** 40%

  G. 4 %　　　**J.** 400%

17. This season, the Marshview soccer team won 0.512 of its games. Find the percent for the decimal.

  A. 5.12%　　　**C.** 51.2%

  B. 50.12%　　　**D.** 512%

18. From last year's scores, the Marshview soccer team improved by 125 percent. Find the mixed number in simplest form for 125 percent.

  F. $1\frac{1}{2}$　　　**H.** $1\frac{1}{6}$

  G. $1\frac{1}{4}$　　　**J.** $1\frac{1}{8}$

19. Of 320 students at Marshview School, only $\frac{1}{4}$ walk to school. The rest take the bus. What percent of students take the bus?

  A. 25%　　　**C.** 60%

  B. 50%　　　**D.** 75%

20. Last year, Karen made 20 percent of 60 foul shots. This year, she made 30 of 60 foul shots. How many more foul shots did Karen make this year?

  F. 6 foul shots　　　**H.** 12 foul shots

  G. 10 foul shots　　　**J.** 18 foul shots

STOP

Read each question carefully. Fill in the correct answer in the space provided.

1. Write the fraction for the shaded part.

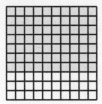

_____

_____

2. Write the ratio for the shaded part.

_____

_____

3. Write 0.42 as a percent.

_____

_____

4. Write $\frac{4}{5}$ as a percent.

_____

_____

5. Write the decimal for the shaded part.

_____

6. Write the percent for the shaded part.

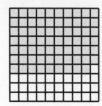

_____

_____

7. Write $\frac{66}{100}$ as a percent.

_____

_____

8. Write 27:100 as a percent.

_____

_____

9. Write $\frac{400}{100}$ as a percent.

_____

_____

10. Write 0.09 as a percent.

_____

GO ON

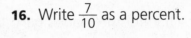
11. Write 90% as a fraction.

_____

12. Write 180% as a mixed number.

_____

13. Write 650% as a mixed number.

_____

14. Write the percent for the unshaded part.

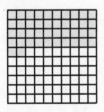

_____

15. Write 0.88 as a percent.

_____

16. Write $\frac{7}{10}$ as a percent.

_____

17. This season the Dover soccer team won 0.422 of its games. Write the percent for the decimal.

_____

18. From last year's scores, the Dover soccer team improved by 140 percent. Write 140% as a mixed number in simplest form.

_____

19. Of 400 students at Dover School, only $\frac{1}{5}$ walk to school and the rest take the bus. What percent of students take the bus?

_____

20. Last year Dan made 50 percent of 40 foul shots. This year he made 30 of 40 foul shots. How many more foul shots did Dan make this year?

_____

STOP

Chapter 28 – Teacher Interview

Core Concept: *Interpret and Make a Circle Graph*

Student Activity: Students demonstrate an understanding of percent and are able to make a circle graph. Provide students with the following problem: Lauren surveyed her class to find out their favorite color. Of the 60 students, 18 chose red, 30 chose blue, 9 chose green, and 3 chose yellow. Ask students to find the percents of the students' choices and then use the percents to make a circle graph.

Teacher Question 1:

- What is the percent for each color choice?

Understanding Student Response	Practice and Improvement
Students who say 60%, 18%, 30%, 9%, and 3%.	Review lesson 2 to help students recognize that they need to find the percent that each number is of 60.
Students who include 60 in the total and find the percent that each number is of 120.	Reread the problem to help students recognize that 60 is the total number of students.

Teacher Question 2:

- How will a circle graph represent this information?

Understanding Student Response	Practice and Improvement
Students who cannot explain how a circle graph represents information.	Review lesson 4 to help students learn about circle graphs.
Students who say the size of the section for each color is related to the number of students who chose each color.	Review lesson 4 to reinforce the concept that the size of each section is related to its central angle.

Teacher Question 3:

- How will you find the central angle of each section?

Understanding Student Response	Practice and Improvement
Students who use the percents as measures for the central angle.	Review lesson 4 to help students understand that each central angle measure is a percent of 360°.
Students who say they will divide each percent by 360°.	Review lesson 4 to help students understand that each central angle measure is calculated by multiplying a percent by 360°.

Chapter 28 – Journal Writing

Encourage students to generate their own journal entries related to math ideas in general or to concepts in this chapter. Present the following journal prompt and have students share their drawing/writing with a partner:

- When you are problem solving, how does logical reasoning help you find the answer to the problem?

    (Responses should indicate that logical reasoning helps you to analyze the information and think about the problem in an organized way.)

JOURNAL WRITING/PROBLEM SOLVING

At baseball practice, Jan caught 60 of 75 baseball throws. What percent did Jan catch? Explain your answer.

Read

Have students find the answer to the problem. Then ask them to write a few sentences telling—

- which information they used to find the answer

- what they did with the information

Have students make up another problem with different information for which they could have followed the same procedure. Then have students solve the problem and supply the correct response.

Plan

Students must correctly find the percent of a number. Students first divide to find the decimal then change the decimal to a percent.

Solve

The correct response to the assigned problem is 80%. Students need to divide 60 by 75 and then rewrite the decimal (0.8) as a percent.

Look Back

A correct response demonstrates the ability to find a percent that one number is of another. (See scoring rubric on page 7.)

Chapter 28 – Monitoring Student Progress

☐ Form A   ☐ Form B

Name _____ Date _____

Directions: For each item that is answered incorrectly, cross out the item number. Then record the number of correct responses in the appropriate Student Score column. If the student has not met the Criterion Score for an objective, circle the student's score. Recommended assignments are listed in the Prescription Table on the next page.

Objective	Item Numbers	Criterion Score	Student Score
A. Find percent of a number.	1, 2, 10, 11, 14, 15	5/6	/6
B. Find what percent one number is of another.	3, 4, 12, 13, 16	4/5	/5
C. Interpret and make circle graphs.	5, 6, 7, 8, 9	4/5	/5
D. Use skills and strategies to solve problems.	17, 18, 19, 20	3/4	/4
Total Test Score		16/20	/20
Total Percent Correct			%

Chapter 28 – Prescription Table

The following chart correlates the tested objectives for this chapter to supplementary materials that meet the individual needs of the students. The Reteach and Practice pages are designed for students who need further instruction in the math concepts taught in this chapter. The Enrich pages are designed for students who need advanced challenges.

Objective	Reteach	Practice	Enrich
A. Find percent of a number.	467	468	469
B. Find what percent one number is of another.	470	471	472
C. Interpret and make circle graphs.	476	477	478
D. Use skills and strategies to solve problems.	473, 474	475	

Name _____

Read each question carefully. Darken the circle on your answer sheet for the correct answer.

1. What is 20% of 175?

   A. 17.5   **B.** 35   **C.** 70   **D.** 140

---

2. What is 60% of $24.00?

   F. $14.40   **H.** $12.00

   G. $13.60   **J.** $9.60

---

3. What percent of 80 is 40?

   A. 60%   **C.** 50%

   B. 55%   **D.** 40%

---

4. What percent of 35 is 7?

   F. 15%   **H.** 25%

   G. 20%   **J.** 35%

Use data from the circle graph for problems 5–9.

Favorite Breed of Dog

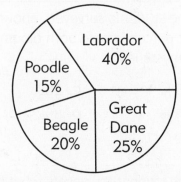

5. If 120 students were surveyed about their favorite breeds of dogs, how many students like Great Danes?

   A. 30 students   **C.** 20 students

   B. 24 students   **D.** 18 students

6. What fraction of the total number of students prefers Beagles?

   F. $\frac{1}{8}$ **H.** $\frac{1}{4}$

   G. $\frac{1}{5}$ **J.** $\frac{1}{3}$

---

7. What percent of students prefer Labradors and Great Danes?

   A. 55%   **C.** 65%

   B. 60%   **D.** 85%

---

8. What percent make up the least favorite 2 breeds?

   F. 35%   **H.** 55%

   G. 40%   **J.** 65%

---

9. Suppose 140 students were surveyed, how many students prefer Beagles?

   A. 14 students

   B. 28 students

   C. 30 students

   D. 56 students

---

10. What is 125% of 60?

   F. 15   **H.** 75

   G. 70   **J.** 90

GO ON

11. What is 45% of 25?

    A. 11.25   **C.** 13.75

    B. 12.25   **D.** 14.75

12. What percent of 50 is 75?

    F. 75%   **H.** 135%

    G. 120%   **J.** 150%

13. What percent of 9 is 3 rounded to the nearest tenth?

    A. 30.3%   **C.** 33.6%

    B. 33.3%   **D.** 66.7%

14. What is 150% of 9.3?

    F. 11.63   **H.** 14.88

    G. 13.95   **J.** 18.60

15. What is 225% of $420.00?

    A. $735.00   **C.** $900.00

    B. $840.00   **D.** $945.00

16. What percent of 30 is 3?

    F. 10%   **H.** 30%

    G. 20%   **J.** 50%

Use the Venn diagram for problems 17–20.

Favorite Kinds of Books

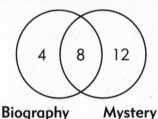

Biography   Mystery

17. How many students were surveyed about favorite kinds of books?

    A. 32 students   **C.** 28 students

    B. 30 students   **D.** 24 students

18. How many students chose only biographies?

    F. 20 students   **H.** 8 students

    G. 12 students   **J.** 4 students

19. Of the students surveyed, about what percent chose both biographies and mysteries?

    A. 33%   **C.** 20%

    B. 24%   **D.** 8%

20. Of the students surveyed, what percent of students chose only mysteries?

    F. 12%   **H.** 50%

    G. 20%   **J.** 83%

STOP

Read each question carefully. Fill in the correct answer in the space provided.

1. What is 20% of 195?

_____

2. What is 40% of $32.00?

_____

3. What percent of 120 is 60?

_____

4. What percent of 30 is 6?

_____

Use the data from the circle graph for problems 5–9.

Favorite Breed of Dog

5. If 160 students were surveyed about their favorite breed of dog, how many students like German Shepherds?

_____

6. What fraction of the total number of students prefers Dalmatians?

_____

7. What percent of students prefer Golden Retrievers and Cocker Spaniels?

_____

8. What percent makes up the two favorite breeds?

_____

9. Suppose 180 students were surveyed, how many students prefer German Shepherds?

_____

10. What is 125% of 80?

_____

GO ON

11. What is 45% of 45?

_____

12. What percent of 60 is 90?

_____

13. What percent of 9 is 6 rounded to the nearest tenth?

_____

14. What is 150% of 12.4?

_____

15. What is 275% of $320.00?

_____

16. What percent of 60 is 6?

_____

Use the Venn diagram for problems 17–20.

Favorite Kinds of Books

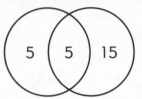

Classics   Adventure

17. How many students were surveyed about favorite kinds of books?

_____

18. How many students chose only classics?

_____

19. Of the students surveyed, what percent chose both classics and adventure books?

_____

20. Of the students surveyed, what percent chose only adventure books?

_____

STOP

Unit 14 Performance Assessment

Yankee Doodle Dandy

- *Target Skill:* Find percent of a number.
- *Additional Skills:* Understand the meaning of percent; interpret percents; change numbers between percents, decimals, and fractions.

**Task
Description:** This task requires students to complete a price list of discounts. The students will be asked to calculate the original price, percent discount, or discounted price, given the other two.

Preparing: You may wish to have the students review how to change a percent to a decimal and a fraction in order to multiply.

Materials	Group Size	Time on Task
Calculator (optional)	1 to 2 students	1 to 2 days

Guiding: Tell students that they will calculate prices using percentages and percentages using prices.

Tell students to decide which calculation they need to perform to reach the needed answer, and then set up the expression to calculate it.

**Observing/
Monitoring:** As you move among the students, pose the following questions:

In which cases is it easier to use multiplication, and in which is division easier?

In which cases is it easier to convert a percent to a fraction?

In which cases is it easier to convert a percent to a decimal?

Unit 14 Performance Assessment Scoring Rubric

Yankee Doodle Dandy

Score	Explanation
3	Students demonstrate an efficient strategy and a thorough approach that enables them to solve the problem completely. A satisfactory answer: • calculates percentages correctly in all three cases; • shows alternate methods for reaching answers. Students are able to complete the problem quickly and have all of the above correct solutions.
2	Students demonstrate a strategy that enables them to solve most of the problem correctly. The strategy is somewhat disorganized, making it less efficient. A solution is found, but errors are contained. Students may: • multiply and divide correctly; • not always use the correct operation to solve the problem. Students may have some difficulty determining all solutions correctly but demonstrate an understanding of general concepts.
1	Students demonstrate a confused strategy, which leads to difficulty solving the problem. Most answers are incorrect, but students demonstrate knowledge of at least one concept being assessed such as calculating percent.

Unit 14 Performance Assessment
Student Activity

Yankee Doodle Dandy

You will need
• calculator (optional)

It is July 6, and Syrena's Notions is having a post–Fourth of July sale. All items are marked down!

Item	Price	% Off	Sale Price
American flag	$20		$15
Uncle Sam hats	$4.89	10%	
Betsy Ross sewing kit		25%	$6
Sparklers	$2.99	40%	
Statue of Liberty bobblehead doll	$20		$11

1. How did you find the sale price if you know the original price and the percent off?

   _____

2. How can you find the percent off if you know the original price and the sale price?

   _____

3. How can you find the original price if you know the percent off and the sale price?

   _____

4. Complete the chart.

   _____

5. On July 13, sparklers were 60 percent off. What is the new sale price?

   _____

Unit 14 – Monitoring Student Progress

☐ Form A   ☐ Form B

Name _____ Date _____

Directions: This test targets selected objectives. For each item that is answered incorrectly, cross out the item number. Then record the number of correct responses in the column labeled **Number of Correct Responses.** Add to find the **Total Number of Correct Responses** and record the total. Use this total to determine the **Total Test Score** and the **Total Percent Correct.**

Strand • Objective(s)	Item Numbers	Number of Correct Responses
Number Sense, Concepts, and Operations • Understand the meaning of percent. • Convert numbers between percents, decimals, and fractions. • Interpret percents. • Find percent of a number. • Find what percent one number is of another. • Interpret and make circle graphs. • Use skills and strategies to solve problems.	1, 2, 3, 4, 5, 6, 7, 8, 9, 10, 11, 12, 13, 14, 15, 16, 17, 18, 19, 20, 21, 22, 23, 24, 25, 26, 27, 28, 29, 30, 31, 32, 33, 34, 35, 36, 37, 38, 39, 40	/40
Total Number of Correct Responses		
Total Test Score		/40
Total Percent Correct		%

Read each question carefully. Darken the circle on your answer sheet for the correct answer.

1. Write $\frac{3}{4}$ as a percent.

   A. 150%   **C.** 50%

   B. 75%   **D.** 25%

7. Write 25% as a decimal.

   A. 25.0   **C.** 0.25

   B. 2.5   **D.** 0.025

2. Find 62% of 90.

   F. 145.1   **H.** 14.51

   G. 55.8   **J.** 5.58

8. Find 30% of 80.

   F. 26.7   **H.** 2.7

   G. 24   **J.** 2.4

3. What percent of 20 is 8?

   A. 250%   **C.** 32%

   B. 40%   **D.** 25%

9. 70 is what percent of 112?

   A. 120%   **C.** 62.5%

   B. 75%   **D.** 50%

4. Write 0.83 as a percent.

   F. 8300%   **H.** 83%

   G. 830%   **J.** 8.3%

10. Write 40% as a fraction.

   F. $\frac{4}{5}$ **H.** $\frac{4}{50}$

   G. $\frac{2}{5}$ **J.** $\frac{2}{50}$

5. Find 145% of 50.

   A. 725   **C.** 72.5

   B. 344.8   **D.** 34.48

11. Find 210% of 30.

   A. 6,300   **C.** 63

   B. 630   **D.** 6.3

6. What percent of 30 is 45?

   F. 150%   **H.** 90%

   G. 120%   **J.** 75%

12. 22 is what percent of 11?

   F. 200%   **H.** 50%

   G. 75%   **J.** 20%

GO ON

Use the circle graph for exercises 13–14.

Trees in Davis Park

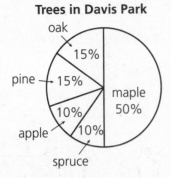

oak
15%
pine → 15%
maple 50%
10%
apple 10%
spruce

13. Of which type of tree is there the most?

A. maple   **C.** oak

B. pine   **D.** apple

14. If there are 300 trees in Davis Park, how many are pine trees?

F. 6   **H.** 45

G. 20   **J.** 6,000

Use the table for exercises 15–16.

Which Is Your Favorite Color?

Color	Percent of Total Responses
red	25%
blue	50%
green	17%
yellow	5%
other	3%

15. Which size central angle would you draw to show "blue" on a circle graph?

A. 180°   **C.** 100°

B. 120°   **D.** 50°

16. Which size central angle would you draw to show "yellow" on a circle graph?

F. 30°   **H.** 18°

G. 25°   **J.** 10°

17. The Rangers basketball team improved its wins over last year by 25%. Last year the team won 12 games. How many did they win this year?

A. 27 games   **C.** 18 games

B. 24 games   **D.** 15 games

18. The Taftly family has completed 10% of a 150-mile trip. How far have they gone?

F. 135 mi   **H.** 30 mi

G. 67.5 mi   **J.** 15 mi

19. Anita answered 90% of the items correctly on her test. What fraction of her test items were correct?

A. $\frac{7}{1}$ **C.** $\frac{1}{2}$

B. $\frac{9}{10}$ **D.** $\frac{1}{10}$

20. The Lee School baseball team plays 25 games in a season. So far, they have played 10 games. What percent of the games have they played?

F. 60%   **H.** 40%

G. 50%   **J.** 30%

GO ON ➡

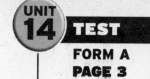
21. Write $\frac{3}{5}$ as a percent.

    A. 90%   **C.** 30%

    B. 60%   **D.** 20%

22. Find 20% of 84.

    F. 168   **H.** 16.8

    G. 42   **J.** 4.2

23. What percent of 20 is 16?

    A. 80%   **C.** 75%

    B. 125%   **D.** 50%

24. Write 0.12 as a percent.

    F. 120%   **H.** 1.2%

    G. 12%   **J.** 0.12%

25. Find 250% of 60.

    A. 150   **C.** 30

    B. 120   **D.** 15

26. What percent of 15 is 45?

    F. 300%   **H.** 66%

    G. 200%   **J.** 33%

27. Write 77% as a decimal.

    A. 77.0   **C.** 0.77

    B. 7.7   **D.** 0.077

28. Find 90% of 120.

    F. 320   **H.** 108

    G. 180   **J.** 10.8

29. 35 is what percent of 140?

    A. 400%   **C.** 75%

    B. 200%   **D.** 25%

30. Write 30% as a fraction.

    F. $\frac{2}{5}$ **H.** $\frac{1}{3}$

    G. $\frac{1}{10}$ **J.** $\frac{3}{10}$

31. Find 115% of 50.

    A. 57.5   **C.** 11.5

    B. 35   **D.** 7.5

32. 40 is what percent of 16?

    F. 300%   **H.** 80%

    G. 250%   **J.** 40%

GO ON

Use the circle graph for exercises 33–34.

Animals on Oates Farm

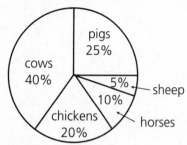

33. Of which type of animal is there the fewest?

A. pigs   **C.** chickens

B. sheep   **D.** cows

34. If there are 200 animals on Oates Farm, how many are cows?

F. 8   **H.** 80

G. 40   **J.** 8,000

Use the table for exercises 35–36.

Which Season Do You Like Best?

Season	Percent of Total Responses
Winter	10%
Spring	30%
Summer	40%
Fall	20%

35. Which size central angle would you draw to show "Summer" on a circle graph?

A. 180°   **B.** 150°   **C.** 144°   **D.** 132°

36. Which size central angle would you draw to show "Winter" on a circle graph?

F. 60°   **H.** 36°

G. 50°   **J.** 18°

37. Cal's tennis team won 50% more games this year than last. Last year they won 20. How many did they win this year?

A. 50 games   **C.** 30 games

B. 40 games   **D.** 25 games

38. Bill drove 25% of a 500-mile trip. How much farther does he need to go?

F. 400 mi   **H.** 250 mi

G. 375 mi   **J.** 125 mi

39. Adele answered 75% of the items correctly on her test. What fraction of her test items were incorrect?

A. $\frac{3}{4}$ **C.** $\frac{1}{3}$

B. $\frac{1}{2}$ **D.** $\frac{1}{4}$

40. Ana's track team has competed in 5 meets so far this season. They have 15 more meets to go. What percent of their total meets have they finished so far?

F. 75%   **H.** $33\frac{1}{3}$%

G. 50%   **J.** 25%

STOP

Read each question carefully. Fill in the correct answer in the space provided.

1. Write $\frac{1}{4}$ as a percent.

_____

6. What percent of 25 is 30?

_____

2. Find 57% of 80.

_____

7. Write 65% as a decimal.

_____

3. What percent of 40 is 24?

_____

8. Find 40% of 90.

_____

4. Write 0.79 as a percent.

_____

9. 60 is what percent of 96?

_____

5. Find 175% of 40.

_____

10. Write 80% as a fraction in simplest form.

_____

GO ON

11. Find 230% of 20.

_____

12. 36 is what percent of 12?

_____

Use the circle graph for exercises 13–14.

Trees in Davis Park

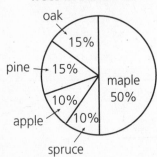

oak
15%
pine → 15%
maple
50%
10%
apple
10%
spruce

13. Of which type of tree is there the least?

_____

14. If there are 200 trees in Davis Park, how many are oak trees?

_____

Use the table for exercises 15–16.

What is your favorite sport?	
Sport	**Percent of Total Responses**
baseball	25%
football	32%
basketball	20%
hockey	10%
soccer	8%
other	5%

15. What size central angle would you draw to show "baseball" on a circle graph?

_____

16. What size central angle would you draw to show "other" on a circle graph?

_____

17. The Terriers softball team improved its wins over last year by 20%. Last year the team won 10 games. How many games did they win this year?

_____

18. The Costa family has completed 20% of a 120-mile trip. How far have they gone?

_____

19. Bruce answered 70% of the items correctly on his test. What fraction of his test items were correct?

_____

20. The Higgins School baseball team plays 30 games in a season. So far they have played 12 games. What percent of the games have they played?

_____

GO ON

21. Write $\frac{3}{10}$ as a percent.

_____

22. Find 30% of 72.

_____

23. What percent of 50 is 37?

_____

24. Write 0.27 as a percent.

_____

25. Find 150 percent of 30.

_____

26. What percent of 40 is 50?

_____

27. Write 93% as a decimal.

_____

28. Find 80% of 110.

_____

29. 45 is what percent of 225?

_____

30. Write 60% as a fraction in simplest form.

_____

GO ON

31. Find 160% of 40.

_____

32. 50 is what percent of 20?

_____

Use the circle graph for exercises 33–34.

Animals on Oates Farm

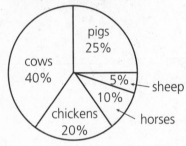

33. Of which type of animal is there the most?

_____

34. If there are 400 animals on Oates Farm, how many are pigs?

_____

Use the table for exercises 35–36.

What is your favorite type of music?	
Music Type	**Percent of Total Responses**
pop	40%
country	25%
hip hop	20%
classical	10%
other	5%

35. What size central angle would you draw to show "hip hop" on a circle graph?

_____

36. What size central angle would you draw to show "pop" on a circle graph?

_____

37. The Tornados baseball team improved its wins over last year by 50%. Last year the team won 12 games. How many games did they win this year?

_____

38. A race car driver has completed 65% of a 300-mile race. How many more miles does he need to go?

_____

39. Leroy answered 90% of the items correctly on his test. What fraction of his test items were incorrect?

_____

40. Carl's bowling team has competed in 8 matches so far this season. They have 12 more matches to play. What percent of their matches have they finished so far?

_____

STOP

Final Test – Monitoring Student Progress

☐ Form A   ☐ Form B

Name _____   Date _____

Directions: This test targets selected objectives. For each item that is answered incorrectly, cross out the item number. Then record the number of correct responses in the column labeled **Number of Correct Responses.** Add to find the **Total Number of Correct Responses** and record the total. Use this total to determine the **Total Test Score** and the **Total Percent Correct.**

Strand • Objective(s)	Item Numbers	Number of Correct Responses
Number Sense • Use place value to read and write whole numbers and decimals. • Add whole numbers and decimals. • Estimate sums and differences of whole numbers and decimals. • Multiply whole numbers and decimals. • Estimate products of whole numbers and decimals. • Express products as powers and evaluate exponential expressions.• Divide decimals by 10, 100, and 1,000. • Divide whole numbers and decimals. • Estimate quotients of whole numbers and decimals. • Identify prime or composite numbers. • Find common factors and the greatest common factors. • Find equivalent fractions and simplify fractions. • Compare and order fractions, mixed numbers, and decimals. • Add mixed numbers. • Subtract mixed numbers. • Multiply mixed numbers and whole numbers. • Divide fractions, mixed numbers, and whole numbers. • Change numbers between percents, decimals, and fractions. • Find percent of a number. • Identify and use properties of multiplication.	1, 2, 3, 4, 5, 6, 7, 8, 9, 10, 11, 12, 13, 14, 21, 22, 29, 30, 31, 33, 35	/23

Strand • Objective(s)	Item Numbers	Number of Correct Responses
Measurement • Change between and compute units of time and find elapsed time. • Change between metric units of measurement. • Choose appropriate units for measurement of length, weight/mass, and capacity. • Find the area of rectangles. • Find the circumference of circles. • Find the volume of rectangular prisms. • Use scale drawings and maps.	23, 24, 26, 32, 37, 39, 40	/7
Geometry and Spatial Sense • Measure, draw, and classify angles. • Find the unknown angles of a figure. • Use order of operations. • Solve multiplication and division equations. • Find equivalent ratios.	25, 27, 38	/3
Data Analysis and Probability • Read and interpret data in a line plot, pictograph, bar graph, and line graph. • Find the range, mean, median, and mode for a set of data. • Find the probability of a simple event. • Use skills and strategies to solve problems.	15, 16, 17, 18, 19, 20, 36	/7
Algebraic Thinking • Write and evaluate algebraic expressions.	28, 34	/2
Total Number of Correct Responses		
Total Test Score		/40
Total Percent Correct		%

Read each question carefully. Darken the circle on your answer sheet for the correct answer.

1. Name the place of the underlined digit.

4,4$\underline{7}$3,952

A. millions

B. hundred thousands

C. ten thousands

D. thousands

2. $9.232 + 48.005 + 6.537 =$ ▢

F. 205.69   **H.** 63.774

G. 122.607   **J.** 20.574

3. Estimate the sum.

$5.763 + 8.054$

A. 12   **C.** 16

B. 14   **D.** 18

4. $2.7 \times 500 =$ ▢

F. 13,500   **H.** 103.5

G. 1,350   **J.** 10.35

5. Estimate the product.

35.7×249

A. 800   **C.** 8,000

B. 900   **D.** 80,000

6. Rewrite using a base and an exponent.

$8 \times 8 \times 8 \times 8 \times 8$

F. 5^8 **H.** 8^5

G. 4^8 **J.** 8^4

7. $94.78 \div 100 =$ ▢

A. 9.478   **C.** 0.09478

B. 0.9478   **D.** 0.009478

8. $39.52 \div 7.6 =$ ▢

F. 50.2   **H.** 5.02

G. 5.2   **J.** 0.502

9. Estimate the quotient.

$4,572 \div 88$

A. 5   **C.** 350

B. 50   **D.** 500

10. What is the greatest common factor (GCF) of 32 and 56?

F 16   **H.** 4

G. 8   **J.** 3

GO ON ▶

11. What is the simplest form of $\frac{20}{35}$?

A. $\frac{4}{5}$ **C.** $\frac{4}{7}$

B. $\frac{5}{7}$ **D.** $\frac{2}{5}$

---

12. Order from least to greatest.

$\frac{1}{4}$, 0.23, $\frac{2}{9}$

F. $\frac{2}{9}$, 0.23, $\frac{1}{4}$ **H.** $\frac{2}{9}$, $\frac{1}{4}$, 0.23

G. 0.23, $\frac{2}{9}$, $\frac{1}{4}$ **J.** $\frac{1}{4}$, $\frac{2}{9}$, 0.23

---

13. $5\frac{1}{3} + 4\frac{5}{6} = $ ☐

A. $10\frac{5}{9}$ **C.** $10\frac{1}{6}$

B. $10\frac{1}{3}$ **D.** $9\frac{5}{9}$

---

14. $4\frac{3}{8} - \frac{9}{10} = $ ☐

F. $4\frac{21}{40}$ **H.** $3\frac{3}{5}$

G. $4\frac{1}{5}$ **J.** $3\frac{19}{40}$

Use the line plot for problems 15–18.

Student Visits to the Ocean Park Aquarium

```
                X
        X   X       X           X
    X   X   X   X   X   X   X
    X   X   X   X   X   X   X
    X   X   X   X   X   X   X
    0   1   2   3   4   5   6
```
Number of Visits

---

15. How many students were included in the survey?

A. 26 students **C.** 20 students

B. 23 students **D.** 6 students

---

16. Find the range of the number of visits.

F. 3 **H.** 5

G. 4 **J.** 6

---

17. Which other kind of display would not be appropriate to show the data?

A. line graph

B. pictograph

C. frequency table

D. double-bar graph

---

18. If each ticket cost $3, what was the total amount of money the students spent on tickets to the Ocean Park Aquarium in the summer?

F. $252 **H.** $177

G. $234 **J.** $63

---

19. Find the mean.

1, 11, 10, 3, 5, 4, 9, 8, 3

A. 8 **C.** 6

B. 7 **D.** 5

---

20. Find the mode.

2, 10, 3, 4, 7, 4, 3, 8, 4

F. 3 **G.** 4 **H.** 5 **J.** 8

GO ON

21. $20\frac{5}{8} \times 15\frac{3}{5} = $ ▨

   A. $3,139\frac{1}{4}$ **C.** $321\frac{3}{4}$

   B. $322\frac{1}{20}$ **D.** $320\frac{4}{5}$

---

22. $82 \div 10\frac{1}{4} = $ ▨

   F. 840.5   **H.** 20.5
   G. 801   **J.** 8

---

23. Find the time that is 4 hours
30 minutes after 7:45 A.M.

   A. 11:15 A.M.   **C.** 12:15 P.M.
   B. 11:45 A.M.   **D.** 12:45 P.M.

---

24. 8 km = ▨ m

   F. 80,000   **H.** 800
   G. 8,000   **J.** 80

---

25. Identify the angle.

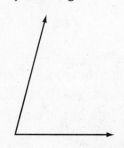

   A. acute   **C.** obtuse
   B. right   **D.** straight

---

26. Find the approximate circumference.
Use 3.14 for pi.

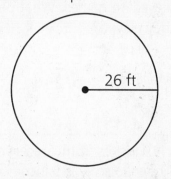

26 ft

   F. 2,122 ft   **H.** 163 ft
   G. 1,061 ft   **J.** 82 ft

---

27. Rob measures the angles of a triangle
as 47° and 68°. What is the measure
of the third angle?

   A. 145°   **C.** 75°
   B. 115°   **D.** 65°

---

28. Solve for p.

   $6p = 84$

   F. 504   **H.** 78
   G. 90   **J.** 14

---

29. Complete the ratio.

   $32:5 = $ ▨ $:20$

   A. 64   **C.** 128
   B. 96   **D.** 160

---

30. Write 45% as a fraction.

   F. $\frac{1}{3}$ **G.** $\frac{2}{5}$ **H.** $\frac{9}{20}$ **J.** $\frac{1}{2}$

GO ON ▶

31. The Bangley Tennis team plays 40 games per season. So far, they have played 14 games. What percent have they played?

    A. 35%   **C.** 30%

    B. $33\frac{1}{3}$%   **D.** 25%

32. Joyess is 9 inches from Gracely on a map. The map scale is 3 inches = 14 miles. How far apart are the towns?

    F. 378 miles   **H.** 84 miles

    G. 126 miles   **J.** 42 miles

33. Identify the property used.

$$4 \times 12\frac{4}{7} = (4 \times 12) + (4 \times \frac{4}{7})$$

    A. Identity Property

    B. Commutative Property

    C. Associative Property

    D. Distributive Property of Multiplication over Addition

34. Write an expression for the situation. Nine times a number n increased by 3.

    F. $9n + 3$ **H.** $9n + 3n$

    G. $3(9n)$ **J.** $9n - 3$

35. Which number is prime?

    A. 9   **C.** 47

    B. 33   **D.** 91

36. Use the spinner.

What is the probability of spinning red?

    F. $\frac{2}{5}$ **G.** $\frac{1}{4}$ **H.** $\frac{3}{4}$ **J.** $\frac{1}{3}$

37. Which is the most reasonable unit for measuring the weight of a kitchen table?

    A. kilogram   **C** centimeter

    B. gram   **D.** milligram

38. Simplify using order of operations.

$$55 + 8 \times 4 - (27 \div 3) = \boxed{}$$

    F. 252 **G.** 87 **H.** 78 **J.** 61

39. Dani is filling a box that is 24 inches by 16 inches by 5 inches. What is its volume?

    A. 1,920 in.^{3} **C.** 384 in.^{3}

    B. 1,168 in.^{3} **D.** 90 in.^{3}

40. The city built a rectangular park that is 150 yards long by 100 yards wide. What is the area of the park?

    F. 250 square yards

    G. 500 square yards

    H. 15,000 square yards

    J. 150,000 square yards

STOP

Read each question carefully. Fill in the correct answer in the space provided.

1. Name the place of the underlined digit.

7,83<u>8</u>,456

_____

_____

2. 49.6 + 18.004 + 222.5 =

_____

3. Estimate the sum.

3.697 + 9.045

_____

_____

4. 3.9 × 600 = _____

_____

5. Estimate the product.

28.7 × 495

_____

6. Rewrite using a base as an exponent.

4 × 4 × 4 × 4 × 4 × 4

_____

_____

7. 28.54 ÷ 100 = _____

_____

8. 48.24 ÷ 6.7 = _____

_____

9. Estimate the quotient.

3,888 ÷ 77

_____

_____

10. Write the greatest common factor (GCF) of 48 and 64.

_____

11. Write $\frac{25}{35}$ in simplest form.

_____

12. Order from least to greatest.

$\frac{1}{4}$, 0.23, $\frac{2}{7}$

_____

_____

13. $7\frac{5}{6} + 2\frac{1}{3} =$ _____

_____

14. $6\frac{1}{8} - \frac{7}{10} =$ _____

_____

Use the line plot for problems 15–18.

Student Visits to the Ocean Park Aquarium

```
                    X
        X   X               X               X
    X   X   X   X   X   X   X
    X   X   X   X   X   X   X
    X   X   X   X   X   X   X
    0   1   2   3   4   5   6
```
Number of Visits

15. How many students visited the aquarium two times?

_____

_____

16. Find the median of the number of visits.

_____

17. Write *true* or *false*. A double-bar graph could also be used to show the data.

_____

18. If each ticket cost $4, what was the total amount of money the students spent on tickets to the Ocean Park Aquarium in the summer?

_____

_____

19. Find the mean.

1, 12, 10, 3, 6, 2, 8, 3, 9

_____

20. Find the mode.

2, 12, 10, 3, 6, 2, 8, 3, 2

_____

21. $5\frac{3}{8} \times 15\frac{2}{5} =$ _____

_____

22. $87 \div 4\frac{1}{7} =$ _____

_____

23. Find the time that is 8 hours 30 minutes after 7:15 A.M.

_____

_____

24. 4 km = _____ m

_____

25. Identify the angle as acute, right, or obtuse.

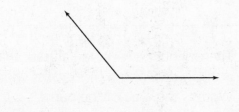

_____

26. Find the circumference. Use 3.14 for pi.

.15 ft

_____

_____

27. Rhonda measures the angles of a triangle as 43° and 52°. What is the measure of the third angle?

_____

_____

28. Solve for m.

$7m = 63$

_____

_____

29. Complete the ratio.

$9:14 =$ _____ $:126$

_____

30. Write 55% as a fraction.

_____

31. The Canton Soccer team plays 20 games per season. So far, they have played 15 games. What percent have they played?

_____

_____

32. Duxbury is 8 inches from Newton on a map. The map scale is 3 inches = 15 miles. How far apart are the towns?

_____

_____

33. Write the property used.

$3 \times 13\frac{3}{8} = (3 \times 13) + (3 \times \frac{3}{8})$

_____

_____

34. Write an expression for the situation.

Seven times a number n increased by 5.

_____

_____

35. Which number is prime?

25   37   57   69

_____

36. Use the spinner.

What is the probability of spinning blue?

_____

_____

37. Write the most reasonable metric unit for measuring the weight of a wooden chair.

_____

_____

38. Simplify using order of operations.

$22 + 7 \times 3 - (12 \div 4)$ _____

_____

39. Rebecca is filling a box that is 32 inches by 10 inches by 3 inches. What is its volume?

_____

_____

40. The city built a rectangular park that is 200 yards long by 120 yards wide. What is the area of the park?

_____

STOP

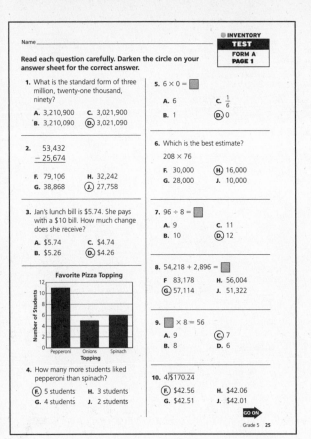

Read each question carefully. Darken the circle on your answer sheet for the correct answer.

1. What is the standard form of three million, twenty-one thousand, ninety?

A. 3,210,900   C. 3,021,900
B. 3,210,090   (D.) 3,021,090

2. 53,432
− 25,674

F. 79,106   H. 32,242
G. 38,868   (J.) 27,758

3. Jan's lunch bill is $5.74. She pays with a $10 bill. How much change does she receive?

A. $5.74   C. $4.74
B. $5.26   (D.) $4.26

Favorite Pizza Topping

(bar graph: Number of Students vs Topping — Pepperoni ~11, Onions ~5, Spinach ~6)

4. How many more students liked pepperoni than spinach?

(F.) 5 students   H. 3 students
G. 4 students   J. 2 students

5. 6 × 0 = ▢

A. 6   C. $\frac{1}{6}$
B. 1   (D.) 0

6. Which is the best estimate?
208 × 76

F. 30,000   (H.) 16,000
G. 28,000   J. 10,000

7. 96 ÷ 8 = ▢

A. 9   C. 11
B. 10   (D.) 12

8. 54,218 + 2,896 = ▢

F 83,178   H. 56,004
(G.) 57,114 J. 51,322

9. ▢ × 8 = 56

A. 9   (C.) 7
B. 8   D. 6

10. 4)$170.24

(F.) $42.56   H. $42.06
G. $42.51   J. $42.01

GO ON

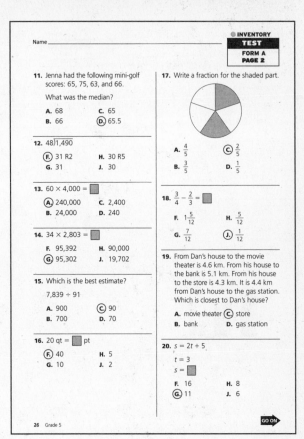

11. Jenna had the following mini-golf scores: 65, 75, 63, and 66.
What was the median?

A. 68   C. 65
B. 66   (D.) 65.5

12. 48)1,490

(F.) 31 R2   H. 30 R5
G. 31   J. 30

13. 60 × 4,000 = ▢

(A.) 240,000   C. 2,400
B. 24,000   D. 240

14. 34 × 2,803 = ▢

F. 95,392   H. 90,000
(G.) 95,302 J. 19,702

15. Which is the best estimate?
7,839 ÷ 91

A. 900   (C.) 90
B. 700   D. 70

16. 20 qt = ▢ pt

(F.) 40   H. 5
G. 10   J. 2

17. Write a fraction for the shaded part.

(circle divided into 5 parts, some shaded)

A. $\frac{4}{5}$ (C.) $\frac{2}{5}$
B. $\frac{3}{5}$ D. $\frac{1}{5}$

18. $\frac{3}{4} - \frac{2}{3} = $ ▢

F. $1\frac{5}{12}$ H. $\frac{5}{12}$
G. $\frac{7}{12}$ (J.) $\frac{1}{12}$

19. From Dan's house to the movie theater is 4.6 km. From his house to the bank is 5.1 km. From his house to the store is 4.3 km. It is 4.4 km from Dan's house to the gas station. Which is closest to Dan's house?

A. movie theater   (C.) store
B. bank   D. gas station

20. $s = 2t + 5$
$t = 3$
$s = $ ▢

F. 16   H. 8
(G.) 11 J. 6

GO ON

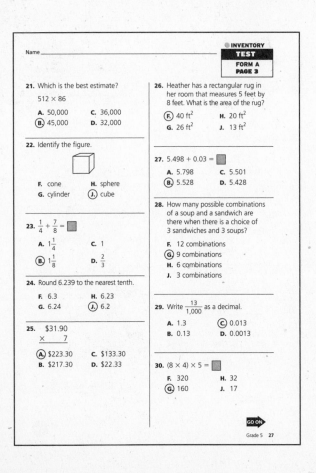

21. Which is the best estimate?
512 × 86

A. 50,000   C. 36,000
(B.) 45,000 D. 32,000

22. Identify the figure.

(cube figure)

F. cone   H. sphere
G. cylinder (J.) cube

23. $\frac{1}{4} + \frac{7}{8} = $ ▢

A. $1\frac{1}{4}$ C. 1
(B.) $1\frac{1}{8}$ D. $\frac{2}{3}$

24. Round 6.239 to the nearest tenth.

F. 6.3   H. 6.23
G. 6.24   (J.) 6.2

25. $31.90
× 7

(A.) $223.30   C. $133.30
B. $217.30   D. $22.33

26. Heather has a rectangular rug in her room that measures 5 feet by 8 feet. What is the area of the rug?

(F.) 40 ft²   H. 20 ft²
G. 26 ft²   J. 13 ft²

27. 5.498 + 0.03 = ▢

A. 5.798   C. 5.501
(B.) 5.528 D. 5.428

28. How many possible combinations of a soup and a sandwich are there when there is a choice of 3 sandwiches and 3 soups?

F. 12 combinations
(G.) 9 combinations
H. 6 combinations
J. 3 combinations

29. Write $\frac{13}{1,000}$ as a decimal.

A. 1.3   (C.) 0.013
B. 0.13   D. 0.0013

30. (8 × 4) × 5 = ▢

F. 320   H. 32
(G.) 160 J. 17

GO ON

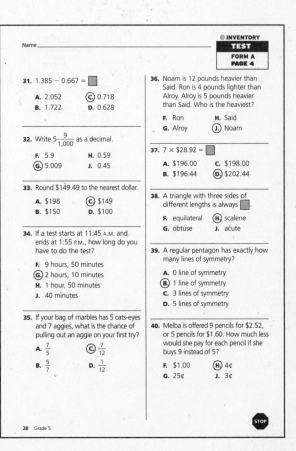

31. 1.385 − 0.667 = ▢

A. 2.052   (C.) 0.718
B. 1.722   D. 0.628

32. Write $5\frac{9}{1,000}$ as a decimal.

F. 5.9   H. 0.59
(G.) 5.009 J. 0.45

33. Round $149.49 to the nearest dollar.

A. $198   (C.) $149
B. $150   D. $100

34. If a test starts at 11:45 A.M. and ends at 1:55 P.M., how long do you have to do the test?

F. 9 hours, 50 minutes
(G.) 2 hours, 10 minutes
H. 1 hour, 50 minutes
J. 40 minutes

35. If your bag of marbles has 5 cats-eyes and 7 aggies, what is the chance of pulling out an aggie on your first try?

A. $\frac{7}{5}$ (C.) $\frac{7}{12}$
B. $\frac{5}{7}$ D. $\frac{1}{12}$

36. Noam is 12 pounds heavier than Said. Ron is 4 pounds lighter than Alroy. Alroy is 5 pounds heavier than Said. Who is the heaviest?

F. Ron   H. Said
G. Alroy (J.) Noam

37. 7 × $28.92 = ▢

A. $196.00   C. $198.00
B. $196.44   (D.) $202.44

38. A triangle with three sides of different lengths is always ▢.

F. equilateral   (H.) scalene
G. obtuse   J. acute

39. A regular pentagon has exactly how many lines of symmetry?

A. 0 line of symmetry
(B.) 1 line of symmetry
C. 3 lines of symmetry
D. 5 lines of symmetry

40. Melba is offered 9 pencils for $2.52, or 5 pencils for $1.60. How much less would she pay for each pencil if she buys 9 instead of 5?

F. $1.00   (H.) 4¢
G. 25¢   J. 3¢

STOP

Inventory

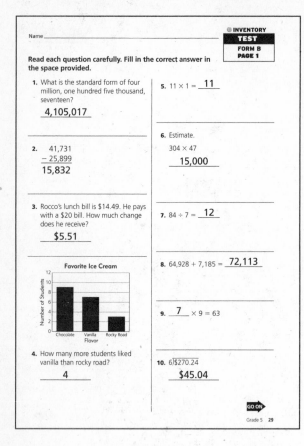

Name _____

● INVENTORY
TEST
FORM B
PAGE 1

Read each question carefully. Fill in the correct answer in the space provided.

1. What is the standard form of four million, one hundred five thousand, seventeen?

4,105,017

2. 41,731
  − 25,899
  15,832

3. Rocco's lunch bill is $14.49. He pays with a $20 bill. How much change does he receive?

$5.51

Favorite Ice Cream

4. How many more students liked vanilla than rocky road?

4

5. 11 × 1 = __11__

6. Estimate.
  304 × 47
  15,000

7. 84 ÷ 7 = __12__

8. 64,928 + 7,185 = __72,113__

9. __7__ × 9 = 63

10. 6)$270.24
  $45.04

GO ON
Grade 5 **29**

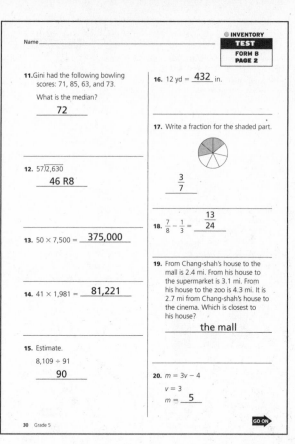

Name _____

● INVENTORY
TEST
FORM B
PAGE 2

11. Gini had the following bowling scores: 71, 85, 63, and 73.
What is the median?
  72

12. 57)2,630
  46 R8

13. 50 × 7,500 = __375,000__

14. 41 × 1,981 = __81,221__

15. Estimate.
  8,109 ÷ 91
  90

16. 12 yd = __432__ in.

17. Write a fraction for the shaded part.

  3
  7

18. $\frac{7}{8} - \frac{1}{3}$ = **13**
  24

19. From Chang-shah's house to the mall is 2.4 mi. From his house to the supermarket is 3.1 mi. From his house to the zoo is 4.3 mi. It is 2.7 mi from Chang-shah's house to the cinema. Which is closest to his house?

  the mall

20. m = 3v − 4
  v = 3
  m = __5__

GO ON

30 Grade 5

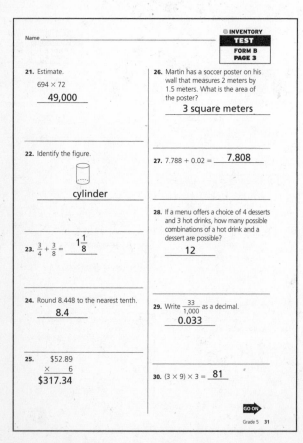

Name _____

● INVENTORY
TEST
FORM B
PAGE 3

21. Estimate.
  694 × 72
  49,000

22. Identify the figure.

  cylinder

23. $\frac{3}{4} + \frac{3}{8}$ = **1$\frac{1}{8}$**

24. Round 8.448 to the nearest tenth.
  8.4

25. $52.89
  ×   6
  $317.34

26. Martin has a soccer poster on his wall that measures 2 meters by 1.5 meters. What is the area of the poster?

  3 square meters

27. 7.788 + 0.02 = __7.808__

28. If a menu offers a choice of 4 desserts and 3 hot drinks, how many possible combinations of a hot drink and a dessert are possible?

  12

29. Write $\frac{33}{1,000}$ as a decimal.

  0.033

30. (3 × 9) × 3 = __81__

GO ON
Grade 5 **31**

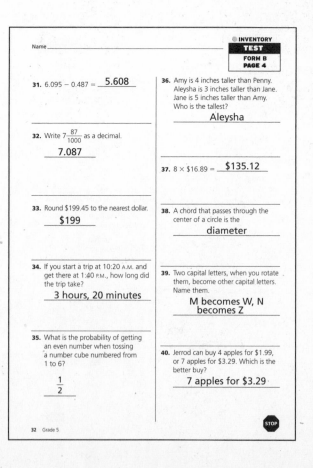

Name _____

● INVENTORY
TEST
FORM B
PAGE 4

31. 6.095 − 0.487 = __5.608__

32. Write $7\frac{87}{1000}$ as a decimal.

  7.087

33. Round $199.45 to the nearest dollar.
  $199

34. If you start a trip at 10:20 A.M. and get there at 1:40 P.M., how long did the trip take?

  3 hours, 20 minutes

35. What is the probability of getting an even number when tossing a number cube numbered from 1 to 6?

  $\frac{1}{2}$

36. Amy is 4 inches taller than Penny. Aleysha is 3 inches taller than Jane. Jane is 5 inches taller than Amy. Who is the tallest?

  Aleysha

37. 8 × $16.89 = __$135.12__

38. A chord that passes through the center of a circle is the

  diameter

39. Two capital letters, when you rotate them, become other capital letters. Name them.

  M becomes W, N becomes Z

40. Jerrod can buy 4 apples for $1.99, or 7 apples for $3.29. Which is the better buy?

  7 apples for $3.29

STOP

32 Grade 5

Chapter 1

Name _____

Read each question carefully. Darken the circle on your answer sheet for the correct answer.

1. Which is the most likely amount of juice in the full glass?

A. 5 ounces   **C.** 10 ounces
B. 6 ounces   D. 15 ounces

2. Which is most likely the number of marbles in the full jar?

F. 60 marbles   **H.** 150 marbles
G. 90 marbles   J. 300 marbles

3. Name the underlined place value.

32<u>1</u>,654

A. ones   C. hundreds
B. tens   **D.** thousands

4. Write fifteen million, three hundred twenty-four thousand, fifty-seven in standard form.

F. 1,532,457   H. 7,542,351
G. 5,732,415   **J.** 15,324,057

5. 30,000,000 + 20,000 + 3,000 + 500 + 10 + 7 =

A. 323,517   **C.** 30,023,517
B. 3,023,517   D. 32,003,517

6. Order from least to greatest.

0.235, 1.05, 0.073, 1.10

F. 0.073, 0.235, 1.05, 1.10
G. 1.10, 1.05, 0.235, 0.073
H. 0.073, 0.235, 1.10, 1.05
J. 1.05, 1.10, 0.235, 0.073

7. Name the underlined place value.

3,113.2<u>0</u>5

A. thousands
B. thousandths
C. hundreds
D. hundredths

8. Which number is greater than 86,507.508?

F. 86,505.329   H. 86,507.041
G. 86,507.093   **J.** 86,507.724

9. Which digit makes the sentence true?

1,238 > 1,2☐8

A. 2   C. 4
B. 3   D. 5

10. Which is the most likely price for the second bunch of bananas?

$2.07

F. $6   **H.** $12
G. $8   J. $20

GO ON

Name _____

11. Order from greatest to least.

1.092, 1.102, 0.805, 0.812

A. 1.092, 1.102, 0.812, 0.805
B. 1.092, 1.102, 0.805, 0.812
C. 1.102, 1.092, 0.812, 0.805
D. 1.102, 1.092, 0.805, 0.812

12. Which number has 7 in the tenths place?

F. 23.07   H. 17.34
G. 72.12   **J.** 56.75

13. Which number is less than 124.0234?

A. 125.0022   C. 124.0321
B. 124.0222   D. 124.1203

14. Which digit makes the sentence true?

0.0285 < 0.02☐5

F. 6   G. 7   H. 8   **J.** 9

15. 40,000,000 + 700,000 + 60,000 + 200 + 90 + 1 = ☐

A. 40, 076,291   C. 47,600,291
B. 40,760,291   D. 47,629,100

16. Write the expanded form.

62,058.7

F. 60,000 + 2,000 + 50 + 8 + 0.7
G. 60,000 + 2,000 + 500 + 8 + 0.7
H. 600,000 + 20,000 + 500 + 80 + 7
J. 600,000 + 20,000 + 5,000 + 80 + 7

17. In the solar system, four planets have a diameter larger than Earth's—Uranus (51,200 km), Saturn (120,540 km), Jupiter (142,980 km), and Neptune (49,500 km). List them from largest to smallest.

A. Jupiter, Saturn, Uranus, Neptune
B. Saturn, Jupiter, Uranus, Neptune
C. Jupiter, Saturn, Neptune, Uranus
D. Saturn, Jupiter, Neptune, Uranus

18. The populations of four cities are: Baltimore (651,154), Memphis (650,100), Milwaukee (596,974), Boston (589,141). Which two cities have about the same population?

F. Milwaukee and Boston
G. Baltimore and Memphis
H. Memphis and Milwaukee
J. Boston and Baltimore

19. Minneapolis has a population of 382,618. Miami has a population of 362,470. Which place value determines which number is greater?

A. millions
B. hundred thousands
C. ten thousands
D. thousands

20. In a 100-meter race, Erin had a time of 13.3 seconds, Dave's time was 14.1 seconds, Sara's was 13.9 seconds and Matias's was 14.2 seconds. List them in order from fastest to slowest.

F. Erin, Sara, Dave, Matias
G. Dave, Matias, Sara, Erin
H. Sara, Erin, Matias, Dave
J. Matias, Dave, Sara, Erin

STOP

Name _____

Read each question carefully. Fill in the correct answer in the space provided.

1. Which is the more likely number of pennies in the full jar, 300 or 600?

300 pennies

2. Which is the more reasonable amount of juice in the full glass, 6 ounces or 12 ounces?

12 ounces

3. Name the underlined place value.

8<u>9</u>2,917

ten thousands

4. Write twenty-seven million, three hundred eight thousand, one hundred seven in standard form.

27,308,107

5. 80,000,000 + 9,000,000 + 50,000 + 6,000 + 100 + 20 + 3 =

89,056,123

6. Order from least to greatest.

12.086, 12.105, 12.720, 12.009

12.009, 12.086, 12.105, 12.720

7. Name the underlined place value.

847.2<u>5</u>3

hundredths

8. Compare. Write >, <, or =.

156,842,370 ◯ 156,842,048

>

9. Write a digit that makes the sentence true.

1.0786 < 1.0☐86

8 or 9

10. Which is the more likely number of pages in the larger book? 150 or 500?

50 pages

150 pages

GO ON

Name _____

11. Order from greatest to least.

17.628, 17.268, 17.609, 17.097

17.628, 17.609, 17.268, 17.097

12. Name the place of the 6 in the number 12.654.

tenths

13. Compare. Write >, <, or =.

13.2 ☐ 13.20

=

14. Write a digit that makes the sentence true.

180.065 > 1__5.324

7, 6, 5, 4, 3, 2, 1, or 0

15. 70,000,000 + 4,000,000 + 3,000 + 900 + 8 =

74,003,908

16. Write the expanded form.

48,562.3

forty-eight thousand five hundred sixty-two and three tenths

17. In the solar system, there are four large planets with a diameter smaller than Earth's—Mars (6,794 km), Venus (12,104 km), Pluto (2,200 km), and Mercury (4,878 km). List these planets from largest to smallest.

Venus, Mars, Mercury, Pluto

18. The populations of four cities are listed below.

Lexington	260,512
Newark	273,546
Anchorage	260,283
Louisville	256,231

Which two cities have about the same population?

Lexington and Anchorage

19. Dallas has a population of 1,188,580. San Antonio has a population of 1,144,646. Which place determines which number is greater?

ten thousands

20. At a track meet, Miguel's longest jump was 11.3 meters, Paul's was 12.4 meters, Lina's was 11.2 meters, and Kylie's was 11.9 meters. List the jumpers in order from shortest to longest jump.

Lina, Miguel, Kylie, Paul

STOP

Chapter 2

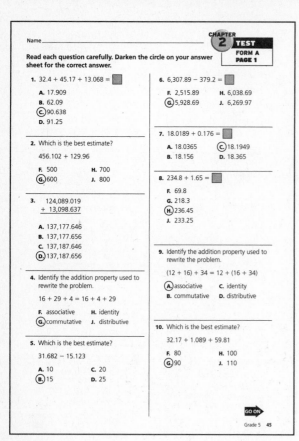

CHAPTER 2 TEST
FORM A
PAGE 1

Read each question carefully. Darken the circle on your answer sheet for the correct answer.

1. 32.4 + 45.17 + 13.068 = ▨

- **A.** 17.909
- **B.** 62.09
- **(C.)** 90.638
- **D.** 91.25

2. Which is the best estimate?

456.102 + 129.96

- **F.** 500
- **(G.)** 600
- **H.** 700
- **J.** 800

3.   124,089.019
  + 13,098.637

- **A.** 137,177.646
- **B.** 137,177.656
- **C.** 137,187.646
- **(D.)** 137,187.656

4. Identify the addition property used to rewrite the problem.

16 + 29 + 4 = 16 + 4 + 29

- **F.** associative
- **(G.)** commutative
- **H.** identity
- **J.** distributive

5. Which is the best estimate?

31.682 − 15.123

- **A.** 10
- **(B.)** 15
- **C.** 20
- **D.** 25

6. 6,307.89 − 379.2 = ▨

- **F.** 2,515.89
- **(G.)** 5,928.69
- **H.** 6,038.69
- **J.** 6,269.97

7. 18.0189 + 0.176 = ▨

- **A.** 18.0365
- **B.** 18.156
- **(C.)** 18.1949
- **D.** 18.365

8. 234.8 + 1.65 = ▨

- **F.** 69.8
- **G.** 218.3
- **(H.)** 236.45
- **J.** 233.25

9. Identify the addition property used to rewrite the problem.

(12 + 16) + 34 = 12 + (16 + 34)

- **(A.)** associative
- **B.** commutative
- **C.** identity
- **D.** distributive

10. Which is the best estimate?

32.17 + 1.089 + 59.81

- **F.** 80
- **(G.)** 90
- **H.** 100
- **J.** 110

GO ON

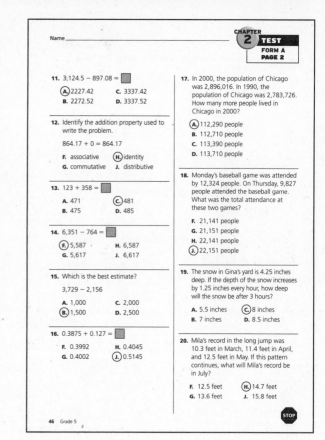

CHAPTER 2 TEST
FORM A
PAGE 2

11. 3,124.5 − 897.08 = ▨

- **(A.)** 2227.42
- **B.** 2272.52
- **C.** 3337.42
- **D.** 3337.52

12. Identify the addition property used to write the problem.

864.17 + 0 = 864.17

- **F.** associative
- **G.** commutative
- **(H.)** identity
- **J.** distributive

13. 123 + 358 = ▨

- **A.** 471
- **B.** 475
- **(C.)** 481
- **D.** 485

14. 6,351 − 764 = ▨

- **(F.)** 5,587
- **G.** 5,617
- **H.** 6,587
- **J.** 6,617

15. Which is the best estimate?

3,729 − 2,156

- **A.** 1,000
- **(B.)** 1,500
- **C.** 2,000
- **D.** 2,500

16. 0.3875 + 0.127 = ▨

- **F.** 0.3992
- **G.** 0.4002
- **H.** 0.4045
- **(J.)** 0.5145

17. In 2000, the population of Chicago was 2,896,016. In 1990, the population of Chicago was 2,783,726. How many more people lived in Chicago in 2000?

- **(A.)** 112,290 people
- **B.** 112,710 people
- **C.** 113,390 people
- **D.** 113,710 people

18. Monday's baseball game was attended by 12,324 people. On Thursday, 9,827 people attended the baseball game. What was the total attendance at these two games?

- **F.** 21,141 people
- **G.** 21,151 people
- **H.** 22,141 people
- **(J.)** 22,151 people

19. The snow in Gina's yard is 4.25 inches deep. If the depth of the snow increases by 1.25 inches every hour, how deep will the snow be after 3 hours?

- **A.** 5.5 inches
- **B.** 7 inches
- **(C.)** 8 inches
- **D.** 8.5 inches

20. Mila's record in the long jump was 10.3 feet in March, 11.4 feet in April, and 12.5 feet in May. If this pattern continues, what will Mila's record be in July?

- **F.** 12.5 feet
- **G.** 13.6 feet
- **(H.)** 14.7 feet
- **J.** 15.8 feet

STOP

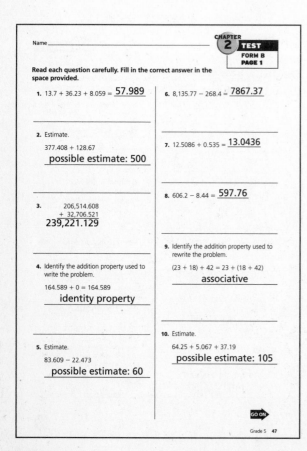

CHAPTER 2 TEST
FORM B
PAGE 1

Read each question carefully. Fill in the correct answer in the space provided.

1. 13.7 + 36.23 + 8.059 = __57.989__

2. Estimate.

377.408 + 128.67

   possible estimate: 500

3.   206,514.608
  + 32,706.521
  239,221.129

4. Identify the addition property used to write the problem.

164.589 + 0 = 164.589

   identity property

5. Estimate.

83.609 − 22.473

   possible estimate: 60

6. 8,135.77 − 268.4 = __7867.37__

7. 12.5086 + 0.535 = __13.0436__

8. 606.2 − 8.44 = __597.76__

9. Identify the addition property used to rewrite the problem.

(23 + 18) + 42 = 23 + (18 + 42)

   associative

10. Estimate.

64.25 + 5.067 + 37.19

   possible estimate: 105

GO ON

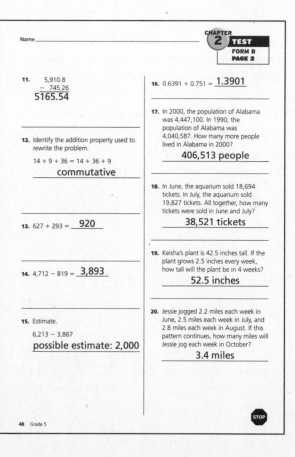

CHAPTER 2 TEST
FORM B
PAGE 2

11.   5,910.8
  − 745.26
  5165.54

12. Identify the addition property used to rewrite the problem.

14 + 9 + 36 = 14 + 36 + 9

   commutative

13. 627 + 293 = __920__

14. 4,712 − 819 = __3,893__

15. Estimate.

6,213 − 3,867

   possible estimate: 2,000

16. 0.6391 + 0.751 = __1.3901__

17. In 2000, the population of Alabama was 4,447,100. In 1990, the population of Alabama was 4,040,587. How many more people lived in Alabama in 2000?

   __406,513 people__

18. In June, the aquarium sold 18,694 tickets. In July, the aquarium sold 19,827 tickets. All together, how many tickets were sold in June and July?

   __38,521 tickets__

19. Keisha's plant is 42.5 inches tall. If the plant grows 2.5 inches every week, how tall will the plant be in 4 weeks?

   __52.5 inches__

20. Jessie jogged 2.2 miles each week in June, 2.5 miles each week in July, and 2.8 miles each week in August. If this pattern continues, how many miles will Jessie jog each week in October?

   __3.4 miles__

STOP

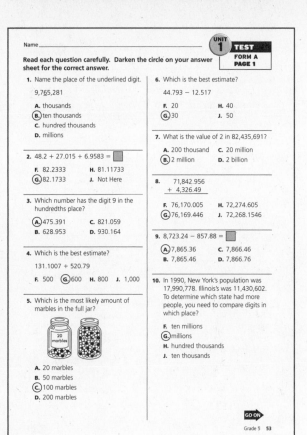

Name _____

UNIT 1 TEST FORM A PAGE 1

Read each question carefully. Darken the circle on your answer sheet for the correct answer.

1. Name the place of the underlined digit.

9,765,281

A. thousands
B. ten thousands ●
C. hundred thousands
D. millions

2. 48.2 + 27.015 + 6.9583 = ☐

F. 82.2333
G. 82.1733 ●
H. 81.11733
J. Not Here

3. Which number has the digit 9 in the hundredths place?

A. 475.391 ●
B. 628.953
C. 821.059
D. 930.164

4. Which is the best estimate?

131.1007 + 520.79

F. 500   G. 600 ●   H. 800   J. 1,000

5. Which is the most likely amount of marbles in the full jar?

A. 20 marbles
B. 50 marbles
C. 100 marbles ●
D. 200 marbles

6. Which is the best estimate?

44.793 − 12.517

F. 20   H. 40
G. 30 ●   J. 50

7. What is the value of 2 in 82,435,691?

A. 200 thousand   C. 20 million
B. 2 million ●   D. 2 billion

8.

71,842.956
+ 4,326.49

F. 76,170.005   H. 72,274.605
G. 76,169.446 ●   J. 72,268.1546

9. 8,723.24 − 857.88 = ☐

A. 7,865.36 ●   C. 7,866.46
B. 7,865.46   D. 7,866.76

10. In 1990, New York's population was 17,990,778. Illinois's was 11,430,602. To determine which state had more people, you need to compare digits in which place?

F. ten millions
G. millions ●
H. hundred thousands
J. ten thousands

GO ON

Grade 5   53

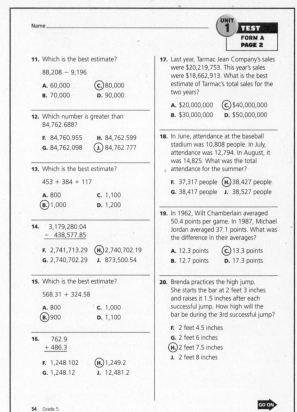

Name _____

UNIT 1 TEST FORM A PAGE 2

11. Which is the best estimate?

88,208 − 9,196

A. 60,000   C. 80,000 ●
B. 70,000   D. 90,000

12. Which number is greater than 84,762.688?

F. 84,760.955   H. 84,762.599
G. 84,762.098   J. 84,762.777 ●

13. Which is the best estimate?

453 + 384 + 117

A. 800   C. 1,100
B. 1,000 ●   D. 1,200

14.

3,179,280.04
− 438,577.85

F. 2,741,713.29   H. 2,740,702.19 ●
G. 2,740,702.29   J. 873,500.54

15. Which is the best estimate?

568.31 + 324.58

A. 800   C. 1,000
B. 900 ●   D. 1,100

16.

762.9
+ 486.3

F. 1,248.102   H. 1,249.2 ●
G. 1,248.12   J. 12,481.2

17. Last year, Tarmac Jean Company's sales were $20,219,753. This year's sales were $18,662,913. What is the best estimate of Tarmac's total sales for the two years?

A. $20,000,000   C. $40,000,000 ●
B. $30,000,000   D. $50,000,000

18. In June, attendance at the baseball stadium was 10,808 people. In July, attendance was 12,794. In August, it was 14,825. What was the total attendance for the summer?

F. 37,317 people   H. 38,427 people ●
G. 38,417 people   J. 38,527 people

19. In 1962, Wilt Chamberlain averaged 50.4 points per game. In 1987, Michael Jordan averaged 37.1 points. What was the difference in their averages?

A. 12.3 points   C. 13.3 points ●
B. 12.7 points   D. 17.3 points

20. Brenda practices the high jump. She starts the bar at 2 feet 3 inches and raises it 1.5 inches after each successful jump. How high will the bar be during the 3rd successful jump?

F. 2 feet 4.5 inches
G. 2 feet 6 inches
H. 2 feet 7.5 inches ●
J. 2 feet 8 inches

GO ON

54   Grade 5

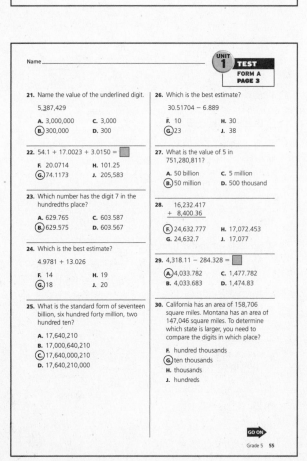

Name _____

UNIT 1 TEST FORM A PAGE 3

21. Name the value of the underlined digit.

5,387,429

A. 3,000,000   C. 3,000
B. 300,000 ●   D. 300

22. 54.1 + 17.0023 + 3.0150 = ☐

F. 20.0714   H. 101.25
G. 74.1173 ●   J. 205,583

23. Which number has the digit 7 in the hundredths place?

A. 629.765   C. 603.587
B. 629.575 ●   D. 603.567

24. Which is the best estimate?

4.9781 + 13.026

F. 14   H. 19
G. 18 ●   J. 20

25. What is the standard form of seventeen billion, six hundred forty million, two hundred ten?

A. 17,640,210
B. 17,000,640,210
C. 17,640,000,210 ●
D. 17,640,210,000

26. Which is the best estimate?

30.51704 − 6.889

F. 10   H. 30
G. 23 ●   J. 38

27. What is the value of 5 in 751,280,811?

A. 50 billion   C. 5 million
B. 50 million ●   D. 500 thousand

28.

16,232.417
+ 8,400.36

F. 24,632.777 ●   H. 17,072.453
G. 24,632.7   J. 17,077

29. 4,318.11 − 284.328 = ☐

A. 4,033.782 ●   C. 1,477.782
B. 4,033.683   D. 1,474.83

30. California has an area of 158,706 square miles. Montana has an area of 147,046 square miles. To determine which state is larger, you need to compare the digits in which place?

F. hundred thousands
G. ten thousands ●
H. thousands
J. hundreds

GO ON

Grade 5   55

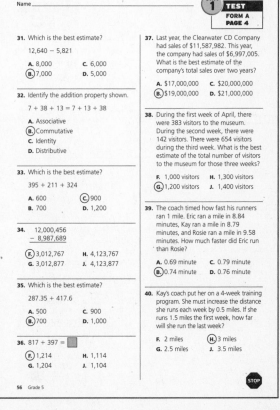

Name _____

UNIT 1 TEST FORM A PAGE 4

31. Which is the best estimate?

12,640 − 5,821

A. 8,000   C. 6,000
B. 7,000 ●   D. 5,000

32. Identify the addition property shown.

7 + 38 + 13 = 7 + 13 + 38

A. Associative
B. Commutative ●
C. Identity
D. Distributive

33. Which is the best estimate?

395 + 211 + 324

A. 600   C. 900 ●
B. 700   D. 1,200

34.

12,000,456
− 8,987,689

F. 3,012,767 ●   H. 4,123,767
G. 3,012,877   J. 4,123,877

35. Which is the best estimate?

287.35 + 417.6

A. 500   C. 900
B. 700 ●   D. 1,000

36. 817 + 397 = ☐

F. 1,214 ●   H. 1,114
G. 1,204   J. 1,104

37. Last year, the Clearwater CD Company had sales of $11,587,982. This year, the company had sales of $6,997,005. What is the best estimate of the company's total sales over two years?

A. $17,000,000   C. $20,000,000
B. $19,000,000 ●   D. $21,000,000

38. During the first week of April, there were 383 visitors to the museum. During the second week, there were 142 visitors. There were 654 visitors during the third week. What is the best estimate of the total number of visitors to the museum for those three weeks?

F. 1,000 visitors   H. 1,300 visitors
G. 1,200 visitors ●   J. 1,400 visitors

39. The coach timed how fast his runners ran 1 mile. Eric ran a mile in 8.84 minutes, Kay ran a mile in 8.79 minutes, and Rosie ran a mile in 9.58 minutes. How much faster did Eric run than Rosie?

A. 0.69 minute   C. 0.79 minute
B. 0.74 minute ●   D. 0.76 minute

40. Kay's coach put her on a 4-week training program. She must increase the distance she runs each week by 0.5 miles. If she runs 1.5 miles the first week, how far will she run the last week?

F. 2 miles   H. 3 miles ●
G. 2.5 miles   J. 3.5 miles

STOP

56   Grade 5

Page 1 (Form B, Page 1)

Name _____

Read each question carefully. Fill in the correct answer in the space provided.

1. Name the place of the underlined digit.

1_8_,076,352

ten millions

2. 3.0378 + 23.9 + 54.816 =

81.7538

3. Which number has the digit 3 in the thousandths place?

3,102.04   4.036   12.093

12.093

4. Estimate.

82.0637 + 294.51

possible estimate: 377

5. Estimate the amount of juice in the full cup.

0.4 liters

possible estimate: 1.2 liters

6. Estimate.

28.726 − 11.418

possible estimate: 20

7. What is the value of 6 in 612,038,541?

600 million

8.
```
  36,142.833
+  5,667.09
```
41,809.923

9. 8,156.71 − 623.55 = **7,533.16**

10. In the 100-meter dash, Erik's time is 11.27 seconds. Darnel's time is 11.24 seconds. To determine the winner of the race, you need to compare digits to which place?

hundredths

GO ON

Page 2 (Form B, Page 2)

Name _____

11. Estimate.

57,816 − 8,149

possible estimate: 50,000

12. Complete. Write <, >, or =

12.090 ◯ 12.09

=

13. Estimate.

273 + 521 + 681

possible estimate: 1,500

14.
```
  8,459,126.38
−   231,667.09
```
8,227,459.29

15. Estimate.

655.13 + 249.78

possible estimate: 900

16.
```
  893.6
+ 358.7
```
1,252.3

17. A theme park's ticket sales were $15,789,021. Sales of food and drinks at the park were $9,328,602. Estimate the total sales at the park.

possible estimate: $25,000,000

18. Kareem Abdul-Jabar scored 38,387 points during his career. Karl Malone scored 35,464 points. Wilt Chamberlain scored 31,419 points. How many points did they score altogether?

105,270 points

19. Carl is 1.37 meters tall. Shelly is 1.64 meters tall. What is the difference in their heights?

0.27 meters

20. Georgia's best swimming time is 1 minute 56.7 seconds. Her time decreased by 1.3 seconds each week. What is Georgia's best swimming time after 2 weeks?

1 minute 59.3 seconds

GO ON

Page 3 (Form B, Page 3)

Name _____

21. Name the value of the underlined digit.

342,5_9_2.093

500

22. 68.7 + 189.230 + 1.55 = **259.48**

23. Which number has the digit 3 in the tenths place?

31.065   19.372   24.035

19.372

24. 56.854 + 7.0396 = **63.8936**

25. What is the standard form of forty-five billion, eight hundred thirty million, three thousand twenty-two?

45,830,003,022

26. Estimate.

43.872 − 9.65

possible estimate: 34

27. What is the value of 9 in 13,290,075?

90 thousand

28.
```
  56,142.783
+  6,002.47
```
62,145.253

29. 1,892.34 − 435.761 = **1456.579**

30. Japan has an area of 234,800 square miles. Sweden has an area of 279,600 square miles. To determine which country is larger, you need to compare the digits in which place?

ten thousands

GO ON

Page 4 (Form B, Page 4)

Name _____

31. Estimate.

17,862 − 5,349

possible estimate: 13,000

32. Identify the addition property shown.

234.85 + 0 = 234.85

identity property

33. Estimate.

514 + 398 + 832

possible estimate: 1,700

34.
```
  19,658,173
−  3,519,277
```
16,138,896

35. Estimate.

514.99 + 176.34

possible estimate: 700

36. 341 + 568 = **909**

37. Last week, 19,087,663 people bought tickets to see a new movie. This week, 6,813,420 people bought tickets. Estimate the number of people who bought tickets during these two weeks.

possible estimate: 26,000,000

38. During November, 742 skiers bought season passes. During December 878 skiers bought season passes. During January, 566 skiers bought season passes. Estimate the number of season passes sold during those three months.

possible estimate: 2,200 passes

39. Ken earns $6.89 per hour. Larry earns $6.78 per hour. Tanya earns $7.23 per hour. How much more per hour does Tanya earn than Ken?

$0.34

40. Each week Karen increases the length of her bike ride by 0.6 miles. If Karen's bike ride is 2.1 miles during the first week, how long will her ride be during the fourth week?

3.9 miles

STOP

Chapter 3

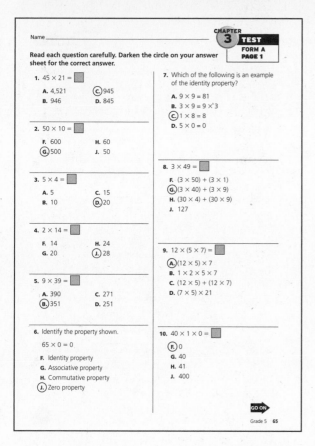

CHAPTER 3 TEST
FORM A
PAGE 1

Read each question carefully. Darken the circle on your answer sheet for the correct answer.

1. 45 × 21 = ▢
- **A.** 4,521
- **B.** 946
- **(C.)** 945
- **D.** 845

2. 50 × 10 = ▢
- **F.** 600
- **(G.)** 500
- **H.** 60
- **J.** 50

3. 5 × 4 = ▢
- **A.** 5
- **B.** 10
- **C.** 15
- **(D.)** 20

4. 2 × 14 = ▢
- **F.** 14
- **G.** 20
- **H.** 24
- **(J.)** 28

5. 9 × 39 = ▢
- **A.** 390
- **(B.)** 351
- **C.** 271
- **D.** 251

6. Identify the property shown.

65 × 0 = 0
- **F.** Identity property
- **G.** Associative property
- **H.** Commutative property
- **(J.)** Zero property

7. Which of the following is an example of the identity property?
- **A.** 9 × 9 = 81
- **B.** 3 × 9 = 9 × 3
- **(C.)** 1 × 8 = 8
- **D.** 5 × 0 = 0

8. 3 × 49 = ▢
- **F.** (3 × 50) + (3 × 1)
- **(G.)** (3 × 40) + (3 × 9)
- **H.** (30 × 4) + (30 × 9)
- **J.** 127

9. 12 × (5 × 7) = ▢
- **(A.)** (12 × 5) × 7
- **B.** 1 × 2 × 5 × 7
- **C.** (12 × 5) + (12 × 7)
- **D.** (7 × 5) × 21

10. 40 × 1 × 0 = ▢
- **(F.)** 0
- **G.** 40
- **H.** 41
- **J.** 400

GO ON

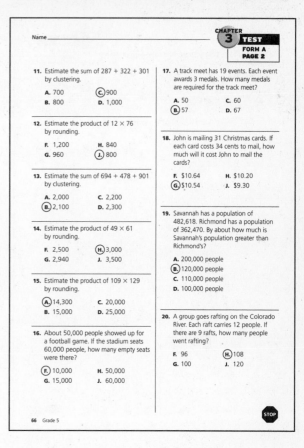

CHAPTER 3 TEST
FORM A
PAGE 2

11. Estimate the sum of 287 + 322 + 301 by clustering.
- **A.** 700
- **B.** 800
- **(C.)** 900
- **D.** 1,000

12. Estimate the product of 12 × 76 by rounding.
- **F.** 1,200
- **G.** 960
- **H.** 840
- **(J.)** 800

13. Estimate the sum of 694 + 478 + 901 by clustering.
- **A.** 2,000
- **(B.)** 2,100
- **C.** 2,200
- **D.** 2,300

14. Estimate the product of 49 × 61 by rounding.
- **F.** 2,500
- **G.** 2,940
- **(H.)** 3,000
- **J.** 3,500

15. Estimate the product of 109 × 129 by rounding.
- **(A.)** 14,300
- **B.** 15,000
- **C.** 20,000
- **D.** 25,000

16. About 50,000 people showed up for a football game. If the stadium seats 60,000 people, how many empty seats were there?
- **(F.)** 10,000
- **G.** 15,000
- **H.** 50,000
- **J.** 60,000

17. A track meet has 19 events. Each event awards 3 medals. How many medals are required for the track meet?
- **A.** 50
- **(B.)** 57
- **C.** 60
- **D.** 67

18. John is mailing 31 Christmas cards. If each card costs 34 cents to mail, how much will it cost John to mail the cards?
- **F.** $10.64
- **(G.)** $10.54
- **H.** $10.20
- **J.** $9.30

19. Savannah has a population of 482,618. Richmond has a population of 362,470. By about how much is Savannah's population greater than Richmond's?
- **A.** 200,000 people
- **(B.)** 120,000 people
- **C.** 110,000 people
- **D.** 100,000 people

20. A group goes rafting on the Colorado River. Each raft carries 12 people. If there are 9 rafts, how many people went rafting?
- **F.** 96
- **G.** 100
- **(H.)** 108
- **J.** 120

STOP

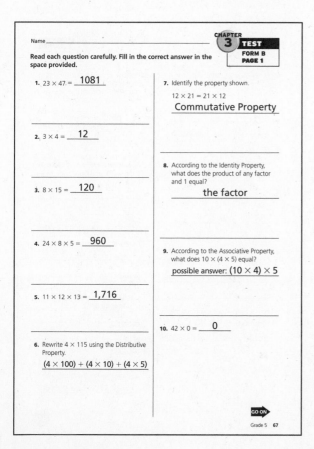

CHAPTER 3 TEST
FORM B
PAGE 1

Read each question carefully. Fill in the correct answer in the space provided.

1. 23 × 47 = __1081__

2. 3 × 4 = __12__

3. 8 × 15 = __120__

4. 24 × 8 × 5 = __960__

5. 11 × 12 × 13 = __1,716__

6. Rewrite 4 × 115 using the Distributive Property.
(4 × 100) + (4 × 10) + (4 × 5)

7. Identify the property shown.

12 × 21 = 21 × 12
Commutative Property

8. According to the Identity Property, what does the product of any factor and 1 equal?
the factor

9. According to the Associative Property, what does 10 × (4 × 5) equal?
possible answer: (10 × 4) × 5

10. 42 × 0 = __0__

GO ON

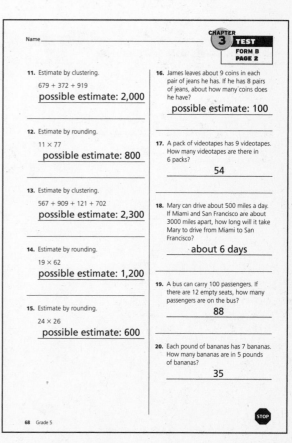

CHAPTER 3 TEST
FORM B
PAGE 2

11. Estimate by clustering.

679 + 372 + 919
possible estimate: 2,000

12. Estimate by rounding.

11 × 77
possible estimate: 800

13. Estimate by clustering.

567 + 909 + 121 + 702
possible estimate: 2,300

14. Estimate by rounding.

19 × 62
possible estimate: 1,200

15. Estimate by rounding.

24 × 26
possible estimate: 600

16. James leaves about 9 coins in each pair of jeans he has. If he has 8 pairs of jeans, about how many coins does he have?
possible estimate: 100

17. A pack of videotapes has 9 videotapes. How many videotapes are there in 6 packs?
54

18. Mary can drive about 500 miles a day. If Miami and San Francisco are about 3000 miles apart, how long will it take Mary to drive from Miami to San Francisco?
about 6 days

19. A bus can carry 100 passengers. If there are 12 empty seats, how many passengers are on the bus?
88

20. Each pound of bananas has 7 bananas. How many bananas are in 5 pounds of bananas?
35

STOP

Chapter 4

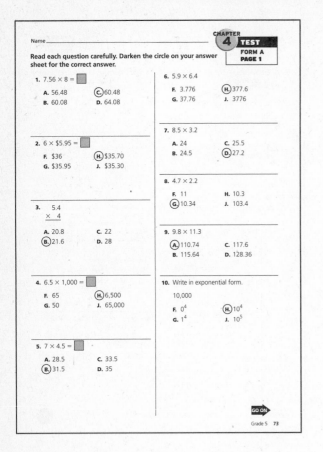

Read each question carefully. Darken the circle on your answer sheet for the correct answer.

1. $7.56 \times 8 = \square$
- A. 56.48
- C. 60.48
- B. 60.08
- D. 64.08

2. $6 \times \$5.95 = \square$
- F. $36
- H. $35.70
- G. $35.95
- J. $35.30

3. $\begin{array}{r} 5.4 \\ \times\ 4 \\ \hline \end{array}$
- A. 20.8
- C. 22
- B. 21.6
- D. 28

4. $6.5 \times 1,000 = \square$
- F. 65
- H. 6,500
- G. 50
- J. 65,000

5. $7 \times 4.5 = \square$
- A. 28.5
- C. 33.5
- B. 31.5
- D. 35

6. 5.9×6.4
- F. 3.776
- H. 377.6
- G. 37.76
- J. 3776

7. 8.5×3.2
- A. 24
- C. 25.5
- B. 24.5
- D. 27.2

8. 4.7×2.2
- F. 11
- H. 10.3
- G. 10.34
- J. 103.4

9. 9.8×11.3
- A. 110.74
- C. 117.6
- B. 115.64
- D. 128.36

10. Write in exponential form.
10,000
- F. 0^4
- H. 10^4
- G. 1^4
- J. 10^5

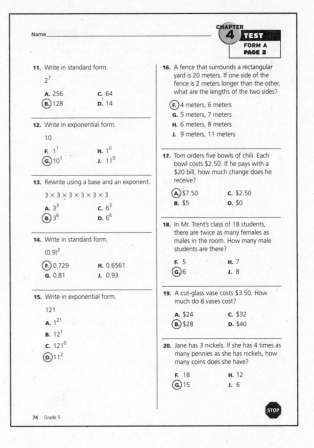

11. Write in standard form.
2^7
- A. 256
- C. 64
- B. 128
- D. 14

12. Write in exponential form.
10
- F. 1^1
- H. 1^0
- G. 10^1
- J. 11^0

13. Rewrite using a base and an exponent.
$3 \times 3 \times 3 \times 3 \times 3 \times 3$
- A. 3^3
- C. 6^3
- B. 3^6
- D. 6^6

14. Write in standard form.
$(0.9)^3$
- F. 0.729
- H. 0.6561
- G. 0.81
- J. 0.93

15. Write in exponential form.
121
- A. 1^{21}
- B. 12^1
- C. 121^0
- D. 11^2

16. A fence that surrounds a rectangular yard is 20 meters. If one side of the fence is 2 meters longer than the other, what are the lengths of the two sides?
- F. 4 meters, 6 meters
- G. 5 meters, 7 meters
- H. 6 meters, 8 meters
- J. 9 meters, 11 meters

17. Tom orders five bowls of chili. Each bowl costs $2.50. If he pays with a $20 bill, how much change does he receive?
- A. $7.50
- C. $2.50
- B. $5
- D. $0

18. In Mr. Trent's class of 18 students, there are twice as many females as males in the room. How many male students are there?
- F. 5
- H. 7
- G. 6
- J. 8

19. A cut-glass vase costs $3.50. How much do 8 vases cost?
- A. $24
- C. $32
- B. $28
- D. $40

20. Jane has 3 nickels. If she has 4 times as many pennies as she has nickels, how many coins does she have?
- F. 18
- H. 12
- G. 15
- J. 6

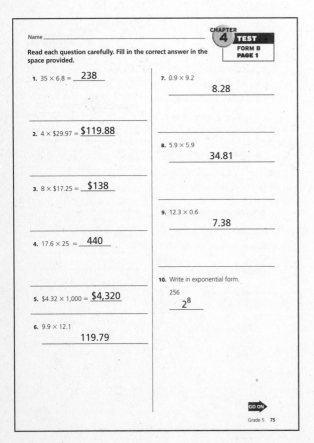

Read each question carefully. Fill in the correct answer in the space provided.

1. $35 \times 6.8 = $ ___238___

2. $4 \times \$29.97 = $ ___$119.88___

3. $8 \times \$17.25 = $ ___$138___

4. $17.6 \times 25 = $ ___440___

5. $\$4.32 \times 1,000 = $ ___$4,320___

6. 9.9×12.1
___119.79___

7. 0.9×9.2
___8.28___

8. 5.9×5.9
___34.81___

9. 12.3×0.6
___7.38___

10. Write in exponential form.
256
___2^8___

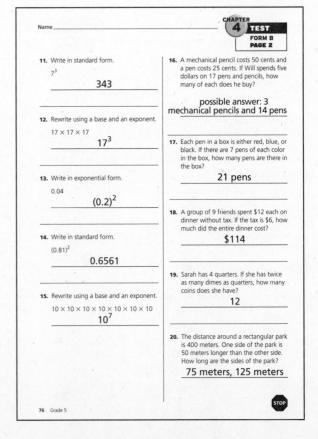

11. Write in standard form.
7^3
___343___

12. Rewrite using a base and an exponent.
$17 \times 17 \times 17$
___17^3___

13. Write in exponential form.
0.04
___$(0.2)^2$___

14. Write in standard form.
$(0.81)^2$
___0.6561___

15. Rewrite using a base and an exponent.
$10 \times 10 \times 10 \times 10 \times 10 \times 10 \times 10$
___10^7___

16. A mechanical pencil costs 50 cents and a pen costs 25 cents. If Will spends five dollars on 17 pens and pencils, how many of each does he buy?
possible answer: 3 mechanical pencils and 14 pens

17. Each pen in a box is either red, blue, or black. If there are 7 pens of each color in the box, how many pens are there in the box?
21 pens

18. A group of 9 friends spent $12 each on dinner without tax. If the tax is $6, how much did the entire dinner cost?
$114

19. Sarah has 4 quarters. If she has twice as many dimes as quarters, how many coins does she have?
12

20. The distance around a rectangular park is 400 meters. One side of the park is 50 meters longer than the other side. How long are the sides of the park?
75 meters, 125 meters

Unit 2

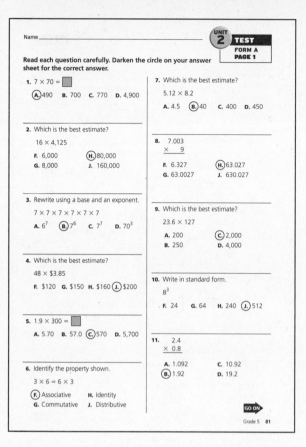

Name_____

Read each question carefully. Darken the circle on your answer sheet for the correct answer.

1. $7 \times 70 = \square$

A. 490   B. 700   C. 770   D. 4,900

2. Which is the best estimate?

$16 \times 4,125$

F. 6,000   H. 80,000
G. 8,000   J. 160,000

3. Rewrite using a base and an exponent.

$7 \times 7 \times 7 \times 7 \times 7 \times 7$

A. 6^7 B. 7^6 C. 7^7 D. 70^3

4. Which is the best estimate?

$48 \times \$3.85$

F. \$120   G. \$150   H. \$160   J. \$200

5. $1.9 \times 300 = \square$

A. 5.70   B. 57.0   C. 570   D. 5,700

6. Identify the property shown.

$3 \times 6 = 6 \times 3$

F. Associative   H. Identity
G. Commutative   J. Distributive

7. Which is the best estimate?

5.12×8.2

A. 4.5   B. 40   C. 400   D. 450

8. 7.003
$\times \quad 9$

F. 6.327   H. 63.027
G. 63.0027   J. 630.027

9. Which is the best estimate?

23.6×127

A. 200   C. 2,000
B. 250   D. 4,000

10. Write in standard form.

8^3

F. 24   G. 64   H. 240   J. 512

11. 2.4
$\times 0.8$

A. 1.092   C. 10.92
B. 1.92   D. 19.2

GO ON

Grade 5   81

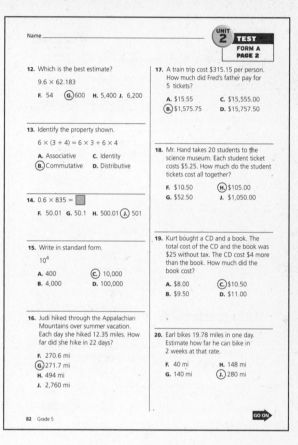

Name_____

12. Which is the best estimate?

9.6×62.183

F. 54   G. 600   H. 5,400   J. 6,200

13. Identify the property shown.

$6 \times (3 + 4) = 6 \times 3 + 6 \times 4$

A. Associative   C. Identity
B. Commutative   D. Distributive

14. $0.6 \times 835 = \square$

F. 50.01   G. 50.1   H. 500.01   J. 501

15. Write in standard form.

10^4

A. 400   C. 10,000
B. 4,000   D. 100,000

16. Judi hiked through the Appalachian Mountains over summer vacation. Each day she hiked 12.35 miles. How far did she hike in 22 days?

F. 270.6 mi
G. 271.7 mi
H. 494 mi
J. 2,760 mi

17. A train trip cost \$315.15 per person. How much did Fred's father pay for 5 tickets?

A. \$15.55   C. \$15,555.00
B. \$1,575.75   D. \$15,757.50

18. Mr. Hand takes 20 students to the science museum. Each student ticket costs \$5.25. How much do the student tickets cost all together?

F. \$10.50   H. \$105.00
G. \$52.50   J. \$1,050.00

19. Kurt bought a CD and a book. The total cost of the CD and the book was \$25 without tax. The CD cost \$4 more than the book. How much did the book cost?

A. \$8.00   C. \$10.50
B. \$9.50   D. \$11.00

20. Earl bikes 19.78 miles in one day. Estimate how far he can bike in 2 weeks at that rate.

F. 40 mi   H. 148 mi
G. 140 mi   J. 280 mi

GO ON

82   Grade 5

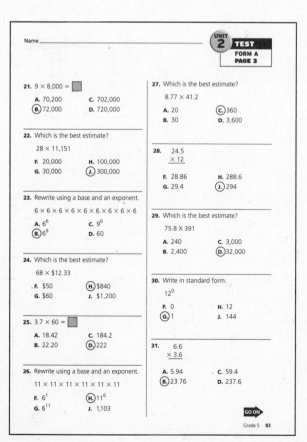

Name_____

21. $9 \times 8,000 = \square$

A. 70,200   C. 702,000
B. 72,000   D. 720,000

22. Which is the best estimate?

$28 \times 11,151$

F. 20,000   H. 100,000
G. 30,000   J. 300,000

23. Rewrite using a base and an exponent.

$6 \times 6 \times 6 \times 6 \times 6 \times 6 \times 6 \times 6 \times 6$

A. 6^6 C. 9^6
B. 6^9 D. 60

24. Which is the best estimate?

$68 \times \$12.33$

F. \$50   H. \$840
G. \$60   J. \$1,200

25. $3.7 \times 60 = \square$

A. 18.42   C. 184.2
B. 22.20   D. 222

26. Rewrite using a base and an exponent.

$11 \times 11 \times 11 \times 11 \times 11 \times 11$

F. 6^1 H. 11^6
G. 6^{11} J. 1,103

27. Which is the best estimate?

8.77×41.2

A. 20   C. 360
B. 30   D. 3,600

28. 24.5
$\times 12$

F. 28.86   H. 288.6
G. 29.4   J. 294

29. Which is the best estimate?

75.8×391

A. 240   C. 3,000
B. 2,400   D. 32,000

30. Write in standard form.

12^0

F. 0   H. 12
G. 1   J. 144

31. 6.6
$\times 3.6$

A. 5.94   C. 59.4
B. 23.76   D. 237.6

GO ON

Grade 5   83

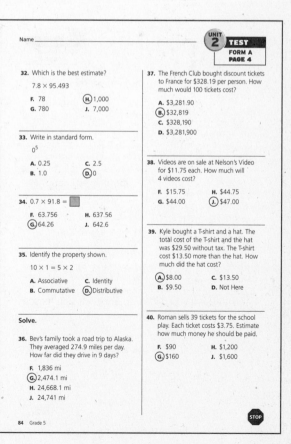

Name_____

32. Which is the best estimate?

7.8×95.493

F. 78   H. 1,000
G. 780   J. 7,000

33. Write in standard form.

0^5

A. 0.25   C. 2.5
B. 1.0   D. 0

34. $0.7 \times 91.8 = \square$

F. 63.756   H. 637.56
G. 64.26   J. 642.6

35. Identify the property shown.

$10 \times 1 = 5 \times 2$

A. Associative   C. Identity
B. Commutative   D. Distributive

Solve.

36. Bev's family took a road trip to Alaska. They averaged 274.9 miles per day. How far did they drive in 9 days?

F. 1,836 mi
G. 2,474.1 mi
H. 24,668.1 mi
J. 24,741 mi

37. The French Club bought discount tickets to France for \$328.19 per person. How much would 100 tickets cost?

A. \$3,281.90
B. \$32,819
C. \$328,190
D. \$3,281,900

38. Videos are on sale at Nelson's Video for \$11.75 each. How much will 4 videos cost?

F. \$15.75   H. \$44.75
G. \$44.00   J. \$47.00

39. Kyle bought a T-shirt and a hat. The total cost of the T-shirt and the hat was \$29.50 without tax. The T-shirt cost \$13.50 more than the hat. How much did the hat cost?

A. \$8.00   C. \$13.50
B. \$9.50   D. Not Here

40. Roman sells 39 tickets for the school play. Each ticket costs \$3.75. Estimate how much money he should be paid.

F. \$90   H. \$1,200
G. \$160   J. \$1,600

STOP

84   Grade 5

Unit 2

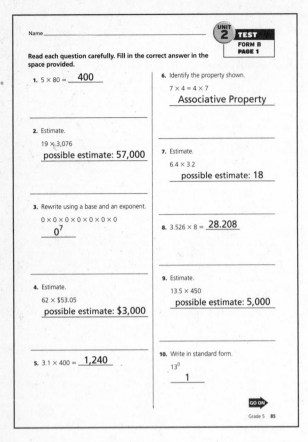

Read each question carefully. Fill in the correct answer in the space provided.

1. 5 × 80 = __400__

2. Estimate.
19 × 3,076
possible estimate: 57,000

3. Rewrite using a base and an exponent.
0 × 0 × 0 × 0 × 0 × 0 × 0
0^7

4. Estimate.
62 × $53.05
possible estimate: $3,000

5. 3.1 × 400 = __1,240__

6. Identify the property shown.
7 × 4 = 4 × 7
Associative Property

7. Estimate.
6.4 × 3.2
possible estimate: 18

8. 3.526 × 8 = __28.208__

9. Estimate.
13.5 × 450
possible estimate: 5,000

10. Write in standard form.
13^0
__1__

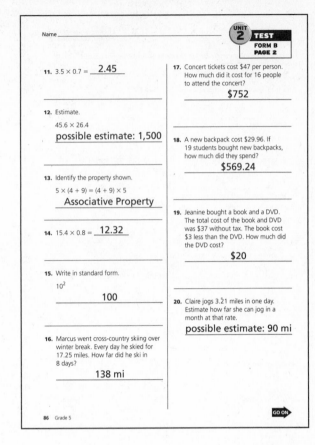

11. 3.5 × 0.7 = __2.45__

12. Estimate.
45.6 × 26.4
possible estimate: 1,500

13. Identify the property shown.
5 × (4 + 9) = (4 + 9) × 5
Associative Property

14. 15.4 × 0.8 = __12.32__

15. Write in standard form.
10^2
__100__

16. Marcus went cross-country skiing over winter break. Every day he skied for 17.25 miles. How far did he ski in 8 days?
138 mi

17. Concert tickets cost $47 per person. How much did it cost for 16 people to attend the concert?
$752

18. A new backpack cost $29.96. If 19 students bought new backpacks, how much did they spend?
$569.24

19. Jeanine bought a book and a DVD. The total cost of the book and DVD was $37 without tax. The book cost $3 less than the DVD. How much did the DVD cost?
$20

20. Claire jogs 3.21 miles in one day. Estimate how far she can jog in a month at that rate.
possible estimate: 90 mi

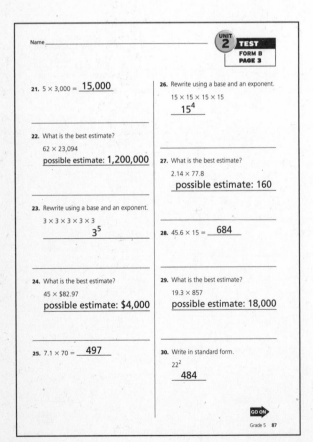

21. 5 × 3,000 = __15,000__

22. What is the best estimate?
62 × 23,094
possible estimate: 1,200,000

23. Rewrite using a base and an exponent.
3 × 3 × 3 × 3 × 3
3^5

24. What is the best estimate?
45 × $82.97
possible estimate: $4,000

25. 7.1 × 70 = __497__

26. Rewrite using a base and an exponent.
15 × 15 × 15 × 15
15^4

27. What is the best estimate?
2.14 × 77.8
possible estimate: 160

28. 45.6 × 15 = __684__

29. What is the best estimate?
19.3 × 857
possible estimate: 18,000

30. Write in standard form.
22^2
__484__

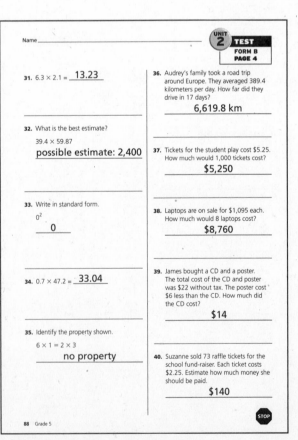

31. 6.3 × 2.1 = __13.23__

32. What is the best estimate?
39.4 × 59.87
possible estimate: 2,400

33. Write in standard form.
0^2
__0__

34. 0.7 × 47.2 = __33.04__

35. Identify the property shown.
6 × 1 = 2 × 3
no property

36. Audrey's family took a road trip around Europe. They averaged 389.4 kilometers per day. How far did they drive in 17 days?
6,619.8 km

37. Tickets for the student play cost $5.25. How much would 1,000 tickets cost?
$5,250

38. Laptops are on sale for $1,095 each. How much would 8 laptops cost?
$8,760

39. James bought a CD and a poster. The total cost of the CD and poster was $22 without tax. The poster cost $6 less than the CD. How much did the CD cost?
$14

40. Suzanne sold 73 raffle tickets for the school fund-raiser. Each ticket costs $2.25. Estimate how much money she should be paid.
$140

Chapter 5

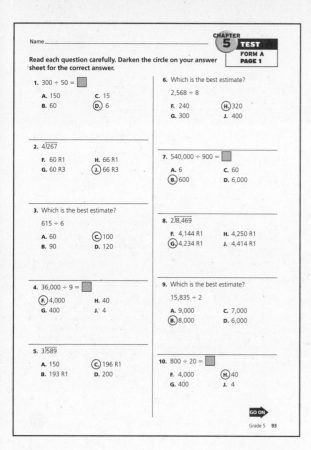

Name _____

CHAPTER 5 TEST
FORM A
PAGE 1

Read each question carefully. Darken the circle on your answer sheet for the correct answer.

1. 300 ÷ 50 = ▨
A. 150　C. 15
B. 60　**D.** 6

2. 4)267
F. 60 R1　H. 66 R1
G. 60 R3　**J.** 66 R3

3. Which is the best estimate?
615 ÷ 6
A. 60　**C.** 100
B. 90　D. 120

4. 36,000 ÷ 9 = ▨
F. 4,000　H. 40
G. 400　J. 4

5. 3)589
A. 150　**C.** 196 R1
B. 193 R1　D. 200

6. Which is the best estimate?
2,568 ÷ 8
F. 240　**H.** 320
G. 300　J. 400

7. 540,000 ÷ 900 = ▨
A. 6　C. 60
B. 600　D. 6,000

8. 2)8,469
F. 4,144 R1　H. 4,250 R1
G. 4,234 R1　J. 4,414 R1

9. Which is the best estimate?
15,835 ÷ 2
A. 9,000　C. 7,000
B. 8,000　D. 6,000

10. 800 ÷ 20 = ▨
F. 4,000　**H.** 40
G. 400　J. 4

GO ON
Grade 5　**93**

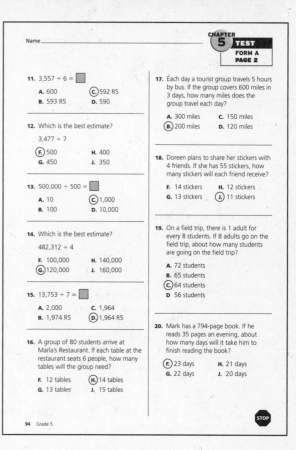

Name _____

CHAPTER 5 TEST
FORM A
PAGE 2

11. 3,557 ÷ 6 = ▨
A. 600　**C.** 592 R5
B. 593 R5　D. 590

12. Which is the best estimate?
3,477 ÷ 7
F. 500　H. 400
G. 450　J. 350

13. 500,000 ÷ 500 = ▨
A. 10　**C.** 1,000
B. 100　D. 10,000

14. Which is the best estimate?
482,312 ÷ 4
F. 100,000　H. 140,000
G. 120,000　J. 160,000

15. 13,753 ÷ 7 = ▨
A. 2,000　C. 1,964
B. 1,974 R5　**D.** 1,964 R5

16. A group of 80 students arrive at Marla's Restaurant. If each table at the restaurant seats 6 people, how many tables will the group need?
F. 12 tables　**H.** 14 tables
G. 13 tables　J. 15 tables

17. Each day a tourist group travels 5 hours by bus. If the group covers 600 miles in 3 days, how many miles does the group travel each day?
A. 300 miles　C. 150 miles
B. 200 miles　D. 120 miles

18. Doreen plans to share her stickers with 4 friends. If she has 55 stickers, how many stickers will each friend receive?
F. 14 stickers　H. 12 stickers
G. 13 stickers　**J.** 11 stickers

19. On a field trip, there is 1 adult for every 8 students. If 8 adults go on the field trip, about how many students are going on the field trip?
A. 72 students
B. 65 students
C. 64 students
D. 56 students

20. Mark has a 794-page book. If he reads 35 pages an evening, about how many days will it take him to finish reading the book?
F. 23 days　H. 21 days
G. 22 days　J. 20 days

STOP
94　Grade 5

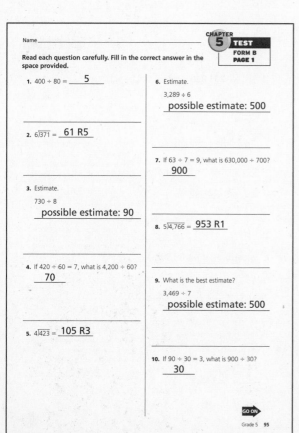

Name _____

CHAPTER 5 TEST
FORM B
PAGE 1

Read each question carefully. Fill in the correct answer in the space provided.

1. 400 ÷ 80 = ___5___

2. 6)371 = ___61 R5___

3. Estimate.
730 ÷ 8
possible estimate: 90

4. If 420 ÷ 60 = 7, what is 4,200 ÷ 60?
___70___

5. 4)423 = ___105 R3___

6. Estimate.
3,289 ÷ 6
possible estimate: 500

7. If 63 ÷ 7 = 9, what is 630,000 ÷ 700?
___900___

8. 5)4,766 = ___953 R1___

9. What is the best estimate?
3,469 ÷ 7
possible estimate: 500

10. If 90 ÷ 30 = 3, what is 900 ÷ 30?
___30___

GO ON
Grade 5　**95**

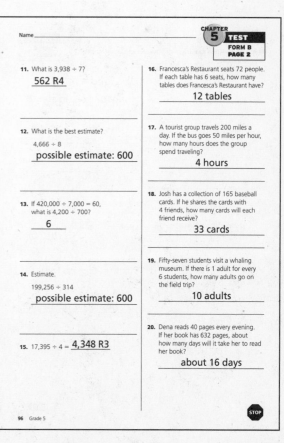

Name _____

CHAPTER 5 TEST
FORM B
PAGE 2

11. What is 3,938 ÷ 7?
___562 R4___

12. What is the best estimate?
4,666 ÷ 8
possible estimate: 600

13. If 420,000 ÷ 7,000 = 60, what is 4,200 ÷ 700?
___6___

14. Estimate.
199,256 ÷ 314
possible estimate: 600

15. 17,395 ÷ 4 = ___4,348 R3___

16. Francesca's Restaurant seats 72 people. If each table has 6 seats, how many tables does Francesca's Restaurant have?
___12 tables___

17. A tourist group travels 200 miles a day. If the bus goes 50 miles per hour, how many hours does the group spend traveling?
___4 hours___

18. Josh has a collection of 165 baseball cards. If he shares the cards with 4 friends, how many cards will each friend receive?
___33 cards___

19. Fifty-seven students visit a whaling museum. If there is 1 adult for every 6 students, how many adults go on the field trip?
___10 adults___

20. Dena reads 40 pages every evening. If her book has 632 pages, about how many days will it take her to read her book?
___about 16 days___

STOP
96　Grade 5

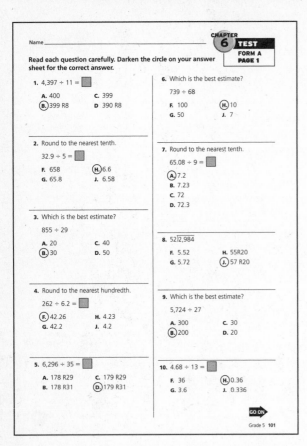

Name _____

Read each question carefully. Darken the circle on your answer sheet for the correct answer.

1. 4,397 ÷ 11 = ☐
A. 400   C. 399
B. 399 R8   D 390 R8

2. Round to the nearest tenth.
32.9 ÷ 5 = ☐
F. 658   **H.** 6.6
G. 65.8   J. 6.58

3. Which is the best estimate?
855 ÷ 29
A. 20   C. 40
B. 30   D. 50

4. Round to the nearest hundredth.
262 ÷ 6.2 = ☐
F. 42.26   H. 4.23
G. 42.2   J. 4.2

5. 6,296 ÷ 35 = ☐
A. 178 R29   C. 179 R29
B. 178 R31   **D.** 179 R31

6. Which is the best estimate?
739 ÷ 68
F. 100   **H.** 10
G. 50   J. 7

7. Round to the nearest tenth.
65.08 ÷ 9 = ☐
A. 7.2
B. 7.23
C. 72
D. 72.3

8. 52)2,984
F. 5.52   H. 55R20
G. 5.72   **J.** 57 R20

9. Which is the best estimate?
5,724 ÷ 27
A. 300   C. 30
B. 200   D. 20

10. 4.68 ÷ 13 = ☐
F. 36   **H.** 0.36
G. 3.6   J. 0.336

GO ON

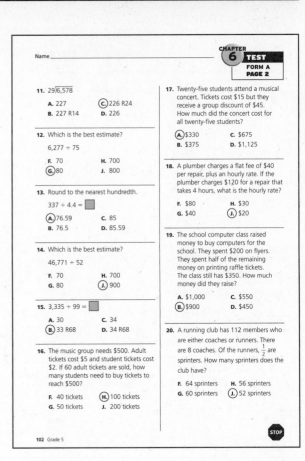

Name _____

11. 29)6,578
A. 227   **C.** 226 R24
B. 227 R14   D. 226

12. Which is the best estimate?
6,277 ÷ 75
F. 70   H. 700
G. 80   J. 800

13. Round to the nearest hundredth.
337 ÷ 4.4 = ☐
A. 76.59   C. 85
B. 76.5   D. 85.59

14. Which is the best estimate?
46,771 ÷ 52
F. 70   H. 700
G. 80   **J.** 900

15. 3,335 ÷ 99 = ☐
A. 30   C. 34
B. 33 R68   D. 34 R68

16. The music group needs $500. Adult tickets cost $5 and student tickets cost $2. If 60 adult tickets are sold, how many students need to buy tickets to reach $500?
F. 40 tickets   **H.** 100 tickets
G. 50 tickets   J. 200 tickets

17. Twenty-five students attend a musical concert. Tickets cost $15 but they receive a group discount of $45. How much did the concert cost for all twenty-five students?
A. $330   C. $675
B. $375   D. $1,125

18. A plumber charges a flat fee of $40 per repair, plus an hourly rate. If the plumber charges $120 for a repair that takes 4 hours, what is the hourly rate?
F. $80   H. $30
G. $40   **J.** $20

19. The school computer class raised money to buy computers for the school. They spent $200 on flyers. They spent half of the remaining money on printing raffle tickets. The class still has $350. How much money did they raise?
A. $1,000   C. $550
B. $900   D. $450

20. A running club has 112 members who are either coaches or runners. There are 8 coaches. Of the runners, $\frac{1}{2}$ are sprinters. How many sprinters does the club have?
F. 64 sprinters   H. 56 sprinters
G. 60 sprinters   **J.** 52 sprinters

STOP

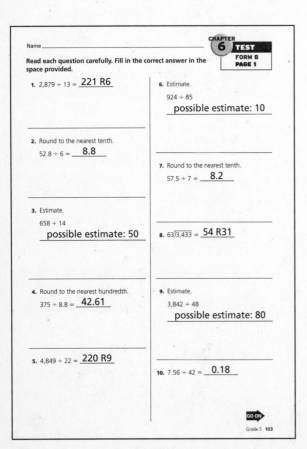

Name _____

Read each question carefully. Fill in the correct answer in the space provided.

1. 2,879 ÷ 13 = __221 R6__

2. Round to the nearest tenth.
52.8 ÷ 6 = __8.8__

3. Estimate.
658 ÷ 14
possible estimate: 50

4. Round to the nearest hundredth.
375 ÷ 8.8 = __42.61__

5. 4,849 ÷ 22 = __220 R9__

6. Estimate.
924 ÷ 85
possible estimate: 10

7. Round to the nearest tenth.
57.5 ÷ 7 = __8.2__

8. 63)3,433 = __54 R31__

9. Estimate.
3,842 ÷ 48
possible estimate: 80

10. 7.56 ÷ 42 = __0.18__

GO ON

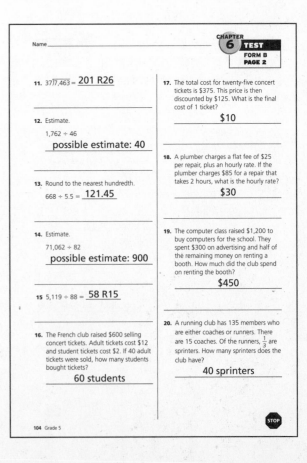

Name _____

11. 37)7,463 = __201 R26__

12. Estimate.
1,762 ÷ 46
possible estimate: 40

13. Round to the nearest hundredth.
668 ÷ 5.5 = __121.45__

14. Estimate.
71,062 ÷ 82
possible estimate: 900

15. 5,119 ÷ 88 = __58 R15__

16. The French club raised $600 selling concert tickets. Adult tickets cost $12 and student tickets cost $2. If 40 adult tickets were sold, how many students bought tickets?
__60 students__

17. The total cost for twenty-five concert tickets is $375. This price is then discounted by $125. What is the final cost of 1 ticket?
__$10__

18. A plumber charges a flat fee of $25 per repair, plus an hourly rate. If the plumber charges $85 for a repair that takes 2 hours, what is the hourly rate?
__$30__

19. The computer class raised $1,200 to buy computers for the school. They spent $300 on advertising and half of the remaining money on renting a booth. How much did the club spend on renting the booth?
__$450__

20. A running club has 135 members who are either coaches or runners. There are 15 coaches. Of the runners, $\frac{1}{3}$ are sprinters. How many sprinters does the club have?
__40 sprinters__

STOP

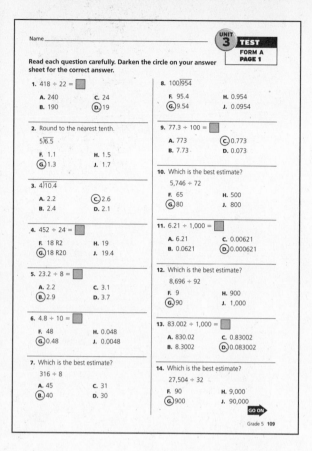

Name_____

UNIT **3** **TEST** FORM A PAGE 1

Read each question carefully. Darken the circle on your answer sheet for the correct answer.

1. $418 \div 22 = \square$

A. 240 C. 24
B. 190 (D.) 19

2. Round to the nearest tenth.
$5\overline{)6.5}$

F. 1.1 H. 1.5
(G.) 1.3 J. 1.7

3. $4\overline{)10.4}$

A. 2.2 (C.) 2.6
B. 2.4 D. 2.1

4. $452 \div 24 = \square$

F. 18 R2 H. 19
(G.) 18 R20 J. 19.4

5. $23.2 \div 8 = \square$

A. 2.2 C. 3.1
(B.) 2.9 D. 3.7

6. $4.8 \div 10 = \square$

F. 48 H. 0.048
(G.) 0.48 J. 0.0048

7. Which is the best estimate?
$316 \div 8$

A. 45 C. 31
(B.) 40 D. 30

8. $100\overline{)954}$

F. 95.4 H. 0.954
(G.) 9.54 J. 0.0954

9. $77.3 \div 100 = \square$

A. 773 (C.) 0.773
B. 7.73 D. 0.073

10. Which is the best estimate?
$5,746 \div 72$

F. 65 H. 500
(G.) 80 J. 800

11. $6.21 \div 1,000 = \square$

A. 6.21 C. 0.00621
B. 0.0621 (D.) 0.000621

12. Which is the best estimate?
$8,696 \div 92$

F. 9 H. 900
(G.) 90 J. 1,000

13. $83.002 \div 1,000 = \square$

A. 830.02 C. 0.83002
B. 8.3002 (D.) 0.083002

14. Which is the best estimate?
$27,504 \div 32$

F. 90 H. 9,000
(G.) 900 J. 90,000

GO ON

Grade 5 **109**

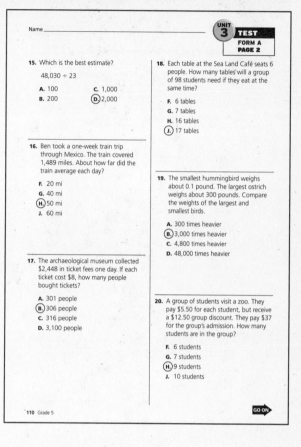

Name_____

UNIT **3** **TEST** FORM A PAGE 2

15. Which is the best estimate?
$48,030 \div 23$

A. 100 C. 1,000
B. 200 (D.) 2,000

16. Ben took a one-week train trip through Mexico. The train covered 1,489 miles. About how far did the train average each day?

F. 20 mi
G. 40 mi
(H.) 50 mi
J. 60 mi

17. The archaeological museum collected $2,448 in ticket fees one day. If each ticket cost $8, how many people bought tickets?

A. 301 people
(B.) 306 people
C. 316 people
D. 3,100 people

18. Each table at the Sea Land Café seats 6 people. How many tables will a group of 98 students need if they eat at the same time?

F. 6 tables
G. 7 tables
H. 16 tables
(J.) 17 tables

19. The smallest hummingbird weighs about 0.1 pound. The largest ostrich weighs about 300 pounds. Compare the weights of the largest and smallest birds.

A. 300 times heavier
(B.) 3,000 times heavier
C. 4,800 times heavier
D. 48,000 times heavier

20. A group of students visit a zoo. They pay $5.50 for each student, but receive a $12.50 group discount. They pay $37 for the group's admission. How many students are in the group?

F. 6 students
G. 7 students
(H.) 9 students
J. 10 students

GO ON

110 Grade 5

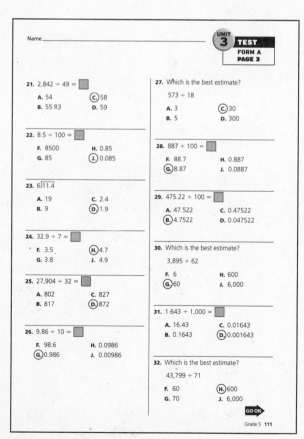

Name_____

UNIT **3** **TEST** FORM A PAGE 3

21. $2,842 \div 49 = \square$

A. 54 (C.) 58
B. 55 R3 D. 59

22. $8.5 \div 100 = \square$

F. 8500 H. 0.85
G. 85 (J.) 0.085

23. $6\overline{)11.4}$

A. 19 C. 2.4
B. 9 (D.) 1.9

24. $32.9 \div 7 = \square$

F. 3.5 (H.) 4.7
G. 3.8 J. 4.9

25. $27,904 \div 32 = \square$

A. 802 C. 827
B. 817 (D.) 872

26. $9.86 \div 10 = \square$

F. 98.6 H. 0.0986
(G.) 0.986 J. 0.00986

27. Which is the best estimate?
$573 \div 18$

A. 3 (C.) 30
B. 5 D. 300

28. $887 \div 100 = \square$

F. 88.7 H. 0.887
(G.) 8.87 J. 0.0887

29. $475.22 \div 100 = \square$

A. 47.522 C. 0.47522
(B.) 4.7522 D. 0.047522

30. Which is the best estimate?
$3,895 \div 62$

F. 6 H. 600
(G.) 60 J. 6,000

31. $1.643 \div 1,000 = \square$

A. 16.43 C. 0.01643
B. 0.1643 (D.) 0.001643

32. Which is the best estimate?
$43,799 \div 71$

F. 60 (H.) 600
G. 70 J. 6,000

GO ON

Grade 5 **111**

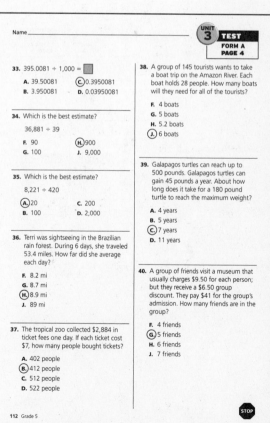

Name_____

UNIT **3** **TEST** FORM A PAGE 4

33. $395.0081 \div 1,000 = \square$

A. 39.50081 (C.) 0.3950081
B. 3.950081 D. 0.03950081

34. Which is the best estimate?
$36,881 \div 39$

F. 90 (H.) 900
G. 100 J. 9,000

35. Which is the best estimate?
$8,221 \div 420$

(A.) 20 C. 200
B. 100 D. 2,000

36. Terri was sightseeing in the Brazilian rain forest. During 6 days, she traveled 53.4 miles. How far did she average each day?

F. 8.2 mi
G. 8.7 mi
(H.) 8.9 mi
J. 89 mi

37. The tropical zoo collected $2,884 in ticket fees one day. If each ticket cost $7, how many people bought tickets?

A. 402 people
(B.) 412 people
C. 512 people
D. 522 people

38. A group of 145 tourists wants to take a boat trip on the Amazon River. Each boat holds 28 people. How many boats will they need for all of the tourists?

F. 4 boats
G. 5 boats
H. 5.2 boats
(J.) 6 boats

39. Galapagos turtles can reach up to 500 pounds. Galapagos turtles can gain 45 pounds a year. About how long does it take for a 180 pound turtle to reach the maximum weight?

A. 4 years
B. 5 years
(C.) 7 years
D. 11 years

40. A group of friends visit a museum that usually charges $9.50 for each person; but they receive a $6.50 group discount. They pay $41 for the group's admission. How many friends are in the group?

F. 4 friends
(G.) 5 friends
H. 6 friends
J. 7 friends

STOP

112 Grade 5

Unit 3

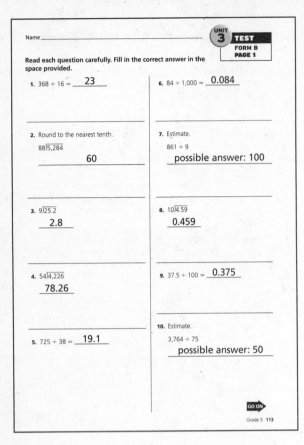

Read each question carefully. Fill in the correct answer in the space provided.

1. $368 \div 16 =$ ___23___

2. Round to the nearest tenth.
88)5,284
60

3. 9)25.2
2.8

4. 54)4,226
78.26

5. $725 \div 38 =$ ___19.1___

6. $84 \div 1,000 =$ ___0.084___

7. Estimate.
$861 \div 9$
possible answer: 100

8. 10)4.59
0.459

9. $37.5 \div 100 =$ ___0.375___

10. Estimate.
$3,764 \div 75$
possible answer: 50

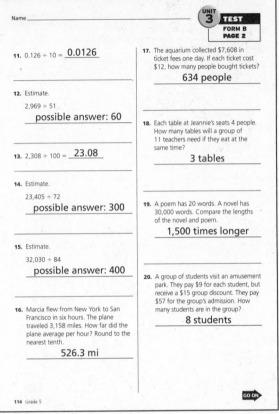

11. $0.126 \div 10 =$ ___0.0126___

12. Estimate.
$2,969 \div 51$
possible answer: 60

13. $2,308 \div 100 =$ ___23.08___

14. Estimate.
$23,405 \div 72$
possible answer: 300

15. Estimate.
$32,030 \div 84$
possible answer: 400

16. Marcia flew from New York to San Francisco in six hours. The plane traveled 3,158 miles. How far did the plane average per hour? Round to the nearest tenth.
526.3 mi

17. The aquarium collected $7,608 in ticket fees one day. If each ticket cost $12, how many people bought tickets?
634 people

18. Each table at Jeannie's seats 4 people. How many tables will a group of 11 teachers need if they eat at the same time?
3 tables

19. A poem has 20 words. A novel has 30,000 words. Compare the lengths of the novel and poem.
1,500 times longer

20. A group of students visit an amusement park. They pay $9 for each student, but receive a $15 group discount. They pay $57 for the group's admission. How many students are in the group?
8 students

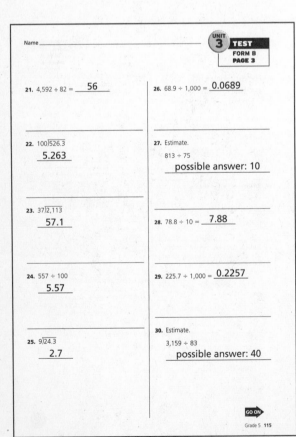

21. $4,592 \div 82 =$ ___56___

22. 100)526.3
5.263

23. 37)2,113
57.1

24. $557 \div 100 =$
5.57

25. 9)24.3
2.7

26. $68.9 \div 1,000 =$ ___0.0689___

27. Estimate.
$813 \div 75$
possible answer: 10

28. $78.8 \div 10 =$ ___7.88___

29. $225.7 \div 1,000 =$ ___0.2257___

30. Estimate.
$3,159 \div 83$
possible answer: 40

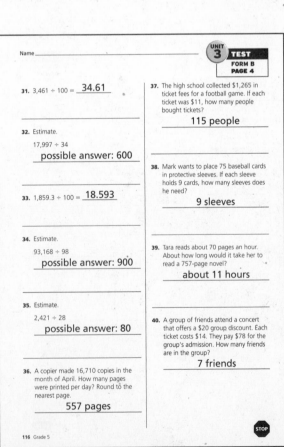

31. $3,461 \div 100 =$ ___34.61___

32. Estimate.
$17,997 \div 34$
possible answer: 600

33. $1,859.3 \div 100 =$ ___18.593___

34. Estimate.
$93,168 \div 98$
possible answer: 900

35. Estimate.
$2,421 \div 28$
possible answer: 80

36. A copier made 16,710 copies in the month of April. How many pages were printed per day? Round to the nearest page.
557 pages

37. The high school collected $1,265 in ticket fees for a football game. If each ticket was $11, how many people bought tickets?
115 people

38. Mark wants to place 75 baseball cards in protective sleeves. If each sleeve holds 9 cards, how many sleeves does he need?
9 sleeves

39. Tara reads about 70 pages an hour. About how long would it take her to read a 757-page novel?
about 11 hours

40. A group of friends attend a concert that offers a $20 group discount. Each ticket costs $14. They pay $78 for the group's admission. How many friends are in the group?
7 friends

## Chapter 7

Top Left — Form A, Page 1

Read each question carefully. Darken the circle on your answer sheet for the correct answer.

Use the line plot for problems 1–6.

Students Who Own CDs

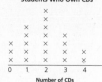

```
                  ×
                  ×
        ×    ×
        ×    ×    ×
   ×    ×    ×    ×
   ×    ×    ×    ×    ×
   ×    ×    ×    ×
   0    1    2    3    4
```
Number of CDs

1. How many students own CDs?

A. 3   B. 10   **C.** 18   D. 21

2. What is the range of the number of CDs?

F. 7   G. 5   **H.** 4   J. 3

3. What is the median number of CDs?

A. 5   B. 4   C. 3   **D.** 2

4. What is the mean of the number of CDs to the nearest tenth?

F. 1.9   H. 3.2
G. 4   J. 2.2

5. What is the mode of the number of CDs?

A. 4   **C.** 2
B. 3   D. 1

6. Which other kind of graph would best show the data?

F. histogram
G. stem-and-leaf plot
H. frequency table
J. double-bar graph

Use the line graph for problems 7–11.

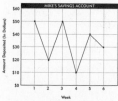

MIKE'S SAVINGS ACCOUNT

7. How much money does Mike save during the 6-week period?

A. $210   **B.** $200   C. $100   D. $50

8. What is the range of money saved in dollar amounts?

F. $50   **G.** $40   H. $20   J. $10

9. What is the mode for the set of data?

A. $10   B. $20   C. $40   **D.** $50

10. In which week does Mike save the least amount of money?

F. Week 2   **H.** Week 4
G. Week 3   J. Week 6

GO ON

Top Right — Form A, Page 2

11. Suppose a pictograph of this set of data shows $$ for week 2. What would the graph show for Week 6?

A. $$$$$$ **C.** $$$
B. $$$$ D. $$

Use the pictograph for problems 12–16.

Favorite After School Sports	
Sport	**Number of Students**
Soccer	👤👤👤👤👤👤👤
Basketball	👤👤👤👤👤👤
Football	👤👤👤👤👤👤👤👤👤
Baseball	👤👤👤👤👤👤👤
Swimming	👤👤👤

Key: each 👤 = 5 students

12. How many students participate in after school sports?

F. 40   G. 80   H. 100   **J.** 200

13. What is the median for the set of data?

A. 50   B. 45   **C.** 40   D. 35

14. What is the mean for this set of data?

F. 35   **G.** 40   H. 45   J. 50

15. Which two sports represent 70 students?

A. Soccer and Basketball
B. Basketball and Football
C. Baseball and Football
D. Swimming and Soccer

16. What other type of graph would best display the data?

F. bar graph   H. double bar graph
G. line graph   J. line plot

17. Which type of display would not be appropriate to show the favorite foods of a group of students?

A. pictograph   **C.** line graph
B. frequency table   D. bar graph

18. A puppy weighed 2 lb at birth and weighed 18 pounds after 4 months. You keep track of the weight on a line graph. Which intervals are most appropriate for the axis showing the number of pounds?

F. intervals of 2 pounds
G. intervals of 5 pounds
H. intervals of 10 pounds
J. intervals of 18 pounds

19. Which type of graph could you use to best display the number of inches of rainfall during a 12-month period?

A. double bar   C. bar graph
graph
B. line graph   D. pictograph

20. Which type of display is best for comparing the costs of four bicycles?

F. double bar graph
G. line graph
H. frequency table
J. bar graph

STOP

Bottom Left — Form B, Page 1

Read each question carefully. Fill in the correct answer in the space provided.

Use the line plot for problems 1–6.

Museum Visits in a Month

```
             ×
        ×    ×    ×
        ×    ×    ×
   ×    ×    ×    ×
   0    1    2    3    4
```
Number of Visits

1. How many students visited the museum?

11 students

2. What is the range of the number of visits to the museum?

4

3. What is the median number of visits?

2

4. What is the mean of the number of visits to the nearest tenth?

2.3

5. What is the mode of the number of visits?

2

6. Which other kind of graph would best show the data?

frequency table

Use the line graph for problems 7–11.

Marla's Walking Times

7. How many minutes does Marla walk during the 6-day period?

95 minutes

8. What is the range of minutes walked?

20 minutes

9. What is the mode for the set of data?

20

10. On which day does Marla walk the least number of minutes?

Day 5

GO ON

Bottom Right — Form B, Page 2

11. Suppose you use a pictograph to display this set of data. You use a picture of one shoe to show a walking distance of 5 minutes. How many shoes would you show for day 6?

3 shoes

Use the pictograph for problems 12–16.

Favorite Musical Instruments	
Instrument	**Number of Students**
Drums	♪♪♪♪♪♪
Piano	♪♪♪♪
Trumpet	♪
Violin	♪♪
Guitar	♪♪♪♪♪♪♪

Key: each ♪ = 5 students

12. How many students play a musical instrument?

100 students

13. What is the median for the set of data?

20

14. What is the mean for this set of data?

20

15. Which two musical instruments represent 25 students?

piano and trumpet

16. Write true or false. A double bar graph could also be used to show the data.

false

17. Which type of display would **not** be appropriate to show the favorite juice drinks of a group of students?

a line graph

18. Jerry planted a seed that grew into a 24-inch tall plant after 4 months. Suppose he makes a line graph to show changes in the plant's height over time. Which intervals are most appropriate for the axis showing the number of inches?

possible answer: 4 inches

19. Which type of graph could you use to best display the number of inches of snowfall during a 6-week period—a double bar graph or a line graph?

line graph

20. Which type of graph might you use to convince your teacher that more students want to visit the science museum than the zoo—a line graph or bar graph?

bar graph

STOP

Chapter 8

Read each question carefully. Darken the circle on your answer sheet for the correct answer.

Use the histogram for problems 1-6.

Earnings: Selling Notepads

(histogram: Number of Students vs Amount (in dollars); intervals 0–25, 26–50, 51–75, 76–100)

1. How many students sold notepads?

(A) 85   **B.** 75   **C.** 50   **D.** 30

2. How many students sold between $26 and $50 worth of notepads?

F. 10   (G) 20   **H.** 25   **J.** 30

3. What is the greatest number of students that could have earned $17 dollars?

A. 10   **B.** 20   **C.** 25   (D) 30

4. How many students sold between $51 and $100 worth of notepads?

F. 55   **G.** 45   (H) 35   **J.** 25

5. Suppose 10 more students earned $115 from selling notepads. Which interval would you add to the histogram?

A. 126–150   (C) 101–125
B. 101–150   **D.** 101–115

6. What other kind of display would best show this data?

F. double bar graph
G. line graph
(H) frequency table
J. pictograph

Use the stem-and-leaf plot for problems 7–11.

Bike Rentals for 2 Weeks

2 | 3 3 4 6
3 | 2 3 3 5 6 6   Key: 2|3 = 23
4 | 1 3 5
5 | 4 6

7. During how many days did people rent more than 36 bikes?

A. 4   (B) 5   **C.** 6   **D.** 7

8. During how many days did people rent fewer than 35 bikes?

F. 2   **G.** 5   (H) 7   **J.** 10

9. Each bike rental costs $7. If 50 bikes were rented during 2 days, how much did the rental shop earn?

A. $250   **C.** $300
B. $275   (D) $350

10. Which stem has the most leaves?

F. 2   (G) 3   **H.** 4   **J.** 5

---

11. Suppose you use a histogram to display this set of data. Which interval would show a gap?

(A) 0–19   **C.** 30–39
B. 20–29   **D.** 40–49

12. In a population of 1,000 people, 150 people are surveyed. What are the people surveyed called?

F. a population   **H.** a representative
(G) a sample   **J.** a survey

13. There are 400 students in a school. If you put all their names in a hat, and choose 100 students, which type of a sample would you have?

(A) random   **C.** representative
B. biased   **D.** population

14. Suppose 2 friends pick 25 students out of a total of 500 students for a survey. What is the population in this example?

F. 2 friends
G. 25 students chosen
H. 475 students not chosen
(J) 500 students

15. A survey asks the 15 youngest members in 3 classes of fifth-graders to name the President of the United States. What kind of a sample is this?

A. population   **C.** representive
B. random   (D) biased

16. If each member of the school population has the same chance of being chosen for a survey, what kind of a sample is that?

(F) random
G. biased
H. population
J. representative

17. Which type of display would best show the average temperatures of 50 cities?

A. line graph
(B) stem-and-leaf plot
C. double bar graph
D. bar graph

18. Which type of graph could you use to best display the prices of hardware stock during one year?

F. histogram   **H.** double bar graph
(G) line graph   **J.** pictograph

19. Which type of graph could you use to best display the number of boys and girls who attended computer camp each year from 2002–2004?

(A) double bar graph   **C.** bar graph
B. line graph   **D.** pictograph

20. Kelly measured the heights of 100 students. She wants to organize her data into 5 groups. Which type of display should she use?

F. double bar graph   **H.** pictograph
G. line graph   (J) histogram

Read each question carefully. Fill in the correct answer in the space provided.

Use the histogram for problems 1–6.

Earnings: Selling Stickers

(histogram: Number of Students vs Amount (in dollars); intervals 0–25, 26–50, 51–75, 76–100)

1. How many students sold stickers?

85

2. How many students sold between $26 and $50 worth of stickers?

30 students

3. What is the greatest number of students that could have earned $63?

25 students

4. How many students sold between $51 and $100 worth of stickers?

35 students

5. 10 more students earned $120 from selling stickers. Which interval would you add to the histogram?

101-125

6. What other kind of display would best show this data?

bar graph

Use the stem-and-leaf plot for problems 7–11.

Kayak Rentals for 2 Weeks

2 | 3 4 4 5
3 | 2 3 4 5 5 6   Key: 2|3 = 23
4 | 1 3 4
5 | 2 8

7. During how many days did people rent more than 25 kayaks?

11 days

8. During how many days did people rent fewer than 36 kayaks?

9 days

9. Each kayak rental costs $9. If 50 kayaks were rented during 2 days, how much did the rental shop earn?

$450

10. Which stem has the least leaves?

5

---

11. Suppose you use a bar graph to display this set of data. Which interval would show a gap?

0–19

12. At a concert, 6 students survey 500 of the 3,000 people who bought tickets. How many people are in the sample?

500 people

13. If you put all the names of students in a hat and choose 200 students of 800 students, which type of a sample would you have?

random

14. Suppose 50 students of a total of 750 were chosen for a survey. How many students are in the population?

750 students

15. A survey asks the 15 oldest members in 3 classes of fifth-graders to name the capital of their state. What kind of a sample is this—representative or biased?

biased

16. Write *true* or *false*. If each member of the school population has the same chance of being chosen for a survey, then the sample would be random.

true

17. Which type of graph could you use to best compare populations of the largest cities in Florida—a line graph or a bar graph?

bar graph

18. Which type of graph would be the best display for showing the prices of eggs during one year—a double bar graph or a line graph?

line graph

19. Which type of graph could you use to best display the number of boys and girls who attended sports camp each year from 2002–2004—a bar graph or a double bar graph?

double bar graph

20. Which type of graph could you use to best display the number of students in a school and their ages in equal intervals—a line graph or a histogram?

histogram

Name_____

Read each question carefully. Darken the circle on your answer sheet for the correct answer.

Use the line plot for exercises 1–6.

Library Visits in a Month

```
        ×
        ×   ×   ×   ×
×   ×   ×   ×   ×
×   ×   ×   ×   ×
0   1   2   3   4   5
     Number of Visits
```

1. How many students were surveyed?

A. 10   B. 12   C. 16   D. Not Here

2. What is the median of the number of visits?

F. 2   G. 3   H. 4   J. 5

3. What is the mode of the number of visits?

A. 2   B. 3   C. 4   D. 5

4. What is the mean of the number of visits to the nearest tenth?

F. 2   G. 2.8   H. 3   J. 3.2

5. What is the range of the number of visits?

A. 1   B. 2   C. 3   D. 5

6. What other kind of display would best show the data?

F. histogram
G. stem-and-leaf plot
H. frequency table
J. double-bar graph

Use the bar graph for exercises 7–11.

Favorite Juices

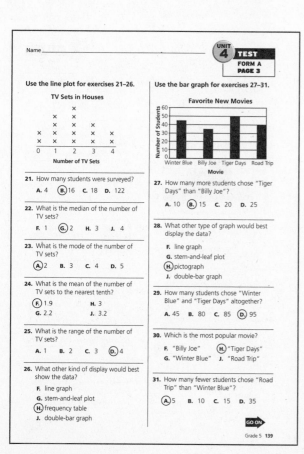

7. How many more students chose orange juice than apple juice?

A. 5   B. 10   C. 20   D. 50

8. What other type of graph would best display the data?

F. line graph
G. stem-and-leaf plot
H. pictograph
J. double-bar graph

9. How many students chose apple juice and grape juice altogether?

A. 10   C. 25
B. 20   D. 35

10. Which is the most popular juice?

F. apple   H. grape
G. orange   J. other

11. How many fewer students chose grape juice than orange juice?

A. 5   B. 10   C. 15   D. 30

GO ON

Grade 5 **137**

Name_____

Use the histogram for exercises 12–14.

Earnings: Selling Mugs

```
Number of Students
30
20
10
 0
    0–19  20–39  40–59  60–79
       Amount (in dollars)
```

12. The fewest number of students earned which amount?

F. $0–$19   H. $40–$59
G. $20–$39   J. $60–$79

13. How many students sold 0–19 dollars worth of mugs?

A. 25   B. 30   C. 35   D. 55

14. How many students sold mugs?

F. 30   G. 50   H. 75   J. 85

Use the stem-and-leaf plot for exercises 15–17.

Canoes Rented Over Two Weeks

```
2 | 4 4 5 6
3 | 3 4 4 5 6
4 | 2 3 4        Key: 2|4 means 24
5 | 1 3
```

15. During how many days did people rent more than 35 canoes?

A. 5   B. 6   C. 7   D. 8

16. Each rental costs $5. During how many days did rentals bring in more than $250?

F. 2   G. 5   H. 10   J. 14

17. During how many days did people rent fewer than 33 canoes?

A. 4   B. 5   C. 6   D. 8

18. Sarah wants to survey bikers to see which bike trails are the most popular in the park. In order to get a random sample, when should she survey the bikers in the park?

F. in the morning
G. in the afternoon
H. in the evening
J. at random times

19. The Amoco Cadiz spilled 68 million gallons of oil. The Braer spilled 25 million, and the Torrey Canyon spilled 37 million. If a bar graph is used to display the data, which intervals are most appropriate for the axis showing the number of gallons?

A. intervals of 10 gallons
B. intervals of 100 gallons
C. intervals of 10 million gallons
D. intervals of 100 million gallons

20. Which type of graph could you use to best display the daily high and low temperatures for 5 days?

F. double-bar graph
G. stem-and-leaf plot
H. histogram
J. line graph

GO ON

138 Grade 5

Name_____

Use the line plot for exercises 21–26.

TV Sets in Houses

```
        ×
    ×   ×
    ×   ×   ×
×   ×   ×   ×   ×
×   ×   ×   ×   ×
0   1   2   3   4
    Number of TV Sets
```

21. How many students were surveyed?

A. 4   B. 16   C. 18   D. 122

22. What is the median of the number of TV sets?

F. 1   G. 2   H. 3   J. 4

23. What is the mode of the number of TV sets?

A. 2   B. 3   C. 4   D. 5

24. What is the mean of the number of TV sets to the nearest tenth?

F. 1.9   H. 3
G. 2.2   J. 3.2

25. What is the range of the number of TV sets?

A. 1   B. 2   C. 3   D. 4

26. What other kind of display would best show the data?

F. line graph
G. stem-and-leaf plot
H. frequency table
J. double-bar graph

Use the bar graph for exercises 27–31.

Favorite New Movies

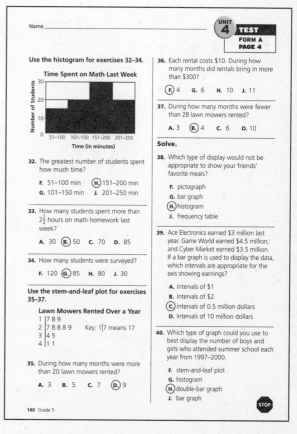

27. How many more students chose "Tiger Days" than "Billy Joe"?

A. 10   B. 15   C. 20   D. 25

28. What other type of graph would best display the data?

F. line graph
G. stem-and-leaf plot
H. pictograph
J. double-bar graph

29. How many students chose "Winter Blue" and "Tiger Days" altogether?

A. 45   B. 80   C. 85   D. 95

30. Which is the most popular movie?

F. "Billy Joe"   H. "Tiger Days"
G. "Winter Blue"   J. "Road Trip"

31. How many fewer students chose "Road Trip" than "Winter Blue"?

A. 5   B. 10   C. 15   D. 35

GO ON

Grade 5 **139**

Name_____

Use the histogram for exercises 32–34.

Time Spent on Math Last Week

```
Number of Students
30
20
10
 0
   51–100 101–150 151–200 201–250
          Time (in minutes)
```

32. The greatest number of students spent how much time?

F. 51–100 min   H. 151–200 min
G. 101–150 min   J. 201–250 min

33. How many students spent more than $2\frac{1}{2}$ hours on math homework last week?

A. 30   B. 50   C. 70   D. 85

34. How many students were surveyed?

F. 120   G. 85   H. 80   J. 30

Use the stem-and-leaf plot for exercises 35–37.

Lawn Mowers Rented Over a Year

```
1 | 7 8 9
2 | 7 8 8 8 9      Key: 1|7 means 17
3 | 4 5
4 | 1 1
```

35. During how many months were more than 20 lawn mowers rented?

A. 3   B. 5   C. 7   D. 9

36. Each rental costs $10. During how many months did rentals bring in more than $300?

F. 4   G. 6   H. 10   J. 11

37. During how many months were fewer than 28 lawn mowers rented?

A. 3   B. 4   C. 6   D. 10

Solve.

38. Which type of display would not be appropriate to show your friends' favorite meals?

F. pictograph
G. bar graph
H. histogram
J. frequency table

39. Ace Electronics earned $3 million last year. Game World earned $4.5 million, and Cyber Market earned $3.5 million. If a bar graph is used to display the data, which intervals are appropriate for the axis showing earnings?

A. intervals of $1
B. intervals of $2
C. intervals of 0.5 million dollars
D. intervals of 10 million dollars

40. Which type of graph could you use to best display the number of boys and girls who attended summer school each year from 1997–2000.

F. stem-and-leaf plot
G. histogram
H. double-bar graph
J. bar graph

STOP

140 Grade 5

Unit 4

Name_____

UNIT 4 TEST FORM B PAGE 1

Read each question carefully. Fill in the correct answer in the space provided.

Use the line plot for exercises 1–6.

Video Store Visits In a Week

```
      ×
      ×       ×
      ×       ×
      ×       ×           ×
  ×   ×   ×               ×
  ×   ×   ×       ×       ×       ×
  0   1   2   3   4   5
        Number of Visits
```

1. How many students were surveyed?

   18

2. What is the range of the number of visits?

   5

3. What is the mean of the number of visits to the nearest tenth?

   2.0. Do not accept 2.

4. What is the median of the number of visits?

   2

5. What is the mode of the number of visits?

   1

6. What other kind of display would best show the data?

   frequency table

Use the bar graph for exercises 7–11.

Favorite Color

(bar graph: Red 40, Yellow 25, Green 15, Blue 5, Purple 5; y-axis Number of Students 10, 20, 30, 40; x-axis Color)

7. How many more students chose yellow than green?

   10 students

8. How many students chose red and purple all together?

   45 students

9. How many fewer students chose blue than red?

   30 students

10. What is the most popular color?

    red

11. What other type of graph would best display the data?

    pictograph

GO ON

Grade 5 **141**

UNIT 4 TEST FORM B PAGE 2

Use the histogram for exercises 12–14.

Money Spent on Snacks

(histogram: 0–19: 15, 20–39: 35, 40–59: 30, 60–79: 15, 80+: 10; y-axis Number of Students 10, 20, 30, 40; x-axis Amount (in dollars))

12. How many students were surveyed?

    105

13. How many students spent 40–59 dollars on snacks?

    possible estimate: 30

14. The least number of students spent what amount?

    $80+

Use the stem-and-leaf plot for exercises 15–17.

Daily Video Game Rentals

```
0 | 7 8 8 9
1 | 0 0 1 2     Key: 1|0 means 10 games
2 | 5
3 | 3 6 8
4 | 1
```

15. During how many days did people rent more than 13 games?

    5 days

16. Each rental costs $3. During how many days did rentals bring in more than $100?

    3 days

17. During how many days did people rent less than 11 games?

    6 days

18. Matt wants to survey joggers to see which jogging trails are the most popular in the park. In order to get a random sample, when should he survey joggers in the park?

    at random times

19. Cathy is 1.4 meters tall. Sean is 1.6 meters tall. If a bar graph is used to display the data, what intervals are most appropriate for the axis showing the number of meters?

    possible answer: 0.1 meter

20. What type of graph could you use to best display the daily high and low temperatures for 5 days?

    double-bar graph

GO ON

142 Grade 5

UNIT 4 TEST FORM B PAGE 3

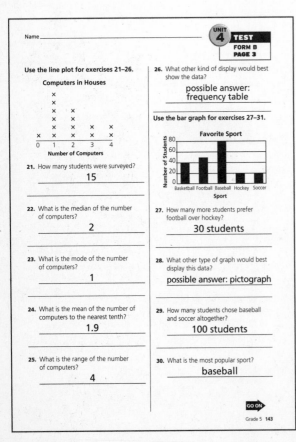

Use the line plot for exercises 21–26.

Computers in Houses

```
      ×
      ×
      ×   ×
      ×   ×
      ×   ×   ×   ×
  ×   ×   ×   ×   ×
  0   1   2   3   4
       Number of Computers
```

21. How many students were surveyed?

    15

22. What is the median of the number of computers?

    2

23. What is the mode of the number of computers?

    1

24. What is the mean of the number of computers to the nearest tenth?

    1.9

25. What is the range of the number of computers?

    4

26. What other kind of display would best show the data?

    possible answer: frequency table

Use the bar graph for exercises 27–31.

Favorite Sport

(bar graph: Basketball 40, Football 50, Baseball 80, Hockey 20, Soccer 20; y-axis Number of Students 20, 40, 60, 80; x-axis Sport)

27. How many more students prefer football over hockey?

    30 students

28. What other type of graph would best display this data?

    possible answer: pictograph

29. How many students chose baseball and soccer altogether?

    100 students

30. What is the most popular sport?

    baseball

GO ON

Grade 5 **143**

UNIT 4 TEST FORM B PAGE 4

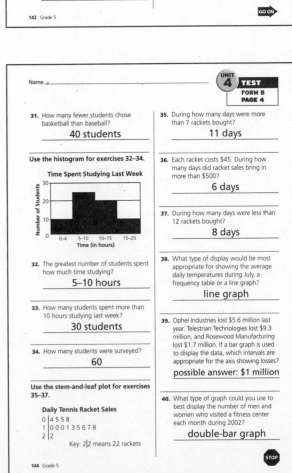

31. How many fewer students chose basketball than baseball?

    40 students

Use the histogram for exercises 32–34.

Time Spent Studying Last Week

(histogram: 0–4: 10, 5–10: 25, 10–15: 20, 15–20: 5; y-axis Number of Students 10, 20, 30; x-axis Time (in hours))

32. The greatest number of students spent how much time studying?

    5–10 hours

33. How many students spent more than 10 hours studying last week?

    30 students

34. How many students were surveyed?

    60

Use the stem-and-leaf plot for exercises 35–37.

Daily Tennis Racket Sales

```
0 | 4 5 5 8
1 | 0 0 0 1 3 5 6 7 8
2 | 2
        Key: 2|2 means 22 rackets
```

35. During how many days were more than 7 rackets bought?

    11 days

36. Each racket costs $45. During how many days did racket sales bring in more than $500?

    6 days

37. During how many days were less than 12 rackets bought?

    8 days

38. What type of display would be most appropriate for showing the average daily temperatures during July, a frequency table or a line graph?

    line graph

39. Ophel Industries lost $5.6 million last year. Telestrian Technologies lost $9.3 million, and Rosewood Manufacturing lost $1.7 million. If a bar graph is used to display the data, which intervals are appropriate for the axis showing losses?

    possible answer: $1 million

40. What type of graph could you use to best display the number of men and women who visited a fitness center each month during 2002?

    double-bar graph

STOP

144 Grade 5

Name _____

Read each question carefully. Darken the circle on your answer sheet for the correct answer.

1. Which number is prime?

A. 14   B. 24   C. 29   D. 26

2. Which number is composite?

F. 50   G. 47   H. 43   J. 41

3. What is the greatest common factor (GCF) of 24 and 64?

A. 2   B. 4   C. 6   D. 8

4. Which is the simplest form of $\frac{60}{100}$?

F. $\frac{4}{15}$ G. $\frac{5}{12}$ H. $\frac{3}{5}$ J. $\frac{1}{2}$

5. What is the greatest common factor (GCF) of 25 and 35?

A. 15   B. 10   C. 5   D. 3

6. Which fraction is equivalent to $\frac{9}{12}$ and $\frac{18}{24}$?

F. $\frac{6}{8}$ G. $\frac{3}{4}$ H. $\frac{5}{8}$ J. $\frac{2}{3}$

7. Which of the following numbers is **not** prime?

A. 11   B. 13   C. 16   D. 17

8. What is the greatest common factor (GCF) of 14, 28, and 35?

F. 2   G. 4   H. 5   J. 7

9. Which of the following is **not** composite?

A. 48   B. 49   C. 50   D. 53

10. Which two fractions are equivalent to $\frac{2}{3}$?

F. $\frac{3}{8}$ and $\frac{9}{18}$

G. $\frac{9}{12}$ and $\frac{18}{24}$

H. $\frac{4}{6}$ and $\frac{8}{12}$

J. $\frac{5}{8}$ and $\frac{10}{16}$

11. Which is the simplest form of $\frac{12}{48}$?

A. $\frac{1}{4}$ B. $\frac{1}{3}$ C. $\frac{1}{5}$ D. $\frac{1}{2}$

12. Which of the numbers is **not** a common factor of 24?

F. 8   G. 6   H. 5   J. 4

13. Which number is composite?

A. 29   B. 32   C. 37   D. 41

GO ON

Name _____

14. Which is an equivalent fraction for $\frac{18}{36}$?

F. $\frac{1}{6}$ G. $\frac{1}{4}$ H. $\frac{1}{3}$ J. $\frac{1}{2}$

15. What is the greatest common factor (GCF) of 21 and 54?

A. 3   B. 4   C. 6   D. 9

16. Students sold tickets to the annual play. The math club sold $\frac{1}{4}$ of the tickets, the science club sold $\frac{3}{8}$ of the tickets, and the music group sold $\frac{1}{8}$ of the tickets. How many tickets did the math club sell? What information is missing to solve the problem?

F. the number of students attending the play

G. the total number of tickets sold

H. the cost of the tickets

J. the group who sold $\frac{1}{3}$ of the tickets

17. On the first night of the play, one row of seats was empty. The auditorium seats 350 people. How many seats were empty? What information is missing to solve the problem?

A. the number of adults attending the performance

B. the number of tickets sold for each performance

C. the number of seats in a row

D. the number of students attending the performance

18. Over 250 students attended the play. Each student bought a ticket. The runner's club sold $\frac{1}{4}$ of the tickets to adults. Student tickets cost $2. How much did the school collect from the students? What extra information is given?

F. Over 250 students attended.

G. The runner's club sold $\frac{1}{4}$ of the tickets to adults.

H. Student tickets cost $2.

J. Each student bought a ticket.

19. At the performance, 27 school ushers wore armbands. No one wanted to wear green armbands. One-half of the ushers wore yellow armbands. A second group wore red. One-third group wore blue. How many ushers word red armbands? What extra information is given?

A. 27 school ushers wore armbands.

B. No one wanted green armbands.

C. One group wore yellow armbands.

D. A second group wore red.

20. On the first night, 250 students and 100 adults attended the performance. Only one row of seats was empty. How many seats were empty? What information is missing?

F. the number of seats in the auditorium

G. the number of performers

H. the number of rows of seats in the auditorium

J. the number of tickets sold

STOP

Name _____

Read each question carefully. Fill in the correct answer in the space provided.

1. Which number is prime?

22   32   37   44

__37__

2. Which number is composite?

29   31   36   37

__36__

3. What is the greatest common factor (GCF) of 18 and 36?

__18__

4. What is the simplest form of $\frac{30}{90}$?

$\frac{1}{3}$

5. What is the greatest common factor (GCF) of 20 and 45?

__5__

6. What fraction is equivalent to $\frac{8}{12}$ and $\frac{16}{24}$?

$\frac{2}{3}$

7. Which number is **not** prime?

13   16   17   19

__16__

8. What is the greatest common factor (GCF) of 27, 36, and 45?

__9__

9. Which number is **not** composite?

22   31   36   40

__31__

10. Write two equivalent fractions for $\frac{2}{5}$.

possible answers: $\frac{4}{10}$, $\frac{8}{20}$

GO ON

Name _____

11. Write $\frac{14}{56}$ in simplest form.

$\frac{1}{4}$

12. Which number is not a common factor of 36?

4   5   6   8

__5__

13. Which number is composite?

23   31   37   42

__42__

14. Which is an equivalent fraction of $\frac{21}{35}$?

$\frac{1}{2}$ $\frac{3}{5}$ $\frac{2}{3}$ $\frac{3}{4}$

$\frac{3}{5}$

15. What is the greatest common factor (GCF) of 32 and 48?

__16__

16. Students sold tickets to the graduation dance. The social committee sold $\frac{3}{8}$ of the tickets, the band sold $\frac{1}{4}$ of the tickets, and the decoration committee sold $\frac{1}{4}$ of the tickets. How many tickets did the band sell? What information is missing to solve the problem?

the total number of tickets sold

17. On the night of the dance, only one table was empty. All the other tables were full. If 8 people sat at each table, how many people attended the dance? What information is missing to solve the problem?

the number of tables in the room

18. A total of 175 tickets were sold to a dance. The social club sold $\frac{1}{8}$ of the tickets to adults. Each ticket costs $3. How much did the dance committees collect in ticket sales? What extra information is given in the problem?

the social club sold $\frac{1}{8}$ of the tickets to adults

19. At the dance, 12 members of the dance committee wore colored bracelets. No one wanted to wear yellow bracelets. One-fourth of the members wore black bracelets. The social committee wore red bracelets. One-third of the members wore blue bracelets. How many members wore red bracelets? What extra information is given in the problem?

no one wanted to wear yellow bracelets

20. On the night of the dance, 175 students and 20 adults attended. Only 5 tables were empty. How many tables were full? What information is missing to solve the problem?

the number of people per table

STOP

Chapter 10

Form A, Page 1

Name _____

CHAPTER 10 TEST FORM A PAGE 1

Read each question carefully. Darken the circle on your answer sheet for the correct answer.

1. What is the least common multiple (LCM) of 3 and 8?
- A. 16
- (C.) 24
- B. 20
- D. 32

2. What is the least common denominator (LCD) for $\frac{1}{2}$ and $\frac{3}{4}$?
- (F.) 4
- H. 12
- G. 8
- J. 16

3. Using the least common denominator (LCD), what are equivalent fractions for $\frac{2}{5}$ and $\frac{2}{3}$?
- A. $\frac{4}{10}$ and $\frac{4}{9}$
- C. $\frac{8}{20}$ and $\frac{4}{9}$
- (B.) $\frac{6}{15}$ and $\frac{10}{15}$
- D. $\frac{5}{15}$ and $\frac{9}{15}$

4. What is the fraction in simplest form for 0.3?
- F. $\frac{3}{1,000}$
- G. $\frac{3}{100}$
- H. $\frac{31}{100}$
- (J.) $\frac{3}{10}$

5. Order $\frac{1}{3}$, $\frac{3}{10}$, $\frac{4}{15}$, and $\frac{1}{4}$ from least to greatest.
- A. $\frac{1}{3}$, $\frac{3}{10}$, $\frac{4}{15}$, $\frac{1}{4}$
- (C.) $\frac{1}{4}$, $\frac{4}{15}$, $\frac{3}{10}$, $\frac{1}{3}$
- B. $\frac{1}{4}$, $\frac{3}{10}$, $\frac{4}{15}$, $\frac{1}{3}$
- D. $\frac{1}{3}$, $\frac{4}{15}$, $\frac{3}{10}$, $\frac{1}{4}$

6. Write $\frac{44}{7}$ as a mixed number in simplest form.
- F. $6\frac{1}{7}$
- H. $7\frac{1}{6}$
- (G.) $6\frac{2}{7}$
- J. $7\frac{2}{7}$

7. Write $3\frac{3}{8}$ as a decimal.
- A. 0.338
- C. 3.38
- B. 0.375
- (D.) 3.375

8. Order $5\frac{5}{8}$, 5.07, $5\frac{7}{8}$, and 5.7 from greatest to least.
- F. $5\frac{5}{8}$, 5.07, $5\frac{7}{8}$, 5.7
- (G.) $5\frac{7}{8}$, 5.7, $5\frac{5}{8}$, 5.07
- H. 5.7, 5.07, $5\frac{7}{8}$, $5\frac{5}{8}$
- J. 5.07, $5\frac{5}{8}$, $5\frac{7}{8}$, and 5.7

9. What is the least common multiple (LCM) of 6 and 18?
- A. 42
- (C.) 18
- B. 24
- D. 6

10. What is the least common denominator (LCD) for $\frac{1}{3}$ and $\frac{5}{8}$?
- F. 32
- H. 15
- (G.) 24
- J. 8

GO ON

Grade 5 **157**

Form A, Page 2

Name _____

CHAPTER 10 TEST FORM A PAGE 2

11. Using the least common denominator (LCD), what are equivalent fractions for $\frac{1}{3}$ and $\frac{5}{12}$?
- (A.) $\frac{4}{12}$ and $\frac{5}{12}$
- C. $\frac{12}{15}$ and $\frac{10}{24}$
- B. $\frac{5}{12}$ and $\frac{5}{12}$
- D. $\frac{3}{24}$ and $\frac{10}{24}$

12. What is the fraction in simplest form for 0.75?
- F. $\frac{1}{4}$
- (H.) $\frac{3}{4}$
- G. $\frac{2}{3}$
- J. $\frac{7}{8}$

13. Write 0.07 as a fraction.
- A. $\frac{7}{1,000}$
- C. $\frac{17}{100}$
- (B.) $\frac{7}{100}$
- D. $\frac{7}{10}$

14. Order $\frac{1}{3}$, $\frac{1}{2}$, $\frac{1}{5}$, and $\frac{1}{4}$ from greatest to least.
- F. $\frac{1}{3}$, $\frac{1}{2}$, $\frac{1}{5}$, $\frac{1}{4}$
- (H.) $\frac{1}{2}$, $\frac{1}{3}$, $\frac{1}{4}$, $\frac{1}{5}$
- G. $\frac{1}{4}$, $\frac{1}{2}$, $\frac{1}{5}$, $\frac{1}{3}$
- J. $\frac{1}{5}$, $\frac{1}{4}$, $\frac{1}{3}$, $\frac{1}{2}$

15. Write $6\frac{6}{9}$ as a mixed number in simplest form.
- A. $7\frac{1}{3}$
- C. $8\frac{1}{3}$
- (B.) $6\frac{2}{3}$
- D. $8\frac{2}{9}$

16. Write $12\frac{9}{10}$ as a decimal.
- F. 12.009
- (H.) 12.9
- G. 12.09
- J. 129

Use the table for problems 17–20.

Favorite Apples	Number of Students
Granny Smith	25
Delicious	20
Gala	15
Cortland	22
Empire	18

17. Which fraction, in simplest form, names the part of the group of students who like Granny Smith apples?
- A. $\frac{1}{2}$
- (C.) $\frac{1}{4}$
- B. $\frac{1}{3}$
- D. $\frac{1}{5}$

18. Which fraction, in simplest form, names the part of the group of students who like Cortland and Empire apples?
- F. $\frac{2}{3}$
- H. $\frac{1}{2}$
- (G.) $\frac{2}{5}$
- J. $\frac{1}{3}$

19. Which decimal names the part of the group of students who like Delicious apples?
- A. 0.18
- C. 0.22
- (B.) 0.20
- D. 0.25

20. Which decimal represents the group of students who like Granny Smith, Cortland, and Empire apples?
- F. 0.45
- H. 0.60
- G. 0.50
- (J.) 0.65

STOP

158 Grade 5

Form B, Page 1

Name _____

CHAPTER 10 TEST FORM B PAGE 1

1. What is the least common multiple (LCM) of 5 and 8?

_40_

2. What is the least common denominator (LCD) for $\frac{1}{3}$ and $\frac{3}{5}$?

_15_

3. Using the least common denominator (LCD), what are equivalent fractions for $\frac{5}{6}$ and $\frac{3}{4}$?

$\frac{10}{12}$ and $\frac{9}{12}$

4. What is the fraction in simplest form for 0.6?

$\frac{3}{5}$

5. Order $\frac{1}{4}$, $\frac{4}{10}$, $\frac{3}{8}$, and $\frac{1}{3}$ from least to greatest.

$\frac{1}{4}$, $\frac{1}{3}$, $\frac{3}{8}$, $\frac{4}{10}$

6. Write $\frac{58}{9}$ as a mixed number in simplest form.

$6\frac{4}{9}$

7. Write $5\frac{7}{8}$ as a decimal.

_5.875_

8. Order $4\frac{5}{6}$, 4.06, $4\frac{1}{6}$, and 4.6 from greatest to least.

$4\frac{5}{6}$, 4.6, $4\frac{1}{6}$, 4.06

9. What is the least common multiple (LCM) of 7 and 21?

_21_

10. What is the least common denominator (LCD) for $\frac{1}{4}$ and $\frac{5}{6}$?

_12_

GO ON

Grade 5 **159**

Form B, Page 2

Name _____

CHAPTER 10 TEST FORM B PAGE 2

11. Using the least common denominator (LCD), what are equivalent fractions for $\frac{1}{5}$ and $\frac{3}{8}$?

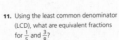

$\frac{8}{40}$ and $\frac{15}{40}$

12. What is the fraction in simplest form for 0.67?

$\frac{67}{100}$

13. Write 0.03 as a fraction.

$\frac{3}{100}$

14. Order $\frac{1}{6}$, $\frac{4}{5}$, $\frac{3}{4}$, and $\frac{2}{3}$ from greatest to least.

$\frac{4}{5}$, $\frac{3}{4}$, $\frac{2}{3}$, $\frac{1}{6}$

15. Write $\frac{68}{8}$ as a mixed number in simplest form.

$8\frac{1}{2}$

16. Write $23\frac{7}{10}$ as a decimal.

_23.7_

Use the table for problems 17–20.

Favorite Vegetable	Number of Students
peas	35
string beans	20
corn	25
broccoli	12
squash	8

17. Which fraction, in simplest form, names the part of the group of students that likes corn?

$\frac{1}{4}$

18. Which fraction, in simplest form, names the part of the group that likes string beans, broccoli, and squash?

$\frac{2}{5}$

19. Which decimal names the part of the group that likes peas and squash?

_0.43_

20. Which decimal represents the group of students that likes peas and string beans?

_0.55_

STOP

160 Grade 5

Name _____

 TEST FORM A PAGE 1

Read each question carefully. Darken the circle on your answer sheet for the correct answer.

1. Which number is prime?

A. 51   B. 76   C. 87   D. 97

2. Which number is composite?

F. 43   G. 61   H. 81   J. 83

3. Which is the simplest form of $\frac{40}{56}$?

A. $\frac{10}{14}$ B. $\frac{5}{7}$ C. $\frac{11}{16}$ D. $\frac{5}{8}$

4. What is the decimal form of $\frac{3}{8}$?

F. 0.38   H. 0.83   G. 0.24   J. 0.375

5. Order $3\frac{7}{9}$, $\frac{29}{8}$, and 3.7 from least to greatest.

A. 3.7, $3\frac{7}{9}$, $\frac{29}{8}$ C. $3\frac{7}{9}$, 3.7, $\frac{29}{8}$

B. $\frac{29}{8}$, 3.7, $3\frac{7}{9}$ D. $3\frac{7}{9}$, $\frac{29}{8}$, 3.7

6. What is the least common multiple (LCM) of 8 and 15?

F. 40   G. 80   H. 90   J. 120

7. Rewrite $\frac{1}{6}$, $\frac{4}{15}$, and $\frac{3}{4}$ using their least common denominator.

A. $\frac{5}{30}$, $\frac{8}{30}$, $\frac{21}{30}$ C. $\frac{15}{90}$, $\frac{24}{90}$, $\frac{60}{90}$

B. $\frac{10}{60}$, $\frac{16}{60}$, $\frac{45}{60}$ D. $\frac{20}{120}$, $\frac{32}{120}$, $\frac{90}{120}$

8. Which is the simplest form of $\frac{12}{54}$?

F. $\frac{1}{6}$ G. $\frac{4}{18}$ H. $\frac{6}{27}$ J. $\frac{2}{9}$

9. Order $\frac{1}{3}$, 0.24, and $\frac{2}{7}$ from least to greatest.

A. 0.24, $\frac{2}{7}$, $\frac{1}{3}$ C. $\frac{2}{7}$, 0.24, $\frac{1}{3}$

B. 0.24, $\frac{1}{3}$, $\frac{2}{7}$ D. $\frac{2}{7}$, $\frac{1}{3}$, 0.24

10. Rewrite $\frac{3}{7}$, $\frac{1}{2}$, and $\frac{2}{3}$ using their least common denominator.

F. $\frac{6}{14}$, $\frac{7}{14}$, $\frac{8}{14}$ H. $\frac{18}{42}$, $\frac{21}{42}$, $\frac{28}{42}$

G. $\frac{12}{28}$, $\frac{14}{28}$, $\frac{18}{28}$ J. $\frac{36}{84}$, $\frac{42}{84}$, $\frac{56}{84}$

11. Write $\frac{46}{6}$ as a mixed number in simplest form.

A. $6\frac{5}{6}$ B. $7\frac{1}{3}$ C. $7\frac{2}{3}$ D. 8

12. Write $\frac{42}{8}$ as a mixed number in simplest form.

F. $5\frac{1}{21}$ G. $5\frac{1}{4}$ H. 6   J. $6\frac{2}{3}$

13. What is the prime factorization of 75?

A. 5×3^2 C. 5×3^5 B. 5×3^3 D. 3×5^2

14. What is the greatest common factor (GCF) of 18 and 81?

F. 3   G. 6   H. 9   J. 18

GO ON

Grade 5   165

Name _____

 TEST FORM A PAGE 2

15. Order $\frac{9}{5}$, 1.2, and $1\frac{2}{5}$ from least to greatest on a number line.

16. Order $1\frac{3}{10}$, $\frac{9}{4}$, and 1.85 from least to greatest.

F. $1\frac{3}{10}$, $\frac{9}{4}$, 1.85   H. 1.85, $\frac{9}{4}$, $1\frac{3}{10}$

G. $1\frac{3}{10}$, 1.85, $\frac{9}{4}$ J. $\frac{9}{4}$, 1.85, $1\frac{3}{10}$

Use the table for problems 17–18.

Favorite Sport	Number of Students
indoor swimming	3
basketball	12
skiing	6
skating	3
volleyball	8

17. Which fraction, in simplest form, names the part of the group of students who like basketball best?

A. $\frac{1}{8}$ B. $\frac{1}{4}$ C. $\frac{5}{16}$ D. $\frac{3}{8}$

18. Which fraction, in simplest form, names the part of the group of students who like volleyball best?

F. $\frac{1}{8}$ G. $\frac{1}{4}$ H. $\frac{5}{16}$ J. $\frac{3}{4}$

19. Three students agreed to sell tickets. Lisa sold $\frac{2}{7}$ of her tickets. Kelly sold $\frac{3}{16}$. Frank sold $\frac{1}{4}$.

What information is needed to find the number of tickets they each sold?

A. the number of students who attended the play

B. the cost of the ticket

C. the number of days the play will be running

D. the total number of tickets they each agreed to sell

20. Three students agreed to sell tickets. Lila sold 0.5 of her tickets. Terry sold 0.25. Vance sold 0.125. Who sold exactly $\frac{1}{8}$ of his or her tickets?

F. Lila   H. Vance   G. Terry

GO ON

166   Grade 5

Name _____

 TEST FORM A PAGE 3

21. Which number is prime?

A. 21   B. 49   C. 52   D. 73

22. Which number is composite?

F. 24   G. 37   H. 61   J. 79

23. Which is the simplest form of $\frac{21}{56}$?

A. $\frac{3}{8}$ B. $\frac{3}{7}$ C. $\frac{5}{7}$ D. $\frac{11}{28}$

24. What is the fractional form of 0.55?

F. $\frac{11}{20}$ H. $\frac{1}{55}$ G. $\frac{3}{20}$ J. $\frac{13}{20}$

25. Order $2\frac{3}{4}$, $\frac{25}{9}$, and 2.76 from least to greatest.

A. $2\frac{3}{4}$, $\frac{25}{9}$, 2.76   C. 2.76, $2\frac{3}{4}$, $\frac{25}{9}$

B. $2\frac{3}{4}$, 2.76, $\frac{25}{9}$ D. Not Here

26. What is the least common multiple (LCM) of 5, 6, and 8?

F. 40   G. 60   H. 120   J. 240

27. Rewrite $\frac{1}{8}$, $\frac{1}{3}$, and $\frac{5}{12}$ using their least common denominator.

A. $\frac{2}{12}$, $\frac{4}{12}$, $\frac{5}{12}$ C. $\frac{6}{48}$, $\frac{16}{48}$, $\frac{20}{48}$

B. $\frac{3}{24}$, $\frac{8}{24}$, $\frac{10}{24}$ D. $\frac{7}{60}$, $\frac{20}{60}$, $\frac{5}{60}$

28. Which is the simplest form of $\frac{58}{12}$?

F. $4\frac{2}{3}$ G. $4\frac{5}{6}$ H. 5   J. $5\frac{1}{2}$

29. Order $\frac{1}{6}$, 0.15, and $\frac{2}{11}$ from least to greatest.

A. $\frac{1}{6}$, 0.15, $\frac{2}{11}$ C. 0.15, $\frac{2}{11}$, $\frac{1}{6}$

B. $\frac{1}{6}$, $\frac{2}{11}$, 0.15   D. 0.15, $\frac{1}{6}$, $\frac{2}{11}$

30. Rewrite $\frac{2}{9}$, $\frac{4}{7}$, and $\frac{10}{21}$ using their least common denominator.

F. $\frac{5}{21}$, $\frac{4}{21}$, $\frac{10}{21}$ H. $\frac{28}{126}$, $\frac{72}{126}$, $\frac{60}{126}$

G. $\frac{14}{63}$, $\frac{36}{63}$, $\frac{30}{63}$ J. $\frac{41}{147}$, $\frac{84}{147}$, $\frac{70}{147}$

31. Write $\frac{75}{9}$ as a mixed number in simplest form.

A. $7\frac{8}{9}$ B. $8\frac{1}{9}$ C. $8\frac{1}{3}$ D. $8\frac{2}{3}$

32. Write $\frac{374}{121}$ as a mixed number in simplest form.

F. 3   G. $3\frac{1}{11}$ H. $3\frac{1}{4}$ J. $3\frac{1}{3}$

33. What is the prime factorization of 72?

A. 7×3^2 C. 3^4 B. $3^2 \times 2^3$ D. 2^5

GO ON

Grade 5   167

Name _____

TEST FORM A PAGE 4

34. What is the greatest common factor (GCF) of 12 and 60?

F. 2   G. 4   H. 6   J. 12

35. Order $1\frac{5}{8}$, $1\frac{1}{4}$, and $\frac{34}{20}$ from least to greatest on a number line.

36. Order $4\frac{2}{3}$, 4.59, and $\frac{24}{5}$ from least to greatest.

F. 4.59, $4\frac{2}{3}$, $\frac{24}{5}$ H. $4\frac{2}{3}$, $\frac{24}{5}$, 4.59

G. 4.59, $\frac{24}{5}$, $4\frac{2}{3}$ J. $\frac{24}{5}$, 4.59, $4\frac{2}{3}$

Use the table for problems 37–38.

Type of Tree	Number of Trees
apple	12
chestnut	14
maple	25
oak	37
pine	12

37. Which fraction, in simplest form, names the part of the trees that are maple?

A. $\frac{3}{18}$ B. $\frac{1}{4}$ C. $\frac{1}{3}$ D. $\frac{5}{12}$

38. Which fraction, in simplest form, names the part of the trees that are chestnut?

F. $\frac{7}{50}$ H. $\frac{7}{10}$ G. $\frac{7}{100}$ J. $\frac{7}{25}$

39. Four students agreed to sell cookies. Ben sold $\frac{1}{4}$ of his cookies. Tom sold $\frac{1}{5}$. Nicki sold $\frac{1}{5}$. Lee sold $\frac{1}{2}$. What information is needed to find the number of cookies they each sold?

A. the number of students who attended the fair

B. the cost of a cookie

C. the total number of cookies they each agreed to sell

D. the number of teachers who attended the fair

40. Brenda did 0.11 of an assignment. Todd did 0.25. Joe did 0.17. Bill did 0.14. Who did about $\frac{1}{7}$ of the job?

F. Brenda   H. Joe   G. Todd   J. Bill

 STOP

168   Grade 5

Unit 5

Page 1

Name

UNIT 5 TEST
FORM B
PAGE 1

Read each question carefully. Fill in the correct answer in the space provided.

1. Which number is prime?

63, 77, 79, or 81

79

2. Which number is composite?

53, 61, 83, or 91

91

3. What is the simplest form of $\frac{56}{64}$?

$\frac{7}{8}$

4. What is the decimal form of $\frac{3}{20}$?

0.15

5. Order $\frac{18}{7}$, 2.5, $\frac{19}{8}$ from greatest to least.

$\frac{18}{7}$, 2.5, $\frac{19}{8}$

6. What is the least common multiple (LCM) of 12 and 16?

48

7. Rewrite $\frac{1}{5}$, $\frac{3}{4}$, and $\frac{5}{6}$ using their least common denominator.

$\frac{12}{60}$, $\frac{45}{60}$, $\frac{50}{60}$

8. What is the simplest form of $\frac{8}{36}$?

$\frac{2}{9}$

9. Order 0.4, $\frac{3}{8}$, and $\frac{7}{19}$ from least to greatest.

$\frac{7}{19}$, $\frac{3}{8}$, 0.4

10. Rewrite $\frac{1}{2}$, $\frac{2}{3}$, and $\frac{5}{8}$ using their least common denominator.

$\frac{12}{24}$, $\frac{16}{24}$, $\frac{15}{24}$

GO ON

Page 2

Name

UNIT 5 TEST
FORM B
PAGE 2

11. Write $\frac{33}{7}$ as a mixed number in simplest form.

$4\frac{5}{7}$

12. Write $\frac{34}{9}$ as a mixed number in simplest form.

$3\frac{7}{9}$

13. What is the prime factorization of 84?

$2^2 \times 3 \times 7$

14. What is the greatest common factor of 72 and 96?

24

15. Order 0.75, $\frac{7}{4}$, and $2\frac{1}{2}$ from least to greatest on a number line.

16. Order $\frac{8}{7}$, $1\frac{3}{10}$, and 1.25 from greatest to least.

$1\frac{3}{10}$, 1.25, $\frac{8}{7}$

Use the table for problems 17–18.

Favorite Movie Genre	Number of People
Action	37
Comedy	18
Drama	8
Horror	12
Suspense	25

17. What fraction, in simplest form, represents the part of the group of people who like suspense best?

$\frac{1}{4}$

18. What fraction, in simplest form, represents the part of the group of people who like comedy best?

$\frac{9}{50}$

19. Four students agreed to sell tickets. Jamal sold $\frac{3}{4}$ of his tickets. Marian sold $\frac{3}{5}$ of her tickets. Gina sold $\frac{7}{8}$ of her tickets, and Julius sold $\frac{1}{2}$ of his tickets. What information is required to determine the total number of tickets they each agreed to sell?

the number of tickets they each sold

20. Three students agreed to sell tickets. Moira sold 0.8 of her tickets. Nina sold 0.55. Tim sold 0.7. Who sold exactly $\frac{11}{20}$ of his or her tickets?

Nina

GO ON

Page 3

Name

UNIT 5 TEST
FORM B
PAGE 3

21. Which number is prime?

27, 51, 63, or 79

79

22. Which number is composite?

41, 43, 45, or 47

45

23. What is the simplest form of $\frac{28}{49}$?

$\frac{4}{7}$

24. What is the fractional form of 0.625?

$\frac{5}{8}$

25. Order 5.6, $\frac{53}{9}$, and $5\frac{3}{4}$ from greatest to least.

$\frac{53}{9}$, $5\frac{3}{4}$, 5.6

26. What is the least common multiple (LCM) of 8, 12, and 18?

72

27. Rewrite $\frac{1}{5}$, $\frac{2}{9}$, and $\frac{7}{30}$ using their least common denominator.

$\frac{18}{90}$, $\frac{20}{90}$, $\frac{21}{90}$

28. What is the simplest form of $\frac{75}{18}$?

$4\frac{1}{6}$

29. Order $4\frac{1}{7}$, 4.25, and $\frac{21}{5}$ from least to greatest.

$4\frac{1}{7}$, $\frac{21}{5}$, 4.25

30. Rewrite $\frac{3}{4}$, $\frac{5}{9}$, and $\frac{13}{18}$ using their least common denominator.

$\frac{27}{36}$, $\frac{20}{36}$, $\frac{26}{36}$

GO ON

Page 4

Name

UNIT 5 TEST
FORM B
PAGE 4

31. Write $\frac{66}{8}$ as a mixed number in simplest form.

$8\frac{1}{4}$

32. Write $\frac{343}{21}$ as a mixed number in simplest form.

$16\frac{1}{3}$

33. What is the prime factorization of 90?

$2 \times 3^2 \times 5$

34. What is the greatest common factor of 91 and 65?

13

35. Order $1\frac{3}{5}$, $\frac{31}{20}$, and 1.5 from least to greatest on a number line.

36. Order 5.01, $\frac{46}{9}$, and $4\frac{7}{8}$ from least to greatest.

$4\frac{7}{8}$, 5.01, $\frac{46}{9}$

Use the table for problems 37–38.

Color of Pen	Number of Pens
Red	10
Green	23
Blue	29
Black	35
Violet	1
Orange	2

37. What fraction, in simplest form, represents the part of the pens that are black?

$\frac{7}{20}$

38. What fraction, in simplest form, represents the part of the pens that are either red or orange?

$\frac{3}{25}$

39. Three students work at a fast-food place. Madeleine served $\frac{1}{8}$ of the customers. Miranda served $\frac{1}{3}$. Antoine served $\frac{2}{7}$. What information is needed to find the number of customers they each served?

the total number of customers

40. Josh did 0.3 of his homework. Scott did 0.72. Caryn did 0.65. Jessica did 0.9. Who did about $\frac{2}{3}$ of his or her homework?

Caryn

STOP

Form A, Page 1

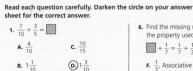

Name _____

CHAPTER 11 TEST FORM A PAGE 1

Read each question carefully. Darken the circle on your answer sheet for the correct answer.

1. $\frac{7}{10} + \frac{3}{5} = \square$

A. $\frac{4}{10}$ C. $\frac{10}{15}$

B. $1\frac{1}{10}$ **D.** $1\frac{3}{10}$

2. $2\frac{1}{4} + 7\frac{5}{6} = \square$

F. $10\frac{1}{12}$ H. $10\frac{1}{6}$

G. $10\frac{1}{4}$ J. $9\frac{11}{12}$

3. Identify the property used.

$\frac{3}{4} + 0 = \frac{3}{4}$

A. Associative Property
B. Commutative Property
C. Identity Property
D. Addition

4. $\frac{1}{10} + \frac{3}{8} = \square$

F. $\frac{19}{80}$ **H.** $\frac{19}{40}$

G. $\frac{9}{10}$ J. $\frac{19}{30}$

5. $3\frac{5}{8} + 9\frac{2}{3} = \square$

A. $12\frac{7}{11}$ C. $13\frac{1}{4}$

B. $12\frac{7}{8}$ **D.** $13\frac{7}{24}$

6. Find the missing number and identify the property used.

$\square + \frac{1}{7} = \frac{1}{7} + \frac{1}{3}$

F. $\frac{1}{3}$, Associative Property
G. $\frac{1}{7}$, Associative Property
H. $\frac{1}{7}$, Commutative Property
J. $\frac{1}{3}$, Commutative Property

7. Find the missing number and identify the property used.

$\frac{1}{3} + (\square + \frac{1}{4}) = (\frac{1}{3} + \frac{1}{6}) + \frac{1}{4}$

A. $\frac{1}{6}$, Associative Property
B. $\frac{1}{3}$, Associative Property
C. $\frac{1}{6}$, Commutative Property
D. $\frac{1}{4}$, Commutative Property

8. $\frac{1}{3} + \frac{8}{9} = \square$

F. $\frac{5}{9}$ G. $1\frac{1}{12}$ **H.** $1\frac{2}{9}$ J. $1\frac{1}{3}$

9. $42\frac{1}{10} + 16\frac{2}{5} = \square$

A. $58\frac{3}{5}$ C. $57\frac{1}{2}$

B. $58\frac{1}{2}$ D. $57\frac{3}{10}$

10. $\frac{2}{3} + \frac{4}{5} = \square$

F. $1\frac{7}{15}$ H. $1\frac{1}{5}$

G. $1\frac{1}{3}$ J. $\frac{3}{4}$

GO ON

Grade 5 **177**

Form A, Page 2

Name _____

CHAPTER 11 TEST FORM A PAGE 2

11. Find the missing number and identify the property used.

$2\frac{2}{3} + \square = \frac{1}{5} + 2\frac{2}{3}$

A. $\frac{1}{5}$, Multiplication Property
B. $\frac{1}{5}$, Identity Property
C. $\frac{1}{5}$, Associative Property
D. $\frac{1}{5}$, Commutative Property

12. $\frac{5}{8} + \frac{1}{6} = \square$

F. $1\frac{1}{2}$ **H.** $\frac{19}{24}$

G. $1\frac{5}{12}$ J. $\frac{6}{14}$

13. $31\frac{1}{3} + 9\frac{1}{6} = \square$

A. $41\frac{1}{3}$ C. $40\frac{1}{3}$

B. $40\frac{2}{3}$ D. $39\frac{2}{3}$

14. Find the missing number and identify the property used.

$(2\frac{1}{10} + 1\frac{1}{8}) + \square = 2\frac{1}{10} + (1\frac{1}{8} + 3\frac{1}{4})$

F. $3\frac{1}{4}$, Associative Property
G. $2\frac{1}{10}$, Commutative Property
H. $1\frac{1}{8}$, Identity Property
J. $3\frac{1}{4}$, Commutative Property

15. $\frac{7}{8} + \frac{3}{16} = \square$

A. $\frac{15}{16}$ C. $1\frac{1}{8}$

B. 1 **D.** $1\frac{1}{16}$

16. $8\frac{2}{3} + 6\frac{7}{15} = \square$

F. $15\frac{1}{15}$ **G.** $15\frac{5}{15}$ H. $15\frac{1}{5}$ J. $15\frac{1}{3}$

17. Janice spent $\frac{1}{3}$ of her savings on an outfit. The next week Janice spent another $\frac{1}{4}$ of her savings on a CD. How much of her total savings does she spend?

A. $\frac{1}{7}$ B. $\frac{5}{12}$ C. $\frac{1}{2}$ **D.** $\frac{7}{12}$

18. Janice's brother, Steve, spent $\frac{1}{3}$ of his weekly allowance of $12 in May. In June, he spent $\frac{1}{2}$ of his weekly allowance on repairing his bike. How much more of his allowance in dollars does he spend in June than in May?

F. $2.00 H. $4.00
G. $3.00 J. $10.00

19. On Tuesday, Rachel made $3\frac{1}{2}$ pounds of meatloaf for her family. On Saturday, she made $5\frac{1}{3}$ pounds for the soccer team. How many pounds of meatloaf does she make in all?

A. $9\frac{1}{3}$ lb **B.** $8\frac{5}{6}$ lb C. $8\frac{1}{6}$ lb D. $1\frac{5}{6}$ lb

20. In Rachel's recipe, she used $\frac{1}{2}$ cup breadcrumbs, $1\frac{3}{4}$ cup tomato sauce, and $\frac{1}{4}$ cup onions. How many cups of the ingredients does she use all together?

F. 2 cups **H.** $2\frac{1}{2}$ cups
G. $2\frac{1}{4}$ cups J. $2\frac{3}{4}$ cups

STOP

178 Grade 5

Form B, Page 1

Name _____

CHAPTER 11 TEST FORM B PAGE 1

Read each question carefully. Fill in the correct answer in the space provided.

1. $\frac{2}{5} + \frac{2}{3} = $ ___ $1\frac{1}{15}$

2. $3\frac{3}{8} + 6\frac{3}{4} = $ ___ $10\frac{1}{8}$

3. Identify the property used.

$\frac{5}{6} + 0 = \frac{5}{6}$

___ **Identity Property**

4. $\frac{3}{5} + \frac{3}{10} = $ ___ $\frac{9}{10}$

5. $5\frac{3}{8} + 7\frac{3}{4} = $ ___ $13\frac{1}{8}$

6. Find the missing number and identify the property used.

$\frac{5}{9} + \square = \frac{1}{3} + \frac{5}{9}$

___ $\frac{1}{3}$, **Commutative Property**

7. Find the missing number and identify the property used.

$(\frac{5}{8} + \square) + \frac{1}{2} = \frac{5}{8} + (\frac{2}{3} + \frac{1}{2})$

___ $\frac{2}{3}$, **Associative Property**

8. $\frac{2}{7} + \frac{11}{14} = $ ___ $1\frac{1}{14}$

9. $24\frac{4}{5} + 18\frac{1}{2} = $ ___ $43\frac{3}{10}$

10. $\frac{1}{4} + \frac{4}{5} = $ ___ $1\frac{1}{20}$

GO ON

Grade 5 **179**

Form B, Page 2

Name _____

CHAPTER 11 TEST FORM B PAGE 2

11. Find the missing number and identify the property used.

$3\frac{1}{2} + \square = \frac{1}{3} + 3\frac{1}{2}$

___ $\frac{1}{3}$, **Commutative Property**

12. $\frac{3}{8} + \frac{5}{6} = $ ___ $1\frac{5}{24}$

13. $46\frac{1}{3} + 5\frac{1}{6} = $ ___ $51\frac{1}{2}$

14. Find the missing number and identify the property used.

$(3\frac{3}{10} + 2\frac{3}{8}) + \square = 3\frac{3}{10} + (2\frac{3}{8} + 1\frac{1}{5})$

___ $1\frac{1}{5}$, **Associative Property**

15. $\frac{3}{4} + \frac{5}{16} = $ ___ $1\frac{1}{16}$

16. $6\frac{11}{15} + 5\frac{1}{3} = $ ___ $12\frac{1}{15}$

17. Tom spent $\frac{1}{4}$ of his allowance on a bike tire. The next week Tom spent another $\frac{2}{3}$ of his allowance on new bike brakes. How much of his total allowance for the two weeks does he spend?

___ $\frac{11}{12}$

18. Sara used her allowance to buy school supplies. In August, she spent $\frac{1}{5}$ of her weekly allowance of $20 on a notepad. She spent $\frac{1}{4}$ of her allowance on rulers and pens in September. How much more of her allowance in dollars does she spend in September than in August?

___ $1.00

19. Paulo cooked $2\frac{3}{4}$ pounds of chicken for a hiking trip. He also made $3\frac{1}{8}$ pounds of meatballs. How many pounds of food does Paulo cook in all?

___ $5\frac{7}{8}$ lb

20. The recipe for meatballs calls for $\frac{3}{4}$ cups breadcrumbs, $2\frac{1}{4}$ cups tomato sauce, and $\frac{1}{2}$ cup tomato paste. How many cups of the ingredients are used altogether in the recipe?

___ $3\frac{1}{2}$ cups

STOP

180 Grade 5

Chapter 12

Form A, Page 1

Name _____

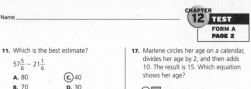

CHAPTER 12 TEST
FORM A
PAGE 1

Read each question carefully. Darken the circle on your answer sheet for the correct answer.

1. $\frac{5}{8} - \frac{1}{8} = \blacksquare$
   A. $\frac{3}{4}$ C. $\frac{3}{8}$
   B. $\frac{1}{2}$ D. $\frac{1}{4}$

6. Which is the best estimate?
   $8\frac{2}{3} + 6\frac{3}{5}$
   F. 14 **H.** 16
   G. 15 J. 17

2. $15\frac{13}{16} - 3 = \blacksquare$
   F. $18\frac{13}{16}$ **H.** $12\frac{13}{16}$
   G. $18\frac{5}{8}$ J. $12\frac{3}{16}$

7. $\frac{3}{4} - \frac{1}{6} = \blacksquare$
   A. $\frac{7}{12}$ C. $\frac{1}{2}$
   B. $\frac{5}{12}$ D. $\frac{1}{3}$

3. Which is the best estimate?
   $3\frac{4}{5} + 1\frac{3}{10}$
   A. 6 C. 4
   B. 5 D. 3

8. Which is the best estimate?
   $4\frac{1}{5} - 1\frac{7}{10}$
   F. 1 H. 3
   G. 2 J. 5

4. $\frac{9}{10} - \frac{2}{10} = \blacksquare$
   F. $\frac{2}{5}$ **H.** $\frac{7}{10}$
   G. $\frac{1}{2}$ J. $1\frac{1}{10}$

9. $19\frac{1}{6} - 6\frac{1}{2} = \blacksquare$
   A. $12\frac{1}{2}$ C. $13\frac{1}{2}$
   B. $12\frac{2}{3}$ D. $13\frac{2}{3}$

5. $25\frac{3}{8} - 23\frac{1}{4} = \blacksquare$
   A. $2\frac{1}{8}$ C. $1\frac{7}{8}$
   B. $2\frac{1}{2}$ D. $1\frac{1}{2}$

10. $\frac{13}{20} - \frac{3}{10} = \blacksquare$
    F. $\frac{9}{10}$ H. $\frac{1}{2}$
    G. $\frac{7}{10}$ **J.** $\frac{7}{20}$

GO ON

Form A, Page 2

Name _____

CHAPTER 12 TEST
FORM A
PAGE 2

11. Which is the best estimate?
    $57\frac{5}{6} - 21\frac{1}{6}$
    A. 80 **C.** 40
    B. 70 D. 30

12. Which is the best estimate?
    $78\frac{11}{12} - 49\frac{7}{12}$
    F. 45 H. 35
    G. 40 **J.** 30

13. $19\frac{9}{10} - 10\frac{1}{4} = \blacksquare$
    A. $10\frac{3}{20}$ **C.** $9\frac{13}{20}$
    B. $9\frac{7}{10}$ D. $9\frac{1}{4}$

14. $\frac{11}{12} - \frac{2}{3} = \blacksquare$
    F. $\frac{1}{4}$ G. $\frac{1}{3}$ H. $\frac{2}{3}$ J. $\frac{3}{4}$

15. $51\frac{1}{2} - 13\frac{3}{4} = \blacksquare$
    A. $38\frac{3}{4}$ **C.** $37\frac{3}{4}$
    B. $38\frac{1}{2}$ D. $37\frac{1}{2}$

16. Gavin circles his age on a calendar, doubles it, and then adds 5. The result is 23. Which equation shows his age?
    F. $\blacksquare \times 2 - 5 = 23$
    G. $\blacksquare \times 2 + 5 = 23$
    H. $\blacksquare + 2 \times 5 = 23$
    J. $\blacksquare + 2 + 5 = 23$

17. Marlene circles her age on a calendar, divides her age by 2, and then adds 10. The result is 15. Which equation shows her age?
    A. $\blacksquare \div 2 + 10 = 15$
    B. $\blacksquare + 2 - 10 = 15$
    C. $\blacksquare - {}^-2 + 10 = 15$
    D. $\blacksquare \div 2 - 10 = 15$

18. A 20-pound bag of nails has $7\frac{1}{4}$ pounds left. How many nails have been removed?
    F. $13\frac{1}{4}$ lb **H.** $12\frac{3}{4}$ lb
    G. $13\frac{1}{8}$ lb J. $12\frac{1}{4}$ lb

19. Luisa has $1\frac{3}{4}$ pound of nails in a large jar. She puts $\frac{1}{2}$ pound into a small jar. How many pounds of nails are left in the large jar?
    A. $1\frac{3}{4}$ lb C. $\frac{3}{4}$ lb
    B. $1\frac{1}{4}$ lb D. $\frac{1}{2}$ lb

20. At a hardware store Marcy buys 5 gallons of white paint and 2 gallons of blue paint. She uses $3\frac{3}{4}$ gallons of white paint on her bedroom walls. How many gallons of white and blue paint does she have left?
    F. 7 gal **H.** $3\frac{1}{4}$ gal
    G. $3\frac{3}{4}$ gal J. 2 gal

STOP

Form B, Page 1

Name _____

CHAPTER 12 TEST
FORM B
PAGE 1

Read each question carefully. Fill in the correct answer in the space provided.

1. $\frac{5}{6} - \frac{1}{6} = \underline{\frac{2}{3}}$

6. Which is the best estimate?
   $9\frac{5}{6} + 3\frac{2}{3}$
   $\underline{14}$

2. $13\frac{7}{8} - 2 = \underline{11\frac{7}{8}}$

7. $\frac{2}{3} - \frac{1}{4} = \underline{\frac{5}{12}}$

3. Which is the best estimate?
   $2\frac{5}{8} + 1\frac{1}{3}$
   $\underline{4}$

8. Which is the best estimate?
   $6\frac{1}{6} - 1\frac{11}{12}$
   $\underline{4}$

4. $\frac{11}{12} - \frac{5}{12} = \underline{\frac{1}{2}}$

9. $17\frac{1}{8} - 5\frac{3}{4} = \underline{11\frac{3}{8}}$

5. $37\frac{5}{8} - 35\frac{1}{4} = \underline{2\frac{3}{8}}$

10. $\frac{15}{21} - \frac{3}{7} = \underline{\frac{2}{7}}$

GO ON

Form B, Page 2

Name _____

CHAPTER 12 TEST
FORM B
PAGE 2

11. Which is the best estimate?
    $48\frac{5}{8} - 23\frac{1}{8}$
    $\underline{30}$

12. Which is the best estimate?
    $67\frac{9}{10} - 49\frac{3}{10}$
    $\underline{20}$

13. $45\frac{7}{10} - 10\frac{1}{3} = \underline{35\frac{11}{30}}$

14. $\frac{7}{12} - \frac{1}{3} = \underline{\frac{1}{4}}$

15. $62\frac{1}{4} - 23\frac{2}{3} = \underline{38\frac{7}{12}}$

16. Gail circles her age on a calendar, doubles it, and then adds 7. The result is 31. Write an equation that shows her age.
    $\underline{\blacksquare} \times 2 + 7 = 31$

17. Rich circles his age on a calendar, divides his age by 2, and then adds 12. The result is 27. Write an equation that shows his age.
    $\blacksquare \div 2 + 12 = 27$

18. A 30-pound bag of shells has $12\frac{1}{2}$ pounds left. How many shells have been removed?
    $17\frac{1}{2}$ lb

19. Dora has $2\frac{1}{2}$ pounds of shells in a large bottle. She puts $\frac{3}{4}$ pound into a small bottle. How many pounds of shells are left in the large bottle?
    $1\frac{3}{4}$ lb

20. Marco buys 4 gallons of cherry stain and 3 gallons of clear stain. He uses $1\frac{1}{3}$ gallons of cherry stain on woodwork. How many gallons of cherry and clear stain does he have left?
    $5\frac{2}{3}$ gal

STOP

Name _____

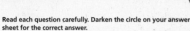

Read each question carefully. Darken the circle on your answer sheet for the correct answer.

1. $1\frac{13}{25} + 2\frac{17}{25} = $ ☐

  A. $3\frac{23}{25}$ **C.** $4\frac{6}{25}$

  B. $4\frac{1}{5}$ **D.** 5

2. $5\frac{7}{8} - 2\frac{3}{8} = $ ☐

  F. $3\frac{1}{4}$ **H.** $3\frac{1}{2}$

  G. $3\frac{3}{8}$ **J.** $3\frac{3}{4}$

3. Identify the property used.

$\frac{7}{9} + \frac{3}{8} = \frac{3}{8} + \frac{7}{9}$

  A. Associative Property
  B. Commutative Property
  C. Identity Property
  D. Distributive Property

4. Which is the best estimate?

$4\frac{2}{3} + 5\frac{11}{13}$

  F. 4   **G.** 5   **H.** 11   **J.** 20

5. $\frac{4}{5} + \frac{3}{4} = $ ☐

  A. $\frac{19}{20}$ **C.** $1\frac{11}{20}$

  B. $1\frac{1}{2}$ **D.** $1\frac{3}{5}$

6. $4\frac{2}{3} + \frac{5}{6} = $ ☐

  F. $5\frac{1}{2}$ **G.** $5\frac{5}{6}$ **H.** $6\frac{1}{6}$ **J.** $6\frac{2}{3}$

7. $\frac{9}{11} - \frac{3}{7} = $ ☐

  A. $\frac{4}{11}$ **B.** $\frac{3}{7}$ **C.** $\frac{30}{77}$ **D.** $\frac{6}{11}$

8. Identify the property used.

$\frac{5}{7} + (\frac{1}{7} + \frac{3}{4}) = (\frac{5}{7} + \frac{1}{7}) + \frac{3}{4}$

  F. Associative Property
  G. Commutative Property
  H. Identity Property
  J. Distributive Property

9. Which is the best estimate?

$7\frac{2}{9} + 11\frac{4}{7}$

  A. 7   **B.** 11   **C.** 19   **D.** 77

10. $2\frac{3}{7} + 4\frac{10}{21} = $ ☐

  F. $5\frac{2}{3}$ **H.** $6\frac{6}{7}$

  G. $6\frac{19}{21}$ **J.** $5\frac{13}{21}$

11. $12\frac{5}{8} - \frac{3}{4} = $ ☐

  A. $11\frac{1}{2}$ **C.** $12\frac{1}{8}$

  B. $11\frac{7}{8}$ **D.** $12\frac{7}{8}$

12. Which is the best estimate?

$9\frac{7}{10} - 4\frac{1}{8}$

  F. 6   **G.** 9   **H.** 13   **J.** 94

GO ON

Name _____

13. Identify the property used.

$4\frac{11}{12} + 0 = 4\frac{11}{12}$

  A. Associative Property
  B. Commutative Property
  C. Identity Property
  D. Distributive Property

14. $16\frac{2}{3} - 4\frac{1}{4} = $ ☐

  F. $12\frac{5}{12}$ **H.** $12\frac{3}{7}$

  G. $12\frac{2}{7}$ **J.** $12\frac{1}{2}$

15. Evaluate.

$8\frac{2}{3} + (6\frac{4}{5} + 2\frac{1}{5}) = $ ☐

  A. $16\frac{2}{3}$ **C.** $17\frac{1}{5}$

  B. $16\frac{14}{15}$ **D.** $17\frac{2}{3}$

16. Which is the best estimate?

$16\frac{1}{3} - 7\frac{5}{6}$

  F. 8   **H.** 23

  G. 16   **J.** 167

17. Dave bought two loaves of bread. One loaf weighed $2\frac{3}{8}$ pounds. The other loaf weighed $1\frac{3}{4}$ pounds. What was the total weight?

  A. $3\frac{1}{2}$ lb   **C.** $4\frac{1}{8}$ lb

  B. 4 lb   **D.** $4\frac{1}{2}$ lb

18. Liz made a loaf of banana bread that weighed $1\frac{5}{8}$ pounds. She gave Tim $\frac{4}{5}$ pound of the bread. How much was left?

  F. $\frac{1}{8}$ lb   **H.** $\frac{33}{40}$ lb

  G. $\frac{3}{40}$ lb   **J.** $\frac{3}{5}$ lb

19. Ginny's family ate $6\frac{1}{24}$ pounds of bread in March. They ate $7\frac{2}{5}$ pounds in April. How much did they eat in those two months?

  A. $13\frac{1}{3}$ lb   **C.** $13\frac{2}{3}$ lb

  B. $13\frac{13}{20}$ lb   **D.** $13\frac{3}{4}$ lb

20. John's family buys $2\frac{5}{9}$ pounds of whole wheat bread each month. They buy $1\frac{4}{5}$ pounds of oat bread. How much more whole wheat than oat bread do they buy?

  F. $\frac{1}{5}$ lb   **H.** $\frac{4}{9}$ lb

  G. $\frac{19}{45}$ lb   **J.** $1\frac{1}{2}$ lb

GO ON

Name _____

21. $3\frac{7}{18} + 2\frac{13}{18} = $ ☐

  A. $6\frac{1}{18}$ **B.** $6\frac{1}{9}$ **C.** $6\frac{1}{3}$ **D.** $6\frac{1}{2}$

22. $4\frac{1}{10} - 2\frac{3}{10} = $ ☐

  F. $1\frac{1}{2}$ **H.** $1\frac{4}{5}$

  G. $1\frac{7}{10}$ **J.** $1\frac{9}{10}$

23. Identify the property used.

$16\frac{3}{8} + \frac{1}{4} + 0 = 16\frac{3}{8} + \frac{1}{4}$

  A. Associative Property
  B. Commutative Property
  C. Identity Property
  D. Distributive Property

24. Which is the best estimate?

$12\frac{5}{9} + 4\frac{1}{18}$

  F. 12   **H.** 28

  G. 17   **J.** 124

25. $\frac{7}{8} + \frac{1}{6} = $ ☐

  A. $1\frac{1}{24}$ **C.** $1\frac{1}{8}$

  B. $1\frac{1}{12}$ **D.** $1\frac{1}{4}$

26. $5\frac{1}{9} + \frac{12}{27} = $ ☐

  F. $5\frac{13}{36}$ **H.** $5\frac{5}{9}$

  G. $5\frac{13}{27}$ **J.** $5\frac{2}{3}$

27. $\frac{12}{17} - \frac{7}{34} = $ ☐

  A. $\frac{5}{34}$ **B.** $\frac{1}{2}$ **C.** $\frac{9}{17}$ **D.** $\frac{3}{34}$

28. Identify the property used.

$\frac{2}{5} + \frac{8}{9} = \frac{8}{9} + \frac{2}{5}$

  F. Associative Property
  G. Commutative Property
  H. Identity Property
  J. Distributive Property

29. Which is the best estimate?

$1\frac{9}{10} + 5\frac{11}{22}$

  A. 5   **B.** 8   **C.** 15   **D.** 51

30. $11\frac{7}{18} + 5\frac{4}{9} = $ ☐

  F. $16\frac{5}{6}$ **H.** $17\frac{1}{18}$

  G. $16\frac{17}{18}$ **J.** $17\frac{5}{6}$

31. $9\frac{2}{3} - \frac{5}{8} = $ ☐

  A. $8\frac{7}{8}$ **C.** $9\frac{1}{12}$

  B. $9\frac{1}{24}$ **D.** $9\frac{1}{8}$

32. Which is the best estimate?

$10\frac{7}{12} - 6\frac{1}{6}$

  F. 5   **H.** 16

  G. 10   **J.** 60

GO ON

Name _____

33. Identify the property used.

$(\frac{4}{5} + \frac{5}{9}) + \frac{4}{9} = \frac{4}{5} + (\frac{5}{9} + \frac{4}{9})$

  A. Associative Property
  B. Commutative Property
  C. Identity Property
  D. Distributive Property

34. $18\frac{3}{5} - 2\frac{3}{4} = $ ☐

  F. $15\frac{17}{20}$ **H.** $15\frac{19}{20}$

  G. $15\frac{3}{4}$ **J.** $16\frac{1}{5}$

35. Evaluate.

$(9\frac{3}{8} + 5\frac{1}{8}) + 4\frac{1}{4} = $ ☐

  A. $18\frac{1}{2}$ **C.** $18\frac{3}{4}$

  B. $18\frac{5}{8}$ **D.** 19

36. Which is the best estimate?

$21\frac{1}{7} - 12\frac{9}{14}$

  F. 8   **H.** 21

  G. 12   **J.** 33

37. Trent picked two bags of apples. One bag weighed $5\frac{4}{5}$ pounds. The other weighed $7\frac{3}{10}$ pounds. What was the total weight?

  A. $12\frac{9}{10}$ lb   **C.** $13\frac{1}{5}$ lb

  B. $13\frac{1}{10}$ lb   **D.** $13\frac{2}{5}$ lb

38. Tony bought an $8\frac{1}{2}$-pound bag of apples. He gave $2\frac{2}{7}$ pounds to his friend. How many pounds were left?

  F. $6\frac{1}{7}$ lb   **H.** $6\frac{2}{7}$ lb

  G. $6\frac{3}{14}$ lb   **J.** $6\frac{5}{14}$ lb

39. Sara made two pies. She used $3\frac{2}{3}$ pounds of apples in one and $3\frac{5}{8}$ pounds in the other. How many pounds did she use in all?

  A. $7\frac{1}{3}$ lb   **C.** $7\frac{7}{24}$ lb

  B. $7\frac{3}{8}$ lb   **D.** $7\frac{2}{3}$ lb

40. Nadja's family ate $15\frac{1}{8}$ pounds of apples in September. They ate $4\frac{1}{2}$ pounds of pears. How many more pounds of apples than pears did they eat?

  F. $10\frac{1}{2}$ lb   **H.** $10\frac{3}{4}$ lb

  G. $10\frac{5}{8}$ lb   **J.** $10\frac{7}{16}$ lb

STOP

Unit 6

Form B — Page 1

Name_____

Read each question carefully. Fill in the correct answer in the space provided.

1. $2\frac{8}{15} + 4\frac{13}{15} = $ ___ $7\frac{2}{5}$

6. $5\frac{3}{7} + \frac{4}{5} = $ ___ $6\frac{8}{35}$

2. $4\frac{7}{9} - 3\frac{5}{9} = $ ___ $1\frac{2}{9}$

7. $\frac{7}{8} - \frac{5}{7} = $ ___ $\frac{9}{56}$

3. Identify the property used.
$\frac{2}{3} + \frac{7}{8} = \frac{7}{8} + \frac{2}{3}$
___ Commutative Property

8. Identify the property used.
$\frac{2}{9} + (\frac{3}{8} + \frac{4}{5}) = (\frac{2}{9} + \frac{3}{8}) + \frac{4}{5}$
___ Associative Property

4. Estimate.
$3\frac{7}{9} + 2\frac{11}{12}$
___ possible answer: 7

9. Estimate.
$\frac{2}{7} + 17\frac{4}{11}$
___ possible answer: 26

5. $\frac{7}{10} + \frac{3}{8} = $ ___ $1\frac{3}{40}$

10. $3\frac{1}{6} + 2\frac{3}{4} = $ ___ $5\frac{11}{12}$

GO ON

Grade 5 197

Form B — Page 2

Name_____

11. $11\frac{3}{8} - \frac{2}{3} = $ ___ $10\frac{17}{24}$

12. Estimate.
$10\frac{7}{9} - 8\frac{1}{4}$
___ possible answer: 3

13. Identify the property used.
$5\frac{9}{10} + 0 = 5\frac{9}{10}$
___ Identity Property

14. $7\frac{1}{2} - 5\frac{4}{9} = $ ___ $2\frac{1}{18}$

15. Evaluate.
$4\frac{3}{4} + (3\frac{5}{6} + 1\frac{1}{3}) = $ ___ $9\frac{11}{12}$

16. Estimate.
$12\frac{1}{10} - 6\frac{5}{7}$
___ possible answer: 5

17. Sasha bought two pies. One pie weighed $17\frac{1}{2}$ ounces. The other weighed $21\frac{2}{3}$ ounces. What was the total weight?
___ $39\frac{1}{6}$ ounces

18. Jason bought a bag of oranges that weighed $9\frac{1}{4}$ pounds. He gave away $2\frac{5}{6}$ pounds of oranges. How much was left?
___ $6\frac{5}{12}$ pounds

19. Casey's family ate $12\frac{2}{5}$ pounds of salad in June. They ate $14\frac{1}{4}$ pounds in July. How much did they eat in those two months?
___ $26\frac{13}{20}$ pounds

20. Karen's family buys $3\frac{3}{7}$ pounds of apples each month. They buy $2\frac{5}{8}$ pounds of grapes. How much more apples than grapes do they buy?
___ $\frac{45}{56}$ pounds

GO ON

198 Grade 5

Form B — Page 3

Name_____

21. $4\frac{5}{12} + 6\frac{7}{12} = $ ___ 11

26. $4\frac{1}{12} + \frac{7}{30} = $ ___ $4\frac{19}{60}$

22. $3\frac{1}{8} - 1\frac{5}{8} = $ ___ $1\frac{1}{2}$

27. $\frac{13}{15} - \frac{11}{30} = $ ___ $\frac{1}{2}$

23. Identify the property used.
$8\frac{1}{2} + 0 = 8\frac{1}{2}$
___ Identity Property

28. Identify the property being used.
$\frac{1}{4} + \frac{9}{10} = \frac{9}{10} + \frac{1}{4}$
___ Commutative Property

24. Estimate.
$9\frac{5}{12} + 18\frac{1}{4}$
___ possible answer: 27

29. Estimate.
$10\frac{7}{8} + 5\frac{2}{3}$
___ possible answer: 17

25. $\frac{5}{8} + \frac{2}{3} = $ ___ $1\frac{7}{24}$

30. $8\frac{3}{5} + 9\frac{1}{4} = $ ___ $17\frac{17}{20}$

GO ON

Grade 5 199

Form B — Page 4

Name_____

31. $3\frac{2}{9} - \frac{2}{3} = $ ___ $2\frac{5}{9}$

32. Estimate.
$12\frac{7}{10} - 5\frac{1}{8}$
___ possible answer: 8

33. Identify the property used.
$(\frac{2}{3} + \frac{4}{7}) + \frac{2}{7} = \frac{2}{3} + (\frac{4}{7} + \frac{2}{7})$
___ Associative Property

34. $8\frac{2}{5} - 4\frac{2}{3} = $ ___ $3\frac{11}{15}$

35. Evaluate.
$(7\frac{1}{3} + 8\frac{1}{5}) + 3\frac{1}{2} = $ ___ $19\frac{1}{30}$

36. Estimate.
$17\frac{1}{11} - 14\frac{3}{4}$
___ possible answer: 2

37. Calvin bought two bags of groceries. One bag weighed $3\frac{1}{3}$ pounds. The other bag weighed $7\frac{4}{5}$ pounds. What was the total weight?
___ $11\frac{2}{15}$

38. Meredith bought a $31\frac{1}{2}$-ounce bag of chocolate. She gave $17\frac{8}{9}$ ounces to her friends. How many ounces were left?
___ $13\frac{11}{18}$ ounces

39. Patrick made two sculptures. He used $7\frac{2}{9}$ pounds of marble for one and $9\frac{3}{14}$ for the other. How many pounds did he use in all?
___ $16\frac{55}{126}$ pounds

40. Yvonne's family ate $12\frac{1}{4}$ pounds of oranges in October. They ate $4\frac{6}{7}$ pounds of cherries. How many more pounds of oranges than cherries did they eat?
___ $7\frac{11}{28}$ pounds

STOP

200 Grade 5

Chapter 13

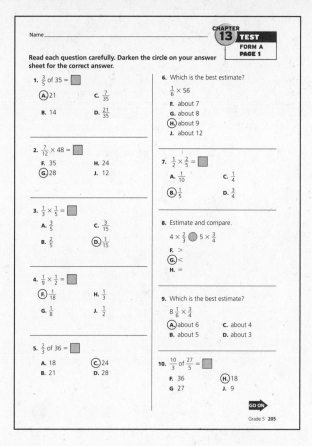

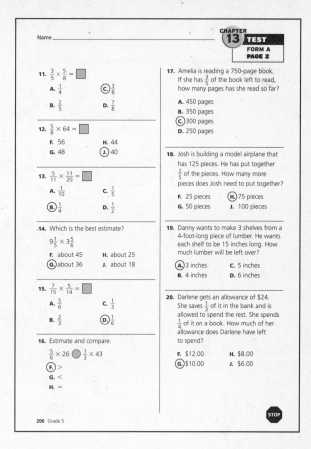

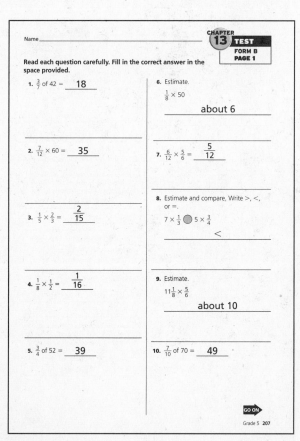

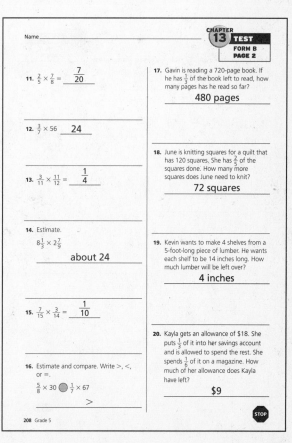

FORM A PAGE 1

Name _____

CHAPTER 14 TEST FORM A PAGE 1

Read each question carefully. Darken the circle on your answer sheet for the correct answer.

1. $3 \times 4\frac{1}{6} =$ ▨

(A.) $12\frac{1}{2}$ **C.** 12

B. $12\frac{1}{6}$ **D.** $7\frac{1}{6}$

2. $3\frac{1}{5} \times \frac{1}{10} =$ ▨

F. $\frac{31}{50}$ **(H.)** $\frac{8}{25}$

G. $\frac{17}{50}$ **J.** $\frac{1}{3}$

3. $28 \times 4\frac{3}{8} =$ ▨

A. $112\frac{3}{8}$ **(C.)** $122\frac{1}{2}$

B. $122\frac{3}{8}$ **D.** $122\frac{3}{4}$

4. $\frac{3}{7} \times 1\frac{1}{3} =$ ▨

(F.) $\frac{4}{7}$ **H.** $\frac{2}{3}$

G. $\frac{1}{2}$ **J.** $2\frac{1}{3}$

5. $\frac{5}{6} \div \frac{5}{12} =$ ▨

A. $\frac{1}{2}$ **C.** $1\frac{5}{6}$

B. $1\frac{1}{2}$ **(D.)** 2

6. $45 \times 3\frac{3}{4} =$ ▨

F. $135\frac{3}{4}$ **H.** $165\frac{1}{6}$

G. $137\frac{1}{4}$ **(J.)** $168\frac{3}{4}$

7. $\frac{3}{4} \div \frac{1}{3} =$ ▨

A. $2\frac{1}{2}$ **C.** $1\frac{1}{2}$

(B.) $2\frac{1}{4}$ **D.** $\frac{1}{4}$

8. $1\frac{7}{9} \times \frac{1}{12} =$ ▨

F. $\frac{1}{3}$ **H.** $\frac{6}{9}$

(G.) $\frac{4}{27}$ **J.** $\frac{5}{6}$

9. $\frac{4}{5} \div 1\frac{1}{2} =$ ▨

A. $\frac{1}{3}$ **(C.)** $\frac{8}{15}$

B. $\frac{2}{5}$ **D.** $\frac{1}{2}$

10. $9 \times 3\frac{2}{3} =$ ▨

F. $27\frac{2}{3}$ **(H.)** 33

G. 30   **J.** 35

GO ON

Grade 5 **213**

FORM A PAGE 2

Name _____

CHAPTER 14 TEST FORM A PAGE 2

11. $\frac{7}{12} \div \frac{1}{12} =$ ▨

A. $\frac{1}{2}$ **B.** $\frac{2}{3}$ **C.** 6   **(D.)** 7

12. $4\frac{2}{3} \times \frac{2}{5} =$ ▨

F. $1\frac{3}{15}$ **G.** $1\frac{3}{5}$ **(H.)** $1\frac{13}{15}$ **J.** $1\frac{4}{5}$

13. $7\frac{1}{2} \div 2\frac{5}{8} =$ ▨

A. $2\frac{5}{7}$ **(B.)** $2\frac{6}{7}$ **C.** $3\frac{5}{7}$ **D.** $3\frac{6}{7}$

14. $2\frac{5}{8} \times 32 =$ ▨

F. $64\frac{5}{8}$ **G.** $65\frac{1}{4}$ **(H.)** 84   **J.** $85\frac{1}{2}$

15. $\frac{5}{6} \div 3\frac{1}{3} =$ ▨

(A.) $\frac{1}{4}$ **C.** $1\frac{1}{3}$

B. $\frac{1}{2}$ **D.** $2\frac{7}{9}$

16. $5\frac{1}{2} \times \frac{1}{8} =$ ▨

(F.) $\frac{11}{16}$ **H.** $\frac{1}{2}$

G. $\frac{5}{8}$ **J.** $\frac{7}{16}$

17. Wanda makes scarves. She can make a scarf with a solid color, a plaid, or a pattern. She can also cut the material into a square or a rectangle. In how many ways can Wanda make a scarf?

A. 3   **B.** 4   **C.** 5   **(D.)** 6

18. George likes to design board games. He draws the board in a zigzag pattern, in a straight line, or in a large circle. He also fills the squares with a solid color, a stripe, or a dotted-line pattern. In how many ways does he design board games?

(F.) 9   **G.** 8   **H.** 7   **J.** 6

19. Christine has two fraction spinners. On one she can spin $\frac{1}{6}$, $\frac{1}{5}$, and $\frac{1}{4}$. On the other she can spin $\frac{1}{3}$ and $\frac{1}{2}$. If she spins both, which products can she find?

A. $\frac{1}{30}$, $\frac{1}{24}$, $\frac{1}{24}$, $\frac{1}{12}$, $\frac{1}{10}$

(B.) $\frac{1}{18}$, $\frac{1}{15}$, $\frac{1}{12}$, $\frac{1}{10}$, $\frac{1}{8}$

C. $\frac{1}{36}$, $\frac{1}{30}$, $\frac{1}{24}$, $\frac{1}{16}$, $\frac{1}{8}$

D. $\frac{1}{18}$, $\frac{1}{9}$, $\frac{1}{5}$, $\frac{1}{5}$, $\frac{1}{6}$

20. Carl has four tiles: a red triangle, a blue square, a yellow rectangle, and a gray rhombus. Jean has an orange triangle, a green square, a purple rectangle, and a white rhombus. If each person uses one tile, how many different pairs of tiles can they make?

F. 20   **(G.)** 16   **H.** 8   **J.** 4

214 Grade 5

STOP

FORM B PAGE 1

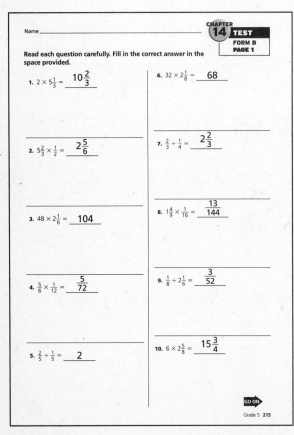

Name _____

CHAPTER 14 TEST FORM B PAGE 1

Read each question carefully. Fill in the correct answer in the space provided.

1. $2 \times 5\frac{1}{3} =$ ___ $10\frac{2}{3}$

2. $5\frac{2}{3} \times \frac{1}{2} =$ ___ $2\frac{5}{6}$

3. $48 \times 2\frac{1}{6} =$ ___ 104

4. $\frac{5}{6} \times \frac{1}{12} =$ ___ $\frac{5}{72}$

5. $\frac{2}{5} \div \frac{1}{5} =$ ___ 2

6. $32 \times 2\frac{1}{8} =$ ___ 68

7. $\frac{2}{3} \div \frac{1}{4} =$ ___ $2\frac{2}{3}$

8. $1\frac{4}{9} \times \frac{1}{16} =$ ___ $\frac{13}{144}$

9. $\frac{1}{8} \div 2\frac{1}{6} =$ ___ $\frac{3}{52}$

10. $6 \times 2\frac{5}{8} =$ ___ $15\frac{3}{4}$

GO ON

Grade 5 **215**

FORM B PAGE 2

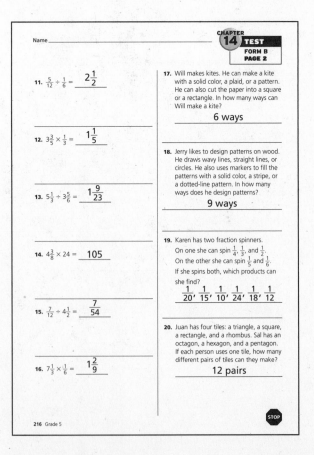

Name _____

CHAPTER 14 TEST FORM B PAGE 2

11. $\frac{5}{12} \div \frac{1}{6} =$ ___ $2\frac{1}{2}$

12. $3\frac{3}{5} \times \frac{1}{3} =$ ___ $1\frac{1}{5}$

13. $5\frac{1}{3} \div 3\frac{5}{6} =$ ___ $1\frac{9}{23}$

14. $4\frac{3}{8} \times 24 =$ ___ 105

15. $\frac{7}{12} \div 4\frac{1}{2} =$ ___ $\frac{7}{54}$

16. $7\frac{1}{3} \times \frac{1}{6} =$ ___ $1\frac{2}{9}$

17. Will makes kites. He can make a kite with a solid color, a plaid, or a pattern. He can also cut the paper into a square or a rectangle. In how many ways can Will make a kite?

___ 6 ways

18. Jerry likes to design patterns on wood. He draws wavy lines, straight lines, or circles. He also uses markers to fill the patterns with a solid color, a stripe, or a dotted-line pattern. In how many ways does he design patterns?

___ 9 ways

19. Karen has two fraction spinners. On one she can spin $\frac{1}{4}$, $\frac{1}{3}$, and $\frac{1}{2}$. On the other she can spin $\frac{1}{5}$ and $\frac{1}{6}$. If she spins both, which products can she find?

$\frac{1}{20}$, $\frac{1}{15}$, $\frac{1}{10}$, $\frac{1}{24}$, $\frac{1}{18}$, $\frac{1}{12}$

20. Juan has four tiles: a triangle, a square, a rectangle, and a rhombus. Sal has an octagon, a hexagon, and a pentagon. If each person uses one tile, how many different pairs of tiles can they make?

___ 12 pairs

216 Grade 5

STOP

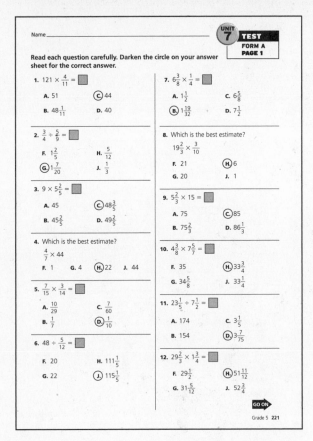

Name_____

Read each question carefully. Darken the circle on your answer sheet for the correct answer.

1. $121 \times \frac{4}{11} =$ ☐
A. 51
C. 44 ✓
B. $48\frac{1}{11}$
D. 40

2. $\frac{3}{4} \div \frac{5}{9} =$ ☐
F. $1\frac{2}{5}$
H. $\frac{5}{12}$
G. $1\frac{7}{20}$ ✓
J. $\frac{1}{3}$

3. $9 \times 5\frac{2}{5} =$ ☐
A. 45
C. $48\frac{3}{5}$ ✓
B. $45\frac{2}{5}$
D. $49\frac{2}{5}$

4. Which is the best estimate?
$\frac{4}{7} \times 44$
F. 1
G. 4
H. 22 ✓
J. 44

5. $\frac{7}{15} \times \frac{3}{14} =$ ☐
A. $\frac{10}{29}$
C. $\frac{7}{60}$
B. $\frac{1}{7}$
D. $\frac{1}{10}$ ✓

6. $48 \div \frac{5}{12} =$ ☐
F. 20
H. $111\frac{1}{5}$
G. 22
J. $115\frac{1}{5}$ ✓

7. $6\frac{3}{8} \times \frac{1}{4} =$ ☐
A. $1\frac{1}{2}$
C. $6\frac{5}{8}$
B. $1\frac{19}{32}$ ✓
D. $7\frac{1}{2}$

8. Which is the best estimate?
$19\frac{2}{3} \times \frac{3}{10}$
F. 21
H. 6 ✓
G. 20
J. 1

9. $5\frac{2}{3} \times 15 =$ ☐
A. 75
C. 85 ✓
B. $75\frac{2}{3}$
D. $86\frac{1}{3}$

10. $4\frac{3}{8} \times 7\frac{5}{7} =$ ☐
F. 35
H. $33\frac{3}{4}$ ✓
G. $34\frac{5}{8}$
J. $33\frac{1}{4}$

11. $23\frac{1}{3} \div 7\frac{1}{2} =$ ☐
A. 174
C. $3\frac{1}{3}$
B. 154
D. $3\frac{7}{75}$ ✓

12. $29\frac{2}{3} \times 1\frac{3}{4} =$ ☐
F. $29\frac{1}{2}$
H. $51\frac{11}{12}$ ✓
G. $31\frac{5}{12}$
J. $52\frac{3}{4}$

GO ON
Grade 5 **221**

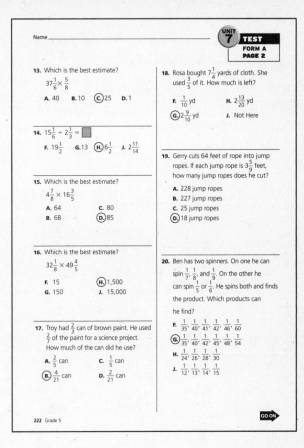

Name_____

13. Which is the best estimate?
$37\frac{1}{6} \times \frac{5}{8}$
A. 40
B. 10
C. 25 ✓
D. 1

14. $15\frac{1}{6} \div 2\frac{1}{3} =$ ☐
F. $19\frac{1}{2}$
G. 13
H. $6\frac{1}{2}$ ✓
J. $2\frac{11}{14}$

15. Which is the best estimate?
$4\frac{7}{8} \times 16\frac{3}{5}$
A. 64
C. 80
B. 68
D. 85 ✓

16. Which is the best estimate?
$32\frac{1}{8} \times 49\frac{4}{5}$
F. 15
H. 1,500 ✓
G. 150
J. 15,000

17. Troy had $\frac{2}{3}$ can of brown paint. He used $\frac{2}{7}$ of the paint for a science project. How much of the can did he use?
A. $\frac{2}{5}$ can
C. $\frac{1}{5}$ can
B. $\frac{4}{21}$ can ✓
D. $\frac{2}{21}$ can

18. Rosa bought $7\frac{1}{4}$ yards of cloth. She used $\frac{3}{5}$ of it. How much is left?
F. $\frac{1}{10}$ yd
H. $2\frac{13}{20}$ yd
G. $2\frac{9}{10}$ yd ✓
J. Not Here

19. Gerry cuts 64 feet of rope into jump ropes. If each jump rope is $3\frac{5}{9}$ feet, how many jump ropes does he cut?
A. 228 jump ropes
B. 227 jump ropes
C. 25 jump ropes
D. 18 jump ropes ✓

20. Ben has two spinners. On one he can spin $\frac{1}{7}$, $\frac{1}{8}$, and $\frac{1}{9}$. On the other he can spin $\frac{1}{5}$ or $\frac{1}{6}$. He spins both and finds the product. Which products can he find?
F. $\frac{1}{35}, \frac{1}{40}, \frac{1}{41}, \frac{1}{42}, \frac{1}{46}, \frac{1}{60}$
G. $\frac{1}{35}, \frac{1}{40}, \frac{1}{42}, \frac{1}{45}, \frac{1}{48}, \frac{1}{54}$ ✓
H. $\frac{1}{24}, \frac{1}{26}, \frac{1}{28}, \frac{1}{30}$
J. $\frac{1}{12}, \frac{1}{13}, \frac{1}{14}, \frac{1}{15}$

GO ON
222 Grade 5

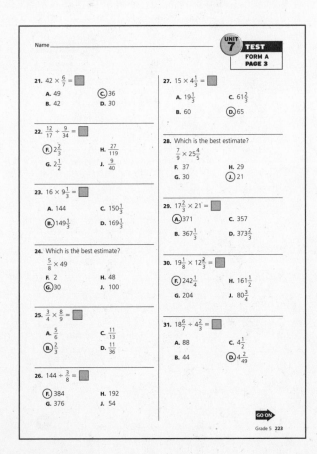

Name_____

21. $42 \times \frac{6}{7} =$ ☐
A. 49
C. 36 ✓
B. 42
D. 30

22. $\frac{12}{17} \div \frac{9}{34} =$ ☐
F. $2\frac{2}{3}$ ✓
H. $\frac{27}{119}$
G. $2\frac{1}{2}$
J. $\frac{9}{40}$

23. $16 \times 9\frac{1}{3} =$ ☐
A. 144
C. $150\frac{1}{3}$
B. $149\frac{1}{3}$ ✓
D. $169\frac{1}{3}$

24. Which is the best estimate?
$\frac{5}{8} \times 49$
F. 2
H. 48
G. 30 ✓
J. 100

25. $\frac{3}{4} \times \frac{8}{9} =$ ☐
A. $\frac{5}{6}$
C. $\frac{11}{13}$
B. $\frac{2}{3}$ ✓
D. $\frac{11}{36}$

26. $144 \div \frac{3}{8} =$ ☐
F. 384 ✓
H. 192
G. 376
J. 54

27. $15 \times 4\frac{1}{3} =$ ☐
A. $19\frac{1}{3}$
C. $61\frac{2}{3}$
B. 60
D. 65 ✓

28. Which is the best estimate?
$\frac{7}{9} \times 25\frac{4}{5}$
F. 37
H. 29
G. 30
J. 21 ✓

29. $17\frac{2}{3} \times 21 =$ ☐
A. 371 ✓
C. 357
B. $367\frac{1}{3}$
D. $373\frac{2}{3}$

30. $19\frac{1}{8} \times 12\frac{2}{3} =$ ☐
F. $242\frac{1}{4}$ ✓
H. $161\frac{1}{2}$
G. 204
J. $80\frac{3}{4}$

31. $18\frac{6}{7} \div 4\frac{2}{3} =$ ☐
A. 88
C. $4\frac{1}{7}$
B. 44
D. $4\frac{2}{49}$ ✓

GO ON
Grade 5 **223**

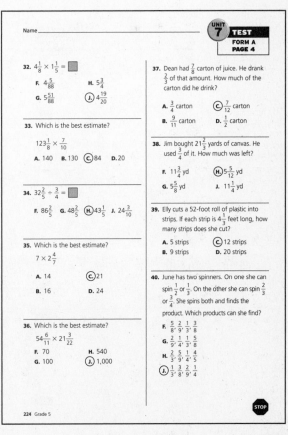

Name_____

32. $4\frac{1}{8} \times 1\frac{1}{5} =$ ☐
F. $4\frac{5}{88}$
H. $5\frac{3}{4}$
G. $5\frac{51}{88}$ ✓
J. $4\frac{19}{20}$

33. Which is the best estimate?
$123\frac{1}{3} \times \frac{7}{10}$
A. 140
B. 130
C. 84 ✓
D. 20

34. $32\frac{2}{5} \div \frac{3}{4} =$ ☐
F. $86\frac{2}{5}$
G. $48\frac{2}{5}$
H. $43\frac{1}{5}$ ✓
J. $24\frac{3}{10}$

35. Which is the best estimate?
$7 \times 2\frac{4}{7}$
A. 14
C. 21 ✓
B. 16
D. 24

36. Which is the best estimate?
$54\frac{6}{11} \times 21\frac{3}{22}$
F. 70
H. 540
G. 100
J. 1,000 ✓

37. Dean had $\frac{7}{8}$ carton of juice. He drank $\frac{2}{3}$ of that amount. How much of the carton did he drink?
A. $\frac{3}{4}$ carton
C. $\frac{7}{12}$ carton ✓
B. $\frac{9}{11}$ carton
D. $\frac{1}{2}$ carton

38. Jim bought $21\frac{2}{3}$ yards of canvas. He used $\frac{3}{4}$ of it. How much was left?
F. $11\frac{3}{4}$ yd
H. $5\frac{5}{12}$ yd ✓
G. $5\frac{5}{8}$ yd
J. $11\frac{1}{4}$ yd

39. Elly cuts a 52-foot roll of plastic into strips. If each strip is $4\frac{1}{3}$ feet long, how many strips does she cut?
A. 5 strips
C. 12 strips ✓
B. 9 strips
D. 20 strips

40. June has two spinners. On one she can spin $\frac{1}{2}$ or $\frac{1}{3}$. On the other she can spin $\frac{2}{3}$ or $\frac{3}{4}$. She spins both and finds the product. Which products can she find?
F. $\frac{5}{8}, \frac{2}{9}, \frac{1}{3}, \frac{3}{8}$
G. $\frac{2}{9}, \frac{1}{4}, \frac{1}{5}, \frac{3}{8}$
H. $\frac{2}{5}, \frac{1}{4}, \frac{1}{5}, \frac{4}{5}$
J. $\frac{1}{3}, \frac{3}{8}, \frac{2}{9}, \frac{1}{4}$ ✓

STOP
224 Grade 5

Grade 5 **463**

Unit 7

Read each question carefully. Fill in the correct answer in the space provided.

1. $132 \times \frac{5}{12} =$ _____ 55

2. $\frac{3}{5} \div \frac{4}{9} =$ _____ $1\frac{7}{20}$

3. $8 \times 6\frac{3}{5} =$ _____ $52\frac{4}{5}$

4. Estimate.
$\frac{5}{9} \times 48$
possible answer: 24

5. $\frac{7}{8} \times \frac{5}{14} =$ _____ $\frac{5}{16}$

6. $64 \div \frac{9}{16} =$ _____ $113\frac{7}{9}$

7. $7\frac{3}{10} \times \frac{1}{5} =$ _____ $1\frac{23}{50}$

8. Estimate.
$17\frac{4}{5} \times \frac{2}{6}$
possible answer: 6

9. $4\frac{3}{4} \times 12 =$ _____ 57

10. $4\frac{4}{7} \times 5\frac{9}{8} =$ _____ 28

---

11. $21\frac{2}{5} \div 4\frac{1}{2} =$ _____ $4\frac{34}{45}$

12. $10\frac{2}{3} \times 1\frac{1}{4} =$ _____ $13\frac{1}{3}$

13. Estimate.
$41\frac{5}{8} \times \frac{5}{6} =$
possible answer: 35

14. $16\frac{5}{6} \div 3\frac{2}{3} =$ _____ $4\frac{13}{22}$

15. Estimate.
$3\frac{7}{8} \times 18\frac{2}{5}$
possible answers: 72 or 80

16. Estimate.
$45\frac{1}{4} \times 52\frac{2}{3}$
possible answer: 2,500

17. Leah has $\frac{3}{4}$ can of red paint. She used $\frac{2}{5}$ of the paint for a social studies project. How much of the can did she use?
$\frac{3}{10}$ of the can

18. John is running $8\frac{1}{2}$ miles. He has run $\frac{3}{5}$ of the course so far. How far has he run?
$5\frac{1}{10}$ miles

19. Betsy cuts 75 feet of rope into jump rope. If each jump rope is $6\frac{1}{4}$ feet, how many jump ropes does she cut?
12 jump ropes

20. Matt has two spinners. On one he can spin $\frac{1}{6}$, $\frac{1}{7}$, and $\frac{1}{9}$. On the other he can spin $\frac{1}{3}$ or $\frac{1}{4}$. If he spins both, what are the possible products he could find?
$\frac{1}{18}, \frac{1}{21}, \frac{1}{24}, \frac{1}{27}, \frac{1}{28}, \frac{1}{36}$

---

21. $35 \times \frac{5}{7} =$ _____ 25

22. $\frac{6}{19} \div \frac{21}{38} =$ _____ $\frac{4}{7}$

23. $18 \times 7\frac{1}{4} =$ _____ $130\frac{1}{2}$

24. Estimate.
$\frac{3}{8} \times 38$
possible answer: 19

25. $\frac{2}{5} \times \frac{7}{9} =$ _____ $\frac{14}{45}$

26. $162 \div \frac{3}{7} =$ _____ 378

27. $21 \times 3\frac{2}{3} =$ _____ 77

28. Estimate.
$\frac{5}{8} \times 41$
possible answer: 25

29. $18\frac{1}{4} \times 22 =$ _____ $401\frac{1}{2}$

30. $17\frac{3}{8} \times 14\frac{1}{3} =$ _____ $249\frac{1}{24}$

---

31. $11\frac{5}{7} \div 5\frac{1}{3} =$ _____ $2\frac{11}{56}$

32. $5\frac{2}{6} \times 1\frac{2}{5} =$ _____ $7\frac{7}{15}$

33. Estimate.
$115\frac{2}{3} \times \frac{4}{5}$
possible answers: 80 or 96

34. $34\frac{3}{5} \div \frac{1}{4} =$ _____ $138\frac{2}{5}$

35. Estimate.
$8 \times 2\frac{5}{7}$
possible answer: 24

36. Estimate.
$51\frac{5}{9} \times 22\frac{1}{19}$
possible answer: 1,000

37. Dwayne had $\frac{9}{10}$ liter of sports drink. He drank $\frac{4}{5}$ of that amount. How much of the sports drink did he drink?
$\frac{18}{25}$ liter

38. Melissa bought $16\frac{1}{4}$ yards of yarn. She used $\frac{4}{5}$ of it. How much was left?
$3\frac{1}{4}$ yards

39. Laz cut a 68-foot-long piece of steel into strips. If each strip is $5\frac{2}{3}$ feet long, how many strips does she cut?
12

40. Elyssia has two spinners. On one she can spin $\frac{3}{4}$ or $\frac{2}{5}$. On the other she can spin $\frac{1}{3}$ and $\frac{1}{4}$. What products can she find if she spins both spinners?
$\frac{1}{4}, \frac{2}{15}, \frac{3}{16}, \frac{1}{10}$

Chapter 15

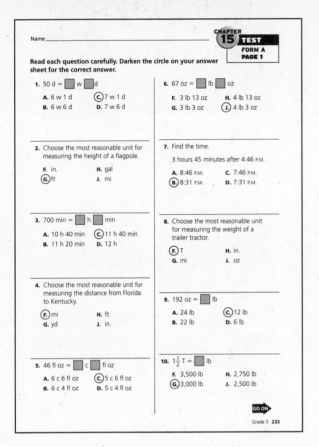

CHAPTER 15 TEST FORM A PAGE 1

Read each question carefully. Darken the circle on your answer sheet for the correct answer.

1. 50 d = [ ] w [ ] d
   A. 6 w 1 d
   C. 7 w 1 d
   B. 6 w 6 d
   D. 7 w 6 d

2. Choose the most reasonable unit for measuring the height of a flagpole.
   F. in.
   H. gal
   G. ft
   J. mi

3. 700 min = [ ] h [ ] min
   A. 10 h 40 min
   C. 11 h 40 min
   B. 11 h 20 min
   D. 12 h

4. Choose the most reasonable unit for measuring the distance from Florida to Kentucky.
   F. mi
   H. ft
   G. yd
   J. in.

5. 46 fl oz = [ ] c [ ] fl oz
   A. 6 c 6 fl oz
   C. 5 c 6 fl oz
   B. 6 c 4 fl oz
   D. 5 c 4 fl oz

6. 67 oz = [ ] lb [ ] oz
   F. 3 lb 13 oz
   H. 4 lb 13 oz
   G. 3 lb 3 oz
   J. 4 lb 3 oz

7. Find the time.
   3 hours 45 minutes after 4:46 P.M.
   A. 8:46 P.M.
   C. 7:46 P.M.
   B. 8:31 P.M.
   D. 7:31 P.M.

8. Choose the most reasonable unit for measuring the weight of a trailer tractor.
   F. T
   H. in.
   G. mi
   J. oz

9. 192 oz = [ ] lb
   A. 24 lb
   C. 12 lb
   B. 22 lb
   D. 6 lb

10. 1½ T = [ ] lb
    F. 3,500 lb
    H. 2,750 lb
    G. 3,000 lb
    J. 2,500 lb

GO ON

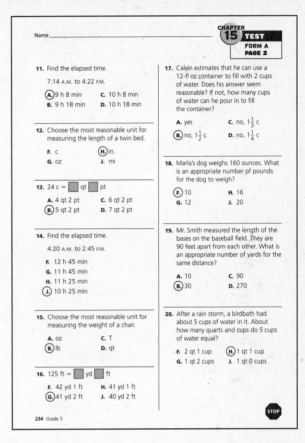

CHAPTER 15 TEST FORM A PAGE 2

11. Find the elapsed time.
    7:14 A.M. to 4:22 P.M.
    A. 9 h 8 min
    C. 10 h 8 min
    B. 9 h 18 min
    D. 10 h 18 min

12. Choose the most reasonable unit for measuring the length of a twin bed.
    F. c
    H. in.
    G. oz
    J. mi

13. 24 c = [ ] qt [ ] pt
    A. 4 qt 2 pt
    C. 6 qt 2 pt
    B. 5 qt 2 pt
    D. 7 qt 2 pt

14. Find the elapsed time.
    4:20 A.M. to 2:45 P.M.
    F. 12 h 45 min
    G. 11 h 45 min
    H. 11 h 25 min
    J. 10 h 25 min

15. Choose the most reasonable unit for measuring the weight of a chair.
    A. oz
    C. T
    B. lb
    D. qt

16. 125 ft = [ ] yd [ ] ft
    F. 42 yd 1 ft
    H. 41 yd 1 ft
    G. 41 yd 2 ft
    J. 40 yd 2 ft

17. Calvin estimates that he can use a 12-fl oz container to fill with 2 cups of water. Does his answer seem reasonable? If not, how many cups of water can he pour in to fill the container?
    A. yes
    C. no, 1⅓ c
    B. no, 1½ c
    D. no, 1¼ c

18. Marla's dog weighs 160 ounces. What is an appropriate number of pounds for the dog to weigh?
    F. 10
    H. 16
    G. 12
    J. 20

19. Mr. Smith measured the length of the bases on the baseball field. They are 90 feet apart from each other. What is an appropriate number of yards for the same distance?
    A. 10
    C. 90
    B. 30
    D. 270

20. After a rain storm, a birdbath had about 5 cups of water in it. About how many quarts and cups do 5 cups of water equal?
    F. 2 qt 1 cup
    H. 1 qt 1 cup
    G. 1 qt 2 cups
    J. 1 qt 0 cups

STOP

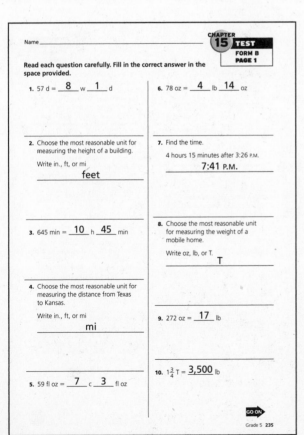

CHAPTER 15 TEST FORM B PAGE 1

Read each question carefully. Fill in the correct answer in the space provided.

1. 57 d = __8__ w __1__ d

2. Choose the most reasonable unit for measuring the height of a building.
   Write in., ft, or mi
   __feet__

3. 645 min = __10__ h __45__ min

4. Choose the most reasonable unit for measuring the distance from Texas to Kansas.
   Write in., ft, or mi
   __mi__

5. 59 fl oz = __7__ c __3__ fl oz

6. 78 oz = __4__ lb __14__ oz

7. Find the time.
   4 hours 15 minutes after 3:26 P.M.
   __7:41 P.M.__

8. Choose the most reasonable unit for measuring the weight of a mobile home.
   Write oz, lb, or T.
   __T__

9. 272 oz = __17__ lb

10. 1¾ T = __3,500__ lb

GO ON

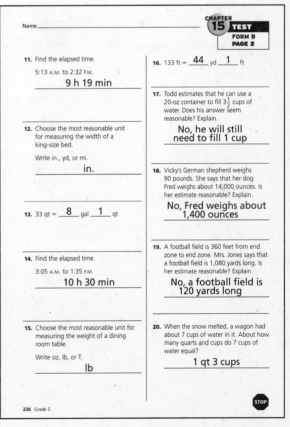

CHAPTER 15 TEST FORM B PAGE 2

11. Find the elapsed time.
    5:13 A.M. to 2:32 P.M.
    __9 h 19 min__

12. Choose the most reasonable unit for measuring the width of a king-size bed.
    Write in., yd, or mi.
    __in.__

13. 33 qt = __8__ gal __1__ qt

14. Find the elapsed time.
    3:05 A.M. to 1:35 P.M.
    __10 h 30 min__

15. Choose the most reasonable unit for measuring the weight of a dining room table.
    Write oz, lb, or T.
    __lb__

16. 133 ft = __44__ yd __1__ ft

17. Todd estimates that he can use a 20-oz container to fill 3⅕ cups of water. Does his answer seem reasonable? Explain.
    __No, he will still need to fill 1 cup__

18. Vicky's German shepherd weighs 90 pounds. She says that her dog Fred weighs about 14,000 ounces. Is her estimate reasonable? Explain.
    __No, Fred weighs about 1,400 ounces__

19. A football field is 360 feet from end zone to end zone. Mrs. Jones says that a football field is 1,080 yards long. Is her estimate reasonable? Explain.
    __No, a football field is 120 yards long__

20. When the snow melted, a wagon had about 7 cups of water in it. About how many quarts and cups do 7 cups of water equal?
    __1 qt 3 cups__

STOP

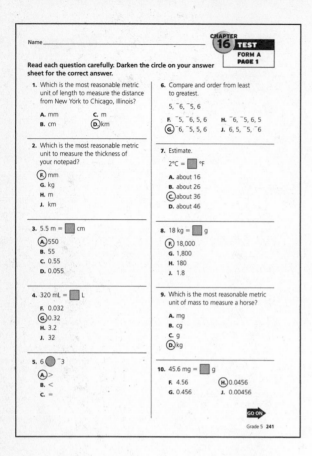

Name_____

Read each question carefully. Darken the circle on your answer sheet for the correct answer.

1. Which is the most reasonable metric unit of length to measure the distance from New York to Chicago, Illinois?
   A. mm   C. m
   B. cm   **D.** km

2. Which is the most reasonable metric unit to measure the thickness of your notepad?
   F. mm
   G. kg
   H. m
   J. km

3. 5.5 m = ☐ cm
   A. 550
   B. 55
   C. 0.55
   D. 0.055

4. 320 mL = ☐ L
   F. 0.032
   G. 0.32
   H. 3.2
   J. 32

5. 6 ◯ ⁻3
   A. >
   B. <
   C. =

6. Compare and order from least to greatest.
   5, ⁻6, ⁻5, 6
   F. ⁻5, ⁻6, 5, 6   H. ⁻6, ⁻5, 6, 5
   G. ⁻6, ⁻5, 5, 6   J. 6, 5, ⁻5, ⁻6

7. Estimate.
   2°C = ☐ °F
   A. about 16
   B. about 26
   C. about 36
   D. about 46

8. 18 kg = ☐ g
   F. 18,000
   G. 1,800
   H. 180
   J. 1.8

9. Which is the most reasonable metric unit of mass to measure a horse?
   A. mg
   B. cg
   C. g
   D. kg

10. 45.6 mg = ☐ g
    F. 4.56   **H.** 0.0456
    G. 0.456   J. 0.00456

GO ON

Grade 5   241

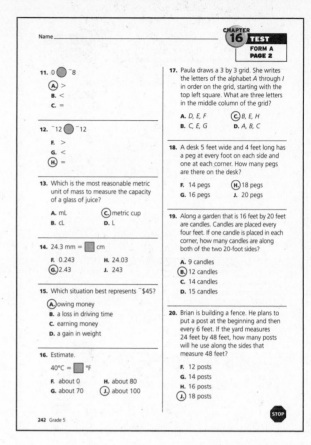

Name_____

11. 0 ◯ ⁻8
    A. >
    B. <
    C. =

12. ⁻12 ◯ ⁻12
    F. >
    G. <
    H. =

13. Which is the most reasonable metric unit of mass to measure the capacity of a glass of juice?
    A. mL   **C.** metric cup
    B. cL   D. L

14. 24.3 mm = ☐ cm
    F. 0.243   H. 24.03
    G. 2.43   J. 243

15. Which situation best represents ⁻$45?
    A. owing money
    B. a loss in driving time
    C. earning money
    D. a gain in weight

16. Estimate.
    40°C = ☐ °F
    F. about 0   H. about 80
    G. about 70   **J.** about 100

17. Paula draws a 3 by 3 grid. She writes the letters of the alphabet A through I in order on the grid, starting with the top left square. What are three letters in the middle column of the grid?
    A. D, E, F   **C.** B, E, H
    B. C, E, G   D. A, B, C

18. A desk 5 feet wide and 4 feet long has a peg at every foot on each side and one at each corner. How many pegs are there on the desk?
    F. 14 pegs   **H.** 18 pegs
    G. 16 pegs   J. 20 pegs

19. Along a garden that is 16 feet by 20 feet are candles. Candles are placed every four feet. If one candle is placed in each corner, how many candles are along both of the two 20-foot sides?
    A. 9 candles
    B. 12 candles
    C. 14 candles
    D. 15 candles

20. Brian is building a fence. He plans to put a post at the beginning and then every 6 feet. If the yard measures 24 feet by 48 feet, how many posts will he use along the sides that measure 48 feet?
    F. 12 posts
    G. 14 posts
    H. 16 posts
    J. 18 posts

STOP

242   Grade 5

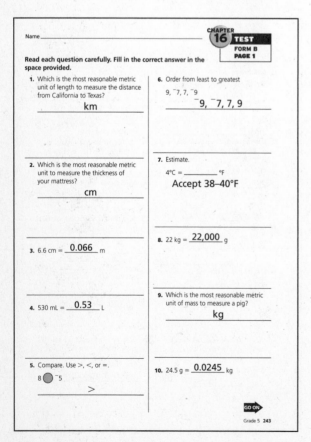

Name_____

Read each question carefully. Fill in the correct answer in the space provided.

1. Which is the most reasonable metric unit of length to measure the distance from California to Texas?
   _____km_____

2. Which is the most reasonable metric unit to measure the thickness of your mattress?
   _____cm_____

3. 6.6 cm = __0.066__ m

4. 530 mL = __0.53__ L

5. Compare. Use >, <, or =.
   8 ◯ ⁻5
   _____>_____

6. Order from least to greatest
   9, ⁻7, 7, ⁻9
   _____⁻9, ⁻7, 7, 9_____

7. Estimate.
   4°C = _____ °F
   Accept 38–40°F

8. 22 kg = __22,000__ g

9. Which is the most reasonable metric unit of mass to measure a pig?
   _____kg_____

10. 24.5 g = __0.0245__ kg

GO ON

Grade 5   243

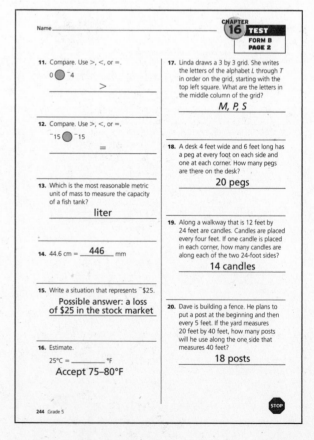

Name_____

11. Compare. Use >, <, or =.
    0 ◯ ⁻4
    _____>_____

12. Compare. Use >, <, or =.
    ⁻15 ◯ ⁻15
    _____=_____

13. Which is the most reasonable metric unit of mass to measure the capacity of a fish tank?
    _____liter_____

14. 44.6 cm = __446__ mm

15. Write a situation that represents ⁻$25.
    Possible answer: a loss of $25 in the stock market

16. Estimate.
    25°C = _____ °F
    Accept 75–80°F

17. Linda draws a 3 by 3 grid. She writes the letters of the alphabet L through T in order on the grid, starting with the top left square. What are the letters in the middle column of the grid?
    _____M, P, S_____

18. A desk 4 feet wide and 6 feet long has a peg at every foot on each side and one at each corner. How many pegs are there on the desk?
    _____20 pegs_____

19. Along a walkway that is 12 feet by 24 feet are candles. Candles are placed every four feet. If one candle is placed in each corner, how many candles are along each of the two 24-foot sides?
    _____14 candles_____

20. Dave is building a fence. He plans to put a post at the beginning and then every 5 feet. If the yard measures 20 feet by 40 feet, how many posts will he use along the one side that measures 40 feet?
    _____18 posts_____

STOP

244   Grade 5

Unit 8

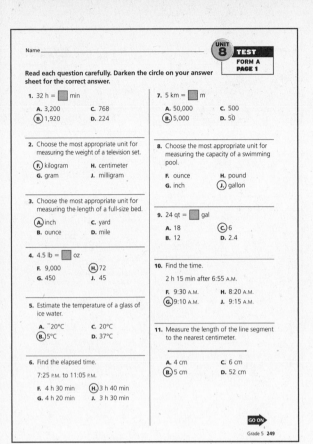

Read each question carefully. Darken the circle on your answer sheet for the correct answer.

1. 32 h = ▢ min
- A. 3,200
- B. 1,920 ●
- C. 768
- D. 224

2. Choose the most appropriate unit for measuring the weight of a television set.
- F. kilogram ●
- G. gram
- H. centimeter
- J. milligram

3. Choose the most appropriate unit for measuring the length of a full-size bed.
- A. inch ●
- B. ounce
- C. yard
- D. mile

4. 4.5 lb = ▢ oz
- F. 9,000
- G. 450
- H. 72 ●
- J. 45

5. Estimate the temperature of a glass of ice water.
- A. ⁻20°C
- B. 5°C ●
- C. 20°C
- D. 37°C

6. Find the elapsed time.
7:25 P.M. to 11:05 P.M.
- F. 4 h 30 min
- G. 4 h 20 min
- H. 3 h 40 min ●
- J. 3 h 30 min

7. 5 km = ▢ m
- A. 50,000
- B. 5,000 ●
- C. 500
- D. 50

8. Choose the most appropriate unit for measuring the capacity of a swimming pool.
- F. ounce
- G. inch
- H. pound
- J. gallon ●

9. 24 qt = ▢ gal
- A. 18
- B. 12
- C. 6 ●
- D. 2.4

10. Find the time.
2 h 15 min after 6:55 A.M.
- F. 9:30 A.M.
- G. 9:10 A.M. ●
- H. 8:20 A.M.
- J. 9:15 A.M.

11. Measure the length of the line segment to the nearest centimeter.
- A. 4 cm
- B. 5 cm ●
- C. 6 cm
- D. 52 cm

GO ON

Grade 5 **249**

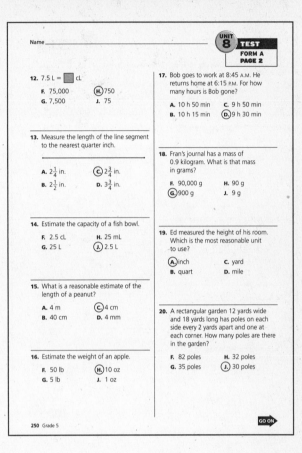

12. 7.5 L = ▢ cL
- F. 75,000
- G. 7,500
- H. 750 ●
- J. 75

13. Measure the length of the line segment to the nearest quarter inch.
- A. $2\frac{1}{4}$ in.
- B. $2\frac{1}{2}$ in.
- C. $2\frac{3}{4}$ in. ●
- D. $3\frac{3}{4}$ in.

14. Estimate the capacity of a fish bowl.
- F. 2.5 cL
- G. 25 L
- H. 25 mL
- J. 2.5 L ●

15. What is a reasonable estimate of the length of a peanut?
- A. 4 m
- B. 40 cm
- C. 4 cm ●
- D. 4 mm

16. Estimate the weight of an apple.
- F. 50 lb
- G. 5 lb
- H. 10 oz ●
- J. 1 oz

17. Bob goes to work at 8:45 A.M. He returns home at 6:15 P.M. For how many hours is Bob gone?
- A. 10 h 50 min
- B. 10 h 15 min
- C. 9 h 50 min
- D. 9 h 30 min ●

18. Fran's journal has a mass of 0.9 kilogram. What is that mass in grams?
- F. 90,000 g
- G. 900 g ●
- H. 90 g
- J. 9 g

19. Ed measured the height of his room. Which is the most reasonable unit to use?
- A. inch ●
- B. quart
- C. yard
- D. mile

20. A rectangular garden 12 yards wide and 18 yards long has poles on each side every 2 yards apart and one at each corner. How many poles are there in the garden?
- F. 82 poles
- G. 35 poles
- H. 32 poles
- J. 30 poles ●

GO ON

250 Grade 5

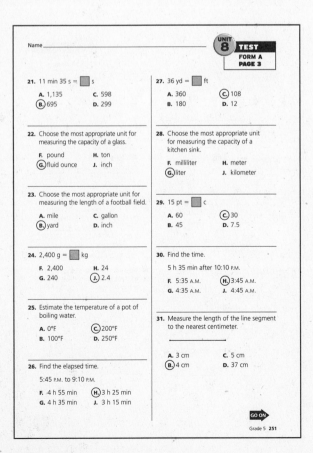

21. 11 min 35 s = ▢ s
- A. 1,135
- B. 695 ●
- C. 598
- D. 299

22. Choose the most appropriate unit for measuring the capacity of a glass.
- F. pound
- G. fluid ounce ●
- H. ton
- J. inch

23. Choose the most appropriate unit for measuring the length of a football field.
- A. mile
- B. yard ●
- C. gallon
- D. inch

24. 2,400 g = ▢ kg
- F. 2,400
- G. 240
- H. 24
- J. 2.4 ●

25. Estimate the temperature of a pot of boiling water.
- A. 0°F
- B. 100°F
- C. 200°F ●
- D. 250°F

26. Find the elapsed time.
5:45 P.M. to 9:10 P.M.
- F. 4 h 55 min
- G. 4 h 35 min
- H. 3 h 25 min ●
- J. 3 h 15 min

27. 36 yd = ▢ ft
- A. 360
- B. 180
- C. 108 ●
- D. 12

28. Choose the most appropriate unit for measuring the capacity of a kitchen sink.
- F. milliliter
- G. liter ●
- H. meter
- J. kilometer

29. 15 pt = ▢ c
- A. 60
- B. 45
- C. 30 ●
- D. 7.5

30. Find the time.
5 h 35 min after 10:10 P.M.
- F. 5:35 A.M.
- G. 4:35 A.M.
- H. 3:45 A.M. ●
- J. 4:45 A.M.

31. Measure the length of the line segment to the nearest centimeter.
- A. 3 cm
- B. 4 cm ●
- C. 5 cm
- D. 37 cm

GO ON

Grade 5 **251**

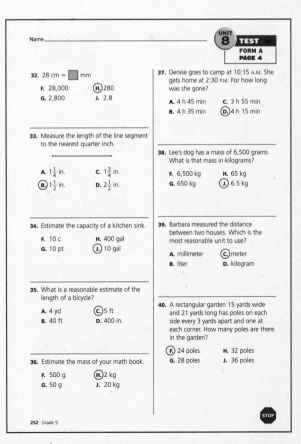

32. 28 cm = ▢ mm
- F. 28,000
- G. 2,800
- H. 280 ●
- J. 2.8

33. Measure the length of the line segment to the nearest quarter inch.
- A. $1\frac{1}{4}$ in.
- B. $1\frac{1}{2}$ in. ●
- C. $1\frac{3}{4}$ in.
- D. $2\frac{1}{2}$ in.

34. Estimate the capacity of a kitchen sink.
- F. 10 c
- G. 10 pt
- H. 400 gal
- J. 10 gal ●

35. What is a reasonable estimate of the length of a bicycle?
- A. 4 yd
- B. 40 ft
- C. 5 ft ●
- D. 400 in.

36. Estimate the mass of your math book.
- F. 500 g
- G. 50 g
- H. 2 kg ●
- J. 20 kg

37. Denise goes to camp at 10:15 A.M. She gets home at 2:30 P.M. For how long was she gone?
- A. 4 h 45 min
- B. 4 h 35 min
- C. 3 h 55 min
- D. 4 h 15 min ●

38. Lee's dog has a mass of 6,500 grams. What is that mass in kilograms?
- F. 6,500 kg
- G. 650 kg
- H. 65 kg
- J. 6.5 kg ●

39. Barbara measured the distance between two houses. Which is the most reasonable unit to use?
- A. millimeter
- B. liter
- C. meter ●
- D. kilogram

40. A rectangular garden 15 yards wide and 21 yards long has poles on each side every 3 yards apart and one at each corner. How many poles are there in the garden?
- F. 24 poles ●
- G. 28 poles
- H. 32 poles
- J. 36 poles

STOP

252 Grade 5

Grade 5 **467**

Unit 8

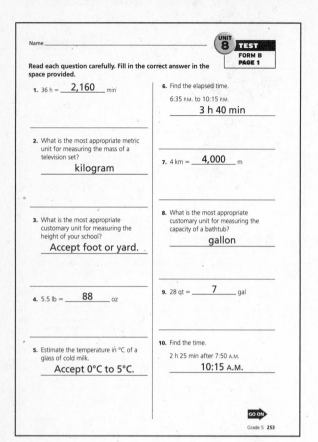

Name_____

UNIT 8 TEST FORM B PAGE 1

Read each question carefully. Fill in the correct answer in the space provided.

1. 36 h = ___2,160___ min

2. What is the most appropriate metric unit for measuring the mass of a television set?
kilogram

3. What is the most appropriate customary unit for measuring the height of your school?
Accept foot or yard.

4. 5.5 lb = ___88___ oz

5. Estimate the temperature in °C of a glass of cold milk.
Accept 0°C to 5°C.

6. Find the elapsed time.
6:35 P.M. to 10:15 P.M.
3 h 40 min

7. 4 km = ___4,000___ m

8. What is the most appropriate customary unit for measuring the capacity of a bathtub?
gallon

9. 28 qt = ___7___ gal

10. Find the time.
2 h 25 min after 7:50 A.M.
10:15 A.M.

GO ON
Grade 5   253

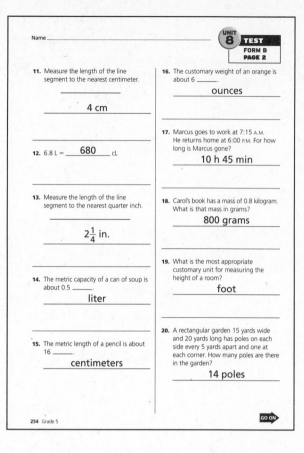

Name_____

UNIT 8 TEST FORM B PAGE 2

11. Measure the length of the line segment to the nearest centimeter.
4 cm

12. 6.8 L = ___680___ cL

13. Measure the length of the line segment to the nearest quarter inch.
$2\frac{1}{4}$ in.

14. The metric capacity of a can of soup is about 0.5 _____.
liter

15. The metric length of a pencil is about 16 _____.
centimeters

16. The customary weight of an orange is about 6 _____.
ounces

17. Marcus goes to work at 7:15 A.M. He returns home at 6:00 P.M. For how long is Marcus gone?
10 h 45 min

18. Carol's book has a mass of 0.8 kilogram. What is that mass in grams?
800 grams

19. What is the most appropriate customary unit for measuring the height of a room?
foot

20. A rectangular garden 15 yards wide and 20 yards long has poles on each side every 5 yards apart and one at each corner. How many poles are there in the garden?
14 poles

254   Grade 5   GO ON

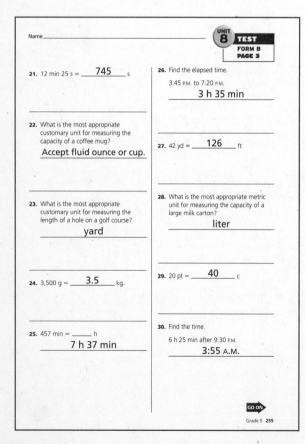

Name_____

UNIT 8 TEST FORM B PAGE 3

21. 12 min 25 s = ___745___ s

22. What is the most appropriate customary unit for measuring the capacity of a coffee mug?
Accept fluid ounce or cup.

23. What is the most appropriate customary unit for measuring the length of a hole on a golf course?
yard

24. 3,500 g = ___3.5___ kg

25. 457 min = _____ h
7 h 37 min

26. Find the elapsed time.
3:45 P.M. to 7:20 P.M.
3 h 35 min

27. 42 yd = ___126___ ft

28. What is the most appropriate metric unit for measuring the capacity of a large milk carton?
liter

29. 20 pt = ___40___ c

30. Find the time.
6 h 25 min after 9:30 P.M.
3:55 A.M.

GO ON
Grade 5   255

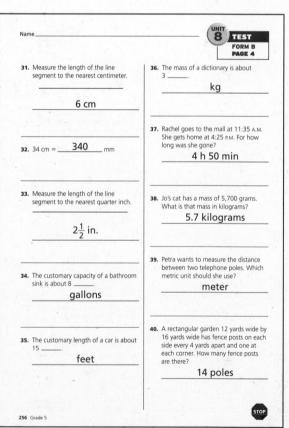

Name_____

UNIT 8 TEST FORM B PAGE 4

31. Measure the length of the line segment to the nearest centimeter.
6 cm

32. 34 cm = ___340___ mm

33. Measure the length of the line segment to the nearest quarter inch.
$2\frac{1}{2}$ in.

34. The customary capacity of a bathroom sink is about 8 _____.
gallons

35. The customary length of a car is about 15 _____.
feet

36. The mass of a dictionary is about 3 _____.
kg

37. Rachel goes to the mall at 11:35 A.M. She gets home at 4:25 P.M. For how long was she gone?
4 h 50 min

38. Jo's cat has a mass of 5,700 grams. What is that mass in kilograms?
5.7 kilograms

39. Petra wants to measure the distance between two telephone poles. Which metric unit should she use?
meter

40. A rectangular garden 12 yards wide by 16 yards wide has fence posts on each side every 4 yards apart and one at each corner. How many fence posts are there?
14 poles

256   Grade 5   STOP

Chapter 17

Name _____

Read each question carefully. Darken the circle on your answer sheet for the correct answer.

1. Evaluate $\frac{a}{6}$, for $a = 420$.

   A. 6   C. 60
   B. 7   **D.** 70

2. Evaluate $7 \times k$, for $k = 63$.

   F. 441   H. 341
   G. 420   J. 320

3. Evaluate. Use the order of operations.

   $4 \times (3 + 9) - 3 \times 5$

   A. 30   C. 90
   B. 33   D. 93

4. Evaluate. Use the order of operations.

   $9 - 24 \div 8 + (6 \times 5)$

   F. 3   H. 17
   G. 13   **J.** 36

5. Evaluate $\frac{1}{3}p$, for $p = 21$.

   A. 18   **C.** 7
   B. 16   D. 6

6. Evaluate. Use the order of operations.

   $6 + 45 \times (4 \times 2) - 3$

   F. 405   H. 231
   G. 363   J. 93

Use the table for problems 7–9.

t	2	4	6
s			

7. Complete the table, if $s = 4t - 2$.

   A. 6, 14, 22   C. 4, 14, 22
   B. 6, 12, 20   D. 4, 12, 20

8. Which ordered pairs match $s = 4t - 2$?

   F. (1, 2), (2, 6), (3, 10)
   G. (1, 2), (2, 10), (3, 14)
   H. (2, 6), (3, 6), (4, 10)
   J. (2, 6), (4, 16), (5, 18)

9. Which ordered pairs match $s = 4t + 2$?

   A. (1, 4), (2, 6), (4, 18)
   B. (1, 6), (2, 8), (5, 18)
   C. (2, 10), (4, 18), (5, 22)
   D. (2, 6), (4, 14), (5, 22)

10. Evaluate $n - 8$, for $n = 17.8$.

    F. 25.8   H. 9.2
    G. 9.8   J. 9

GO ON

Grade 5   261

Name _____

11. Evaluate. Use the order of operations.

    $(20 - 8) \div 3 + 9$

    A. 13   B. 18   C. 27   D. 45

Use data from the graph for problems 12–14.

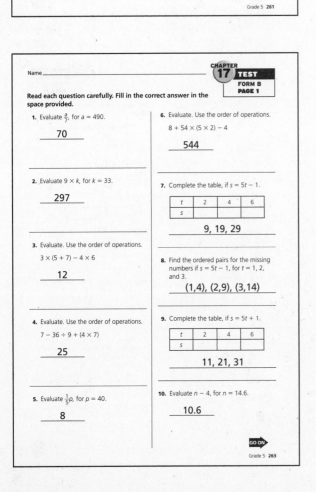

12. Find the coordinates for B.

    F. (1, 3)   **H.** (3, 6)
    G. (2, 4)   J. (7, 3)

13. Find the point for (8, 5).

    A. F   B. E   **C.** C   D. B

14. Find the coordinates for D and F.

    F. (2, 4) and (5, 5)   H. (5, 5) and (6, 3)
    G. (2, 4) and (8, 5)   J. (5, 5) and (3, 6)

15. Find an expression for this situation.

    Miguel read 10 more pages than Bob. Miguel read p pages. How many pages did Bob read?

    A. $10 + p$ C. $10 \times p$
    B. $10 - p$ D. $10 \div p$

16. Evaluate. Use the order of operations.

    $30 - 12 \div 3 - 4$

    F. 30   **G.** 22   H. 3   J. 2

Use data from the graph for problems 17–20.

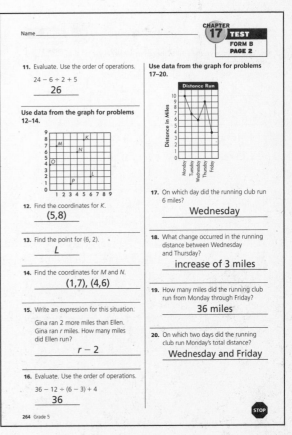

17. On which day did the swim team swim 400 meters?

    A. Monday   **C.** Wednesday
    B. Tuesday   D. Thursday

18. What change occurred in the distance swam between Wednesday and Thursday?

    F. increased by 400 meters
    G. decreased by 400 meters
    H. increased by 200 meters
    J. decreased by 200 meters

19. How many meters did the swim team swim from Monday through Friday?

    A. 2,400 meters   C. 2,800 meters
    B. 2,600 meters   D. 3,000 meters

20. On which two days did the swim team swim Friday's total distance?

    F. Monday and Wednesday
    G. Tuesday and Thursday
    H. Monday and Tuesday
    J. Tuesday and Thursday

STOP

262   Grade 5

Name _____

Read each question carefully. Fill in the correct answer in the space provided.

1. Evaluate $\frac{a}{7}$, for $a = 490$.

   __70__

2. Evaluate $9 \times k$, for $k = 33$.

   __297__

3. Evaluate. Use the order of operations.

   $3 \times (5 + 7) - 4 \times 6$

   __12__

4. Evaluate. Use the order of operations.

   $7 - 36 \div 9 + (4 \times 7)$

   __25__

5. Evaluate $\frac{1}{5}p$, for $p = 40$.

   __8__

6. Evaluate. Use the order of operations.

   $8 + 54 \times (5 \times 2) - 4$

   __544__

7. Complete the table, if $s = 5t - 1$.

t	2	4	6
s			

   __9, 19, 29__

8. Find the ordered pairs for the missing numbers if $s = 5t - 1$, for $t = 1, 2,$ and 3.

   __(1,4), (2,9), (3,14)__

9. Complete the table, if $s = 5t + 1$.

t	2	4	6
s			

   __11, 21, 31__

10. Evaluate $n - 4$, for $n = 14.6$.

    __10.6__

GO ON

Grade 5   263

Name _____

11. Evaluate. Use the order of operations.

    $24 - 6 \div 2 + 5$

    __26__

Use data from the graph for problems 12–14.

12. Find the coordinates for K.

    __(5,8)__

13. Find the point for (6, 2).

    __L__

14. Find the coordinates for M and N.

    __(1,7), (4,6)__

15. Write an expression for this situation.

    Gina ran 2 more miles than Ellen. Gina ran r miles. How many miles did Ellen run?

    __$r - 2$__

16. Evaluate. Use the order of operations.

    $36 - 12 \div (6 - 3) + 4$

    __36__

Use data from the graph for problems 17–20.

17. On which day did the running club run 6 miles?

    __Wednesday__

18. What change occurred in the running distance between Wednesday and Thursday?

    __increase of 3 miles__

19. How many miles did the running club run from Monday through Friday?

    __36 miles__

20. On which two days did the running club run Monday's total distance?

    __Wednesday and Friday__

STOP

264   Grade 5

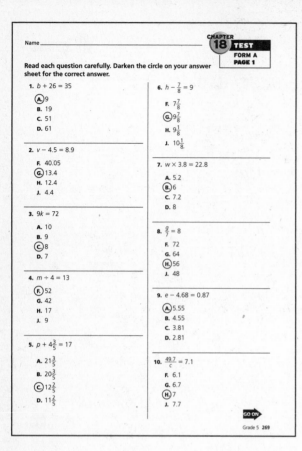

Name_____

Read each question carefully. Darken the circle on your answer sheet for the correct answer.

1. $b + 26 = 35$
  - (A) 9
  - B. 19
  - C. 51
  - D. 61

2. $v - 4.5 = 8.9$
  - F. 40.05
  - (G) 13.4
  - H. 12.4
  - J. 4.4

3. $9k = 72$
  - A. 10
  - B. 9
  - (C) 8
  - D. 7

4. $m \div 4 = 13$
  - (F) 52
  - G. 42
  - H. 17
  - J. 9

5. $p + 4\frac{3}{5} = 17$
  - A. $21\frac{3}{5}$
  - B. $20\frac{3}{5}$
  - (C) $12\frac{2}{5}$
  - D. $11\frac{2}{5}$

6. $h - \frac{7}{8} = 9$
  - F. $7\frac{7}{8}$
  - (G) $9\frac{7}{8}$
  - H. $9\frac{1}{8}$
  - J. $10\frac{1}{8}$

7. $w \times 3.8 = 22.8$
  - A. 5.2
  - (B) 6
  - C. 7.2
  - D. 8

8. $\frac{g}{7} = 8$
  - F. 72
  - G. 64
  - (H) 56
  - J. 48

9. $e - 4.68 = 0.87$
  - (A) 5.55
  - B. 4.55
  - C. 3.81
  - D. 2.81

10. $\frac{49.7}{c} = 7.1$
  - F. 6.1
  - G. 6.7
  - (H) 7
  - J. 7.7

GO ON

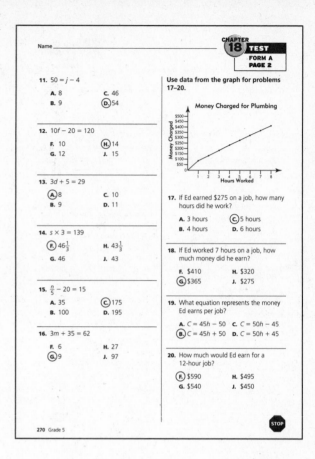

Name_____

11. $50 = j - 4$
  - A. 8
  - B. 9
  - C. 46
  - (D) 54

12. $10f - 20 = 120$
  - F. 10
  - G. 12
  - (H) 14
  - J. 15

13. $3d + 5 = 29$
  - (A) 8
  - B. 9
  - C. 10
  - D. 11

14. $s \times 3 = 139$
  - (F) $46\frac{1}{3}$
  - G. 46
  - H. $43\frac{1}{3}$
  - J. 43

15. $\frac{n}{5} - 20 = 15$
  - A. 35
  - B. 100
  - (C) 175
  - D. 195

16. $3m + 35 = 62$
  - F. 6
  - (G) 9
  - H. 27
  - J. 97

Use data from the graph for problems 17–20.

Money Charged for Plumbing

17. If Ed earned $275 on a job, how many hours did he work?
  - A. 3 hours
  - B. 4 hours
  - (C) 5 hours
  - D. 6 hours

18. If Ed worked 7 hours on a job, how much money did he earn?
  - F. $410
  - G. $365
  - H. $320
  - J. $275

19. What equation represents the money Ed earns per job?
  - A. $C = 45h - 50$
  - (B) $C = 45h + 50$
  - C. $C = 50h - 45$
  - D. $C = 50h + 45$

20. How much would Ed earn for a 12-hour job?
  - (F) $590
  - G. $540
  - H. $495
  - J. $450

STOP

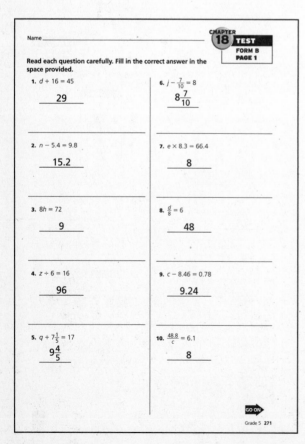

Name_____

Read each question carefully. Fill in the correct answer in the space provided.

1. $d + 16 = 45$

  29

2. $n - 5.4 = 9.8$

  15.2

3. $8h = 72$

  9

4. $z \div 6 = 16$

  96

5. $q + 7\frac{1}{5} = 17$

  $9\frac{4}{5}$

6. $j - \frac{7}{10} = 8$

  $8\frac{7}{10}$

7. $e \times 8.3 = 66.4$

  8

8. $\frac{d}{8} = 6$

  48

9. $c - 8.46 = 0.78$

  9.24

10. $\frac{48.8}{c} = 6.1$

  8

GO ON

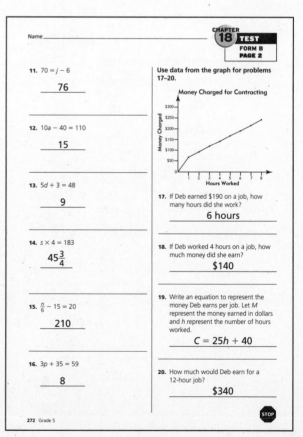

Name_____

11. $70 = j - 6$

  76

12. $10a - 40 = 110$

  15

13. $5d + 3 = 48$

  9

14. $s \times 4 = 183$

  $45\frac{3}{4}$

15. $\frac{n}{6} - 15 = 20$

  210

16. $3p + 35 = 59$

  8

Use data from the graph for problems 17–20.

Money Charged for Contracting

17. If Deb earned $190 on a job, how many hours did she work?

  6 hours

18. If Deb worked 4 hours on a job, how much money did she earn?

  $140

19. Write an equation to represent the money Deb earns per job. Let M represent the money earned in dollars and h represent the number of hours worked.

  $C = 25h + 40$

20. How much would Deb earn for a 12-hour job?

  $340

STOP

Page 1 — Form A

Name_____

UNIT 9 TEST FORM A PAGE 1

Read each question carefully. Darken the circle on your answer sheet for the correct answer.

1. Simplify using order of operations.

$5 - 15 \div 5 + (7 \times 3) = \square$

(A) 23   C. 19
B. 21   D. 15

2. Evaluate $2x + 18 \div 3$ for $x = 8$.

F. 22.66   H. 14
(G) 22   J. 11.333

3. Simplify using order of operations.

$9 - 54 \div 6 + 5 \times (4 - 2) = \square$

A. 48   (C) 10
B. 18   D. ¯12

4. Simplify using order of operations.

$15 + 24 \times (6 \div 3) - 9 = \square$

F. 84   H. 27
(G) 54   J. 23

5. Evaluate $t + 4^2 - 42 \div 7$ for $t = 3$.

A. 25   (C) 13
B. 15   D. 27

6. Write an expression for the situation.

7 less than eight times a number n

F. $8n + 7$ H. $8n \div 7$
G. $7(8n)$ (J) $8n - 7$

7. Simplify using order of operations.

$4 \times (6 + 5) - 8 \times 5 = \square$

A. 160   B. 105   C. 26   (D) 4

8. Write an expression for the situation.

Jannell can read 15 pages in an hour. At that rate, how many pages can she read in h hours?

F. $15 + h$ (H) $15h$
G. $h - 15$ J. $15 \div h$

Use the information below for exercises 9–12.

Ms. Gonzales took 5 children to the movies. She spent t dollars for each child's ticket and $8 for her tickets.

9. Which expression represents the total amount, in dollars, that Ms. Gonzales paid for tickets?

A. $8t + 5$ C. $5t - 8$
(B) $5t + 8$ D. $5 \times (t + 8)$

10. If Ms. Gonzales paid a total of $28 for tickets, how much did each child's ticket cost?

F. $5.60   (H) $4.00
G. $5.00   J. $3.00

GO ON

Grade 5 **277**

Page 2 — Form A

Name_____

UNIT 9 TEST FORM A PAGE 2

11. Suppose each child's ticket cost $6. Which table shows how to find the price of admission for 1, 2, 3, or 4 children?

A.
Number of children	1	2	3	4
Price	$4	$8	$12	$16

(B)
Number of children	1	2	3	4
Price	$6	$12	$18	$2

C.
Number of children	1	2	3	4
Price	$5	$10	$15	$20

D.
Number of children	1	2	3	4
Price	$14	$20	$28	$32

12. Suppose each child's ticket cost $6 and Ms. Gonzales bought $9 worth of popcorn. How much did she spend for popcorn and the tickets for herself and the 5 children?

F. $48   H. $39
(G) $47   J. $38

13. Solve for x. $5x - 10 = 45$

A. 55   B. 22   (C) 11   D. 7

14. Solve for t. $9 + 3t = 81$

F. 30   (G) 24   H. 12   J. 9

15. Solve for a. $4a = 12$

A. 48   (B) 3   C. 16   D. 8

16. Solve for p. $p \div 30 = 5$

F. 350   (G) 150   H. $\frac{1}{6}$ J. $\frac{1}{5}$

Use the following graph for exercises 17–18.

17. Which change in the temperature occurred between 9 A.M. and 10 A.M.?

A. Increase of 5 degrees
B. Decrease of 5 degrees
(C) Increase of 10 degrees
D. Decrease of 10 degrees

18. As time passes, what happens to the temperature?

(F) It increases.
G. It stays the same.
H. It decreases.

19. Terri charges $12 to rake a yard. How did she earn from raking 7 yards?

(A) $84   B. $42   C. $38   D. $19

20. The beach is 15 miles from Lisa's house. She took a bus 10 miles of this distance. Then she walked the rest of the way at the rate of 2.5 miles per hour. How long did it take her to walk to the beach?

F. 5 h   G. 3 h   (H) 2 h   J. 1 h

GO ON

278 Grade 5

Page 3 — Form A

Name_____

UNIT 9 TEST FORM A PAGE 3

21. Simplify using order of operations.

$22 + 21 \div 7 - (3 \times 4) = \square$

A. 88   C. $12\frac{4}{7}$
(B) 13   D. ¯$6\frac{5}{7}$

22. Evaluate $42 + 3x$ for $x = 5$.

(F) 57   H. 22
G. 27   J. 15

23. Simplify using order of operations.

$3^3 + 18 \times (5 + 1) - 11 = \square$

A. 259   C. 106
(B) 124   D. 89

24. Write an expression for the situation.

Three times a number n, increased by 44.

(F) $3n + 44$ H. $3 + n + 44$
G. $3 + n + 44$ J. $3n - 44$

25. Evaluate $20 - 3b + 9b^3$ for $b = 2$.

A. 98   C. 68
(B) 86   D. 89

26. Write an expression for the situation.

Cal can bike 5 miles in an hour. At that rate, how far can he bike in h hours?

F. $5 \div h$ H. $h - 5$
G. $5 + h$ (J) $5h$

27. Simplify using order of operations.

$81 \div 9 - 4 + 8(6 + 1) + 7 = \square$

A. $176\frac{2}{5}$ C. 61
(B) 68   D. 52

28. Simplify using order of operations.

$15 \times (9 - 7) + 6 \times 2 = \square$

F. 268   H. 72
G. 150   (J) 42

Use the information below for exercises 29–32.

Tim had read 32 pages of a book by Monday. He can read 18 pages in an hour.

29. Tim read for h hours on Monday. Which expression represents the number of pages he read?

A. $18 \div h + 32$ C. $18 - h + 32$
B. $h + 18 + 32$ (D) $18h + 32$

30. Suppose Tim had read 150 pages by the end of Tuesday and he read h hours on Wednesday. Write a new expression that shows how much he read by the end of Wednesday.

F. $18h - 150$ (H) $18h + 150$
G. $18h \div 150$ J. $18h(150)$

GO ON

Grade 5 **279**

Page 4 — Form A

Name_____

UNIT 9 TEST FORM A PAGE 4

31. Suppose Tim read 5 hours each day for 5 days. Which table shows how to find the number of pages he could have read?

A.
Days	1	2	3	4	5
Total Number of Pages	5	25	30	35	40

B.
Days	1	2	3	4	5
Total Number of Pages	45	90	150	185	500

(C)
Days	1	2	3	4	5
Total Number of Pages	90	180	270	360	450

D.
Days	1	2	3	4	5
Total Number of Pages	90	180	360	720	1,440

32. Suppose Tim read 122 pages by the end of Monday. For how many hours did he read?

F. 7 h   G. 6 h   (H) 5 h   J. 4 h

33. Solve for a. $12 + 22a = 78$

A. $6\frac{1}{2}$ B. 5   C. $4\frac{1}{11}$ (D) 3

34. Solve for t. $18t - 6 = 156$

F. 14   G. 11   (H) 9   J. $8\frac{1}{3}$

35. Solve for m. $3m = 15$

A. 45   (B) 5   C. 18   D. 12

36. Solve for r. $r \div 9 = 18$

F. 0.5   G. 2   H. 9   (J) 162

Use the following graph for exercises 37–38.

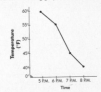

37. Which change in the temperature occurred between 7 P.M. and 8 P.M.?

A. Increase of 5 degrees
(B) Decrease of 5 degrees
C. Increase of 10 degrees
D. Decrease of 10 degrees

38. As time passes, what happens to the temperature?

F. It increases.
G. It stays the same.
(H) It decreases.

39. Ben washed cars for $15 each. How much did he earn from washing 11 cars?

A. $300.00   C. $85.00
(B) $165.00   D. $82.50

40. Erin earned $3 per hour babysitting. In addition, she got $4 allowance each week. How much did she get altogether during a week when she babysat for 8 hours?

F. $70.00   H. $35.00
G. $64.00   (J) $28.00

STOP

280 Grade 5

Unit 9

Page 1

Name _____

 TEST FORM B PAGE 1

Read each question carefully. Fill in the correct answer in the space provided.

1. Simplify using the order of operations.

$9 - 24 \div 8 + (5 \times 6) =$ ___36___

2. Evaluate $3x + 28 \div 4$ for $x = 7$

28

3. Simplify using the order of operations.

$8 - 48 \div 6 + 2 \times (7 - 4) =$ ___6___

4. Simplify using the order of operations.

$12 + 36 \times (12 \div 4) - 8 =$ ___112___

5. Evaluate $m + 5^2 - 56 \div 7$ for $m = 4$.

21

6. Write an expression for the situation.

8 more than seven times a number g

$7g + 8$

7. Simplify using the order of operations.

$5 \times (4 + 8) - 7 \times 6 =$

18

8. Write an expression for the situation.

Harold can type 75 words in a minute. At that rate, how many words can he type in t minutes?

$75t$

Use the information below for exercises 9–12.

Mr. Costanza took 4 of his children to the amusement park. He spent a dollars for each child's ticket and $25 for his ticket.

9. Write an expression that represents the total amount, in dollars, that Mr. Costanza paid for the tickets.

$4a + 25$

10. If Mr. Costanza paid a total of $85 for tickets, how much did each child's ticket cost?

$15

GO ON

Grade 5 **281**

Page 2

Name _____

 TEST FORM B PAGE 2

11. Suppose each child's ticket cost $8. Complete the table to show the price of admission for 1, 2, 3, or 4 children.

Number of children	1	2	3	4
Price	$8	$16	$24	$32

12. Suppose each child's ticket cost $8 and Mr. Costanza spent $25 at lunch. How much did he spend for lunch and the tickets for himself and his 4 children?

$82

13. Solve for p. $6p - 8 = 64$

$p = 12$

14. Solve for w. $7 + 3w = 52$

$w = 15$

15. Solve for b. $4b = 24$

$b = 6$

16. Solve for v. $v \div 40 = 7$

$v = 280$

Use the following graph for exercises 17–18.

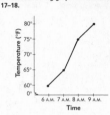

17. How much did the temperature increase between 6 A.M. and 7 A.M.?

$5°F$

18. What happens to the temperature as time passes?

It rises.

19. Laura charges $15 to mow the lawn. How much did she earn from mowing 6 lawns?

$90

20. Rick earns $5 per hour baby-sitting and he gets $9 allowance each week. How much does he get in a week when he baby-sat for 7 hours?

$44

GO ON

Page 3

Name _____

 TEST FORM B PAGE 3

21. Simplify using the order of operations.

$28 + 27 \div 9 - (5 \times 2) =$ ___21___

22. Evaluate $51 + 4x$ for $x = 4$.

67

23. Simplify using the order of operations.

$4^3 + 15 \times (4 + 3) - 12 =$ ___157___

24. Write an expression for the situation.

Four times a number z, increased by 37.

$4z + 37$

25. Evaluate $22 - 4y + 8y^3$, for $y = 2$.

78

26. Write an expression for the situation. Kellie can walk 4 miles in an hour. At that rate how far can she walk in h hours?

$4h$

27. Simplify using the order of operations.

$72 \div 9 - 6 + 7(5 + 2) + 8 =$ ___59___

28. Simplify using the order of operations.

$12 \times (8 - 5) + 5 \times 8 =$ ___76___

Use the information below for exercises 29–32.

Nia had read 28 pages of a book by Friday. She can read 22 pages in an hour.

29. Nia read for h hours on Friday. Write an expression that represents the number of pages she read.

$22h$

30. Suppose Nia had read 176 pages by the end of Saturday and she read h hours on Sunday. Write a new expression that shows how much she read by the end of Sunday.

$22h + 176$

GO ON

Grade 5 **283**

Page 4

Name _____

 TEST FORM B PAGE 4

31. Suppose Nia read 4 hours each day. Complete the table to show how many pages she read for 1, 2, 3, or 4 days.

Number of Days	1	2	3	4
Total Number of Pages	88	176	264	352

32. Suppose Nia read 138 pages by the end of Friday. For how many hours did she read?

5 hours

33. Solve for q. $15 + 18q = 87$

$q = 4$

34. Solve for p. $25p - 12 = 188$

$p = 8$

35. Solve for u. $5u = 45$

$u = 9$

36. Solve for s. $s \div 8 = 19$.

$s = 152$

Use the following graph for exercises 37–38.

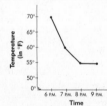

37. What was the change in temperature between 6 P.M. and 7 P.M.?

It dropped 10 degrees.

38. As time passes, what happens to the temperature?

It decreases.

39. Barry washed cars for $16 each. How much did he get for washing 14 cars?

$224

40. Lynn earned $7 per hour baby-sitting. In addition she earns $10 allowance each week. How much did she get during a week when she baby-sat 9 hours?

$73

STOP

Chapter 19

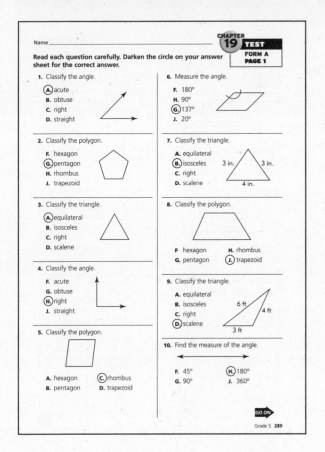

Name _____

CHAPTER 19 TEST
FORM A
PAGE 1

Read each question carefully. Darken the circle on your answer sheet for the correct answer.

1. Classify the angle.
- **(A.)** acute
- **B.** obtuse
- **C.** right
- **D.** straight

6. Measure the angle.
- **F.** 180°
- **H.** 90°
- **(G.)** 137°
- **J.** 20°

2. Classify the polygon.
- **F.** hexagon
- **(G.)** pentagon
- **H.** rhombus
- **J.** trapezoid

7. Classify the triangle.
- **A.** equilateral
- **(B.)** isosceles
- **C.** right
- **D.** scalene

3 in. 3 in.
4 in.

3. Classify the triangle.
- **(A.)** equilateral
- **B.** isosceles
- **C.** right
- **D.** scalene

8. Classify the polygon.
- **F.** hexagon
- **H.** rhombus
- **G.** pentagon
- **(J.)** trapezoid

4. Classify the angle.
- **F.** acute
- **G.** obtuse
- **(H.)** right
- **J.** straight

9. Classify the triangle.
- **A.** equilateral
- **B.** isosceles
- **C.** right
- **(D.)** scalene

6 ft   4 ft
3 ft

5. Classify the polygon.
- **A.** hexagon
- **(C.)** rhombus
- **B.** pentagon
- **D.** trapezoid

10. Find the measure of the angle.
- **F.** 45°
- **(H.)** 180°
- **G.** 90°
- **J.** 360°

GO ON

Grade 5 **289**

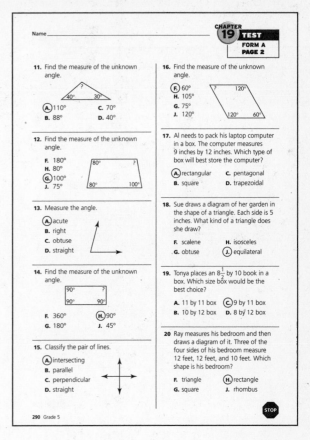

Name _____

CHAPTER 19 TEST
FORM A
PAGE 2

11. Find the measure of the unknown angle.

40° 30° ?

- **(A.)** 110°
- **C.** 70°
- **B.** 88°
- **D.** 40°

16. Find the measure of the unknown angle.

? 120°
120° 60°

- **(F.)** 60°
- **H.** 105°
- **G.** 75°
- **J.** 120°

12. Find the measure of the unknown angle.

80° ?
80° 100°

- **F.** 180°
- **H.** 80°
- **(G.)** 100°
- **J.** 75°

17. Al needs to pack his laptop computer in a box. The computer measures 9 inches by 12 inches. Which type of box will best store the computer?
- **(A.)** rectangular
- **C.** pentagonal
- **B.** square
- **D.** trapezoidal

13. Measure the angle.
- **(A.)** acute
- **B.** right
- **C.** obtuse
- **D.** straight

18. Sue draws a diagram of her garden in the shape of a triangle. Each side is 5 inches. What kind of a triangle does she draw?
- **F.** scalene
- **H.** isosceles
- **G.** obtuse
- **(J.)** equilateral

14. Find the measure of the unknown angle.

90° ?
90° 90°

- **F.** 360°
- **(H.)** 90°
- **G.** 180°
- **J.** 45°

19. Tonya places an $8\frac{1}{2}$ by 10 book in a box. Which size box would be the best choice?
- **A.** 11 by 11 box
- **(C.)** 9 by 11 box
- **B.** 10 by 12 box
- **D.** 8 by 12 box

15. Classify the pair of lines.
- **(A.)** intersecting
- **B.** parallel
- **C.** perpendicular
- **D.** straight

20 Ray measures his bedroom and then draws a diagram of it. Three of the four sides of his bedroom measure 12 feet, 12 feet, and 10 feet. Which shape is his bedroom?
- **F.** triangle
- **(H.)** rectangle
- **G.** square
- **J.** rhombus

STOP

290 Grade 5

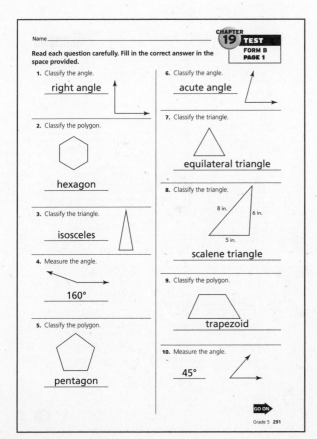

Name _____

CHAPTER 19 TEST
FORM B
PAGE 1

Read each question carefully. Fill in the correct answer in the space provided.

1. Classify the angle.

right angle

6. Classify the angle.

acute angle

2. Classify the polygon.

hexagon

7. Classify the triangle.

equilateral triangle

3. Classify the triangle.

isosceles

8. Classify the triangle.

8 in.   6 in.
5 in.

scalene triangle

4. Measure the angle.

160°

9. Classify the polygon.

trapezoid

5. Classify the polygon.

pentagon

10. Measure the angle.

45°

GO ON

Grade 5 **291**

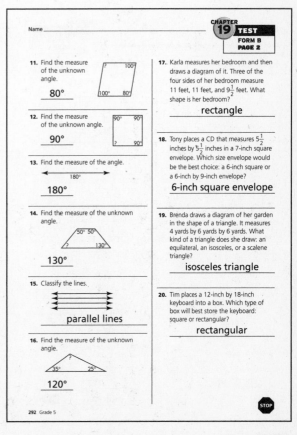

Name _____

CHAPTER 19 TEST
FORM B
PAGE 2

11. Find the measure of the unknown angle.

? 100°
100° 80°

80°

17. Karla measures her bedroom and then draws a diagram of it. Three of the four sides of her bedroom measure 11 feet, 11 feet, and $9\frac{1}{2}$ feet. What shape is her bedroom?

rectangle

12. Find the measure of the unknown angle.

90° 90°
? 90°

90°

18. Tony places a CD that measures $5\frac{1}{2}$ inches by $5\frac{1}{2}$ inches in a 7-inch square envelope. Which size envelope would be the best choice: a 6-inch square or a 6-inch by 9-inch envelope?

6-inch square envelope

13. Find the measure of the angle.

180°

180°

19. Brenda draws a diagram of her garden in the shape of a triangle. It measures 4 yards by 6 yards by 6 yards. What kind of a triangle does she draw: an equilateral, an isosceles, or a scalene triangle?

isosceles triangle

14. Find the measure of the unknown angle.

50° 50°
? 130°

130°

15. Classify the lines.

parallel lines

20. Tim places a 12-inch by 18-inch keyboard into a box. Which type of box will best store the keyboard: square or rectangular?

rectangular

16. Find the measure of the unknown angle.

?
35° 25°

120°

STOP

292 Grade 5

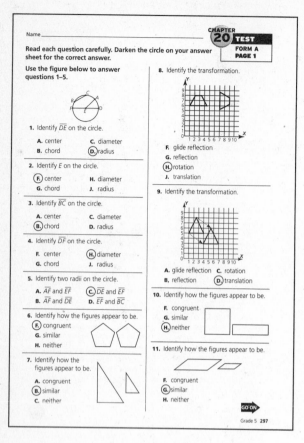

Name_____

Read each question carefully. Darken the circle on your answer sheet for the correct answer.

Use the figure below to answer questions 1–5.

1. Identify $\overline{DE}$ on the circle.
   A. center
   B. chord
   C. diameter
   D. radius

2. Identify E on the circle.
   F. center
   G. chord
   H. diameter
   J. radius

3. Identify $\overline{BC}$ on the circle.
   A. center
   B. chord
   C. diameter
   D. radius

4. Identify $\overline{DF}$ on the circle.
   F. center
   G. chord
   H. diameter
   J. radius

5. Identify two radii on the circle.
   A. $\overline{AF}$ and $\overline{EF}$
   B. $\overline{AF}$ and $\overline{DE}$
   C. $\overline{DE}$ and $\overline{EF}$
   D. $\overline{EF}$ and $\overline{BC}$

6. Identify how the figures appear to be.
   F. congruent
   G. similar
   H. neither

7. Identify how the figures appear to be.
   A. congruent
   B. similar
   C. neither

8. Identify the transformation.
   F. glide reflection
   G. reflection
   H. rotation
   J. translation

9. Identify the transformation.
   A. glide reflection
   B. reflection
   C. rotation
   D. translation

10. Identify how the figures appear to be.
    F. congruent
    G. similar
    H. neither

11. Identify how the figures appear to be.
    F. congruent
    G. similar
    H. neither

GO ON

Name_____

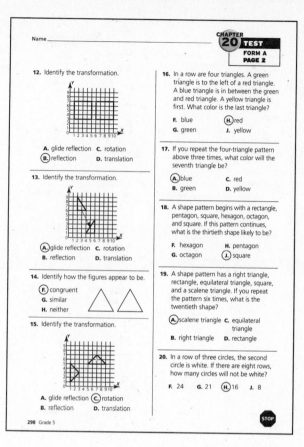

12. Identify the transformation.
    A. glide reflection
    B. reflection
    C. rotation
    D. translation

13. Identify the transformation.
    A. glide reflection
    B. reflection
    C. rotation
    D. translation

14. Identify how the figures appear to be.
    F. congruent
    G. similar
    H. neither

15. Identify the transformation.
    A. glide reflection
    B. reflection
    C. rotation
    D. translation

16. In a row are four triangles. A green triangle is to the left of a red triangle. A blue triangle is in between the green and red triangle. A yellow triangle is first. What color is the last triangle?
    F. blue
    G. green
    H. red
    J. yellow

17. If you repeat the four-triangle pattern above three times, what color will the seventh triangle be?
    A. blue
    B. green
    C. red
    D. yellow

18. A shape pattern begins with a rectangle, pentagon, square, hexagon, octagon, and square. If this pattern continues, what is the thirtieth shape likely to be?
    F. hexagon
    G. octagon
    H. pentagon
    J. square

19. A shape pattern has a right triangle, rectangle, equilateral triangle, square, and a scalene triangle. If you repeat the pattern six times, what is the twentieth shape?
    A. scalene triangle
    B. right triangle
    C. equilateral triangle
    D. rectangle

20. In a row of three circles, the second circle is white. If there are eight rows, how many circles will not be white?
    F. 24
    G. 21
    H. 16
    J. 8

STOP

Name_____

Read each question carefully. Fill in the correct answer in the space provided.

Use the figure below to answer questions 1–5.

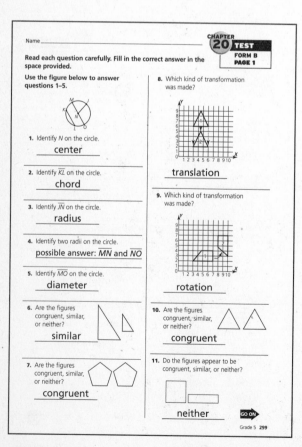

1. Identify N on the circle.
   center

2. Identify $\overline{KL}$ on the circle.
   chord

3. Identify $\overline{JN}$ on the circle.
   radius

4. Identify two radii on the circle.
   possible answer: $\overline{MN}$ and $\overline{NO}$

5. Identify $\overline{MO}$ on the circle.
   diameter

6. Are the figures congruent, similar, or neither?
   similar

7. Are the figures congruent, similar, or neither?
   congruent

8. Which kind of transformation was made?
   translation

9. Which kind of transformation was made?
   rotation

10. Are the figures congruent, similar, or neither?
    congruent

11. Do the figures appear to be congruent, similar, or neither?
    neither

GO ON

Name_____

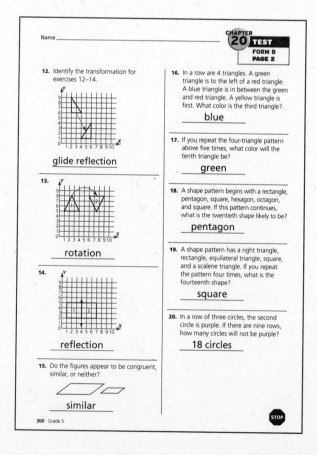

12. Identify the transformation for exercises 12–14.
    glide reflection

13.
    rotation

14.
    reflection

15. Do the figures appear to be congruent, similar, or neither?
    similar

16. In a row are 4 triangles. A green triangle is to the left of a red triangle. A blue triangle is in between the green and red triangle. A yellow triangle is first. What color is the third triangle?
    blue

17. If you repeat the four-triangle pattern above five times, what color will the tenth triangle be?
    green

18. A shape pattern begins with a rectangle, pentagon, square, hexagon, octagon, and square. If this pattern continues, what is the twentieth shape likely to be?
    pentagon

19. A shape pattern has a right triangle, rectangle, equilateral triangle, square, and a scalene triangle. If you repeat the pattern four times, what is the fourteenth shape?
    square

20. In a row of three circles, the second circle is purple. If there are nine rows, how many circles will not be purple?
    18 circles

STOP

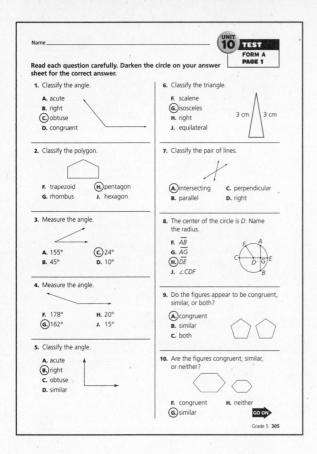

Name_____

Read each question carefully. Darken the circle on your answer sheet for the correct answer.

1. Classify the angle.

A. acute
B. right
C. obtuse ●
D. congruent

2. Classify the polygon.

F. trapezoid
G. rhombus
H. pentagon ●
J. hexagon

3. Measure the angle.

A. 155°
B. 45°
C. 24° ●
D. 10°

4. Measure the angle.

F. 178°
G. 162° ●
H. 20°
J. 15°

5. Classify the angle.

A. acute
B. right ●
C. obtuse
D. similar

6. Classify the triangle.

F. scalene
G. isosceles ●
H. right
J. equilateral

3 cm   3 cm

7. Classify the pair of lines.

A. intersecting ●
B. parallel
C. perpendicular
D. right

8. The center of the circle is *D*. Name the radius.

F. $\overline{AB}$
G. $\overline{AG}$
H. $\overline{DE}$ ●
J. ∠CDF

9. Do the figures appear to be congruent, similar, or both?

A. congruent ●
B. similar
C. both

10. Are the figures congruent, similar, or neither?

F. congruent
G. similar ●
H. neither

GO ON

Grade 5 305

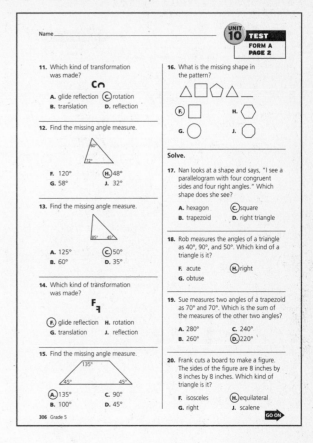

Name_____

11. Which kind of transformation was made?

Cᴖ

A. glide reflection
B. translation
C. rotation ●
D. reflection

12. Find the missing angle measure.

60°
72°

F. 120°
G. 58°
H. 48° ●
J. 32°

13. Find the missing angle measure.

85°   45°

A. 125°
B. 60°
C. 50° ●
D. 35°

14. Which kind of transformation was made?

F�879

F. glide reflection ●
G. translation
H. rotation
J. reflection

15. Find the missing angle measure.

135°
45°   45°

A. 135° ●
B. 100°
C. 90°
D. 45°

16. What is the missing shape in the pattern?

△ □ ⬠ △ __

F. □
G. ○
H. ⬡
J. ⬡

Solve.

17. Nan looks at a shape and says, "I see a parallelogram with four congruent sides and four right angles." Which shape does she see?

A. hexagon
B. trapezoid
C. square ●
D. right triangle

18. Rob measures the angles of a triangle as 40°, 90°, and 50°. Which kind of a triangle is it?

F. acute
G. obtuse
H. right ●

19. Sue measures two angles of a trapezoid as 70° and 70°. Which is the sum of the measures of the other two angles?

A. 280°
B. 260°
C. 240°
D. 220° ●

20. Frank cuts a board to make a figure. The sides of the figure are 8 inches by 8 inches by 8 inches. Which kind of triangle is it?

F. isosceles
G. right
H. equilateral ●
J. scalene

GO ON

306 Grade 5

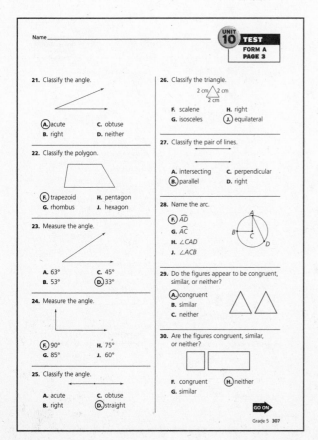

Name_____

21. Classify the angle.

A. acute ●
B. right
C. obtuse
D. neither

22. Classify the polygon.

F. trapezoid ●
G. rhombus
H. pentagon
J. hexagon

23. Measure the angle.

A. 63°
B. 53°
C. 45°
D. 33° ●

24. Measure the angle.

F. 90° ●
G. 85°
H. 75°
J. 60°

25. Classify the angle.

A. acute
B. right
C. obtuse
D. straight ●

26. Classify the triangle.

2 cm   2 cm
2 cm

F. scalene
G. isosceles
H. right
J. equilateral ●

27. Classify the pair of lines.

A. intersecting
B. parallel ●
C. perpendicular
D. right

28. Name the arc.

F. $\overset{\frown}{AD}$ ●
G. $\overset{\frown}{AC}$
H. ∠CAD
J. ∠ACB

29. Do the figures appear to be congruent, similar, or neither?

A. congruent ●
B. similar
C. neither

30. Are the figures congruent, similar, or neither?

F. congruent
G. similar
H. neither ●

GO ON

Grade 5 307

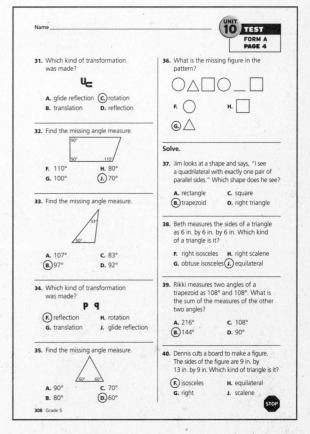

Name_____

31. Which kind of transformation was made?

Uᴄ

A. glide reflection
B. translation
C. rotation ●
D. reflection

32. Find the missing angle measure.

90°
90°   110°

F. 110°
G. 100°
H. 80°
J. 70° ●

33. Find the missing angle measure.

33°
50°

A. 107°
B. 97° ●
C. 83°
D. 92°

34. Which kind of transformation was made?

P q

F. reflection ●
G. translation
H. rotation
J. glide reflection

35. Find the missing angle measure.

60°   60°

A. 90°
B. 80°
C. 70°
D. 60° ●

36. What is the missing figure in the pattern?

○ △ □ ○ __ □

F. ○
G. △ ●
H. □

Solve.

37. Jim looks at a shape and says, "I see a quadrilateral with exactly one pair of parallel sides." Which shape does he see?

A. rectangle
B. trapezoid ●
C. square
D. right triangle

38. Beth measures the sides of a triangle as 6 in. by 6 in. by 6 in. Which kind of a triangle is it?

F. right isosceles
G. obtuse isosceles
H. right scalene
J. equilateral ●

39. Rikki measures two angles of a trapezoid as 108° and 108°. What is the sum of the measures of the other two angles?

A. 216°
B. 144° ●
C. 108°
D. 90°

40. Dennis cuts a board to make a figure. The sides of the figure are 9 in. by 13 in. by 9 in. Which kind of triangle is it?

F. isosceles ●
G. right
H. equilateral
J. scalene

STOP

308 Grade 5

Unit 10

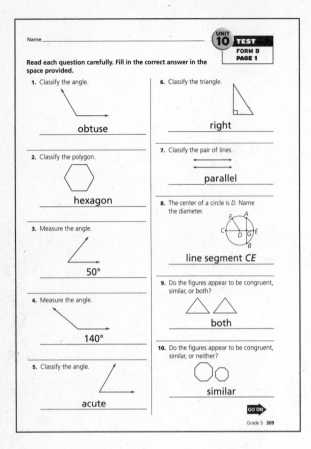

Read each question carefully. Fill in the correct answer in the space provided.

1. Classify the angle.

obtuse

2. Classify the polygon.

hexagon

3. Measure the angle.

50°

4. Measure the angle.

140°

5. Classify the angle.

acute

6. Classify the triangle.

right

7. Classify the pair of lines.

parallel

8. The center of a circle is *D*. Name the diameter.

line segment *CE*

9. Do the figures appear to be congruent, similar, or both?

both

10. Do the figures appear to be congruent, similar, or neither?

similar

GO ON

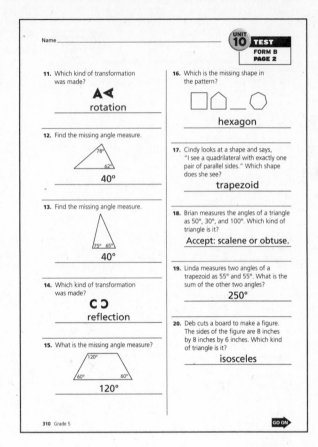

11. Which kind of transformation was made?

rotation

12. Find the missing angle measure.

40°

13. Find the missing angle measure.

40°

14. Which kind of transformation was made?

reflection

15. What is the missing angle measure?

120°

16. Which is the missing shape in the pattern?

hexagon

17. Cindy looks at a shape and says, "I see a quadrilateral with exactly one pair of parallel sides." Which shape does she see?

trapezoid

18. Brian measures the angles of a triangle as 50°, 30°, and 100°. Which kind of triangle is it?

Accept: scalene or obtuse.

19. Linda measures two angles of a trapezoid as 55° and 55°. What is the sum of the other two angles?

250°

20. Deb cuts a board to make a figure. The sides of the figure are 8 inches by 8 inches by 6 inches. Which kind of triangle is it?

isosceles

GO ON

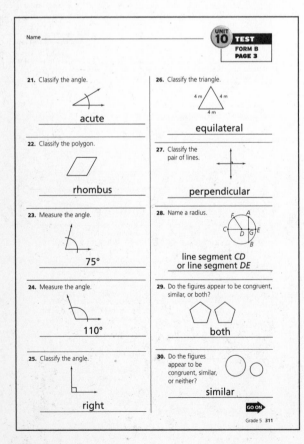

21. Classify the angle.

acute

22. Classify the polygon.

rhombus

23. Measure the angle.

75°

24. Measure the angle.

110°

25. Classify the angle.

right

26. Classify the triangle.

equilateral

27. Classify the pair of lines.

perpendicular

28. Name a radius.

line segment *CD*
or line segment *DE*

29. Do the figures appear to be congruent, similar, or both?

both

30. Do the figures appear to be congruent, similar, or neither?

similar

GO ON

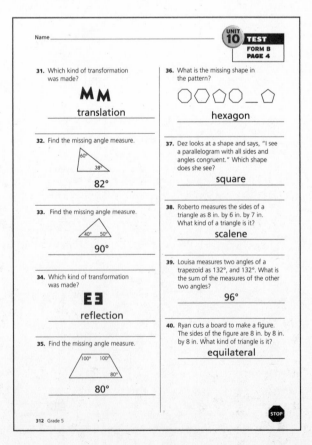

31. Which kind of transformation was made?

translation

32. Find the missing angle measure.

82°

33. Find the missing angle measure.

90°

34. Which kind of transformation was made?

reflection

35. Find the missing angle measure.

80°

36. What is the missing shape in the pattern?

hexagon

37. Dez looks at a shape and says, "I see a parallelogram with all sides and angles congruent." Which shape does she see?

square

38. Roberto measures the sides of a triangle as 8 in. by 6 in. by 7 in. What kind of triangle is it?

scalene

39. Louisa measures two angles of a trapezoid as 132°, and 132°. What is the sum of the measures of the other two angles?

96°

40. Ryan cuts a board to make a figure. The sides of the figure are 8 in. by 8 in. by 8 in. What kind of triangle is it?

equilateral

STOP

Chapter 21

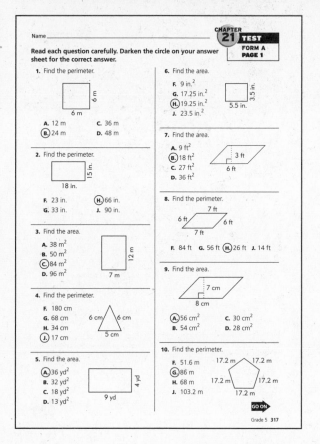

CHAPTER 21 TEST — FORM A — PAGE 1

Name _____

Read each question carefully. Darken the circle on your answer sheet for the correct answer.

1. Find the perimeter.

6 m, 6 m

- A. 12 m
- **B.** 24 m
- C. 36 m
- D. 48 m

2. Find the perimeter.

15 in., 18 in.

- F. 23 in.
- G. 33 in.
- **H.** 66 in.
- J. 90 in.

3. Find the area.

12 m, 7 m

- A. 38 m²
- B. 50 m²
- **C.** 84 m²
- D. 96 m²

4. Find the perimeter.

6 cm, 6 cm, 5 cm

- F. 180 cm
- G. 68 cm
- H. 34 cm
- **J.** 17 cm

5. Find the area.

9 yd, 4 yd

- **A.** 36 yd²
- B. 32 yd²
- C. 18 yd²
- D. 13 yd²

6. Find the area.

5.5 in., 3.5 in.

- F. 9 in.²
- G. 17.25 in.²
- **H.** 19.25 in.²
- J. 23.5 in.²

7. Find the area.

3 ft, 6 ft

- A. 9 ft²
- **B.** 18 ft²
- C. 27 ft²
- D. 36 ft²

8. Find the perimeter.

7 ft, 6 ft, 6 ft, 7 ft

- F. 84 ft
- G. 56 ft
- **H.** 26 ft
- J. 14 ft

9. Find the area.

7 cm, 8 cm

- **A.** 56 cm²
- B. 54 cm²
- C. 30 cm²
- D. 28 cm²

10. Find the perimeter.

17.2 m (pentagon)

- F. 51.6 m
- **G.** 86 m
- H. 68 m
- J. 103.2 m

GO ON

Grade 5 **317**

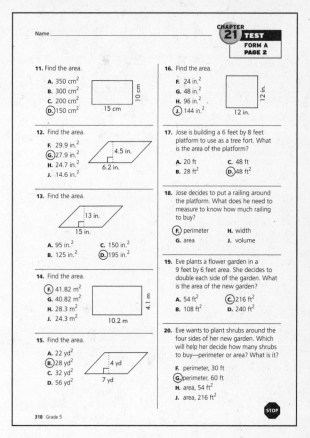

CHAPTER 21 TEST — FORM A — PAGE 2

Name _____

11. Find the area.

15 cm, 10 cm

- A. 350 cm²
- B. 300 cm²
- C. 200 cm²
- **D.** 150 cm²

12. Find the area.

4.5 in., 6.2 in.

- F. 29.9 in.²
- **G.** 27.9 in.²
- H. 24.7 in.²
- J. 14.6 in.²

13. Find the area.

13 in., 15 in.

- A. 95 in.²
- B. 125 in.²
- C. 150 in.²
- **D.** 195 in.²

14. Find the area.

4.1 m, 10.2 m

- **F.** 41.82 m²
- G. 40.82 m²
- H. 28.3 m²
- J. 24.3 m²

15. Find the area.

4 yd, 7 yd

- A. 22 yd²
- **B.** 28 yd²
- C. 32 yd²
- D. 56 yd²

16. Find the area.

12 in., 12 in.

- F. 24 in.²
- G. 48 in.²
- H. 96 in.²
- **J.** 144 in.²

17. Jose is building a 6 feet by 8 feet platform to use as a tree fort. What is the area of the platform?

- A. 20 ft
- B. 28 ft²
- C. 48 ft
- **D.** 48 ft²

18. Jose decides to put a railing around the platform. What does he need to measure to know how much railing to buy?

- **F.** perimeter
- G. area
- H. width
- J. volume

19. Eve plants a flower garden in a 9 feet by 6 feet area. She decides to double each side of the garden. What is the area of the new garden?

- A. 54 ft²
- B. 108 ft²
- **C.** 216 ft²
- D. 240 ft²

20. Eve wants to plant shrubs around the four sides of her new garden. Which will help her decide how many shrubs to buy—perimeter or area? What is it?

- F. perimeter, 30 ft
- **G.** perimeter, 60 ft
- H. area, 54 ft²
- J. area, 216 ft²

STOP

318 Grade 5

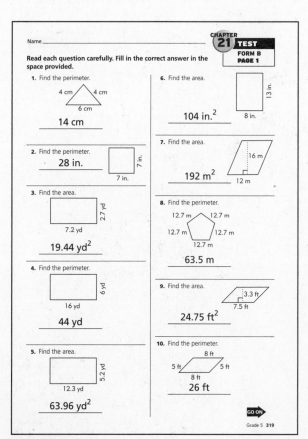

CHAPTER 21 TEST — FORM B — PAGE 1

Name _____

Read each question carefully. Fill in the correct answer in the space provided.

1. Find the perimeter.

4 cm, 4 cm, 6 cm

14 cm

2. Find the perimeter.

7 in.

28 in.

3. Find the area.

2.7 yd, 7.2 yd

19.44 yd²

4. Find the perimeter.

6 yd, 16 yd

44 yd

5. Find the area.

5.2 yd, 12.3 yd

63.96 yd²

6. Find the area.

13 in., 8 in.

104 in.²

7. Find the area.

16 m, 12 m

192 m²

8. Find the perimeter.

12.7 m (pentagon)

63.5 m

9. Find the area.

3.3 ft, 7.5 ft

24.75 ft²

10. Find the perimeter.

8 ft, 5 ft, 5 ft, 8 ft

26 ft

GO ON

Grade 5 **319**

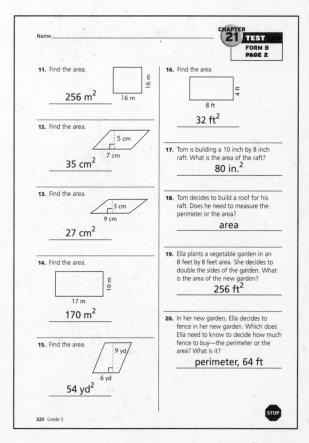

CHAPTER 21 TEST — FORM B — PAGE 2

Name _____

11. Find the area.

16 m, 16 m

256 m²

12. Find the area.

5 cm, 7 cm

35 cm²

13. Find the area.

3 cm, 9 cm

27 cm²

14. Find the area.

10 m, 17 m

170 m²

15. Find the area.

9 yd, 6 yd

54 yd²

16. Find the area.

8 ft, 4 ft

32 ft²

17. Tom is building a 10 inch by 8 inch raft. What is the area of the raft?

80 in.²

18. Tom decides to build a roof for his raft. Does he need to measure the perimeter or the area?

area

19. Ella plants a vegetable garden in an 8 feet by 8 feet area. She decides to double the sides of the garden. What is the area of the new garden?

256 ft²

20. In her new garden, Ella decides to fence in her new garden. Which does Ella need to know to decide how much fence to buy—the perimeter or the area? What is it?

perimeter, 64 ft

STOP

320 Grade 5

Name _____

Read each question carefully. Darken the circle on your answer sheet for the correct answer.

1. Find the area.
- **A.** 20 in.²
- **(B.)** 30 in.²
- **C.** 45 in.²
- **D.** 60 in.²

10 in. / 6 in.

2. Find the area.
- **F.** 36 ft²
- **G.** 18 ft²
- **(H.)** 9 ft²
- **J.** 6 ft²

2 ft / 3 ft / 4 ft

3. Estimate to find the area. Each square = 1 in.².
- **A.** 8 in.²
- **B.** 7 in.²
- **(C.)** 6 in.²
- **D.** 5 in.²

4. Find the approximate circumference of the circle. Use π ≈ 3.14. Round to the nearest hundredth if necessary.
- **F.** 36.68 cm
- **(G.)** 37.68 cm
- **H.** 75.36 cm
- **J.** 150.72 cm

12 cm

5. Find the area.
- **(A.)** 14 m²
- **B.** 28 m²
- **C.** 42 m²
- **D.** 56 m²

4 m / 7 m

6. Find the area.
- **F.** 108 cm²
- **G.** 72 cm²
- **H.** 54 cm²
- **(J.)** 36 cm²

4 cm / 6 cm / 8 cm

7. Find the area. Each square = 1 cm².
- **A.** 15 cm²
- **(B.)** 16 cm²
- **C.** 17 cm²
- **D.** 18 cm²

4 cm 3 cm / 2 cm 2 cm / 5 cm

8. Find the approximate circumference of the circle. Use π ≈ 3.14. Round to the nearest tenth if necessary.
- **F.** 150.2 in.
- **G.** 100.2 in.
- **(H.)** 50.2 in.
- **J.** 25.5 in.

16 in.

9. Estimate to find the area. Each square = 1 cm².
- **A.** 12 cm²
- **B.** 13 cm²
- **(C.)** 14 cm²
- **D.** 15 cm²

10. Find the approximate circumference of the circle. Use π ≈ 3.14. Round to the nearest hundredth if necessary.
- **F.** 14.13 m
- **(G.)** 28.26 m
- **H.** 56.52 m
- **J.** 113.04 m

4.5 m

GO ON

Grade 5 **325**

Name _____

11. Find the area. Each square = 1 cm².
- **(A.)** 38 cm²
- **B.** 40 cm²
- **C.** 41 cm²
- **D.** 43 cm²

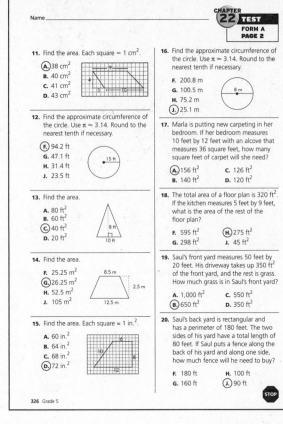

9 / 3 10

12. Find the approximate circumference of the circle. Use π ≈ 3.14. Round to the nearest tenth if necessary.
- **(F.)** 94.2 ft
- **G.** 47.1 ft
- **H.** 31.4 ft
- **J.** 23.5 ft

15 ft

13. Find the area.
- **A.** 80 ft²
- **B.** 60 ft²
- **(C.)** 40 ft²
- **D.** 20 ft²

8 ft / 10 ft

14. Find the area.
- **F.** 25.25 m²
- **(G.)** 26.25 m²
- **H.** 52.5 m²
- **J.** 105 m²

8.5 m / 2.5 m / 12.5 m

15. Find the area. Each square = 1 in.².
- **A.** 60 in.²
- **B.** 64 in.²
- **C.** 68 in.²
- **(D.)** 72 in.²

6 / 10 / 8 / 12

16. Find the approximate circumference of the circle. Use π ≈ 3.14. Round to the nearest tenth if necessary.
- **F.** 200.8 m
- **G.** 100.5 m
- **H.** 75.2 m
- **(J.)** 25.1 m

8 m

17. Marla is putting new carpeting in her bedroom. If her bedroom measures 10 feet by 12 feet with an alcove that measures 36 square feet, how many square feet of carpet will she need?
- **(A.)** 156 ft²
- **B.** 140 ft²
- **C.** 126 ft²
- **D.** 120 ft²

18. The total area of a floor plan is 320 ft². If the kitchen measures 5 feet by 9 feet, what is the area of the rest of the floor plan?
- **F.** 595 ft²
- **G.** 298 ft²
- **(H.)** 275 ft²
- **J.** 45 ft²

19. Saul's front yard measures 50 feet by 20 feet. His driveway takes up 350 ft² of the front yard, and the rest is grass. How much grass is in Saul's front yard?
- **A.** 1,000 ft²
- **(B.)** 650 ft²
- **C.** 550 ft²
- **D.** 350 ft²

20. Saul's back yard is rectangular and has a perimeter of 180 feet. The two sides of his yard have a total length of 80 feet. If Saul puts a fence along the back of his yard and along one side, how much fence will he need to buy?
- **F.** 180 ft
- **G.** 160 ft
- **H.** 100 ft
- **(J.)** 90 ft

STOP

326 Grade 5

Name _____

Read each question carefully. Fill in the correct answer in the space provided.

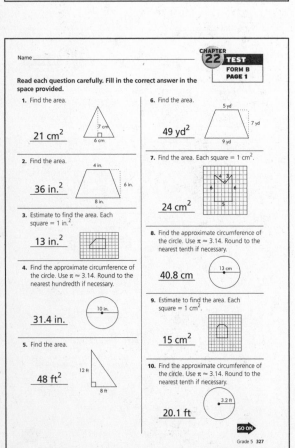

1. Find the area.

___21 cm²___

7 cm / 6 cm

2. Find the area.

___36 in.²___

4 in. / 6 in. / 8 in.

3. Estimate to find the area. Each square = 1 in.².

___13 in.²___

4. Find the approximate circumference of the circle. Use π ≈ 3.14. Round to the nearest hundredth if necessary.

___31.4 in.___

10 in.

5. Find the area.

___48 ft²___

12 ft / 8 ft

6. Find the area.

___49 yd²___

5 yd / 7 yd / 9 yd

7. Find the area. Each square = 1 cm².

___24 cm²___

4 3 / 6 6 / 5

8. Find the approximate circumference of the circle. Use π ≈ 3.14. Round to the nearest tenth if necessary.

___40.8 cm___

13 cm

9. Estimate to find the area. Each square = 1 cm².

___15 cm²___

10. Find the approximate circumference of the circle. Use π ≈ 3.14. Round to the nearest tenth if necessary.

___20.1 ft___

3.2 ft

GO ON

Grade 5 **327**

Name _____

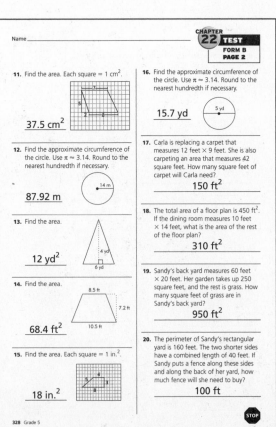

11. Find the area. Each square = 1 cm².

___37.5 cm²___

7 / 5 / 2 8

12. Find the approximate circumference of the circle. Use π ≈ 3.14. Round to the nearest hundredth if necessary.

___87.92 m___

14 m

13. Find the area.

___12 yd²___

4 yd / 6 yd

14. Find the area.

___68.4 ft²___

8.5 ft / 7.2 ft / 10.5 ft

15. Find the area. Each square = 1 in.².

___18 in.²___

5 4 / 3 / 8

16. Find the approximate circumference of the circle. Use π ≈ 3.14. Round to the nearest hundredth if necessary.

___15.7 yd___

5 yd

17. Carla is replacing a carpet that measures 12 feet × 9 feet. She is also carpeting an area that measures 42 square feet. How many square feet of carpet will Carla need?

___150 ft²___

18. The total area of a floor plan is 450 ft². If the dining room measures 10 feet × 14 feet, what is the area of the rest of the floor plan?

___310 ft²___

19. Sandy's back yard measures 60 feet × 20 feet. Her garden takes up 250 square feet, and the rest is grass. How many square feet of grass are in Sandy's back yard?

___950 ft²___

20. The perimeter of Sandy's rectangular yard is 160 feet. The two shorter sides have a combined length of 40 feet. If Sandy puts a fence along these sides and along the back of her yard, how much fence will she need to buy?

___100 ft___

STOP

328 Grade 5

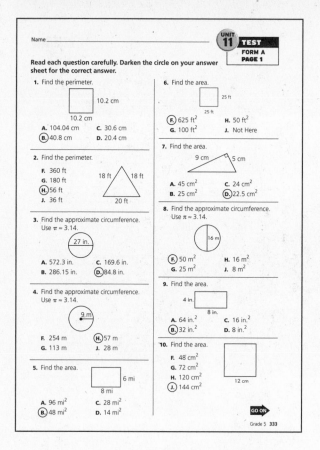

Name _____

Read each question carefully. Darken the circle on your answer sheet for the correct answer.

1. Find the perimeter.

10.2 cm
10.2 cm

A. 104.04 cm **C.** 30.6 cm
B. 40.8 cm **D.** 20.4 cm

2. Find the perimeter.

18 ft 18 ft
20 ft

F. 360 ft
G. 180 ft
H. 56 ft
J. 36 ft

3. Find the approximate circumference. Use π ≈ 3.14.

27 in.

A. 572.3 in. **C.** 169.6 in.
B. 286.15 in. **D.** 84.8 in.

4. Find the approximate circumference. Use π ≈ 3.14.

9 m

F. 254 m **H.** 57 m
G. 113 m **J.** 28 m

5. Find the area.

6 mi
8 mi

A. 96 mi² **C.** 28 mi²
B. 48 mi² **D.** 14 mi²

6. Find the area.

25 ft
25 ft

F. 625 ft² **H.** 50 ft²
G. 100 ft² **J.** Not Here

7. Find the area.

9 cm 5 cm

A. 45 cm² **C.** 24 cm²
B. 25 cm² **D.** 22.5 cm²

8. Find the approximate circumference. Use π ≈ 3.14.

16 m

F. 50 m² **H.** 16 m²
G. 25 m² **J.** 8 m²

9. Find the area.

4 in.
8 in.

A. 64 in.² **C.** 16 in.²
B. 32 in.² **D.** 8 in.²

10. Find the area.

12 cm

F. 48 cm²
G. 72 cm²
H. 120 cm²
J. 144 cm²

GO ON

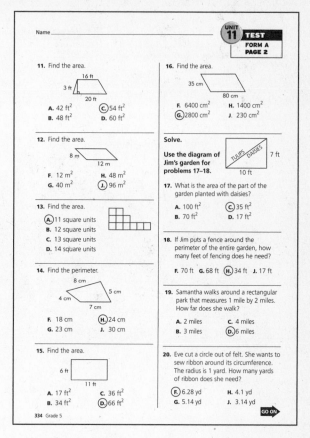

Name _____

11. Find the area.

16 ft
3 ft
20 ft

A. 42 ft² **C.** 54 ft²
B. 48 ft² **D.** 60 ft²

12. Find the area.

8 m
12 m

F. 12 m² **H.** 48 m²
G. 40 m² **J.** 96 m²

13. Find the area.

A. 11 square units
B. 12 square units
C. 13 square units
D. 14 square units

14. Find the perimeter.

8 cm
4 cm 5 cm
7 cm

F. 18 cm **H.** 24 cm
G. 23 cm **J.** 30 cm

15. Find the area.

6 ft
11 ft

A. 17 ft² **C.** 36 ft²
B. 34 ft² **D.** 66 ft²

16. Find the area.

35 cm
80 cm

F. 6400 cm² **H.** 1400 cm²
G. 2800 cm² **J.** 230 cm²

Solve.

Use the diagram of Jim's garden for problems 17–18.

TULIPS DAISIES 7 ft
10 ft

17. What is the area of the part of the garden planted with daisies?

A. 100 ft² **C.** 35 ft²
B. 70 ft² **D.** 17 ft²

18. If Jim puts a fence around the perimeter of the entire garden, how many feet of fencing does he need?

F. 70 ft **G.** 68 ft **H.** 34 ft **J.** 17 ft

19. Samantha walks around a rectangular park that measures 1 mile by 2 miles. How far does she walk?

A. 2 miles **C.** 4 miles
B. 3 miles **D.** 6 miles

20. Eve cut a circle out of felt. She wants to sew ribbon around its circumference. The radius is 1 yard. How many yards of ribbon does she need?

F. 6.28 yd **H.** 4.1 yd
G. 5.14 yd **J.** 3.14 yd

GO ON

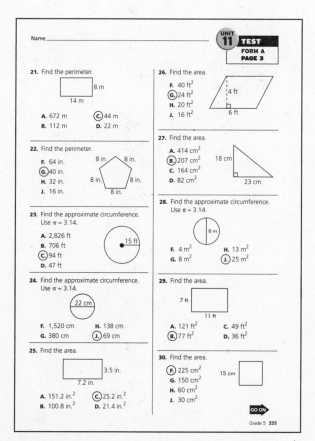

Name _____

21. Find the perimeter.

8 m
14 m

A. 672 m **C.** 44 m
B. 112 m **D.** 22 m

22. Find the perimeter.

8 in. 8 in.
8 in. 8 in.
8 in.

F. 64 in.
G. 40 in.
H. 32 in.
J. 16 in.

23. Find the approximate circumference. Use π ≈ 3.14.

15 ft

A. 2,826 ft
B. 706 ft
C. 94 ft
D. 47 ft

24. Find the approximate circumference. Use π ≈ 3.14.

22 cm

F. 1,520 cm **H.** 138 cm
G. 380 cm **J.** 69 cm

25. Find the area.

3.5 in.
7.2 in.

A. 151.2 in.² **C.** 25.2 in.²
B. 100.8 in.² **D.** 21.4 in.²

26. Find the area.

4 ft
6 ft

F. 40 ft²
G. 24 ft²
H. 20 ft²
J. 16 ft²

27. Find the area.

18 cm
23 cm

A. 414 cm²
B. 207 cm²
C. 164 cm²
D. 82 cm²

28. Find the approximate circumference. Use π ≈ 3.14.

8 m

F. 4 m² **H.** 13 m²
G. 8 m² **J.** 25 m²

29. Find the area.

7 ft
11 ft

A. 121 ft² **C.** 49 ft²
B. 77 ft² **D.** 36 ft²

30. Find the area.

15 cm

F. 225 cm²
G. 150 cm²
H. 60 cm²
J. 30 cm²

GO ON

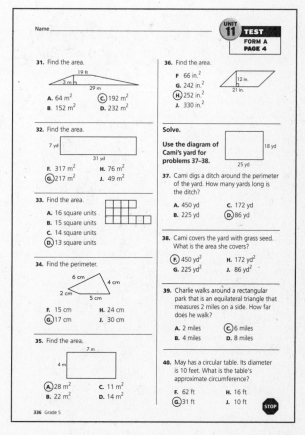

Name _____

31. Find the area.

19 ft
3 m
29 m

A. 64 m² **C.** 192 m²
B. 152 m² **D.** 232 m²

32. Find the area.

7 yd
31 yd

F. 317 m² **H.** 76 m²
G. 217 m² **J.** 49 m²

33. Find the area.

A. 16 square units
B. 15 square units
C. 14 square units
D. 13 square units

34. Find the perimeter.

6 cm 4 cm
2 cm 5 cm

F. 15 cm **H.** 24 cm
G. 17 cm **J.** 30 cm

35. Find the area.

7 m
4 m

A. 28 m² **C.** 11 m²
B. 22 m² **D.** 14 m²

36. Find the area.

12 in.
21 in.

F. 66 in.²
G. 242 in.²
H. 252 in.²
J. 330 in.²

Solve.

Use the diagram of Cami's yard for problems 37–38.

18 yd
25 yd

37. Cami digs a ditch around the perimeter of the yard. How many yards long is the ditch?

A. 450 yd **C.** 172 yd
B. 225 yd **D.** 86 yd

38. Cami covers the yard with grass seed. What is the area she covers?

F. 450 yd² **H.** 172 yd²
G. 225 yd² **J.** 86 yd²

39. Charlie walks around a rectangular park that is an equilateral triangle that measures 2 miles on a side. How far does he walk?

A. 2 miles **C.** 6 miles
B. 4 miles **D.** 8 miles

40. May has a circular table. Its diameter is 10 feet. What is the table's approximate circumference?

F. 62 ft **H.** 16 ft
G. 31 ft **J.** 10 ft

STOP

Unit 11

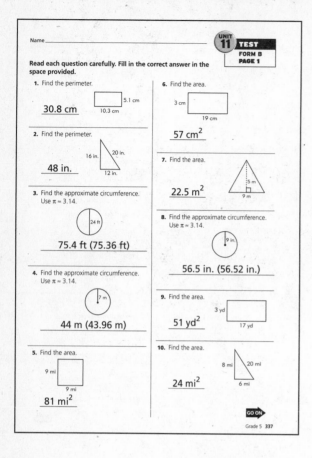

Name _____

Read each question carefully. Fill in the correct answer in the space provided.

1. Find the perimeter.

5.1 cm
10.3 cm

30.8 cm

2. Find the perimeter.

16 in.   20 in.
12 in.

48 in.

3. Find the approximate circumference.
Use π ≈ 3.14.

24 ft

75.4 ft (75.36 ft)

4. Find the approximate circumference.
Use π ≈ 3.14.

7 m

44 m (43.96 m)

5. Find the area.

9 mi
9 mi

81 mi²

6. Find the area.

3 cm
19 cm

57 cm²

7. Find the area.

5 m
9 m

22.5 m²

8. Find the approximate circumference.
Use π ≈ 3.14.

9 in.

56.5 in. (56.52 in.)

9. Find the area.

3 yd
17 yd

51 yd²

10. Find the area.

8 mi   20 mi
6 mi

24 mi²

GO ON
Grade 5 **337**

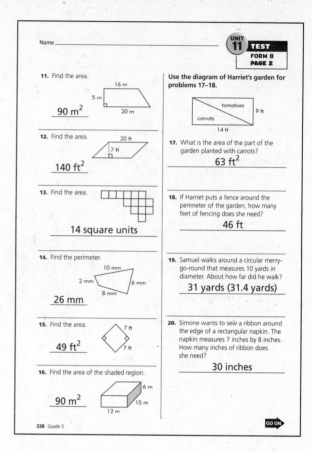

Name _____

11. Find the area.

16 m
5 m
20 m

90 m²

12. Find the area.

20 ft
7 ft

140 ft²

13. Find the area.

14 square units

14. Find the perimeter.

10 mm
2 mm   6 mm
8 mm

26 mm

15. Find the area.

7 ft
7 ft

49 ft²

16. Find the area of the shaded region.

6 m
15 m
12 m

90 m²

Use the diagram of Harriet's garden for problems 17–18.

tomatoes
9 ft
carrots
14 ft

17. What is the area of the part of the garden planted with carrots?

63 ft²

18. If Harriet puts a fence around the perimeter of the garden, how many feet of fencing does she need?

46 ft

19. Samuel walks around a circular merry-go-round that measures 10 yards in diameter. About how far did he walk?

31 yards (31.4 yards)

20. Simone wants to sew a ribbon around the edge of a rectangular napkin. The napkin measures 7 inches by 8 inches. How many inches of ribbon does she need?

30 inches

338 Grade 5

GO ON

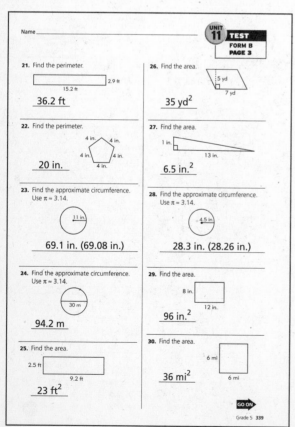

Name _____

21. Find the perimeter.

15.2 ft   2.9 ft

36.2 ft

22. Find the perimeter.

4 in.   4 in.
4 in.   4 in.
4 in.

20 in.

23. Find the approximate circumference.
Use π ≈ 3.14.

11 in.

69.1 in. (69.08 in.)

24. Find the approximate circumference.
Use π ≈ 3.14.

30 m

94.2 m

25. Find the area.

2.5 ft
9.2 ft

23 ft²

26. Find the area.

5 yd
7 yd

35 yd²

27. Find the area.

1 in.
13 in.

6.5 in.²

28. Find the approximate circumference.
Use π ≈ 3.14.

4.5 in.

28.3 in. (28.26 in.)

29. Find the area.

8 in.
12 in.

96 in.²

30. Find the area.

6 mi
6 mi

36 mi²

GO ON
Grade 5 **339**

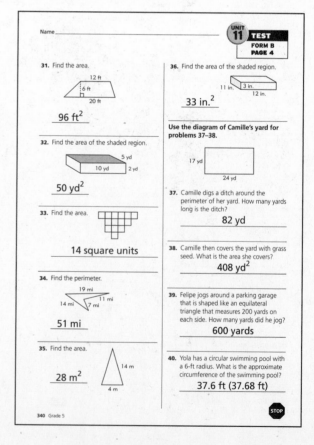

Name _____

31. Find the area.

12 ft
6 ft
20 ft

96 ft²

32. Find the area of the shaded region.

5 yd
10 yd   2 yd

50 yd²

33. Find the area.

14 square units

34. Find the perimeter.

19 mi
14 mi   11 mi
7 mi

51 mi

35. Find the area.

14 m
4 m

28 m²

36. Find the area of the shaded region.

11 in.   3 in.
12 in.

33 in.²

Use the diagram of Camille's yard for problems 37–38.

17 yd
24 yd

37. Camille digs a ditch around the perimeter of her yard. How many yards long is the ditch?

82 yd

38. Camille then covers the yard with grass seed. What is the area she covers?

408 yd²

39. Felipe jogs around a parking garage that is shaped like an equilateral triangle that measures 200 yards on each side. How many yards did he jog?

600 yards

40. Yola has a circular swimming pool with a 6-ft radius. What is the approximate circumference of the swimming pool?

37.6 ft (37.68 ft)

340 Grade 5

STOP

---

480 Grade 5

Chapter 23

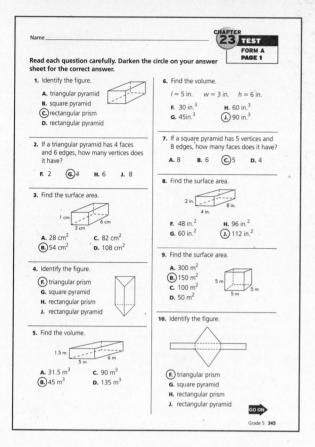

Name _____

Read each question carefully. Darken the circle on your answer sheet for the correct answer.

1. Identify the figure.
- **A.** triangular pyramid
- **B.** square pyramid
- **(C.)** rectangular prism
- **D.** rectangular pyramid

2. If a triangular pyramid has 4 faces and 6 edges, how many vertices does it have?
- **F.** 2   **(G.)** 4   **H.** 6   **J.** 8

3. Find the surface area.
1 cm   6 cm   3 cm
- **A.** 28 cm^2 **C.** 82 cm^2
- **(B.)** 54 cm^2 **D.** 108 cm^2

4. Identify the figure.
- **(F.)** triangular prism
- **G.** square pyramid
- **H.** rectangular prism
- **J.** rectangular pyramid

5. Find the volume.
1.5 m   5 m   6 m
- **A.** 31.5 m^3 **C.** 90 m^3
- **(B.)** 45 m^3 **D.** 135 m^3

6. Find the volume.
$l = 5$ in. $w = 3$ in. $h = 6$ in.
- **F.** 30 in.^{3} **H.** 60 in.^{3}
- **G.** 45in.^{3} **(J.)** 90 in.^{3}

7. If a square pyramid has 5 vertices and 8 edges, how many faces does it have?
- **A.** 8   **B.** 6   **(C.)** 5   **D.** 4

8. Find the surface area.
2 in.   4 in.   8 in.
- **F.** 48 in.^{2} **H.** 96 in.^{2}
- **G.** 60 in.^{2} **(J.)** 112 in.^{2}

9. Find the surface area.
5 m   5 m   5 m
- **A.** 300 m^2
- **(B.)** 150 m^2
- **C.** 100 m^2
- **D.** 50 m^2

10. Identify the figure.
- **(F.)** triangular prism
- **G.** square pyramid
- **H.** rectangular prism
- **J.** rectangular pyramid

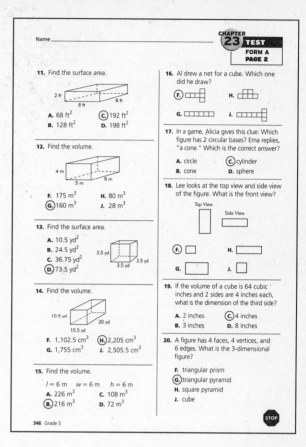

Name _____

11. Find the surface area.
2 ft   8 ft   8 ft
- **A.** 68 ft^2 **(C.)** 192 ft^2
- **B.** 128 ft^2 **D.** 198 ft^2

12. Find the volume.
4 m   5 m   8 m
- **F.** 175 m^3 **H.** 80 m^3
- **(G.)** 160 m^3 **J.** 28 m^3

13. Find the surface area.
3.5 yd   3.5 yd   3.5 yd
- **A.** 10.5 yd^2
- **B.** 24.5 yd^2
- **C.** 36.75 yd^2
- **(D.)** 73.5 yd^2

14. Find the volume.
10.5 yd   20 yd   10.5 yd
- **F.** 1,102.5 cm^3 **(H.)** 2,205 cm^3
- **G.** 1,755 cm^3 **J.** 2,505.5 cm^3

15. Find the volume.
$l = 6$ m $w = 6$ m $h = 6$ m
- **A.** 226 m^3 **C.** 108 m^3
- **(B.)** 216 m^3 **D.** 72 m^3

16. Al drew a net for a cube. Which one did he draw?
- **(F.)**   **H.**
- **G.**   **J.**

17. In a game, Alicia gives this clue: Which figure has 2 circular bases? Ema replies, "a cone." Which is the correct answer?
- **A.** circle   **(C.)** cylinder
- **B.** cone   **D.** sphere

18. Lee looks at the top view and side view of the figure. What is the front view?
Top View   Side View
- **(F.)**   **H.**
- **G.**   **J.**

19. If the volume of a cube is 64 cubic inches and 2 sides are 4 inches each, what is the dimension of the third side?
- **A.** 2 inches   **(C.)** 4 inches
- **B.** 3 inches   **D.** 8 inches

20. A figure has 4 faces, 4 vertices, and 6 edges. What is the 3-dimensional figure?
- **F.** triangular prism
- **(G.)** triangular pyramid
- **H.** square pyramid
- **J.** cube

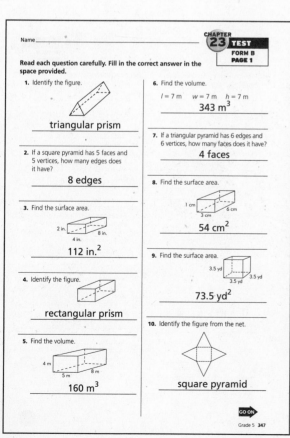

Name _____

Read each question carefully. Fill in the correct answer in the space provided.

1. Identify the figure.

triangular prism

2. If a square pyramid has 5 faces and 5 vertices, how many edges does it have?

8 edges

3. Find the surface area.
2 in.   4 in.   8 in.

112 in.^{2}

4. Identify the figure.

rectangular prism

5. Find the volume.
4 m   5 m   8 m

160 m^3

6. Find the volume.
$l = 7$ m $w = 7$ m $h = 7$ m

343 m^3

7. If a triangular pyramid has 6 edges and 6 vertices, how many faces does it have?

4 faces

8. Find the surface area.
1 cm   3 cm   6 cm

54 cm^2

9. Find the surface area.
3.5 yd   3.5 yd   3.5 yd

73.5 yd^2

10. Identify the figure from the net.

square pyramid

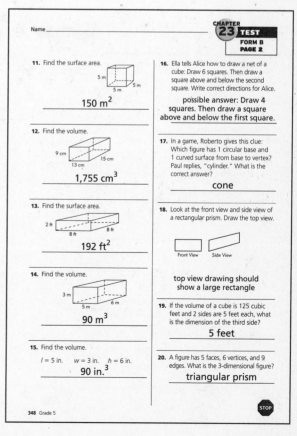

Name _____

11. Find the surface area.
5 m   5 m   5 m

150 m^2

12. Find the volume.
9 cm   13 cm   15 cm

1,755 cm^3

13. Find the surface area.
2 ft   8 ft   8 ft

192 ft^2

14. Find the volume.
3 m   5 m   6 m

90 m^3

15. Find the volume.
$l = 5$ in. $w = 3$ in. $h = 6$ in.

90 in.^{3}

16. Ella tells Alice how to draw a net of a cube: Draw 6 squares. Then draw a square above and below the second square. Write correct directions for Alice.

possible answer: Draw 4 squares. Then draw a square above and below the first square.

17. In a game, Roberto gives this clue: Which figure has 1 circular base and 1 curved surface from base to vertex? Paul replies, "cylinder." What is the correct answer?

cone

18. Look at the front view and side view of a rectangular prism. Draw the top view.
Front View   Side View

top view drawing should show a large rectangle

19. If the volume of a cube is 125 cubic feet and 2 sides are 5 feet each, what is the dimension of the third side?

5 feet

20. A figure has 5 faces, 6 vertices, and 9 edges. What is the 3-dimensional figure?

triangular prism

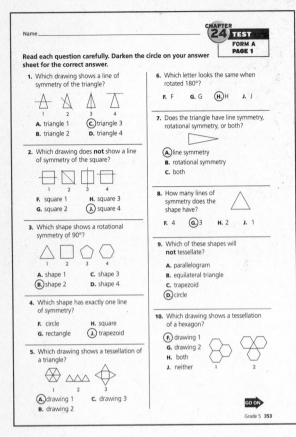

Read each question carefully. Darken the circle on your answer sheet for the correct answer.

1. Which drawing shows a line of symmetry of the triangle?

   1   2   3   4

   A. triangle 1   **C.** triangle 3
   B. triangle 2   **D.** triangle 4

2. Which drawing does **not** show a line of symmetry of the square?

   1   2   3   4

   F. square 1   **H.** square 3
   G. square 2   **J.** square 4

3. Which shape shows a rotational symmetry of 90°?

   1   2   3   4

   A. shape 1   **C.** shape 3
   B. shape 2   **D.** shape 4

4. Which shape has exactly one line of symmetry?

   F. circle   **H.** square
   G. rectangle   **J.** trapezoid

5. Which drawing shows a tessellation of a triangle?

   1   2   3

   A. drawing 1   **C.** drawing 3
   B. drawing 2

6. Which letter looks the same when rotated 180°?

   F. F   **G.** G   **H.** H   **J.** J

7. Does the triangle have line symmetry, rotational symmetry, or both?

   A. line symmetry
   B. rotational symmetry
   C. both

8. How many lines of symmetry does the shape have?

   F. 4   **G.** 3   **H.** 2   **J.** 1

9. Which of these shapes will **not** tessellate?

   A. parallelogram
   B. equilateral triangle
   C. trapezoid
   D. circle

10. Which drawing shows a tessellation of a hexagon?

    1   2

    F. drawing 1
    G. drawing 2
    H. both
    J. neither

GO ON

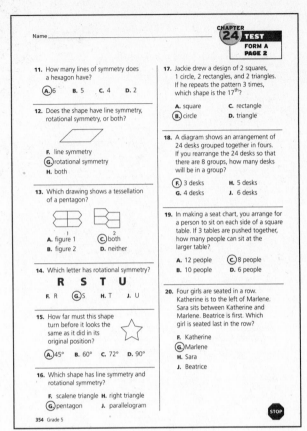

11. How many lines of symmetry does a hexagon have?

    A. 6   **B.** 5   **C.** 4   **D.** 2

12. Does the shape have line symmetry, rotational symmetry, or both?

    F. line symmetry
    G. rotational symmetry
    H. both

13. Which drawing shows a tessellation of a pentagon?

    1   2

    A. figure 1   **C.** both
    B. figure 2   **D.** neither

14. Which letter has rotational symmetry?

    R   S   T   U

    F. R   **G.** S   **H.** T   **J.** U

15. How far must this shape turn before it looks the same as it did in its original position?

    A. 45°   **B.** 60°   **C.** 72°   **D.** 90°

16. Which shape has line symmetry and rotational symmetry?

    F. scalene triangle   **H.** right triangle
    G. pentagon   **J.** parallelogram

17. Jackie drew a design of 2 squares, 1 circle, 2 rectangles, and 2 triangles. If he repeats the pattern 3 times, which shape is the 17th?

    A. square   **C.** rectangle
    B. circle   **D.** triangle

18. A diagram shows an arrangement of 24 desks grouped together in fours. If you rearrange the 24 desks so that there are 8 groups, how many desks will be in a group?

    F. 3 desks   **H.** 5 desks
    G. 4 desks   **J.** 6 desks

19. In making a seat chart, you arrange for a person to sit on each side of a square table. If 3 tables are pushed together, how many people can sit at the larger table?

    A. 12 people   **C.** 8 people
    B. 10 people   **D.** 6 people

20. Four girls are seated in a row. Katherine is to the left of Marlene. Sara sits between Katherine and Marlene. Beatrice is first. Which girl is seated last in the row?

    F. Katherine
    G. Marlene
    H. Sara
    J. Beatrice

STOP

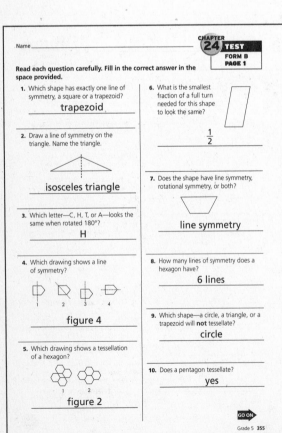

Read each question carefully. Fill in the correct answer in the space provided.

1. Which shape has exactly one line of symmetry, a square or a trapezoid?

   trapezoid

2. Draw a line of symmetry on the triangle. Name the triangle.

   isosceles triangle

3. Which letter—C, H, T, or A—looks the same when rotated 180°?

   H

4. Which drawing shows a line of symmetry?

   1   2   3   4

   figure 4

5. Which drawing shows a tessellation of a hexagon?

   1   2

   figure 2

6. What is the smallest fraction of a full turn needed for this shape to look the same?

   1/2

7. Does the shape have line symmetry, rotational symmetry, or both?

   line symmetry

8. How many lines of symmetry does a hexagon have?

   6 lines

9. Which shape—a circle, a triangle, or a trapezoid will **not** tessellate?

   circle

10. Does a pentagon tessellate?

    yes

GO ON

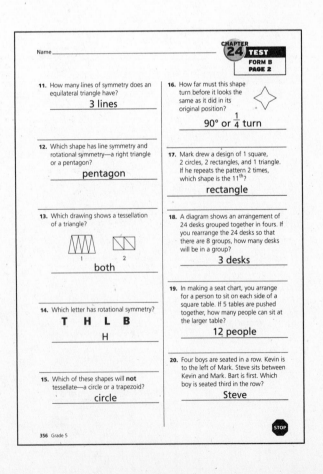

11. How many lines of symmetry does an equilateral triangle have?

    3 lines

12. Which shape has line symmetry and rotational symmetry—a right triangle or a pentagon?

    pentagon

13. Which drawing shows a tessellation of a triangle?

    1   2

    both

14. Which letter has rotational symmetry?

    T   H   L   B

    H

15. Which of these shapes will **not** tessellate—a circle or a trapezoid?

    circle

16. How far must this shape turn before it looks the same as it did in its original position?

    90° or 1/4 turn

17. Mark drew a design of 1 square, 2 circles, 2 rectangles, and 1 triangle. If he repeats the pattern 2 times, which shape is the 11th?

    rectangle

18. A diagram shows an arrangement of 24 desks grouped together in fours. If you rearrange the 24 desks so that there are 8 groups, how many desks will be in a group?

    3 desks

19. In making a seat chart, you arrange for a person to sit on each side of a square table. If 5 tables are pushed together, how many people can sit at the larger table?

    12 people

20. Four boys are seated in a row. Kevin is to the left of Mark. Steve sits between Kevin and Mark. Bart is first. Which boy is seated third in the row?

    Steve

STOP

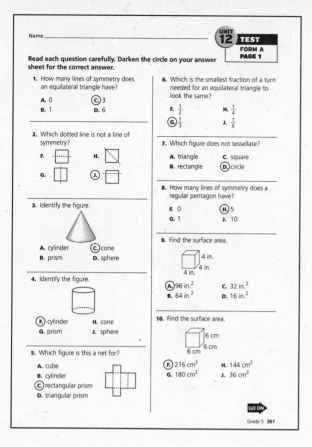

Name_____

UNIT 12 TEST FORM A PAGE 1

Read each question carefully. Darken the circle on your answer sheet for the correct answer.

1. How many lines of symmetry does an equilateral triangle have?

A. 0　　(C.) 3
B. 1　　D. 6

2. Which dotted line is not a line of symmetry?

F.　　H.
G.　　(J.)

3. Identify the figure.

A. cylinder　　(C.) cone
B. prism　　D. sphere

4. Identify the figure.

(F.) cylinder　　H. cone
G. prism　　J. sphere

5. Which figure is this a net for?

A. cube
B. cylinder
(C.) rectangular prism
D. triangular prism

6. Which is the smallest fraction of a turn needed for an equilateral triangle to look the same?

F. $\frac{1}{2}$　　H. $\frac{1}{4}$
(G.) $\frac{1}{3}$　　J. $\frac{1}{6}$

7. Which figure does not tessellate?

A. triangle　　C. square
B. rectangle　　(D.) circle

8. How many lines of symmetry does a regular pentagon have?

F. 0　　(H.) 5
G. 1　　J. 10

9. Find the surface area.

4 in.　4 in.　4 in.

(A.) 96 in.^{2}　　C. 32 in.^{2}
B. 64 in.^{2}　　D. 16 in.^{2}

10. Find the surface area.

6 cm　6 cm　6 cm

(F.) 216 cm^2　　H. 144 cm^2
G. 180 cm^2　　J. 36 cm^2

GO ON

Grade 5　**361**

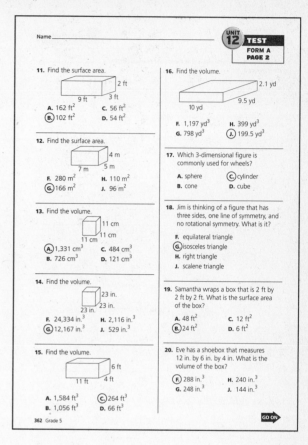

Name_____

UNIT 12 TEST FORM A PAGE 2

11. Find the surface area.

9 ft　2 ft　3 ft

A. 162 ft^2　　C. 56 ft^2
(B.) 102 ft^2　　D. 54 ft^2

12. Find the surface area.

7 m　4 m　5 m

F. 280 m^2　　H. 110 m^2
(G.) 166 m^2　　J. 96 m^2

13. Find the volume.

11 cm　11 cm　11 cm

(A.) 1,331 cm^3　　C. 484 cm^3
B. 726 cm^3　　D. 121 cm^3

14. Find the volume.

23 in.　23 in.　23 in.

F. 24,334 in.^{3}　　H. 2,116 in.^{3}
(G.) 12,167 in.^{3}　　J. 529 in.^{3}

15. Find the volume.

11 ft　6 ft　4 ft

A. 1,584 ft^3　　(C.) 264 ft^3
B. 1,056 ft^3　　D. 66 ft^3

16. Find the volume.

10 yd　2.1 yd　9.5 yd

F. 1,197 yd^3　　H. 399 yd^3
G. 798 yd^3　　(J.) 199.5 yd^3

17. Which 3-dimensional figure is commonly used for wheels?

A. sphere　　(C.) cylinder
B. cone　　D. cube

18. Jim is thinking of a figure that has three sides, one line of symmetry, and no rotational symmetry. What is it?

F. equilateral triangle
(G.) isosceles triangle
H. right triangle
J. scalene triangle

19. Samantha wraps a box that is 2 ft by 2 ft by 2 ft. What is the surface area of the box?

A. 48 ft^2　　C. 12 ft^2
(B.) 24 ft^2　　D. 6 ft^2

20. Eve has a shoebox that measures 12 in. by 6 in. by 4 in. What is the volume of the box?

(F.) 288 in.^{3}　　H. 240 in.^{3}
G. 248 in.^{3}　　J. 144 in.^{3}

GO ON

362　Grade 5

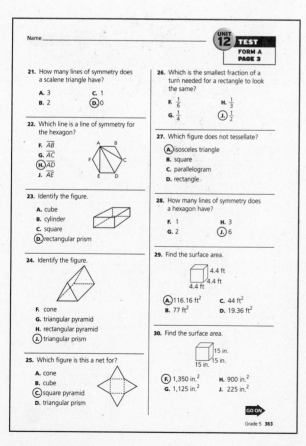

Name_____

UNIT 12 TEST FORM A PAGE 3

21. How many lines of symmetry does a scalene triangle have?

A. 3　　C. 1
B. 2　　(D.) 0

22. Which line is a line of symmetry for the hexagon?

F. $\overline{AB}$
G. $\overline{AC}$
(H.) $\overline{AD}$
J. $\overline{AE}$

23. Identify the figure.

A. cube
B. cylinder
C. square
(D.) rectangular prism

24. Identify the figure.

F. cone
G. triangular pyramid
H. rectangular pyramid
(J.) triangular prism

25. Which figure is this a net for?

A. cone
B. cube
(C.) square pyramid
D. triangular prism

26. Which is the smallest fraction of a turn needed for a rectangle to look the same?

F. $\frac{1}{6}$　　H. $\frac{1}{3}$
G. $\frac{1}{4}$　　(J.) $\frac{1}{2}$

27. Which figure does not tessellate?

(A.) isosceles triangle
B. square
C. parallelogram
D. rectangle

28. How many lines of symmetry does a hexagon have?

F. 1　　H. 3
G. 2　　(J.) 6

29. Find the surface area.

4.4 ft　4.4 ft　4.4 ft

(A.) 116.16 ft^2　　C. 44 ft^2
B. 77 ft^2　　D. 19.36 ft^2

30. Find the surface area.

15 in.　15 in.　15 in.

(F.) 1,350 in.^{2}　　H. 900 in.^{2}
G. 1,125 in.^{2}　　J. 225 in.^{2}

GO ON

Grade 5　**363**

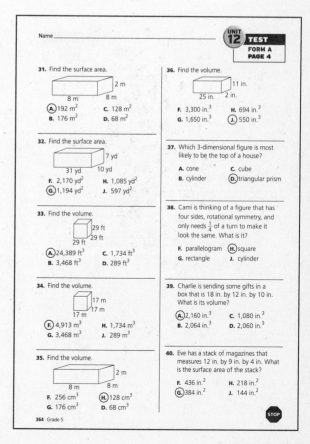

Name_____

UNIT 12 TEST FORM A PAGE 4

31. Find the surface area.

8 m　2 m　8 m

(A.) 192 m^2　　C. 128 m^2
B. 176 m^2　　D. 68 m^2

32. Find the surface area.

31 yd　7 yd　10 yd

F. 2,170 yd^2　　H. 1,085 yd^2
(G.) 1,194 yd^2　　J. 597 yd^2

33. Find the volume.

29 ft　29 ft　29 ft

(A.) 24,389 ft^3　　C. 1,734 ft^3
B. 3,468 ft^3　　D. 289 ft^3

34. Find the volume.

17 m　17 m　17 m

(F.) 4,913 m^3　　H. 1,734 m^3
G. 3,468 m^3　　J. 289 m^3

35. Find the volume.

8 m　2 m　8 m

F. 256 cm^3　　(H.) 128 cm^3
G. 176 cm^3　　D. 68 cm^3

36. Find the volume.

25 in.　11 in.　2 in.

F. 3,300 in.^{3}　　H. 694 in.^{3}
G. 1,650 in.^{3}　　(J.) 550 in.^{3}

37. Which 3-dimensional figure is most likely to be the top of a house?

A. cone　　C. cube
B. cylinder　　(D.) triangular prism

38. Cami is thinking of a figure that has four sides, rotational symmetry, and only needs $\frac{1}{4}$ of a turn to make it look the same. What is it?

F. parallelogram　　(H.) square
G. rectangle　　J. cylinder

39. Charlie is sending some gifts in a box that is 18 in. by 12 in. by 10 in. What is its volume?

(A.) 2,160 in.^{3}　　C. 1,080 in.^{3}
B. 2,064 in.^{3}　　D. 2,060 in.^{3}

40. Eve has a stack of magazines that measures 12 in. by 9 in. by 4 in. What is the surface area of the stack?

F. 436 in.^{2}　　H. 218 in.^{2}
(G.) 384 in.^{2}　　J. 144 in.^{2}

STOP

364　Grade 5

Grade 5　**483**

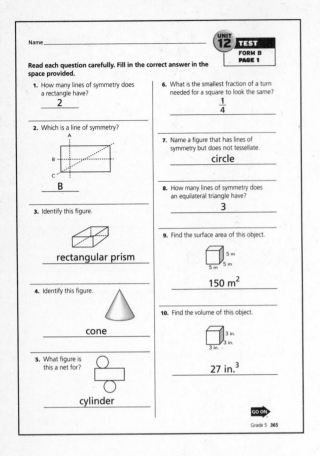

Name_____

Read each question carefully. Fill in the correct answer in the space provided.

1. How many lines of symmetry does a rectangle have?

2

2. Which is a line of symmetry?

B

3. Identify this figure.

rectangular prism

4. Identify this figure.

cone

5. What figure is this a net for?

cylinder

6. What is the smallest fraction of a turn needed for a square to look the same?

$\frac{1}{4}$

7. Name a figure that has lines of symmetry but does not tessellate.

circle

8. How many lines of symmetry does an equilateral triangle have?

3

9. Find the surface area of this object.

150 m^2

10. Find the volume of this object.

27 in.^{3}

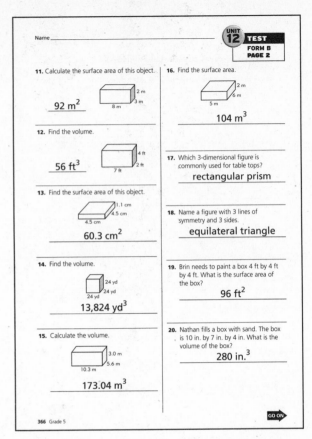

11. Calculate the surface area of this object.

92 m^2

12. Find the volume.

56 ft^3

13. Find the surface area of this object.

60.3 cm^2

14. Find the volume.

13,824 yd^3

15. Calculate the volume.

173.04 m^3

16. Find the surface area.

104 m^3

17. Which 3-dimensional figure is commonly used for table tops?

rectangular prism

18. Name a figure with 3 lines of symmetry and 3 sides.

equilateral triangle

19. Brin needs to paint a box 4 ft by 4 ft by 4 ft. What is the surface area of the box?

96 ft^2

20. Nathan fills a box with sand. The box is 10 in. by 7 in. by 4 in. What is the volume of the box?

280 in.^{3}

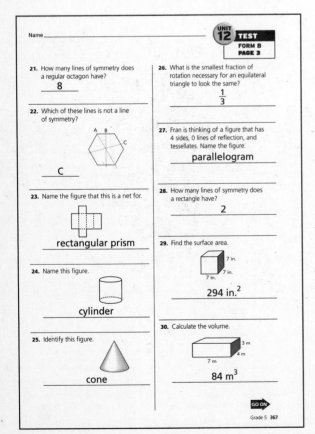

21. How many lines of symmetry does a regular octagon have?

8

22. Which of these lines is not a line of symmetry?

C

23. Name the figure that this is a net for.

rectangular prism

24. Name this figure.

cylinder

25. Identify this figure.

cone

26. What is the smallest fraction of rotation necessary for an equilateral triangle to look the same?

$\frac{1}{3}$

27. Fran is thinking of a figure that has 4 sides, 0 lines of reflection, and tessellates. Name the figure.

parallelogram

28. How many lines of symmetry does a rectangle have?

2

29. Find the surface area.

294 in.^{2}

30. Calculate the volume.

84 m^3

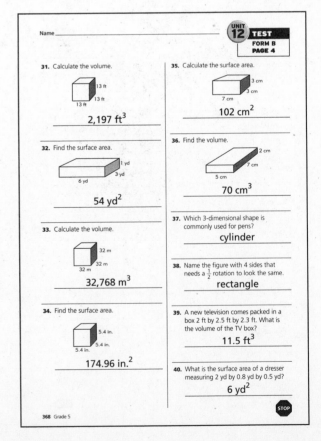

31. Calculate the volume.

2,197 ft^3

32. Find the surface area.

54 yd^2

33. Calculate the volume.

32,768 m^3

34. Find the surface area.

174.96 in.^{2}

35. Calculate the surface area.

102 cm^2

36. Find the volume.

70 cm^3

37. Which 3-dimensional shape is commonly used for pens?

cylinder

38. Name the figure with 4 sides that needs a $\frac{1}{2}$ rotation to look the same.

rectangle

39. A new television comes packed in a box 2 ft by 2.5 ft by 2.3 ft. What is the volume of the TV box?

11.5 ft^3

40. What is the surface area of a dresser measuring 2 yd by 0.8 yd by 0.5 yd?

6 yd^2

Chapter 25

FORM A, PAGE 1

Name _____

Read each question carefully. Darken the circle on your answer sheet for the correct answer.

1. Which ratio is equivalent to 9 to 15?

A. $\frac{2}{3}$ C. $\frac{2}{5}$

B. $\frac{3}{5}$ D. $\frac{10}{30}$

(B circled)

2. Which number makes the ratio equivalent?

$1:5 = n:20$

F. 4   H. 10

G. 5   J. 15

(F circled)

3. Find the unit rate for $64 in 4 hours.

A. $16 per 1h

B. $20 per 1h

C. $22 per 1h

D. $24 per 1h

(A circled)

4. Find the unit rate for 300 miles in 5 hours.

F. 100 mi per 1 h

G. 60 mi per 1 h

H. 50 mi per 1 h

J. 40 mi per 1 h

(G circled)

5. Find the unit rate for 180 miles on 5 gallons of gas.

A. 60 mi per 1 gal

B. 56 mi per 1 gal

C. 36 mi per 1 gal

D. 30 mi per 1 gal

(C circled)

6. Which number makes the ratios equivalent?

$\frac{n}{10} = \frac{6}{30}$

F. 6   H. 3

G. 5   J. 2

(J circled)

7. Which ratio is equivalent to 5:9?

A. 15:19   C. 25:45

B. 30:45   D. 45:90

(C circled)

8. Find the unit rate for 72 miles in 8 days.

F. 16 mi per 1 d

G. 12 mi per 1 d

H. 9 mi per 1 d

J. 8 mi per 1 d

(H circled)

9. Find the unit rate for $360 in 12 months.

A. $24 per 1 mo

B. $30 per 1 mo

C. $32 per 1 mo

D. $36 per 1 mo

(B circled)

10. Which two ratios are equivalent to 3:4?

F. $\frac{8}{12}$ and $\frac{12}{16}$ H. $\frac{9}{12}$ and $\frac{21}{32}$

G. $\frac{9}{12}$ and $\frac{24}{32}$ J. $\frac{10}{12}$ and $\frac{20}{24}$

(G circled)

GO ON

FORM A, PAGE 2

Name _____

11. Which ratio is equivalent to $\frac{4}{3}$?

A. $\frac{1}{2}$ B. $\frac{3}{4}$ C. $\frac{5}{4}$ D. $\frac{8}{6}$

(D circled)

12. Find the unit rate for 90 meters in 5 minutes.

F. 15 m per 1 min   H. 30 m per 1 min

G. 18 m per 1 min   J. 45 m per 1 min

(G circled)

13. Alicia is making a floor plan of a sunroom. She is using the scale 2 in. = 3 feet. One wall is 9 feet. How long should it be on her floor plan?

A. 3 inches   C. 6 inches

B. 4 inches   D. 9 inches

(C circled)

14. Terry makes a map of her neighborhood. She uses a scale of 1 in. = 1 mi. If the neighborhood convenience store is 5 miles away from her house, where will she draw the store on her map?

F. 2 inches away from her house

G. 3 inches away from her house

H. 4 inches away from her house

J. 5 inches away from her house

(J circled)

15. Randy is making a floor plan of a clubhouse. He is using the scale 2 cm = 1 m. The length of the clubhouse is 4 cm on the plan. How long is the actual length in meters?

A. 8 cm   B. 2 m   C. 3 m   D. 4 m

(B circled)

16. On a map, Lake Victoria is 1.5 inches long. The actual length of the lake is 15 miles. What is the scale on the map?

F. 1 inch = 5 miles   H. 1 inch = 15 miles

G. 1 inch = 10 miles   J. 1 inch = 20 miles

(G circled)

17. Margo can drive 20 miles in 30 minutes. Is it reasonable to expect that Margo will drive 50 miles in 1 hour? If not, how many miles will she drive in an hour?

A. yes, 50 miles   C. no, 40 miles

B. no, 30 miles   D. no, 60 miles

(C circled)

18. A convenience store sells a package of 12 pocket tissues for $3.00. At the local supermarket, a package of 3 pocket tissues cost $.60. Lane believes that the convenience store is the better buy. Explain why Lane's answer is not reasonable.

F. convenience store cost $.25 each, supermarket $.20 each

G. convenience store cost $.30 each, supermarket $.25 each

H. convenience store cost $.30 each, supermarket $.20 each

J. convenience store cost $.25 each, supermarket $.25 each

(F circled)

19. Tyler spends $15.75 on a CD. She gives the clerk $20 and expects to receive $5.75 in change. Tyler's answer is not reasonable. What change should she receive?

A. $4.75   B. $4.25   C. $3.75   D. $3.25

(B circled)

20. Mark can run 5 miles in 50 minutes. Why is it reasonable to expect that Mark will run 2.5 miles in 25 minutes?

F. $\frac{5}{25} = \frac{2.5}{50}$ H. $\frac{50}{25} = \frac{5}{2.5}$

G. $\frac{25}{5} = \frac{50}{10}$ J. $\frac{2.5}{5} = \frac{25}{50}$

(J circled)

STOP

FORM B, PAGE 1

Name _____

Read each question carefully. Fill in the correct answer in the space provided.

1. Find an equivalent ratio to 8 to 24.

possible answer: $\frac{1}{3}$

2. Find an equivalent ratio.

$1:7 = n:35$

5

3. Find the unit rate.

$56 in 7 h = $8 per 1 h

4. Find the unit rate.

400 mi in 8 h = 50 mi per 1 h

5. Find the unit rate.

168 mi on 6 gal = 28 mi per 1 gal

6. Find an equivalent ratio.

$\frac{n}{10} = \frac{24}{60}$

4

7. Find an equivalent ratio.

$5:8 = n:40$

25

8. Find the unit rate.

54 mi in 6 d = 9 mi per 1 d

9. Find the unit rate.

$720 in 1 y = $60 in 1 mo

10. Name two equivalent ratios for 5:6.

possible answers: $\frac{10}{12}$, $\frac{20}{24}$

GO ON

FORM B, PAGE 2

Name _____

11. Name an equivalent ratio for $\frac{7}{5}$.

possible answer: $\frac{14}{10}$

12. Find the unit rate.

105 ft in 3 min = 35 ft per 1 min

13. Alex is making a floor plan of a playroom. He is using the scale 3 in. = 6 feet. One wall is 9 feet. How long should it be on her floor plan?

4.5 inches

14. Kerry makes a map of her neighborhood. She uses a scale of 1 in. = 1 mi. If the neighborhood gas station is 3.5 miles away from her house, how far away from her house will the gas station be on her map?

3.5 inches

15. Ralph is making a floor plan of a tree house. He is using the scale 3 cm = 1 m. The length of the tree house is 9 cm on the plan. How long is the actual length in meters?

3 m

16. On a map, Lake Lorraine is 3.5 inches long. The actual length of the lake is 17.5 miles. What is the scale on the map?

1 inch = 5 mi

17. Gale can drive 25 miles in 30 minutes. Is it reasonable to expect that Gale will drive 60 miles in 1 hour? If not, how many miles will she drive in an hour?

not reasonable, 50 mi

18. One office supply store sells a package of 12 small note pads for $4.00. Another office supply store has a special of 3 small notepads for $1.05. Selena believes that 3 small notepads for $1.05 is the better buy. Explain why Selena's answer is not reasonable.

possible answer: $\frac{$4.00}{12} = $.33$ each

and $\frac{$1.05}{3} = $.35$ each

19. Amanda spends $35.75 on 2 CDs. She gives the clerk $40 and expects to receive $5.75 in change. Amanda's answer is not reasonable. What change should she receive?

miscalculated change, $4.25

20. Maura can swim 18 laps in 15 minutes. Why is it reasonable to expect that Maura will swim 36 laps in 30 minutes?

possible answer: $18 \times 30 = 15 \times 36$

STOP

Chapter 26

Form A — Page 1

Name _____

CHAPTER 26 TEST
FORM A
PAGE 1

Read each question carefully. Darken the circle on your answer sheet for the correct answer.

Use the spinner for exercises 1–4.

1. Which outcome is most likely?

A. blue   C. yellow
B. red

2. Which possible outcome is least likely?

F. blue   **H.** yellow
G. red

3. What is the probability of spinning a blue?

A. $\frac{1}{10}$ B. $\frac{1}{5}$ **C.** $\frac{2}{5}$ D. $\frac{1}{2}$

4. What is the probability of spinning a red or yellow?

F. $\frac{3}{5}$ G. $\frac{1}{2}$ H. $\frac{2}{5}$ J. $\frac{1}{5}$

Questions 5–11 are about a number cube with the numbers 1, 2, 3, 4, 5, and 6 on the faces.

5. What is the probability of tossing an even number?

A. $\frac{1}{6}$ B. $\frac{1}{3}$ **C.** $\frac{1}{2}$ D. $\frac{5}{6}$

6. What is the probability of tossing a number less than 5?

F. $\frac{1}{6}$ H. $\frac{1}{2}$
G. $\frac{1}{3}$ **J.** $\frac{2}{3}$

7. What is the probability of tossing a 1 or a 4?

A. $\frac{1}{3}$ C. $\frac{2}{3}$
B. $\frac{1}{2}$ D. $\frac{5}{6}$

8. What is the probability of tossing a 0?

F. certain   H. more likely
G. impossible   J. less likely

9. About how many times will you toss an even number in 30 tosses?

A. about 25 times **C.** about 15 times
B. about 20 times D. about 10 times

10. If you toss the number cube 100 times, how many times do you predict you will toss a number greater than 4?

F. about 22 times H. about 55 times
G. about 33 times J. about 66 times

11. If you toss the number cube 24 times, how many times do you predict you will toss a 3?

A. about 12 times C. about 6 times
B. about 8 times **D.** about 4 times

GO ON

Form A — Page 2

Name _____

CHAPTER 26 TEST
FORM A
PAGE 2

Questions 12–15, are about 2 number cubes with the numbers 1, 2, 3, 4, 5, and 6 on the faces.

12. How many outcomes are possible if you toss both number cubes?

F. 72   H. 12
G. 36   J. 6

13. What is the probability of tossing a sum of 5?

A. $\frac{1}{9}$ C. $\frac{1}{3}$
B. $\frac{1}{4}$ D. $\frac{1}{2}$

14. Which sum of the two number cubes are you most likely to toss?

F. 9   **H.** 7
G. 8   J. 6

15. Suppose you add a third number cube, what are the total possible outcomes?

A. 8   **C.** 216
B. 42   D. 252

16. You pick a marble from a bag filled with marbles that come in 4 colors and 2 patterns. What is the number of possible outcomes?

F. 6   H. 12
G. 8   J. 20

Use the data for problems 17–20.

Frequency of Vowels from 20 Lines of Text

Vowel	Frequency
a	120
e	115
i	114
o	110
u	98

17. Which 2 vowels appear most in print?

A. i, u   B. a, o   C. e, i   **D.** a, e

18. Which vowel had a frequency of 10 less than vowel *a*?

F. vowel *e*   **H.** vowel *o*
G. vowel *i*   J. vowel *u*

19. Suppose you added the letter *y* to the experiment. How would the frequencies for the other vowels change?

A. change dramatically
B. more vowel *a*
C. more vowel *u*
D. remain the same

20. If you used 20 different lines of text from the same book, what is the likely outcome?

F. similar frequencies
G. different frequencies
H. more vowel *i* used
J. more vowel *e* used

STOP

Form B — Page 1

Name _____

CHAPTER 26 TEST
FORM B
PAGE 1

Read each question carefully. Fill in the correct answer in the space provided.

Use the spinner for exercises 1–4.

1. Which outcome is least likely?

yellow

2. Which outcome is most likely?

blue

3. What is the probability of spinning a red?

$\frac{3}{10}$

4. What is the probability of spinning a blue or a yellow?

$\frac{7}{10}$

Questions 5–11, are about a number cube with the numbers 1, 2, 3, 4, 5, and 6 on the faces.

5. What is the probability of tossing an odd number?

$\frac{1}{2}$

6. What is the probability of tossing a number greater than 4?

$\frac{1}{3}$

7. What is the probability of tossing a 2 or a 5?

$\frac{1}{3}$

8. Is the probability of tossing a 0 *certain* or *impossible*?

impossible

9. About how many times will you toss an even number in 60 tosses?

30 tosses

10. If you toss the number cube 100 times, how many times do you predict you will toss a number less than 4?

50 times

11. If you toss the number cube 30 times, how many times do you predict you will toss a 5?

5 times

GO ON

Form B — Page 2

Name _____

CHAPTER 26 TEST
FORM B
PAGE 2

Questions 12–15, are about 2 number cubes with the numbers 1, 2, 3, 4, 5, and 6 on the faces.

12. How many outcomes are possible if you toss both number cubes?

36 outcomes

13. What is the possibility of tossing a sum of 4?

$\frac{1}{12}$

14. Which sum of the two number cubes are you least likely to toss?

2 or 12

15. If there are 1,296 possible outcomes for 4 number cubes, how many outcomes are there for 3 number cubes?

216

16. If you pick a marble from a bag filled with marbles that come in 5 colors and 3 patterns, what is the number of possible outcomes?

15

Use the data for problems 17–20.

Frequency of Vowels from 20 Lines of Text

Vowel	Frequency
a	100
e	95
i	94
o	84
u	72

17. Which 2 vowels appear least in print?

o, u

18. Which vowel had a frequency of 6 less than vowel *a*?

i

19. Suppose you added the letter *y* to the experiment. Would the frequencies for the other vowels change?

No. They would remain the same.

20. If you used 20 different lines of text from the same book in the experiment, what would the results probably show—frequencies that are *about the same* or *very different*?

about the same

STOP

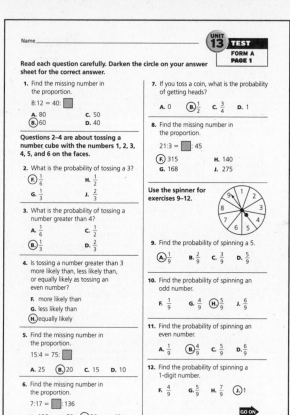

Name_____

Read each question carefully. Darken the circle on your answer sheet for the correct answer.

1. Find the missing number in the proportion.

8:12 = 40: ▊

A. 80   C. 50
B. 60   D. 40

Questions 2–4 are about tossing a number cube with the numbers 1, 2, 3, 4, 5, and 6 on the faces.

2. What is the probability of tossing a 3?

F. $\frac{1}{6}$ H. $\frac{1}{2}$

G. $\frac{1}{3}$ J. $\frac{2}{3}$

3. What is the probability of tossing a number greater than 4?

A. $\frac{1}{6}$ C. $\frac{1}{2}$

B. $\frac{1}{3}$ D. $\frac{2}{3}$

4. Is tossing a number greater than 3 more likely than, less likely than, or equally likely as tossing an even number?

F. more likely than
G. less likely than
H. equally likely

5. Find the missing number in the proportion.

15:4 = 75: ▊

A. 25   B. 20   C. 15   D. 10

6. Find the missing number in the proportion.

7:17 = ▊ :136

F. 126   G. 70   H. 56   J. 49

7. If you toss a coin, what is the probability of getting heads?

A. 0   B. $\frac{1}{2}$ C. $\frac{3}{4}$ D. 1

8. Find the missing number in the proportion.

21:3 = ▊ : 45

F. 315   H. 140
G. 168   J. 275

Use the spinner for exercises 9–12.

9. Find the probability of spinning a 5.

A. $\frac{1}{9}$ B. $\frac{2}{9}$ C. $\frac{3}{9}$ D. $\frac{5}{9}$

10. Find the probability of spinning an odd number.

F. $\frac{1}{9}$ G. $\frac{4}{9}$ H. $\frac{5}{9}$ J. $\frac{6}{9}$

11. Find the probability of spinning an even number.

A. $\frac{1}{9}$ B. $\frac{4}{9}$ C. $\frac{5}{9}$ D. $\frac{6}{9}$

12. Find the probability of spinning a 1-digit number.

F. $\frac{4}{9}$ G. $\frac{5}{9}$ H. $\frac{7}{9}$ J. 1

GO ON

Name_____

Use the scale drawing for exercises 13–16.

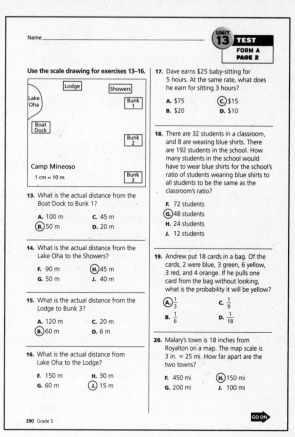

Camp Mineoso
1 cm = 10 m

13. What is the actual distance from the Boat Dock to Bunk 1?

A. 100 m   C. 45 m
B. 50 m   D. 20 m

14. What is the actual distance from the Lake Oha to the Showers?

F. 90 m   H. 45 m
G. 50 m   J. 40 m

15. What is the actual distance from the Lodge to Bunk 3?

A. 120 m   C. 20 m
B. 60 m   D. 6 m

16. What is the actual distance from Lake Oha to the Lodge?

F. 150 m   H. 30 m
G. 60 m   J. 15 m

17. Dave earns $25 baby-sitting for 5 hours. At the same rate, what does he earn for sitting 3 hours?

A. $75   C. $15
B. $20   D. $10

18. There are 32 students in a classroom, and 8 are wearing blue shirts. There are 192 students in the school. How many students in the school would have to wear blue shirts for the school's ratio of students wearing blue shirts to all students to be the same as the classroom's ratio?

F. 72 students
G. 48 students
H. 24 students
J. 12 students

19. Andrew put 18 cards in a bag. Of the cards, 2 were blue, 3 green, 6 yellow, 3 red, and 4 orange. If he pulls one card from the bag without looking, what is the probability it will be yellow?

A. $\frac{1}{3}$ C. $\frac{1}{9}$

B. $\frac{1}{6}$ D. $\frac{1}{18}$

20. Malary's town is 18 inches from Royalton on a map. The map scale is 3 in. = 25 mi. How far apart are the two towns?

F. 450 mi   H. 150 mi
G. 200 mi   J. 100 mi

GO ON

Name_____

21. Find the missing number in the proportion.

5:11 = 35: ▊

A. 77   C. 50
B. 55   D. 41

Questions 22–24 are about tossing a number cube with the numbers 1, 2, 3, 4, 5, and 6 on the faces.

22. What is the probability of tossing a 2?

F. $\frac{2}{3}$ H. $\frac{1}{3}$

G. $\frac{1}{2}$ J. $\frac{1}{6}$

23. What is the probability of tossing a number less than 3?

A. $\frac{2}{3}$ C. $\frac{1}{3}$

B. $\frac{1}{2}$ D. $\frac{1}{6}$

24. Is tossing an odd number more likely than, less likely than, or equally likely as tossing a number greater than 4?

F. more likely than
G. less likely than
H. equally likely

25. Find the missing number in the proportion.

25:3 = 100: ▊

A. 78   C. 12
B. 30   D. 6

26. Find the missing number in the proportion

9:14 = ▊ :126

F. 121   G. 81   H. 72   J. 36

27. If you toss a coin, what is the probability of getting tails?

A. 1   B. $\frac{3}{4}$ C. $\frac{1}{2}$ D. 0

28. Find the missing number in the proportion.

40:8 = ▊ :32

F. 160   G. 80   H. 32   J. 22

Use the spinner for exercises 29–32.

29. Find the probability of spinning a 7.

A. $\frac{3}{8}$ B. $\frac{1}{4}$ C. $\frac{1}{8}$ D. 0

30. Find the probability of spinning an odd number.

F. $\frac{5}{8}$ G. $\frac{4}{8}$ H. $\frac{3}{8}$ J. $\frac{1}{8}$

31. Find the probability of spinning an even number.

A. $\frac{5}{8}$ B. $\frac{3}{8}$ C. $\frac{1}{8}$ D. $\frac{2}{8}$

GO ON

Name_____

32. Find the probability of spinning a 1-digit number.

F. $\frac{1}{8}$ G. $\frac{2}{8}$ H. $\frac{3}{8}$ J. $\frac{4}{8}$

Use the scale drawing for exercises 33–36.

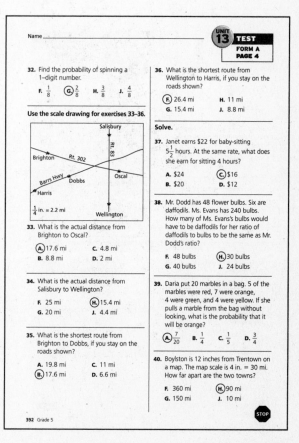

$\frac{1}{4}$ in. = 2.2 mi

33. What is the actual distance from Brighton to Oscal?

A. 17.6 mi   C. 4.8 mi
B. 8.8 mi   D. 2 mi

34. What is the actual distance from Salisbury to Wellington?

F. 25 mi   H. 15.4 mi
G. 20 mi   J. 4.4 mi

35. What is the shortest route from Brighton to Dobbs, if you stay on the roads shown?

A. 19.8 mi   C. 11 mi
B. 17.6 mi   D. 6.6 mi

36. What is the shortest route from Wellington to Harris, if you stay on the roads shown?

F. 26.4 mi   H. 11 mi
G. 15.4 mi   J. 8.8 mi

Solve.

37. Janet earns $22 for baby-sitting $5\frac{1}{2}$ hours. At the same rate, what does she earn for sitting 4 hours?

A. $24   C. $16
B. $20   D. $12

38. Mr. Dodd has 48 flower bulbs. Six are daffodils. Ms. Evans has 240 bulbs. How many of Ms. Evans's bulbs would have to be daffodils for her ratio of daffodils to bulbs to be the same as Mr. Dodd's ratio?

F. 48 bulbs   H. 30 bulbs
G. 40 bulbs   J. 24 bulbs

39. Daria put 20 marbles in a bag. 5 of the marbles were red, 7 were orange, 4 were green, and 4 were yellow. If she pulls a marble from the bag without looking, what is the probability that it will be orange?

A. $\frac{7}{20}$ B. $\frac{1}{4}$ C. $\frac{1}{5}$ D. $\frac{3}{4}$

40. Boylston is 12 inches from Trentown on a map. The map scale is 4 in. = 30 mi. How far apart are the two towns?

F. 360 mi   H. 90 mi
G. 150 mi   J. 10 mi

STOP

Page 1

Name _____

Read each question carefully. Fill in the correct answer in the space provided.

1. Find the missing number in the proportion.

$9:15 = 36:\boxed{}$

60

Questions 2–4 are about tossing a number cube with the numbers 1, 2, 3, 4, 5, and 6 on the faces.

2. What is the probability of tossing a 4?

$\frac{1}{6}$

3. What is the probability of tossing a number less than 3?

$\frac{1}{3}$

4. Is tossing a number greater than 4 more likely than, less likely than, or equally likely as tossing a 1 or 2?

equally likely

5. Find the missing number in the proportion.

$21:8 = 84:\boxed{}$

32

6. Find the missing number in the proportion.

$9:22 = \boxed{}:154$

63

7. If you toss a coin, what is the probability of getting tails?

$\frac{1}{2}$

8. Find the missing number in the proportion.

$18:3 = \boxed{}:36$

216

Use the spinner for exercises 9–12.

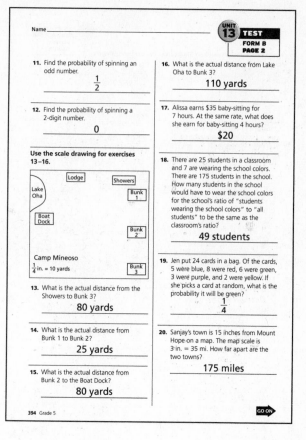

9. Find the probability of spinning a 6.

$\frac{1}{8}$

10. Find the probability of spinning an even number.

$\frac{1}{2}$

GO ON

Grade 5 **393**

Page 2

Name _____

11. Find the probability of spinning an odd number.

$\frac{1}{2}$

12. Find the probability of spinning a 2-digit number.

0

Use the scale drawing for exercises 13–16.

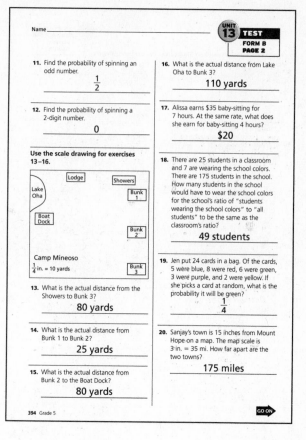

13. What is the actual distance from the Showers to Bunk 3?

80 yards

14. What is the actual distance from Bunk 1 to Bunk 2?

25 yards

15. What is the actual distance from Bunk 2 to the Boat Dock?

80 yards

16. What is the actual distance from Lake Oha to Bunk 3?

110 yards

17. Alissa earns $35 baby-sitting for 7 hours. At the same rate, what does she earn for baby-sitting 4 hours?

$20

18. There are 25 students in a classroom and 7 are wearing the school colors. There are 175 students in the school. How many students in the school would have to wear the school colors for the school's ratio of "students wearing the school colors" to "all students" to be the same as the classroom's ratio?

49 students

19. Jen put 24 cards in a bag. Of the cards, 5 were blue, 8 were red, 6 were green, 3 were purple, and 2 were yellow. If she picks a card at random, what is the probability it will be green?

$\frac{1}{4}$

20. Sanjay's town is 15 inches from Mount Hope on a map. The map scale is $3\frac{1}{2}$ in. = 35 mi. How far apart are the two towns?

175 miles

394 Grade 5

GO ON

Page 3

Name _____

21. Find the missing number in the proportion.

$7:13 = 42:\boxed{}$

78

Questions 22–24 are about tossing a number cube with the numbers 1, 2, 3, 4, 5, and 6 on the faces.

22. What is the probability of tossing a 5?

$\frac{1}{6}$

23. What is the probability of tossing a number greater than 1?

$\frac{5}{6}$

24. Is tossing a number less than 5 more likely than, less likely than, or equally likely as tossing an odd number?

more likely

25. Find the missing number in the proportion.

$75:7 = 300:\boxed{}$

28

26. Find the missing number in the proportion.

$11:16 = \boxed{}:144$

99

27. If you toss a coin, what is the probability of getting heads or tails?

1

28. Find the missing number in the proportion.

$35:5 = \boxed{}:20$

140

Use the spinner for exercises 29–32.

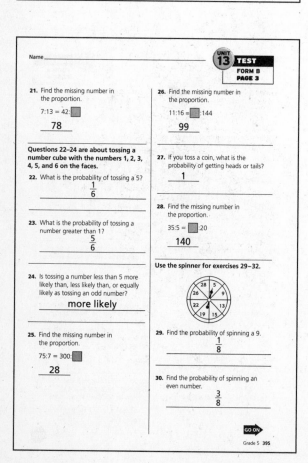

29. Find the probability of spinning a 9.

$\frac{1}{8}$

30. Find the probability of spinning an even number.

$\frac{3}{8}$

GO ON

Grade 5 **395**

Page 4

Name _____

31. Find the probability of spinning an odd number.

$\frac{5}{8}$

32. Find the probability of spinning a 2-digit number.

$\frac{3}{4}$

Use the scale drawing for exercises 33–36.

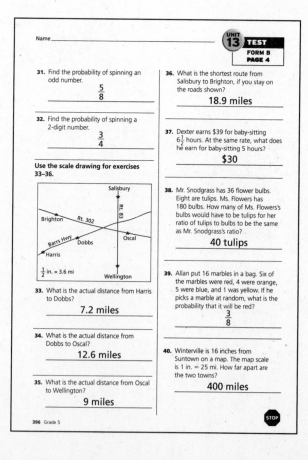

33. What is the actual distance from Harris to Dobbs?

7.2 miles

34. What is the actual distance from Dobbs to Oscal?

12.6 miles

35. What is the actual distance from Oscal to Wellington?

9 miles

36. What is the shortest route from Salisbury to Brighton, if you stay on the roads shown?

18.9 miles

37. Dexter earns $39 for baby-sitting $6\frac{1}{2}$ hours. At the same rate, what does he earn for baby-sitting 5 hours?

$30

38. Mr. Snodgrass has 36 flower bulbs. Eight are tulips. Ms. Flowers has 180 bulbs. How many of Ms. Flowers's bulbs would have to be tulips for her ratio of tulips to bulbs to be the same as Mr. Snodgrass's ratio?

40 tulips

39. Allan put 16 marbles in a bag. Six of the marbles were red, 4 were orange, 5 were blue, and 1 was yellow. If he picks a marble at random, what is the probability that it will be red?

$\frac{3}{8}$

40. Winterville is 16 inches from Suntown on a map. The map scale is 1 in. = 25 mi. How far apart are the two towns?

400 miles

396 Grade 5

STOP

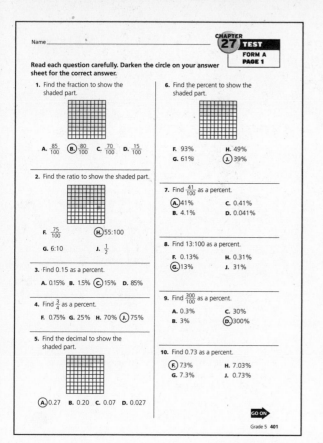

Name _____

Read each question carefully. Darken the circle on your answer sheet for the correct answer.

1. Find the fraction to show the shaded part.

A. $\frac{85}{100}$ B. $\frac{80}{100}$ C. $\frac{70}{100}$ D. $\frac{15}{100}$

2. Find the ratio to show the shaded part.

F. $\frac{75}{100}$ H. 55:100

G. 6:10 J. $\frac{1}{2}$

3. Find 0.15 as a percent.

A. 0.15% B. 1.5% C. 15% D. 85%

4. Find $\frac{3}{4}$ as a percent.

F. 0.75% G. 25% H. 70% J. 75%

5. Find the decimal to show the shaded part.

A. 0.27 B. 0.20 C. 0.07 D. 0.027

6. Find the percent to show the shaded part.

F. 93% H. 49%

G. 61% J. 39%

7. Find $\frac{41}{100}$ as a percent.

A. 41% C. 0.41%

B. 4.1% D. 0.041%

8. Find 13:100 as a percent.

F. 0.13% H. 0.31%

G. 13% J. 31%

9. Find $\frac{300}{100}$ as a percent.

A. 0.3% C. 30%

B. 3% D. 300%

10. Find 0.73 as a percent.

F. 73% H. 7.03%

G. 7.3% J. 0.73%

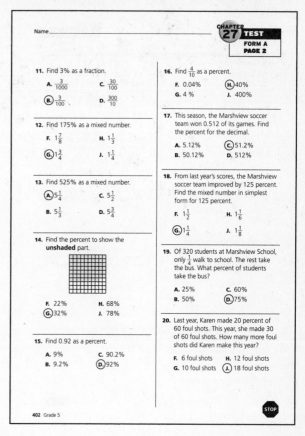

Name _____

11. Find 3% as a fraction.

A. $\frac{3}{1000}$ C. $\frac{30}{100}$

B. $\frac{3}{100}$ D. $\frac{300}{10}$

12. Find 175% as a mixed number.

F. $1\frac{7}{8}$ H. $1\frac{1}{3}$

G. $1\frac{3}{4}$ J. $1\frac{1}{4}$

13. Find 525% as a mixed number.

A. $5\frac{1}{4}$ C. $5\frac{1}{2}$

B. $5\frac{1}{3}$ D. $5\frac{3}{4}$

14. Find the percent to show the **unshaded** part.

F. 22% H. 68%

G. 32% J. 78%

15. Find 0.92 as a percent.

A. 9% C. 90.2%

B. 9.2% D. 92%

16. Find $\frac{4}{10}$ as a percent.

F. 0.04% H. 40%

G. 4 % J. 400%

17. This season, the Marshview soccer team won 0.512 of its games. Find the percent for the decimal.

A. 5.12% C. 51.2%

B. 50.12% D. 512%

18. From last year's scores, the Marshview soccer team improved by 125 percent. Find the mixed number in simplest form for 125 percent.

F. $1\frac{1}{2}$ H. $1\frac{1}{6}$

G. $1\frac{1}{4}$ J. $1\frac{1}{8}$

19. Of 320 students at Marshview School, only $\frac{1}{4}$ walk to school. The rest take the bus. What percent of students take the bus?

A. 25% C. 60%

B. 50% D. 75%

20. Last year, Karen made 20 percent of 60 foul shots. This year, she made 30 of 60 foul shots. How many more foul shots did Karen make this year?

F. 6 foul shots H. 12 foul shots

G. 10 foul shots J. 18 foul shots

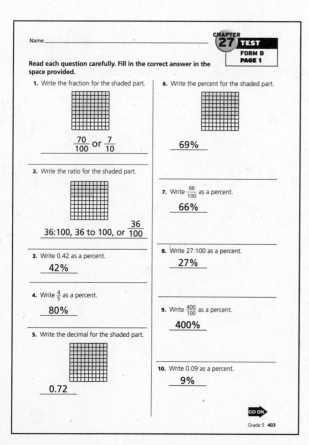

Name _____

Read each question carefully. Fill in the correct answer in the space provided.

1. Write the fraction for the shaded part.

$\frac{70}{100}$ or $\frac{7}{10}$

2. Write the ratio for the shaded part.

36:100, 36 to 100, or $\frac{36}{100}$

3. Write 0.42 as a percent.

42%

4. Write $\frac{4}{5}$ as a percent.

80%

5. Write the decimal for the shaded part.

0.72

6. Write the percent for the shaded part.

69%

7. Write $\frac{66}{100}$ as a percent.

66%

8. Write 27:100 as a percent.

27%

9. Write $\frac{400}{100}$ as a percent.

400%

10. Write 0.09 as a percent.

9%

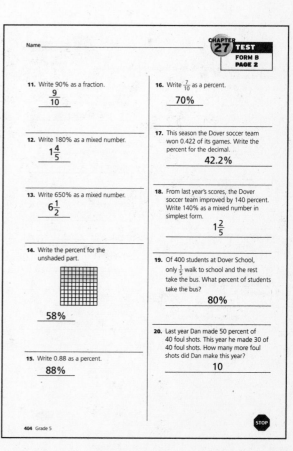

Name _____

11. Write 90% as a fraction.

$\frac{9}{10}$

12. Write 180% as a mixed number.

$1\frac{4}{5}$

13. Write 650% as a mixed number.

$6\frac{1}{2}$

14. Write the percent for the unshaded part.

58%

15. Write 0.88 as a percent.

88%

16. Write $\frac{7}{10}$ as a percent.

70%

17. This season the Dover soccer team won 0.422 of its games. Write the percent for the decimal.

42.2%

18. From last year's scores, the Dover soccer team improved by 140 percent. Write 140% as a mixed number in simplest form.

$1\frac{2}{5}$

19. Of 400 students at Dover School, only $\frac{1}{5}$ walk to school and the rest take the bus. What percent of students take the bus?

80%

20. Last year Dan made 50 percent of 40 foul shots. This year he made 30 of 40 foul shots. How many more foul shots did Dan make this year?

10

Chapter 28

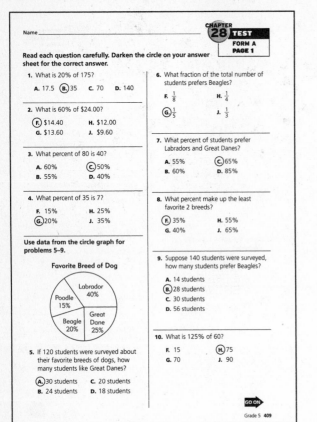

Read each question carefully. Darken the circle on your answer sheet for the correct answer.

1. What is 20% of 175?

A. 17.5   B. 35   C. 70   D. 140

2. What is 60% of $24.00?

F. $14.40   H. $12.00
G. $13.60   J. $9.60

3. What percent of 80 is 40?

A. 60%   C. 50%
B. 55%   D. 40%

4. What percent of 35 is 7?

F. 15%   H. 25%
G. 20%   J. 35%

Use data from the circle graph for problems 5–9.

Favorite Breed of Dog

Labrador 40%
Poodle 15%
Great Dane 25%
Beagle 20%

5. If 120 students were surveyed about their favorite breeds of dogs, how many students like Great Danes?

A. 30 students   C. 20 students
B. 24 students   D. 18 students

6. What fraction of the total number of students prefers Beagles?

F. $\frac{1}{8}$ H. $\frac{1}{4}$
G. $\frac{1}{5}$ J. $\frac{1}{3}$

7. What percent of students prefer Labradors and Great Danes?

A. 55%   C. 65%
B. 60%   D. 85%

8. What percent make up the least favorite 2 breeds?

F. 35%   H. 55%
G. 40%   J. 65%

9. Suppose 140 students were surveyed, how many students prefer Beagles?

A. 14 students
B. 28 students
C. 30 students
D. 56 students

10. What is 125% of 60?

F. 15   H. 75
G. 70   J. 90

GO ON

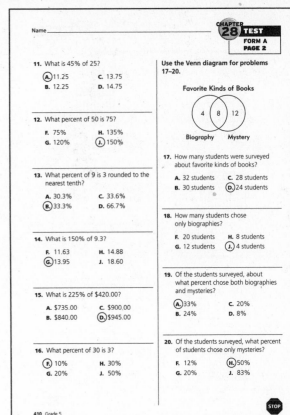

11. What is 45% of 25?

A. 11.25   C. 13.75
B. 12.25   D. 14.75

12. What percent of 50 is 75?

F. 75%   H. 135%
G. 120%   J. 150%

13. What percent of 9 is 3 rounded to the nearest tenth?

A. 30.3%   C. 33.6%
B. 33.3%   D. 66.7%

14. What is 150% of 9.3?

F. 11.63   H. 14.88
G. 13.95   J. 18.60

15. What is 225% of $420.00?

A. $735.00   C. $900.00
B. $840.00   D. $945.00

16. What percent of 30 is 3?

F. 10%   H. 30%
G. 20%   J. 50%

Use the Venn diagram for problems 17–20.

Favorite Kinds of Books

4   8   12
Biography   Mystery

17. How many students were surveyed about favorite kinds of books?

A. 32 students   C. 28 students
B. 30 students   D. 24 students

18. How many students chose only biographies?

F. 20 students   H. 8 students
G. 12 students   J. 4 students

19. Of the students surveyed, about what percent chose both biographies and mysteries?

A. 33%   C. 20%
B. 24%   D. 8%

20. Of the students surveyed, what percent of students chose only mysteries?

F. 12%   H. 50%
G. 20%   J. 83%

STOP

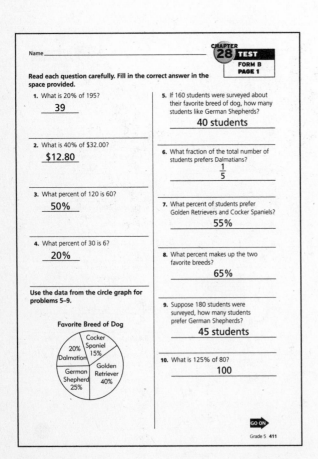

Read each question carefully. Fill in the correct answer in the space provided.

1. What is 20% of 195?

39

2. What is 40% of $32.00?

$12.80

3. What percent of 120 is 60?

50%

4. What percent of 30 is 6?

20%

Use the data from the circle graph for problems 5–9.

Favorite Breed of Dog

Cocker Spaniel 15%
Dalmation 20%
German Shepherd 25%
Golden Retriever 40%

5. If 160 students were surveyed about their favorite breed of dog, how many students like German Shepherds?

40 students

6. What fraction of the total number of students prefers Dalmatians?

$\frac{1}{5}$

7. What percent of students prefer Golden Retrievers and Cocker Spaniels?

55%

8. What percent makes up the two favorite breeds?

65%

9. Suppose 180 students were surveyed, how many students prefer German Shepherds?

45 students

10. What is 125% of 80?

100

GO ON

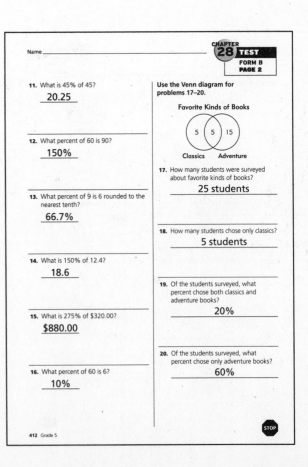

11. What is 45% of 45?

20.25

12. What percent of 60 is 90?

150%

13. What percent of 9 is 6 rounded to the nearest tenth?

66.7%

14. What is 150% of 12.4?

18.6

15. What is 275% of $320.00?

$880.00

16. What percent of 60 is 6?

10%

Use the Venn diagram for problems 17–20.

Favorite Kinds of Books

5   5   15
Classics   Adventure

17. How many students were surveyed about favorite kinds of books?

25 students

18. How many students chose only classics?

5 students

19. Of the students surveyed, what percent chose both classics and adventure books?

20%

20. Of the students surveyed, what percent chose only adventure books?

60%

STOP

Unit 14

Page 1

Name_____

UNIT 14 TEST FORM A PAGE 1

Read each question carefully. Darken the circle on your answer sheet for the correct answer.

1. Write $\frac{3}{4}$ as a percent.
- **A.** 150%
- **C.** 50%
- **B.** 75%
- **D.** 25%

2. Find 62% of 90.
- **F.** 145.1
- **H.** 14.51
- **G.** 55.8
- **J.** 5.58

3. What percent of 20 is 8?
- **A.** 250%
- **C.** 32%
- **B.** 40%
- **D.** 25%

4. Write 0.83 as a percent.
- **F.** 8300%
- **H.** 83%
- **G.** 830%
- **J.** 8.3%

5. Find 145% of 50.
- **A.** 725
- **C.** 72.5
- **B.** 344.8
- **D.** 34.48

6. What percent of 30 is 45?
- **F.** 150%
- **H.** 90%
- **G.** 120%
- **J.** 75%

7. Write 25% as a decimal.
- **A.** 25.0
- **C.** 0.25
- **B.** 2.5
- **D.** 0.025

8. Find 30% of 80.
- **F.** 26.7
- **H.** 2.7
- **G.** 24
- **J.** 2.4

9. 70 is what percent of 112?
- **A.** 120%
- **C.** 62.5%
- **B.** 75%
- **D.** 50%

10. Write 40% as a fraction.
- **F.** $\frac{4}{5}$
- **H.** $\frac{4}{50}$
- **G.** $\frac{2}{5}$
- **J.** $\frac{2}{50}$

11. Find 210% of 30.
- **A.** 6,300
- **C.** 63
- **B.** 630
- **D.** 6.3

12. 22 is what percent of 11?
- **F.** 200%
- **H.** 50%
- **G.** 75%
- **J.** 20%

GO ON

Grade 5 **417**

Page 2

Name_____

UNIT 14 TEST FORM A PAGE 2

Use the circle graph for exercises 13–14.

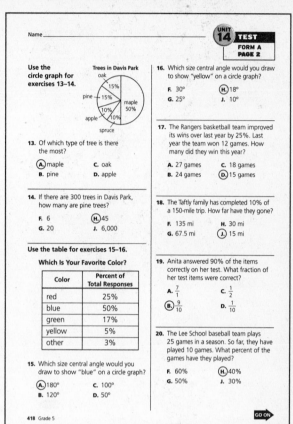

Trees in Davis Park
- oak 15%
- pine 15%
- maple 50%
- apple 10%
- spruce 10%

13. Of which type of tree is there the most?
- **A.** maple
- **C.** oak
- **B.** pine
- **D.** apple

14. If there are 300 trees in Davis Park, how many are pine trees?
- **F.** 6
- **H.** 45
- **G.** 20
- **J.** 6,000

Use the table for exercises 15–16.

Which Is Your Favorite Color?

Color	Percent of Total Responses
red	25%
blue	50%
green	17%
yellow	5%
other	3%

15. Which size central angle would you draw to show "blue" on a circle graph?
- **A.** 180°
- **C.** 100°
- **B.** 120°
- **D.** 50°

16. Which size central angle would you draw to show "yellow" on a circle graph?
- **F.** 30°
- **H.** 18°
- **G.** 25°
- **J.** 10°

17. The Rangers basketball team improved its wins over last year by 25%. Last year the team won 12 games. How many did they win this year?
- **A.** 27 games
- **C.** 18 games
- **B.** 24 games
- **D.** 15 games

18. The Taftly family has completed 10% of a 150-mile trip. How far have they gone?
- **F.** 135 mi
- **H.** 30 mi
- **G.** 67.5 mi
- **J.** 15 mi

19. Anita answered 90% of the items correctly on her test. What fraction of her test items were correct?
- **A.** $\frac{7}{1}$
- **C.** $\frac{1}{2}$
- **B.** $\frac{9}{10}$
- **D.** $\frac{1}{10}$

20. The Lee School baseball team plays 25 games in a season. So far, they have played 10 games. What percent of the games have they played?
- **F.** 60%
- **H.** 40%
- **G.** 50%
- **J.** 30%

GO ON

418 Grade 5

Page 3

Name_____

UNIT 14 TEST FORM A PAGE 3

21. Write $\frac{3}{5}$ as a percent.
- **A.** 90%
- **C.** 30%
- **B.** 60%
- **D.** 20%

22. Find 20% of 84.
- **F.** 168
- **H.** 16.8
- **G.** 42
- **J.** 4.2

23. What percent of 20 is 16?
- **A.** 80%
- **C.** 75%
- **B.** 125%
- **D.** 50%

24. Write 0.12 as a percent.
- **F.** 120%
- **H.** 1.2%
- **G.** 12%
- **J.** 0.12%

25. Find 250% of 60.
- **A.** 150
- **C.** 30
- **B.** 120
- **D.** 15

26. What percent of 15 is 45?
- **F.** 300%
- **H.** 66%
- **G.** 200%
- **J.** 33%

27. Write 77% as a decimal.
- **A.** 77.0
- **C.** 0.77
- **B.** 7.7
- **D.** 0.077

28. Find 90% of 120.
- **F.** 320
- **H.** 108
- **G.** 180
- **J.** 10.8

29. 35 is what percent of 140?
- **A.** 400%
- **C.** 75%
- **B.** 200%
- **D.** 25%

30. Write 30% as a fraction.
- **F.** $\frac{2}{5}$
- **H.** $\frac{1}{3}$
- **G.** $\frac{1}{10}$
- **J.** $\frac{3}{10}$

31. Find 115% of 50.
- **A.** 57.5
- **C.** 11.5
- **B.** 35
- **D.** 7.5

32. 40 is what percent of 16?
- **F.** 300%
- **H.** 80%
- **G.** 250%
- **J.** 40%

GO ON

Grade 5 **419**

Page 4

Name_____

UNIT 14 TEST FORM A PAGE 4

Use the circle graph for exercises 33–34.

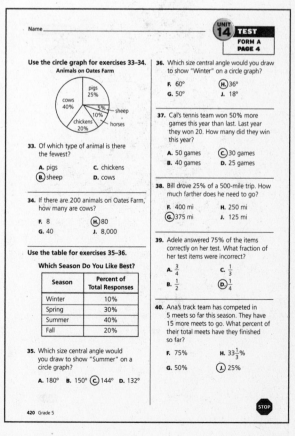

Animals on Oates Farm
- pigs 25%
- cows 40%
- sheep 5%
- horses 10%
- chickens 20%

33. Of which type of animal is there the fewest?
- **A.** pigs
- **C.** chickens
- **B.** sheep
- **D.** cows

34. If there are 200 animals on Oates Farm, how many are cows?
- **F.** 8
- **H.** 80
- **G.** 40
- **J.** 8,000

Use the table for exercises 35–36.

Which Season Do You Like Best?

Season	Percent of Total Responses
Winter	10%
Spring	30%
Summer	40%
Fall	20%

35. Which size central angle would you draw to show "Summer" on a circle graph?
- **A.** 180°
- **B.** 150°
- **C.** 144°
- **D.** 132°

36. Which size central angle would you draw to show "Winter" on a circle graph?
- **F.** 60°
- **H.** 36°
- **G.** 50°
- **J.** 18°

37. Cal's tennis team won 50% more games this year than last. Last year they won 20. How many did they win this year?
- **A.** 50 games
- **C.** 30 games
- **B.** 40 games
- **D.** 25 games

38. Bill drove 25% of a 500-mile trip. How much farther does he need to go?
- **F.** 400 mi
- **H.** 250 mi
- **G.** 375 mi
- **J.** 125 mi

39. Adele answered 75% of the items correctly on her test. What fraction of her test items were incorrect?
- **A.** $\frac{3}{4}$
- **C.** $\frac{1}{3}$
- **B.** $\frac{1}{2}$
- **D.** $\frac{1}{4}$

40. Ana's track team has competed in 5 meets so far this season. They have 15 more meets to go. What percent of their total meets have they finished so far?
- **F.** 75%
- **H.** $33\frac{1}{9}$%
- **G.** 50%
- **J.** 25%

STOP

420 Grade 5

Unit 14

Page 1

Name _____

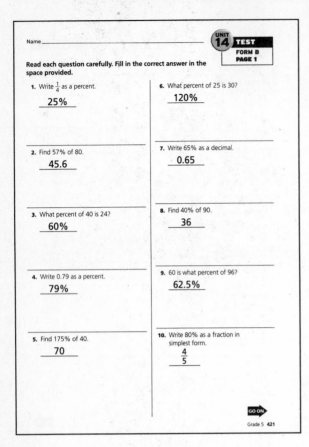

UNIT 14 TEST
FORM B
PAGE 1

Read each question carefully. Fill in the correct answer in the space provided.

1. Write $\frac{1}{4}$ as a percent.

25%

6. What percent of 25 is 30?

120%

2. Find 57% of 80.

45.6

7. Write 65% as a decimal.

0.65

3. What percent of 40 is 24?

60%

8. Find 40% of 90.

36

4. Write 0.79 as a percent.

79%

9. 60 is what percent of 96?

62.5%

5. Find 175% of 40.

70

10. Write 80% as a fraction in simplest form.

$\frac{4}{5}$

GO ON

Grade 5 **421**

Page 2

Name _____

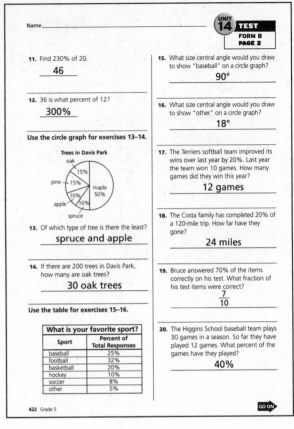

UNIT 14 TEST
FORM B
PAGE 2

11. Find 230% of 20.

46

12. 36 is what percent of 12?

300%

Use the circle graph for exercises 13–14.

Trees in Davis Park

oak 15%
pine 15%
maple 50%
apple 10%
spruce 10%

13. Of which type of tree is there the least?

spruce and apple

14. If there are 200 trees in Davis Park, how many are oak trees?

30 oak trees

Use the table for exercises 15–16.

What is your favorite sport?	
Sport	Percent of Total Responses
baseball	25%
football	32%
basketball	20%
hockey	10%
soccer	8%
other	5%

15. What size central angle would you draw to show "baseball" on a circle graph?

90°

16. What size central angle would you draw to show "other" on a circle graph?

18°

17. The Terriers softball team improved its wins over last year by 20%. Last year the team won 10 games. How many games did they win this year?

12 games

18. The Costa family has completed 20% of a 120-mile trip. How far have they gone?

24 miles

19. Bruce answered 70% of the items correctly on his test. What fraction of his test items were correct?

$\frac{7}{10}$

20. The Higgins School baseball team plays 30 games in a season. So far they have played 12 games. What percent of the games have they played?

40%

GO ON

422 Grade 5

Page 3

Name _____

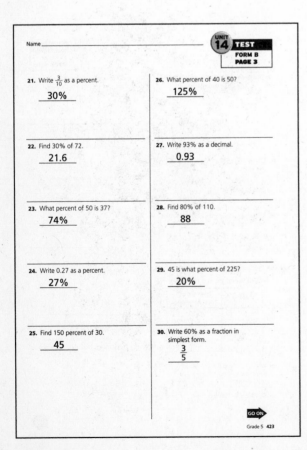

UNIT 14 TEST
FORM B
PAGE 3

21. Write $\frac{3}{10}$ as a percent.

30%

26. What percent of 40 is 50?

125%

22. Find 30% of 72.

21.6

27. Write 93% as a decimal.

0.93

23. What percent of 50 is 37?

74%

28. Find 80% of 110.

88

24. Write 0.27 as a percent.

27%

29. 45 is what percent of 225?

20%

25. Find 150 percent of 30.

45

30. Write 60% as a fraction in simplest form.

$\frac{3}{5}$

GO ON

Grade 5 **423**

Page 4

Name _____

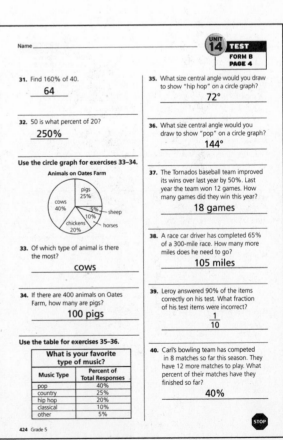

UNIT 14 TEST
FORM B
PAGE 4

31. Find 160% of 40.

64

32. 50 is what percent of 20?

250%

Use the circle graph for exercises 33–34.

Animals on Oates Farm

pigs 25%
cows 40%
sheep 5%
horses 10%
chickens 20%

33. Of which type of animal is there the most?

cows

34. If there are 400 animals on Oates Farm, how many are pigs?

100 pigs

Use the table for exercises 35–36.

What is your favorite type of music?	
Music Type	Percent of Total Responses
pop	40%
country	25%
hip hop	20%
classical	10%
other	5%

35. What size central angle would you draw to show "hip hop" on a circle graph?

72°

36. What size central angle would you draw to show "pop" on a circle graph?

144°

37. The Tornados baseball team improved its wins over last year by 50%. Last year the team won 12 games. How many games did they win this year?

18 games

38. A race car driver has completed 65% of a 300-mile race. How many more miles does he need to go?

105 miles

39. Leroy answered 90% of the items correctly on his test. What fraction of his test items were incorrect?

$\frac{1}{10}$

40. Carl's bowling team has competed in 8 matches so far this season. They have 12 more matches to play. What percent of their matches have they finished so far?

40%

STOP

424 Grade 5

Final

Name_____

Read each question carefully. Darken the circle on your answer sheet for the correct answer.

1. Name the place of the underlined digit.

4,4<u>7</u>3,952

A. millions
B. hundred thousands
C. ten thousands *(circled)*
D. thousands

2. 9.232 + 48.005 + 6.537 = ☐

F. 205.69
G. 122.607
H. 63.774 *(circled)*
J. 20.574

3. Estimate the sum.

5.763 + 8.054

A. 12
B. 14 *(circled)*
C. 16
D. 18

4. 2.7 × 500 = ☐

F. 13,500
G. 1,350 *(circled)*
H. 103.5
J. 10.35

5. Estimate the product.

35.7 × 249

A. 800
B. 900
C. 8,000 *(circled)*
D. 80,000

6. Rewrite using a base and an exponent.

$8 \times 8 \times 8 \times 8 \times 8$

F. 5^8
G. 4^8
H. 8^5 *(circled)*
J. 8^4

7. 94.78 ÷ 100 = ☐

A. 9.478
B. 0.9478 *(circled)*
C. 0.09478
D. 0.009478

8. 39.52 ÷ 7.6 = ☐

F. 50.2
G. 5.2 *(circled)*
H. 5.02
J. 0.502

9. Estimate the quotient.

4,572 ÷ 88

A. 5
B. 50 *(circled)*
C. 350
D. 500

10. What is the greatest common factor (GCF) of 32 and 56?

F. 16
G. 8 *(circled)*
H. 4
J. 3

GO ON

Grade 5 **427**

Name_____

11. What is the simplest form of $\frac{20}{35}$?

A. $\frac{4}{5}$
B. $\frac{5}{7}$
C. $\frac{4}{7}$ *(circled)*
D. $\frac{2}{5}$

12. Order from least to greatest.

$\frac{1}{4}, 0.23, \frac{2}{9}$

F. $\frac{2}{9}, 0.23, \frac{1}{4}$ *(circled)*
G. $0.23, \frac{2}{9}, \frac{1}{4}$
H. $\frac{2}{9}, \frac{1}{4}, 0.23$
J. $\frac{1}{4}, \frac{2}{9}, 0.23$

13. $5\frac{1}{3} + 4\frac{5}{6} =$ ☐

A. $10\frac{5}{9}$
B. $10\frac{1}{3}$
C. $10\frac{1}{6}$ *(circled)*
D. $9\frac{5}{9}$

14. $4\frac{3}{8} - \frac{9}{10} =$ ☐

F. $4\frac{21}{40}$
G. $4\frac{1}{5}$
H. $3\frac{3}{5}$
J. $3\frac{19}{40}$ *(circled)*

Use the line plot for problems 15–18.

Student Visits to the Ocean Park Aquarium

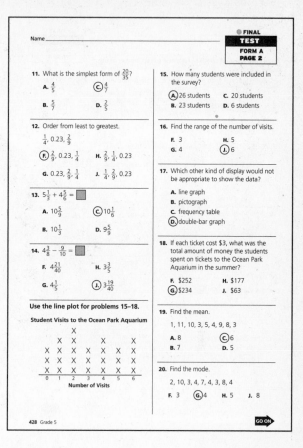

15. How many students were included in the survey?

A. 26 students *(circled)*
B. 23 students
C. 20 students
D. 6 students

16. Find the range of the number of visits.

F. 3
G. 4
H. 5
J. 6 *(circled)*

17. Which other kind of display would not be appropriate to show the data?

A. line graph
B. pictograph
C. frequency table
D. double-bar graph *(circled)*

18. If each ticket cost $3, what was the total amount of money the students spent on tickets to the Ocean Park Aquarium in the summer?

F. $252
G. $234 *(circled)*
H. $177
J. $63

19. Find the mean.

1, 11, 10, 3, 5, 4, 9, 8, 3

A. 8
B. 7
C. 6 *(circled)*
D. 5

20. Find the mode.

2, 10, 3, 4, 7, 4, 3, 8, 4

F. 3
G. 4 *(circled)*
H. 5
J. 8

GO ON

428 Grade 5

Name_____

21. $20\frac{5}{8} \times 15\frac{3}{5} =$ ☐

A. $3,139\frac{1}{4}$
B. $322\frac{1}{20}$
C. $321\frac{3}{4}$ *(circled)*
D. $320\frac{4}{5}$

22. $82 \div 10\frac{1}{4} =$ ☐

F. 840.5
G. 801
H. 20.5
J. 8 *(circled)*

23. Find the time that is 4 hours 30 minutes after 7:45 A.M.

A. 11:15 A.M.
B. 11:45 A.M.
C. 12:15 P.M. *(circled)*
D. 12:45 P.M.

24. 8 km = ☐ m

F. 80,000
G. 8,000 *(circled)*
H. 800
J. 80

25. Identify the angle.

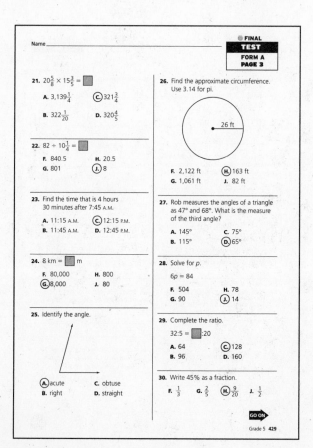

A. acute *(circled)*
B. right
C. obtuse
D. straight

26. Find the approximate circumference. Use 3.14 for pi.

26 ft

F. 2,122 ft
G. 1,061 ft
H. 163 ft *(circled)*
J. 82 ft

27. Rob measures the angles of a triangle as 47° and 68°. What is the measure of the third angle?

A. 145°
B. 115°
C. 75°
D. 65° *(circled)*

28. Solve for p.

6p = 84

F. 504
G. 90
H. 78
J. 14 *(circled)*

29. Complete the ratio.

32:5 = ☐:20

A. 64
B. 96
C. 128 *(circled)*
D. 160

30. Write 45% as a fraction.

F. $\frac{1}{3}$
G. $\frac{2}{5}$
H. $\frac{9}{20}$ *(circled)*
J. $\frac{1}{2}$

GO ON

Grade 5 **429**

Name_____

31. The Bangley Tennis team plays 40 games per season. So far, they have played 14 games. What percent have they played?

A. 35% *(circled)*
B. $33\frac{1}{3}$%
C. 30%
D. 25%

32. Joyess is 9 inches from Gracely on a map. The map scale is 3 inches = 14 miles. How far apart are the towns?

F. 378 miles
G. 126 miles
H. 84 miles
J. 42 miles *(circled)*

33. Identify the property used.

$4 \times 12\frac{4}{7} = (4 \times 12) + (4 \times \frac{4}{7})$

A. Identity Property
B. Commutative Property
C. Associative Property
D. Distributive Property of Multiplication over Addition *(circled)*

34. Write an expression for the situation. Nine times a number n increased by 3.

F. $9n + 3$ *(circled)*
G. $3(9n)$
H. $9n + 3n$
J. $9n - 3$

35. Which number is prime?

A. 9
B. 33
C. 47 *(circled)*
D. 91

36. Use the spinner.

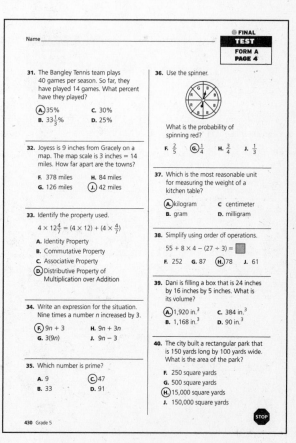

What is the probability of spinning red?

F. $\frac{2}{5}$
G. $\frac{1}{4}$ *(circled)*
H. $\frac{3}{4}$
J. $\frac{1}{3}$

37. Which is the most reasonable unit for measuring the weight of a kitchen table?

A. kilogram *(circled)*
B. gram
C. centimeter
D. milligram

38. Simplify using order of operations.

$55 + 8 \times 4 - (27 \div 3) =$ ☐

F. 252
G. 87
H. 78 *(circled)*
J. 61

39. Dani is filling a box that is 24 inches by 16 inches by 5 inches. What is its volume?

A. 1,920 in.³ *(circled)*
B. 1,168 in.³
C. 384 in.³
D. 90 in.³

40. The city built a rectangular park that is 150 yards long by 100 yards wide. What is the area of the park?

F. 250 square yards
G. 500 square yards
H. 15,000 square yards *(circled)*
J. 150,000 square yards

STOP

430 Grade 5

Final

Final

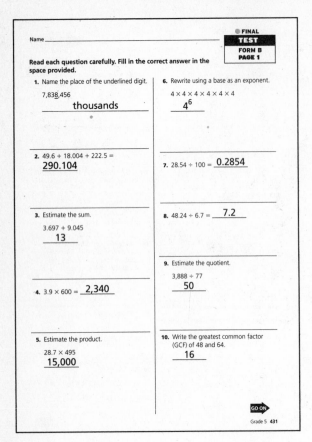

Name _____

● FINAL
TEST
FORM B
PAGE 1

Read each question carefully. Fill in the correct answer in the space provided.

1. Name the place of the underlined digit.

7,83<u>8</u>,456

thousands

2. 49.6 + 18.004 + 222.5 =

290.104

3. Estimate the sum.

3.697 + 9.045

13

4. 3.9 × 600 = **2,340**

5. Estimate the product.

28.7 × 495

15,000

6. Rewrite using a base as an exponent.

4 × 4 × 4 × 4 × 4 × 4

4^6

7. 28.54 ÷ 100 = **0.2854**

8. 48.24 ÷ 6.7 = **7.2**

9. Estimate the quotient.

3,888 ÷ 77

50

10. Write the greatest common factor (GCF) of 48 and 64.

16

GO ON

Grade 5   **431**

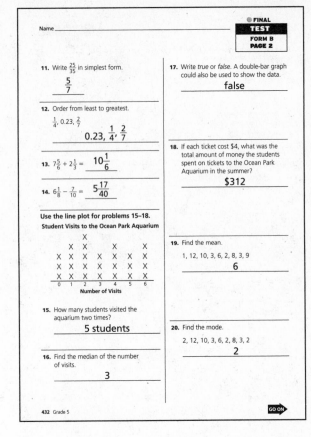

Name _____

● FINAL
TEST
FORM B
PAGE 2

11. Write $\frac{25}{35}$ in simplest form.

$\frac{5}{7}$

12. Order from least to greatest.

$\frac{1}{4}$, 0.23, $\frac{2}{7}$

0.23, $\frac{1}{4}$, $\frac{2}{7}$

13. $7\frac{5}{6} + 2\frac{1}{3}$ = **$10\frac{1}{6}$**

14. $6\frac{1}{8} - \frac{7}{10}$ = **$5\frac{17}{40}$**

Use the line plot for problems 15–18.
Student Visits to the Ocean Park Aquarium

```
                X
        X   X       X           X
X   X   X   X   X   X   X
X   X   X   X       X   X   X
X   X   X   X   X   X   X
0   1   2   3   4   5   6
      Number of Visits
```

15. How many students visited the aquarium two times?

5 students

16. Find the median of the number of visits.

3

17. Write *true* or *false*. A double-bar graph could also be used to show the data.

false

18. If each ticket cost $4, what was the total amount of money the students spent on tickets to the Ocean Park Aquarium in the summer?

$312

19. Find the mean.

1, 12, 10, 3, 6, 2, 8, 3, 9

6

20. Find the mode.

2, 12, 10, 3, 6, 2, 8, 3, 2

2

432   Grade 5

GO ON

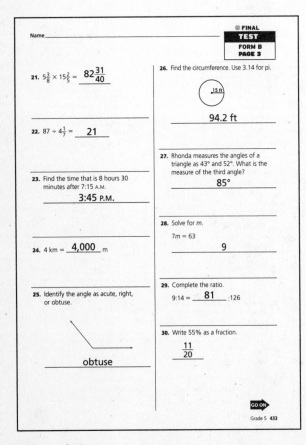

Name _____

● FINAL
TEST
FORM B
PAGE 3

21. $5\frac{3}{8} \times 15\frac{2}{5}$ = **$82\frac{31}{40}$**

22. $87 \div 4\frac{1}{7}$ = **21**

23. Find the time that is 8 hours 30 minutes after 7:15 A.M.

3:45 P.M.

24. 4 km = **4,000** m

25. Identify the angle as acute, right, or obtuse.

obtuse

26. Find the circumference. Use 3.14 for pi.

(15 ft)

94.2 ft

27. Rhonda measures the angles of a triangle as 43° and 52°. What is the measure of the third angle?

85°

28. Solve for *m*.

7*m* = 63

9

29. Complete the ratio.

9:14 = **81** :126

30. Write 55% as a fraction.

$\frac{11}{20}$

GO ON

Grade 5   **433**

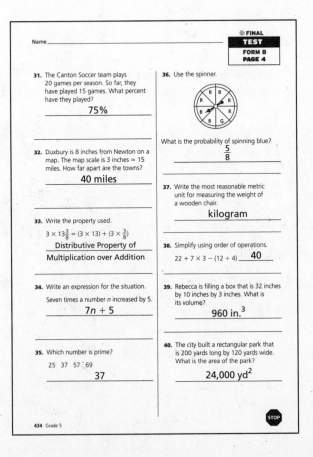

Name _____

● FINAL
TEST
FORM B
PAGE 4

31. The Canton Soccer team plays 20 games per season. So far, they have played 15 games. What percent have they played?

75%

32. Duxbury is 8 inches from Newton on a map. The map scale is 3 inches = 15 miles. How far apart are the towns?

40 miles

33. Write the property used.

$3 \times 13\frac{3}{8} = (3 \times 13) + (3 \times \frac{3}{8})$

Distributive Property of Multiplication over Addition

34. Write an expression for the situation.

Seven times a number *n* increased by 5.

7*n* + 5

35. Which number is prime?

25   37   57   69

37

36. Use the spinner.

What is the probability of spinning blue?

$\frac{5}{8}$

37. Write the most reasonable metric unit for measuring the weight of a wooden chair.

kilogram

38. Simplify using order of operations.

22 + 7 × 3 − (12 ÷ 4)   **40**

39. Rebecca is filling a box that is 32 inches by 10 inches by 3 inches. What is its volume?

960 in.^{3}

40. The city built a rectangular park that is 200 yards long by 120 yards wide. What is the area of the park?

24,000 yd^2

STOP

434   Grade 5

---

494   Grade 5